Advances in
MICROBIAL ECOLOGY

Volume 12

ADVANCES IN MICROBIAL ECOLOGY

Sponsored by the International Committee on Microbial Ecology
(ICOME), a committee of the International Union of
Microbiological Societies (IUMS) and the International Union of
Biological Sciences (IUBS)

EDITORIAL BOARD

AContinuation Order Plan is available for this series. A continuation order will bring delivery of
each new volume immediately upon publication. Volumes are billed only upon actual shipment.
For further information please contact the publisher.

Advances in
MICROBIAL ECOLOGY

Volume 12

Edited by

K. C. Marshall

University of New South Wales
Kensington, New South Wales, Australia

PLENUM PRESS · NEW YORK AND LONDON

The Library of Congress cataloged the first volume of this title as follows:

Advances in microbial ecology. v. 1–
  New York, Plenum Press c1977–
  v. ill. 24 cm.
  Key title: Advances in microbial ecology, ISSN 0147-4863
  1. Microbial ecology — Collected works.
QR100.A36   576′.15   77-649698

ISBN 0-306-44266-3

© 1992 Plenum Press, New York
A Division of Plenum Publishing Corporation
233 Spring Street, New York, N.Y. 10013

Printed in the United States of America

Contributors

Muhammad Arshad, Department of Soil Science, University of Agriculture, Faisalabad, Pakistan

Ronald M. Atlas, Department of Biology, University of Louisville, Louisville, Kentucky 40292

Richard Bartha, Department of Biochemistry and Microbiology, Cook College, Rutgers University, New Brunswick, New Jersey 08903

Mary M. Bateson, Department of Microbiology, Montana State University, Bozeman, Montana 59717

Douglas E. Caldwell, Department of Applied Microbiology and Food Science, University of Saskatchewan, Saskatoon, Saskatchewan S7N 0W0, Canada

Craig A. Carlson, Horn Point Environmental Laboratories, University of Maryland–CEES, Cambridge, Maryland 21613

Grant Daggard, School of Biological Sciences, Macquarie University, Sydney NSW 2109, Australia

Hugh W. Ducklow, Horn Point Environmental Laboratories, University of Maryland–CEES, Cambridge, Maryland 21613

W. T. Frankenberger, Jr., Department of Soil and Environmental Sciences, University of California, Riverside, California 92521

Gary M. King, Darling Marine Center, University of Maine, Walpole, Maine 04573

Paul E. Kolenbrander, Laboratory of Microbial Ecology, National Institute of Dental Research, National Institutes of Health, Bethesda, Maryland 20892

Darren R. Korber, Department of Applied Microbiology and Food Science, University of Saskatchewan, Saskatoon, Saskatchewan S7N 0W0, Canada

John R. Lawrence, National Hydrology Research Institute, Environment Canada, Saskatoon, Saskatchewan S7N 3H5, Canada

Jack London, Laboratory of Microbial Ecology, National Institute of Dental Research, National Institutes of Health, Bethesda, Maryland 20892

Alyson L. Ruff-Roberts, Department of Microbiology, Montana State University, Bozeman, Montana 59717

Alexandre Semenov, Institute of Microbiology, USSR Academy of Sciences, Moscow, USSR

James T. Staley, Department of Microbiology, University of Washington, Seattle, Washington 98195

H. W. Stokes, School of Biological Sciences, Macquarie University, Sydney NSW 2109, Australia

Duncan A. Veal, School of Biological Sciences, Macquarie University, Sydney NSW 2109, Australia

David M. Ward, Department of Microbiology, Montana State University, Bozeman, Montana 59717

Roland Weller, Department of Microbiology, Montana State University, Bozeman, Montana 59717

Julian W. T. Wimpenny, School of Pure and Applied Biology, University of Wales, College of Cardiff, Cardiff CF1 3TL, United Kingdom

Preface

Advances in Microbial Ecology was established by the International Committee on Microbial Ecology (ICOME) to provide a vehicle for in-depth, critical, and even provocative reviews to emphasize recent trends in the important field of microbial ecology. *Advances in Microbial Ecology* is now recognized as a major source of information and inspiration both for practicing and for prospective microbial ecologists. Most reviews appearing in *Advances* have been prepared by leaders in particular areas following invitations issued by the Editorial Board. Individuals are encouraged, however, to submit outlines of unsolicited contributions to any member of the Editorial Board for consideration for publication in *Advances*.

With the publication of Volume 12 of *Advances in Microbial Ecology* there will be a change of Editor and the entire Editorial Board. The current Editor wishes to take this opportunity to thank the present Editorial Board, Ron Atlas, Bo Barker Jørgensen, and Gwyn Jones, as well as past members of the Board, for their assistance and encouragement over the years. The new Editor of *Advances in Microbial Ecology* will be Gwyn Jones, with Bernhard Schink, Warwick F. Vincent, and David M. Ward as members of the Editorial Board. The outgoing Board wish the new Board every success in continuing the traditions established by Martin Alexander, the founding Editor of *Advances in Microbial Ecology*.

The topics featured in Volume 12 of *Advances* include some related to the metabolic activities of bacteria; namely, bioremediation of oil spills, by R. M. Atlas and R. Bartha; methane oxidation, by G. M. King; and biosynthesis of ethylene, by M. Arshad and W. T. Frankenberger, Jr. The ecology of polyprosthecate bacteria is considered by A. Semenov and J. T. Staley. Particular ecosystems considered include bacterial production in oceans, by H. W. Ducklow and C. A. Carlson, and coaggregation in oral bacteria, by P. E. Kolenbrander and J. London. Three-dimensional consideration of microorganisms in nature includes a discussion on patterns in time and space by J. W. T. Wimpenny and the use of confocal laser microscopy and image analysis in ecology by D. E. Caldwell, D. R. Korber, and J. R. Lawrence. Genetic approaches in microbial ecology include an update by D. M. Ward, M. M. Bateson, R. Weller, and A. L. Ruff-Roberts on 16S rRNA analyses of natural microbial communities and a review of genetic exchange in nature by D. A. Veal, H. W. Stokes, and G. Daggard.

K. C. Marshall, Editor
R. M. Atlas
B. B. Jørgensen
J. G. Jones

Contents

Chapter 2

Microbial Biosynthesis of Ethylene and Its Influence on Plant Growth

Muhammad Arshad and W. T. Frankenberger, Jr.

Chapter 3

Oceanic Bacterial Production

Hugh W. Ducklow and Craig A. Carlson

Chapter 4

Ecological Significance of Coaggregation among Oral Bacteria

Paul E. Kolenbrander and Jack London

Chapter 5

Ribosomal RNA Analysis of Microorganisms as They Occur in Nature

David M. Ward, Mary M. Bateson, Roland Weller, and Alyson L. Ruff-Roberts

Chapter 6

Hydrocarbon Biodegradation and Oil Spill Bioremediation

Ronald M. Atlas and Richard Bartha

Chapter 7

Ecology of Polyprosthecate Bacteria

Alexandre Semenov and James T. Staley

Chapter 8

Genetic Exchange in Natural Microbial Communities

Duncan A. Veal, H. W. Stokes, and Grant Daggard

Chapter 9

Ecological Aspects of Methane Oxidation, a Key Determinant of Global Methane Dynamics

Gary M. King

Chapter 10

Microbial Systems: Patterns in Time and Space

Julian W. T. Wimpenny

Confocal Laser Microscopy and Digital Image Analysis in Microbial Ecology

DOUGLAS E. CALDWELL, DARREN R. KORBER, and JOHN R. LAWRENCE

1. Introduction

Microbial ecologists have extensively explored the potential applications of light microscopy for more than five decades (Henrici and Johnson, 1935; Perfil'ev and Gabe, 1969;
Casida, 1969, 1972, 1975, 1976; Staley, 1971; Caldwell and Hirsch, 1973; Caldwell *et
al.*, 1973, 1975; Caldwell and Tiedje, 1975a,b; Labeda *et al.*, 1976; Hirsch, 1977,
1980; Geesey *et al.*, 1978; Marshall, 1986). Now traditional microscopy has given
way to "microvisualization" (Friedhoff, 1991) greatly accelerating research. Microorganisms are no longer merely photographed; instead, they are digitally "imaged"
using fluorescent molecular probes, confocal laser microscopy, and computer image
analysis. The chemical and biological relationships between a microorganism and its
microenvironment are seen directly, nondestructively, *in situ,* and in "real time" (Lawrence and Caldwell, 1990). Consequently, it is no longer necessary to disrupt microbial
communities when studying the molecular or behavioral aspects of their ecology.

The microbial world is one millionth the size of our human frame of reference. Its
smallest free-living inhabitants, the bacteria, are approximately 1.5 μm as compared to
1.7 m for the average human being. A square kilometer of forest is thus analogous to a
bacterial ecosystem occupying only a square millimeter. Bacterial and other microecosystems include biofilms, bioaggregates, neuston, anaerobic consortia, aufwuchs,
marine snow, soil aggregates, sulphureta, and other discrete microbial communities
which are spatially organized, which exchange mass and energy internally, which possess well-defined physical boundaries, and which create their own microenvironments.
Microbial ecosystems possess a high degree of spatial organization on a microscopic

DOUGLAS E. CALDWELL and DARREN R. KORBER • Department of Applied Microbiology and Food
Science, University of Saskatchewan, Saskatoon, Saskatchewan S7N 0W0, Canada.   JOHN R. LAW-
RENCE • National Hydrology Research Institute, Environment Canada, Saskatoon, Saskatchewan S7N 3H5,
Canada.

Advances in Microbial Ecology, Vol. 12, edited by K.C. Marshall. Plenum Press, New York, 1992.

scale, and thus there is not necessarily any equivalence between macroenvironment and microenvironment. Consequently, microenvironments are different from the macroenvironments measured when using conventional experimental methods to study bulk samples. While the macroenvironment is aerobic, the microenvironment can be anaerobic. While the macroenvironment is neutral, microenvironments are often acidic or alkaline. While there is a high concentration of antibiotics in the macroenvironment, bacteria in microenvironments are often sequestered from their effects (Anwar *et al.*, 1989). Plate counts of aggregating microbial populations can decrease, while population size may actually increase. Conversely, plate counts of dispersing microbial aggregates sometimes increase while the population size of these organisms decreases due to death or predation. Consequently, the search for direct optical methods has continued.

Digital microscopy is one of the most promising new methods used to study the spatial heterogeneity of microecosystems. In much the same way that the Earth and its neighboring planets have been monitored remotely using satellites and microwave beams, the microbial world is monitored using the optical microscope, laser beams, fluorescent molecular probes, and computer image analysis. Prior to the introduction of laser microscopy and image processing technology, optical microscopy was qualitative, two-dimensional, and labor-intensive. With the development of image processing methods as well as inexpensive and highly light-sensitive video equipment, it became possible to analyze the growth and behavior of microorganisms as they colonized surface microenvironments (Caldwell and Lawrence, 1986; Lawrence *et al.*, 1987, 1989a,b; Korber *et al.*, 1989a,b). The introduction of confocal laser microscopy (CLM) and 3-D image analysis has established a new standard of analytical precision by virtually eliminating interference from out-of-focus objects and by creating computer reconstructions of 3-D microbial biofilms and bioaggregates. This development makes it possible to apply computer image analysis to complex consortia rather than restricting it to the 2-D analysis of cell monolayers which form during the initial stages of surface colonization (Caldwell and Lawrence, 1986, 1988).

Using fluorescent molecular probes, CLM, computer image analysis, and other methods, it is possible to visualize not only the organisms themselves but also their positioning behavior, growth, metabolism, gene expression, genetic sequencing, as well as the ambient physicochemical and biochemical microenvironment surrounding each cell. In some cases this can be done dynamically, nondestructively, and during an *in situ* time course. The results include not only numerical analyses but also a video display showing a 3-D rotating image with a pseudocolor rendering of biochemistry, metabolism, pH, gene expression, or any parameter of interest which can be visualized using a fluorescent molecular probe, lux insertion, difference imaging, etc. In the future, computer-based holographic imaging will be used to display these visualizations. Texas Instrument's multiplanar display system is already capable of rendering them as translucent objects floating in space, without the aid of 3-D glasses (Emmett, 1991). 3-D image analysis is used to directly and nondestructively determine the biovolume of 3-D objects. The alternative is either to estimate these volumes from 2-D photographs (collapsed 2-D projections of 3-D objects) using stereological formulas (Jenkinson *et al.*, 1976; van Veen and Paul, 1979; Fry and Davies, 1985; Fry, 1988; Wynn-Williams, 1988a,b; Gaju

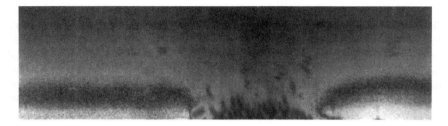

Figure 1. A vertical (sagittal), optodigital thin section showing a microcolony of *Pseudomonas fluorescens* attached to the upper surface of a continuous-flow slide culture and perturbing the surface microenvironment associated with the glass surface. Continuous-flow slide cultures were inoculated at time zero and subsequently irrigated with sterile medium. Fluorescein was used as a pH-sensitive, fluorescent molecular probe. The cells within the microcolony appear dark due to the lack of fluorescein penetration. The surface microenvironment associated with the glass surface is seen as a dark band or cloud, approximately 3 μm thick, extending parallel to the surface. The dark band may be due to either a physiochemical interaction which inhibits fluorescence (most likely reduced pH), shadow or reflection patterns (an artifact, although this is unlikely due to the curvature of the band as it meets the colony), or differential penetration (concentration) of the fluor. (Laser micrograph of a vertical optodigital section showing living cells, *in situ* within a flow cell, and obtained using fluorescein as a fluorescent negative stain; diameter of the microcolony is 14 μm).

et al., 1989; Getliff and Fry, 1989) or to dehydrate and then embed the organisms in plastic, mechanically thin section with a diamond knife, observe using transmission electron microscopy, and apply stereological formulas to the sections (Caldwell and Caldwell, 1978).

Numerous technical difficulties remain, including the development of lenses with longer working distances and improved axial resolution, new fluorescent molecular probes, and 3-D image analysis software to complement existing 3-D rendering software. However, the capability to directly visualize ecological interactions and interrelationships already exists. Perhaps the most significant application is confirmation that bacterial microenvironments do exist (Fig. 1) and can be quantified in terms of magnitude and extent by using fluorescent ph, E_h, lectin, dextran, antibody, enzymatic, and other molecular probes.

2. Computer Image Analysis

2.1. Computer Image Analysis and Microbial Ecology

Early studies of microbiological growth, attachment, and behavior involved either manual microscopic observation or the analysis of a photomicrographic time series. Studies of bacterial motility or chemotaxis primarily relied upon time-exposure photography, cinematographic film, or television images (Vaitzus and Doetsch, 1969; Edgar, 1979; Cooksey and Cooksey, 1988); however, these approaches proved to be tedious and time-consuming. In recent years, computers have become commonplace in the microbiological laboratory, and image processing is now routinely used as a rapid means for the enumeration of microorganisms accumulating on microscope slides or on agar plates (Costello and Monk, 1985; Sieracki *et al.*, 1985; Verran and Rocliffe, 1986; Sjollema *et al.*, 1989; Korber *et al.*, 1989a, 1990). Computer-enhanced microscopy (CEM) has also been applied to the separation of biological growth events from abiotic materials (Caldwell and Germida, 1985), the classification of bacterial species recovered from environmental samples (Meijer *et al.*, 1990), the formation of biofilms under various conditions (Zanyk *et al.*, 1991), the analysis of microbial motion and chemotaxis (Berg and Brown, 1972; Davenport, 1973; Berg, 1985; Gualtieri *et al.*, 1985, 1988; Korber *et al.*, 1989b), the determination of bacterial habitat domain (Peters, 1990), the estimation of bacterial biovolumes (Fry and Davies, 1985; Fry, 1988; Wynn-Williams, 1988a; Getliff and Fry, 1989), and the evaluation of cell viability (Singh *et al.*, 1990).

2.2. Input Devices

To perform image analysis a video camera is used to create an analog video signal, which is then converted to a digital image by a dedicated image processing computer or an add-on video-digitizing device (frame grabber board and personal computer). On-line image analysis is performed by mounting a video camera on a photomicroscope and directing the magnified image to the video camera rather than the ocular lens, thereby permitting quantitation of cell growth and behavior over time. Video cameras for such applications vary in terms of their horizontal resolution, light sensitivity, intrascene dynamic range (latitude), blooming characteristics, geometric distortion, and spectral response (Inoué, 1986). Manual adjustment of the camera gain and voltage control is desirable, as self-adjusting cameras may alter their light sensitivity in response to changes in inter- or intrascene brightness, leading to errors in the measurement of object size, number, and morphology (Lawrence *et al.*, 1989a). Low-light applications require the use of either SIT (silicone intensification target, limiting low-level illuminance, 10^{-3} lux) or ISIT (intensified silicone intensification target, limiting low-level illuminance, 10^{-5} lux) detector, and are generally more expensive than less sensitive units. However, these devices are more susceptible to electronic noise interference, thereby lowering the signal-to-noise ratio. Midsensitivity CCD (charge-coupled device, limiting low-level illuminance, 10^{-3} lux) cameras are not as susceptible to electronic noise and geometric distortion as are the tube cameras, and in recent years have become less expensive. Extremely light-sensitive cameras, such as photon-counting or liquid-cooled CCD cameras (Astromed Ltd., Cambridge, U.K.) are sensitive to exceptionally low-intensity light signals (limiting low-level illuminance, 10^{-11} lux); however, these devices are suitable only for highly specialized applications (e.g., observation of bacterial bioluminescence, lux gene expression), and are not generally applicable to most microbiological analyses.

Cameras with Plumbicon, Chalnicon, Newvicon, or standard CCD detectors are generally less expensive, less light-sensitive (limiting low-level illuminance, $\sim 10^{1}$ to 10^{-2} lux), and require that the objects of interest be brightly illuminated (source illumination of 1.4 to 2.5 $\times$ 10^{5} lux) (Lawrence *et al.*, 1989a). This may cause errors during behavioral and growth studies of living bacteria. A number of workers have

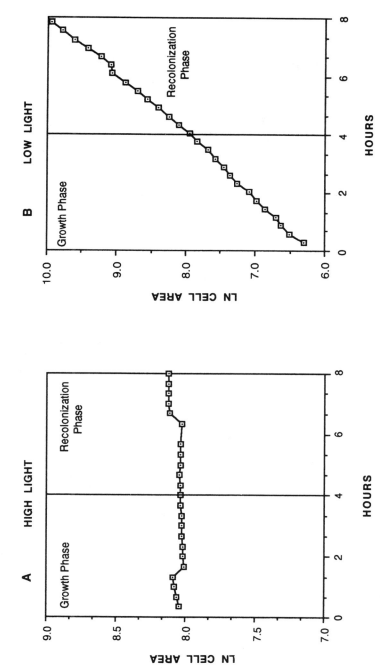

Figure 2. Effect of lighting conditions on the growth rate of bacteria in continuous-flow slide culture. Normal growth of *Pseudomonas fluorescens* occurred under the low light level required by the SIT camera (A, cell doubling time was 1.4 hr) but was inhibited at higher light intensities required for the plumbicon camera (B, cell doubling time was 100 hr). (From Lawrence *et al.*, 1989a, *J. Microbiol. Methods* **10:**123–138, reprinted with permission.)

demonstrated light-induced effects on living cells. Early studies by Kuhn and Starr (1970) demonstrated that intense illumination caused heating (melting of microscopic crystals exposed to microscope illumination) which may inhibit growth or cause cell death. It has also been shown that specific wavelengths elicit positive phytoplankton responses while other wavelengths are nonstimulatory (Davenport, 1973). Lawrence *et al.* (1989a) found that growth of *Pseudomonas fluorescens* in continuous-flow slide culture was completely inhibited with 1.2×10^{-1} lux visible light (faceplate illumination, 400–700 nm). Cells immediately adjacent to illuminated areas (but outside the zone of illumination) developed into mature biofilms at normal rates of growth. Use of a Bosch SIT camera at lower levels of irradiation (faceplate illumination of 10^{-3} lux) resulted in confluent growth with no apparent illumination effects (Figs. 2 and 3). Motility and recolonization of these cells were also adversely affected within zones of high light intensity. Other examples exist whereby microorganisms display phototactic responses (Gualtieri *et al.*, 1988); thus, light intensity and wavelength must be considered during experimental design to avoid adverse effects.

2.3. Selection of the Appropriate Microscope and Video System for Specific Ecological Studies

High-magnification ($100\times$ objective) phase microscopy has been used to analyze individual cells or microcolonies, as opposed to cell populations (Caldwell and Lawrence, 1986; Lawrence *et al.*, 1987, 1989a). The growth of cell monolayers may be quantitated using phase-contrast and digital image analysis. The area occupied by the 2-D projections of 3-D cells in 2-D images is referred to as cell area. In the case of cell monolayers formed by some pseudomonads and other bacteria, the cell area is directly proportional to increases in cell biomass and cell number during exponential growth (Caldwell and Lawrence, 1986). Thus, areal measurements may be used to precisely define the rates of cell growth in slide culture within a single cell division cycle, providing that the cells remain within a single plane. However, the use of high-magnification phase microscopy in conjunction with image analysis has several disadvantages: limited information on populations, small sample size, and lack of automation necessary to take full advantage of digital microscopy and image analysis.

Low-magnification ($10\times$ objective) darkfield microscopy has been used to analyze larger numbers of individuals (populations as opposed to individual cells and small microcolonies) and their behavior, and may be automated to function repetitively over extended periods of time. It is difficult to automate on-line growth studies in slide culture at high magnification due to low depth of field and thus the increased probability that the specimen will drift out of focus. Darkfield microscopy produces a high-contrast image by light scattering, allowing visualization of objects normally below the limits of resolution. This factor and the increased depth of field at low magnification makes darkfield an important tool in studies of microbial growth on surfaces and in biofilm development (Lawrence *et al.*, 1989a; Korber *et al.*, 1989a). The low-magnification darkfield image of the developing biofilm can normally contain a much broader range of object size, motion, brightness, and intrascene dynamic range (latitude) as the biofilm develops than

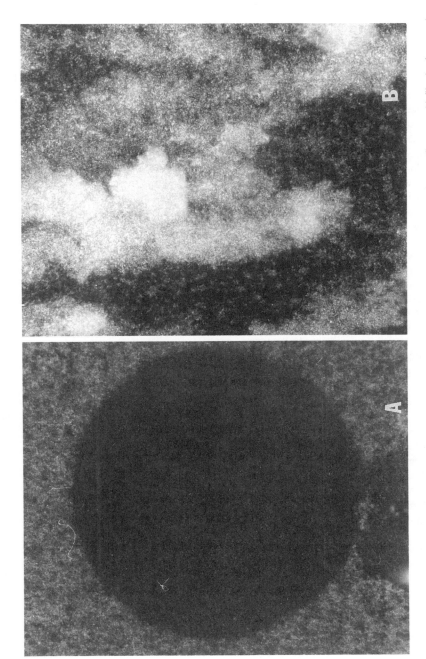

Figure 3. The effect of high light conditions (plumbicon camera)(A) and low light conditions (SIT camera)(B) on *Pseudomonas fluorescens* biofilm development. A circular zone of inhibition (left) corresponding to the lamp diaphragm aperture is apparent in the developing biofilm exposed to the high light intensities required by the plumbicon camera. The unilluminated control is shown on the right. (From Lawrence, *et al.*, 1989a, *J. Microbiol. Methods* **10**:123–138, reprinted with permission.) Darkfield photograph.

do high-magnification phase images. The cells appear as light objects on a dark background, facilitating the conversion of the image into binary format for image processing. This also facilitates the detection of solitary cells in adsorption studies. However, in low-magnification darkfield images, cell area no longer represents the projection of a 3-D cell on a 2-D surface. Instead, each object represents a point light source, the brighter the source, the larger the appearance (2-D area) of the object, and the greater the cell number and/or biomass at the light source. Darkfield measurements could be improved further if the brightness of the pixels (picture elements) within each object was integrated with object size to measure growth.

Differential interference contrast (DIC) may be used to create a signal with maximum information content for objects of interest while virtually eliminating other signals. DIC was used by McLean *et al.* (1991) during a study of struvite crystal formation and dissolution within *Proteus mirabilis* biofilms. Using phase-contrast microscopy, the crystals were obscured by the bacterial biofilm. DIC virtually eliminated the cells and organics within the biofilm, creating an image in which crystal formation could easily be monitored.

Fluorescence microscopy extends the range of information that can be obtained by image analyses from size, shape, and behavior information to include the identification of cells, proteins, carbohydrates, and nucleic acids. However, the low signal intensity and tendency of fluorescent molecular probes to fade, requires the use of light-sensitive television cameras (see previous section), and extensive image processing to accurately define the cell boundary (Sieracki *et al.*, 1989).

Videocassette (tape) recorders (VCR or VTR) are frequently used to store image data, enabling retrieval and playback to an image processing computer at a later time. This is useful because videotape allows repeated analysis of recorded images to test new hypotheses, measure new parameters, or to change the interval between image analysis in time-course studies (to a minimum of 1/30 sec) at a small fraction of the cost for digital image storage. Time-lapse recorders have also proved useful for specific applications, such as the analysis of bacterial growth and motion (Power and Marshall, 1988; Korber *et al.*, 1989b). The capability to simultaneously insert time/date information onto the tape, thereby providing a permanent record of time and identification reference information, is necessary for most scientific applications. Video recording equipment varies in terms of quality and expense. The limiting factor in image resolution for standard video analysis is the VCR (approximately 300-line resolution for many standard models) and not the camera or the monitor (frequently 600-line resolution); thus, selection of an inappropriate VCR, television camera, or monitor may result in appreciable losses in image quality, illumination, and field size. Additional information concerning video microscopy has been summarized by Inoué (1986).

2.4. Image Analysis Systems

There are a number of different image analysis systems currently available. The systems vary in system architecture (parallel or pipeline), gray level resolution (64, 128, or 256 gray levels), programming languages, computer–user interface (menu or command driven), potential for software modification, system memory configurations and capacity, and whether the system is a dedicated image processor or an add-on unit configured for use with PCs (personal computers). Add-on digitizer boards represent the most economical means for entry-level image processing primarily because they may be interfaced with existing laboratory computer equipment. For example, Meijer *et al.* (1990) used an IBM PC/AT computer equipped with a video digitizer board to characterize bacterial species using morphological analysis. The video board contained RAM sufficient for the digitization and storage of four 512 × 512 pixel images, including memory for overlays and lookup tables. Dedicated systems have higher initial and coincident costs, but characteristically operate more rapidly and are more flexible in the types of analyses which may be conducted. Gualtieri *et al.* (1988) used an integrated computer/digitizer system to study the motion of microorganisms. A VDC 501 image processor (Tesak, Florence), which digitized analog signals using an 8-bit analog–digital (A–D) converter, was interfaced with a PDP-11 computer, which controlled the image processing functions as well as videotape positioning. Custom programming of this system allowed the user to analyze microorganism position and direction, and also provided more advanced decision-making power than commonly available in less-expensive systems. Our group utilized an IBAS 2000 image processing computer (Kontron, Eching, FRG) during the analyses of various microbial growth and behavioral events (Lawrence *et al.*, 1987, 1989a,b; Korber *et al.*, 1989a,b, 1990). The computer consisted of a parallel-architecture image array processor integrated with a host computer, allowing real-time digitization, manipulation, and storage of up to 14–512 × 512 pixel images. The end-use of the image analysis system and the sophistication of the image processing steps desired must be of primary consideration prior to the purchase of an image processing system (DeYoung, 1988). Reductions in the cost of computer RAM memory and increases in microprocessor operating speeds have resulted in more powerful, add-on image processing capabilities. Thus, current-generation add-on systems are suitable for the majority of microbiological analysis. For a complete review of image analysis systems, refer to Russ (1990).

2.5. Image Processing

Image analysis involves a number of functions linked together to form a path of computer operations common to most, if not all, image analysis procedures. These steps include image acquisition, image processing, image segmentation and object recognition, object measurement, and data output (summarized in Fig. 4).

2.5.1. Primary Image

Initially, an analog image must be converted into a digitized image (a matrix of pixels assigned gray values ranging from black to white) before storage in computer RAM or disk memory. The manner by which the primary image is digitized is dependent on the intended analysis. Image averaging improves the quality of the primary image by reducing nonimage electrical interference (electric noise or snow, pixel dropout) com-

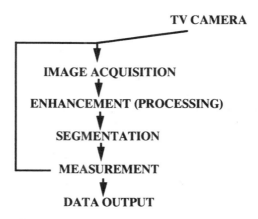

Figure 4. A summary of the procedure most commonly used for digital image processing and analysis.

mon to all television cameras (Inoué, 1986), and by eliminating objects which move during the image averaging process. Averaging a large number of images, or image summing, has been utilized to bring out faintly visible or low-intensity signals common to fluorescence applications (Inoué, 1986). Thus, as the application requires and where hardware permits, the benefits of image averaging should always be exploited. For example, image averaging may be used to improve the quality of images where stationary objects are of primary interest, as in the case of attached bacteria or the analysis of biofilms at discrete time intervals (Korber *et al.*, 1989a; Lawrence *et al.*, 1989b).

Situations where image averaging is not applicable include the analysis of moving objects or where the elimination of stationary or nongrowing objects is the objective of the analysis. Korber *et al.* (1989b) digitized single TV images to determine the total number of diatoms present with the field of analysis (stationary and moving) at any given point in time. The single image input "froze" all moving objects allowing their enumeration. As well, images may not require image averaging provided that they are of sufficient quality for processing without any enhancement. This will increase the speed of analysis and also free memory locations for other computer operations. For difference imagery applications, collection of two single images, followed by image subtraction will result in the elimination of all nonmoving or nongrowing cells (Caldwell, 1985; Lawrence *et al.*, 1989a).

2.5.2. Image Enhancement

There are a number of operations which may be used to enhance images prior to measurement of the desired parameters, including: transformation of the gray level distribution, filtration operations (median, low-pass, nonlinear low-pass, Gaussian, Laplacian, gradient, contrast enhancement, etc.), image subtraction, addition, multiplication, object erosion, and object dilation. These operations may be followed by or preceded by manual image editing, allowing the user to alter the image interactively.

Optical imperfections and microscope misalignment frequently result in the uneven illumination of the primary image, often causing analysis difficulties during subsequent image processing steps (Caldwell, 1985). Thus, primary images should be corrected for uneven illumination prior to image processing. Peters (1990) used shading corrections to eliminate uneven lighting and also to remove particulate debris present within the optical system. Generally, shading corrections involve the digitization and storage of the study surface illuminated under study conditions before inoculation (reference image). The microorganisms are then added to the system and the objects may then be digitized, correcting each digital image against the stored reference image prior to parameter measurement. If the system is aligned and no debris is present, the gray level shading correction will have a zero gray level value. If uneven illumination exists, the gray level of the shading correction will be subtracted from the gray level of the image, thereby eliminating localized bright spots or surface imperfections but not the cells introduced after collection of the reference image (Caldwell, 1985).

Image processors detect changes in object size, brightness, or position by relating the gray levels of individual pixels with neighboring pixels. Ideally, the gray level distribution of an image should encompass the entire range available (0–255), resulting in a high-contrast image. As this is rarely the case, image normalization may be used to improve the overall contrast of the image. Gray level normalization determines the spread of the gray level distribution and reassigns new pixel gray level values to each image pixel, resulting in a new distribution of image gray level values which utilize the entire intensity range. Korber *et al.* (1989b) used gray level histogram analyses of diatom images, finding that the gray level distribution was not normally partitioned over the usable gray level range. This resulted in a relatively low-contrast image which led to underestimation of the measured parameter. Following gray level normalization, the entire gray level range was utilized and image contrast was enhanced.

Image filtration may also be used to improve images of poor quality (Korber *et al.,* 1989b; Sjollema *et al.,* 1989). Digital filtration proceeds in a pixel-by-pixel fashion, altering the values of individual pixels with respect to a matrix of surrounding pixels. A low-pass, or smoothing, filter averages the brightness of a central pixel with respect to a matrix (i.e., 3 × 3) of neighboring pixel brightness values. The filtration algorithm is applied to all pixels contained in the original image, replacing the old image with an "enhanced" version. This type of computer operation is similar for most filtration enhancement steps; however, the algorithm specifying the specific computations varies. Korber *et al.* (1989b) utilized nonlinear low-pass filtration to improve the quality of images obtained from a video recorder. The low-quality primary images obtained from a copied videotape dictated the enhancement of the image; however, the blurring effect of the smoothing filter (low-pass) was not acceptable. Use of nonlinear low-pass filtration eliminated random noise interference without blurring the edges of larger objects (diatoms). For theory and review of these and other filtration operations, readers should consult Gonzalez and Wintz (1977).

2.5.3. Object Recognition

Once the image has been sufficiently processed to allow unbiased measurement, object recognition (thresholding or discrimination) within an image may either be performed manually or using a probabilistic model (Lawrence *et al.*, 1989a; Sieracki *et al.*, 1989). During object recognition by thresholding, pixels with a gray value below a defined threshold value (a pixel brightness of between 0 and 256) are considered background (gray value reset to 0) and pixels with a gray level above the threshold value are redefined as objects (gray level reset to 256), each set of contiguous object pixels being considered an individual object within a newly created binary image. However, problems may arise from poorly defined threshold values, resulting in either over- or underestimation of areal measurements. In most image analysis programs the user may interactively change the specified threshold value and see its effect on the resulting binary image. More advanced methods of thresholding are also commonly used. These often include digital filters and other mathematical transformations as an integral part of the thresholding process, to more accurately define object boundaries.

There are a number of methods whereby the user may accurately define the threshold value. Histogram analysis was used by Gualtieri *et al.* (1988) to facilitate the placement of the gray-value threshold during study of euglenoid motility. When the threshold level was set within the dip between the image histogram peaks (where the peaks represented objects and background), the most effective images were obtained. Sieracki *et al.* (1989) evaluated automated threshold selection during the analysis of fluorescent objects and found that user threshold selection usually resulted in an overestimation of the object size. Because the optical nature of the fluorescent object edge is different from that of images generated from transmitted light, they determined that thresholding fluorescent images required special consideration. The authors tested a number of different automated thresholding algorithms and found that a nondirectional, second-derivative-finding filter (Laplacian filter) offered the best performance during measurement of fluorescent objects without being subject to user-defined visual thresholding. Automated thresholding functions should not be universally applied to all image analysis situations, as automatic settings do not necessarily agree with each other or with the manual settings of an experienced operator.

Following thresholding and formation of a binary image, the user may then choose to interactively edit the image to remove minor imperfections (automatically fill holes, eliminate electronic noise, etc.), or measure the desired parameters directly. Objects may then be selected or eliminated on the basis of size (Lawrence *et al.*, 1989a), shape (Meijer *et al.*, 1990), direction of movement (Gualtieri *et al.*, 1985, 1988; Korber *et al.*, 1989b), or position (Caldwell and Germida, 1985). Other measurement parameters include area or volume determinations (Bjornsen, 1986; Lawrence and Caldwell, 1987), morphometric analysis (Sjollema *et al.*, 1989), nearest-neighbor analysis (Korber *et al.*, 1990), enumeration (Sieracki *et al.*, 1985, 1989), and densitometric analyses. Analysis for parameters not supplied with software packages may often be programmed by the user if support software exists for this purpose.

2.5.4. Difference Imagery

Difference imagery (the digitization of two sequential images and subtraction of their respective gray values) may be used to detect changes within the field of analysis over discrete time intervals, showing the difference between the two images as black objects on a gray background (Caldwell, 1985). This technique is commonly used in the electronics industry, with an "ideal" circuit board image stored in memory and compared with newly produced circuit boards as a means for quality control, and also in satellite remote sensing applications. During microbiological analyses, difference imagery may be used to detect the number of moving objects within the field of analysis, or may identify those cells or microcolonies which exhibit growth over a defined interval. Caldwell and Germida (1985) used difference imagery to study the growth kinetics of *Ensifer adherens* in agar slide culture, evaluating the potential for distinguishing growing cells from fine clay particles. Difference imagery has also been used to enumerate the number of motile cells present within the hydrodynamic boundary layer of continuous-flow slide culture chambers during the recolonization phase of surface-colonizing bacteria (Fig. 5) (Korber *et al.*, 1989a; Lawrence *et al.*, 1989a). This 2-D procedure was restricted in that only cells moving within the focal plane could effectively be detected and quantified. The possibility of creating 3-D volumetric reconstructions of thick biofilms and processing them using difference imaging methods, would permit a better understanding of more complex 3-D movements and of time-dependent changes in microenvironmental chemistry.

Alternately, image summation may also be performed. Lawrence *et al.* (1989b) used image summation and Helmert transformation (Gonzalez and Wintz, 1977) to electronically increase the depth of field. Phase micrographs were obtained from different focal planes, enhanced, aligned, and summed to create composite 2-D images for discrimination and quantitative analysis of *Pedomicrobium* sp. growth and development. Using summed images, growth rates were determined for mother and daughter cells which were not developing within the same focal plane. Thus, this technique increased the effective resolution and operating depth of field for the light microscope.

2.5.5. Pseudocolor

In images where the gray level histogram is narrowly distributed, normalizing the gray level distribution throughout the 0–255 range (gray level transformation) can serve to increase image contrast. However, when the image utilizes the full dynamic range of the display device, there are no unrepresented gray values, and thus contrast cannot be further enhanced. To more fully appreciate and interpret information contained in gray level images, pseudocolor transformation techniques that reassign the gray values for pixels to color values defined in a color lookup table may be used to increase contrast, since the human eye can distinguish many more colors than shades of gray (DeYoung, 1988). This is especially important where small changes in gray value represent a significant change in some biological parameter (e.g., use of pH- or E_h-sensitive fluorescent probes) (Lawrence and Caldwell, 1990).

Using pseudocolor representation, subtle changes in gray level which define the boundary of a bacterium, may be easily visualized. Figure 6A (see color insert) shows a pseudocolor representation of a bacterium, *Vibrio parahaemolyticus,* clearly defining the boundary of the cells which the computer uses during area measurement (the area of

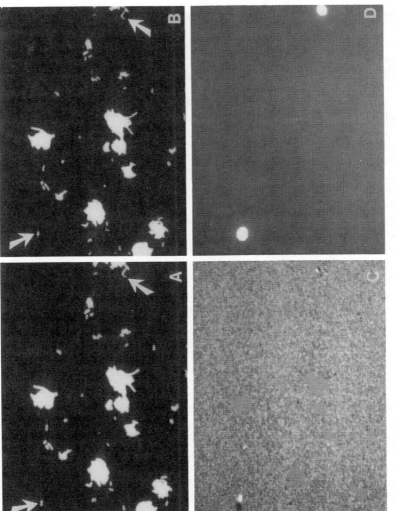

Figure 5. A summary of the image processing steps necessary to analyze cell motility by difference imaging. (A) Primary darkfield image showing vibrio colonies and moving cells (arrows); (B) second primary image taken after a time delay; (C) difference image (the result of subtracting images A and B); (D) discriminated, dilated display image showing the location and number of moving cells. (From Lawrence *et al.*, 1989a, *J. Microbiol. Methods* **10:**123–138, reprinted with permission.) Image processing of digitized video images.

blue-to-red transition). In the original gray value image (Fig. 6B; see color insert) these boundaries are difficult to locate by inspecting the image visually. Thus, exact boundaries, as defined by user thresholding, may be visualized using pseudocolor. Pseudocolor can also be used to create a color map in which each color represents a specific pH, E_h, protein concentration, carbohydrate concentration, nucleic acid concentration, calcium concentration, etc. within an image (see Section 8.0).

2.5.6. 3-D Image Analysis, Processing, and Rendering

To date, most CEM digital processing relies on 2-D image information. However, most real-world events occur in three dimensions. This problem has been overcome by recent advances in laser microscopy which permit the optical sectioning of biological materials without optical interference from other focal planes (Agard et al., 1989a,b; Carlsson et al., 1989; Carlsson and Lileborg, 1989; Shotton, 1989; Shotton and White, 1989). This allows the reconstruction of 3-D biofilms, cell aggregates, and microcolonies as 3-D digital images based on the information contained in optodigital thin sections (Lawrence et al., 1991). Software packages which permit the analysis of cell volume and other biofilm parameters using 3-D image processing are currently available, although limitations do exist. Image processing involving three dimensions is memory intensive, due to the large data base required to perform these calculations (i.e., a 512 × 512 × 512 pixel image would require approximately 135 Mbytes of storage space). The individual spots of light of which a 2-D digital image is composed are referred to as picture elements or pixels. 3-D volumetric, digital images are composed of volume elements or voxels. It should be noted that a 3-D stereo pair or a 3-D, red–blue image is not a 3-D image in the fullest sense of a 3-D volumetric image. The stereo pair and red–blue image represent illusions which are visually perceived as being three-dimensional. However, a 3-D digital image consists of an array of voxels which completely fill an imaginary 3-D space and which contain more information than can be presented in a single 2-D image. Consequently, the viewer is presented with a 2-D illusion of the 3-D simulation.

Indec (Indec Systems, Sunnyvale, Calif.) offers the MicroVoxel package, an IBM-compatible OS-2 system which requires a minimum of 4-Mbyte RAM and 70-Mbyte hard disk space. This package is capable of viewing orthogonal slices in the x, y, and z planes, image transformations, image rendering, extraction and viewing of volumes of images, image animation, and image analysis. A Macintosh-compatible package for the visualization of volumetric data is Spyglass (Spyglass Inc., Champaign, Ill.), a system which permits loading of 3-D data sets and simultaneous display as a set of horizontal, vertical, or parallel slices.

3-D image analysis is not only memory intensive but extremely slow. For example, to measure the diameter of a cell in 2-D requires that the center of gravity for the cell be computed. A series of lines are then drawn through the cell in all directions within the plane of the surface. Most commonly, 32 lines are drawn. The longest of these is then used as the maximum dimension or length of the object (D_{max}) and the shortest of these is taken as the minimum dimension or width of the object (D_{min}). However, to perform the same analysis volumetrically requires that the 32 lines also be drawn at 32 angles around the axis of the cell. This specifies that a total of 1024 lines be measured and increases the computational time by a factor of 32.

There are two primary types of rendering that can be performed on 3-D digital images. These are volumetric and surface rendering. The process of rendering is a series of steps during which a 3-D array of numbers (the brightness and/or color) of a set of voxels (in 3-D space) is presented as a 3-D image on a 2-D computer monitor. In the case of volume rendering, all of the voxels in a specific range of brightness are set to a specific color or made translucent. Using MicroVoxel, a video animation can be created through volumetric rendering, in which the rendered objects rotate in 3-D as they fade in and out (becoming periodically translucent) to reveal a subset of objects within, rendered in a different color. Also using MicroVoxel, one or more imaginary colored light sources can be projected onto a hypothetical surface, producing shadows behind surface protrusions and irregularities. This surface rendering technique highlights surface topography and produces images that appear similar to scanning electron micrographs although produced using a light microscope. Using Spyglass, the positioning of objects within is rendered volumetrically by showing a series of thin sections standing in a row, like dominoes, with enough space between each to see the organization of objects within the original 3-D cube. Using Spyglass, these sections can also be represented as color-coded contour maps.

2.5.7. Data Output

Data may be output in either visual or numerical formats, depending on the end-use or whether the data are to be processed further in another computer system. Visual forms of data include graphic representations, video printer outputs, or screen photographs. Screen photographs of enhanced images may be obtained by photographing the computer monitor using shutter speeds longer (greater than 1/4 sec) than the raster scan rate of the monitor device (usually 1/30 sec) (Korber *et al.*, 1989b; Lawrence *et al.*, 1991). Dedicated flat-screen monitors with CRT (cathode-ray tube) cones function well for these applications and reduce spherical aberrations common to curved television screens. Data may also be downloaded from the image processing computer to PCs for plotting. Zanyk *et al.* (1991) used an RS-232 interface and terminal emulation to transport data from an IBAS 2000 image processor to a Macintosh to produce 4-D images using MacSpin software. This was then used to analyze the growth and development of *Pseudomonas fragi* microcolonies in continuous-flow slide culture. Many PC-based image analysis systems also store data as ASCII files, which can be accessed using numerous spreadsheet or graphics packages.

2.5.8. Deconvolution

Deconvolution is a process whereby the haze caused by stray light (which is due primarily to diffraction in diffraction-limited lens systems) is removed from a digital image. This is done by determining the point-spread function (PSF) of a specific optical

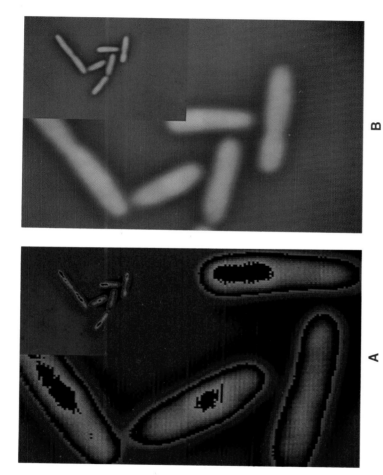

A

B

Figure 6. Pseudocolor rendering of *Vibrio parahaemolyticus* electronically enlarged twofold, enhancing contrast between the cell and its background to better define the boundary used by the computer during area measurements (A). A color lookup table was used to show a color change at the gray level where thresholding was applied. The outer cell boundary is marked by a color transition from black to light blue, forming a light-blue halo encircling each cell. At high magnification, each boundary pixel is clearly shown as either blue or black. The inset shows an unmagnified pseudocolor image of the same field of bacteria. B shows a gray value representation of the same bacteria electronically enlarged twofold. The inset contains an unmagnified image of the same field of bacteria as that shown in A. Human visual perception is less sensitive to changes in levels of gray as compared to color changes, making the cell boundary in the gray level image difficult to consistently define. (Pseudocolor rendering of a digitized video image.)

Figure 25. A 20-μm-thick *Vibrio parahaemolyticus* biofilm. Continuous-flow slide cultures were inoculated at time zero and subsequently irrigated with sterile medium. (3-D laser micrograph shown as a red–blue anaglyph projection which was constructed from a set of seven serial laser micrographs showing living cells, *in situ*, and obtained using fluorescein as a fluorescent negative stain. View with red/blue 3-D glasses.)

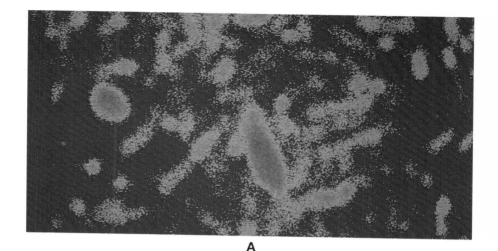

A

B

Figure 26. Horizontal (x, y) optical thin sections showing (A) penetration of a 35,000-mol. wt. FITC dextran at the base of a *Vibrio parahaemolyticus* biofilm (red coloration indicates fluorescence intensity equal to that in the bulk phase); (B) penetration of a 487,000-mol. wt. FITC dextran at the same depth in the *Vibrio* biofilm. Note that the 35,600-mol. wt. dextran penetrated to the base of the biofilm, whereas the 487,000-mol. wt. dextran was effectively excluded. Continuous-flow slide cultures were inoculated at time zero and subsequently irrigated with sterile medium. (Pseudocolor rendering of laser micrographs showing living cells, *in situ*, and obtained using fluoroscein-conjugated dextrans of varying molecular weights as fluorescent negative stains.)

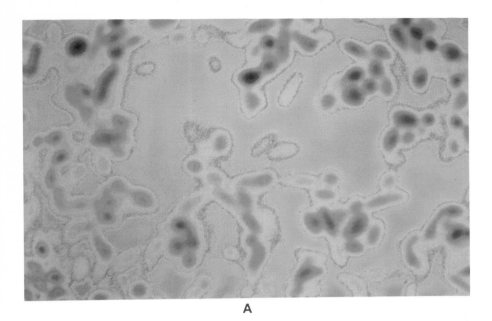

A

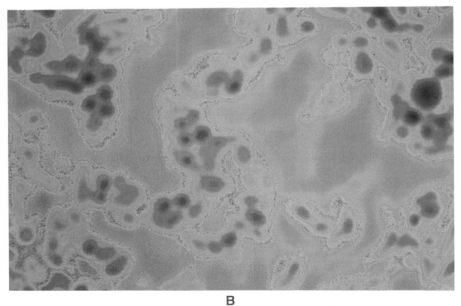

B

Figure 28. Pseudocolor images within a 10-μm thick *Vibrio parahaemolyticus* biofilm showing variations in fluorescence intensity of the pH-sensitive molecular probe, 5 and 6 carboxyfluorescein. Each image is an optodigital thin section at a different depth (0.5 μm, 2.5 μm, 6.0 μm, and 10.0 μm) within the biofilm. Continuous-flow slide cultures were inoculated at time zero and subsequently irrigated with sterile medium. Blue areas indicate the lack of fluorescence due to the lack of penetration by the probe (cells) or areas where

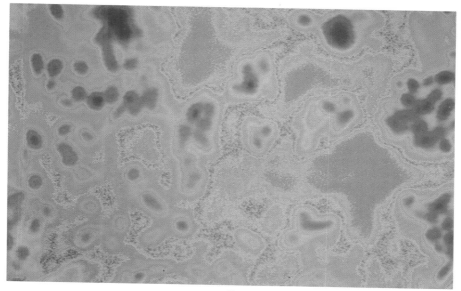

C

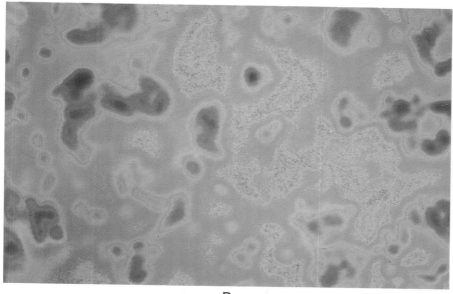

D

fluorescence of the probe is inhibited by low pH. Orange indicates areas where the fluorescence of the probe was not suppressed by lack of penetration or reduced pH. Note that pH gradients surrounded all of the cells and cell aggregates. Note the void spaces and channels within the biofilm. (Laser micrographs of living cells, *in situ* within a flow cell, obtained using 5 and 6 carboxyfluorescein as a fluorescent negative stain.)

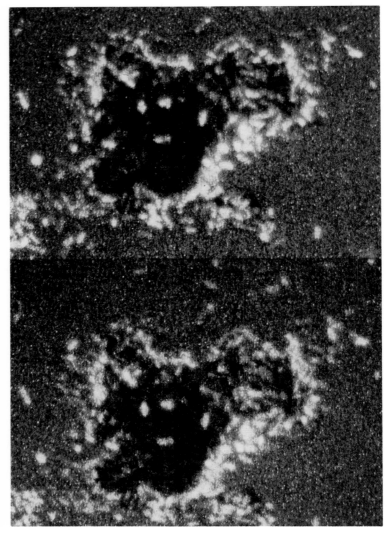

Figure 29. Dual-channel, red–blue anaglyph projection of a series of thin sections from *Vibrio parahaemolyticus* forming a corrosion pit on a mild steel coupon after a 48-hr incubation period in batch culture. Fluorescence gradients occurred from the surface and outer edge of the pit to the center, suggesting pH/E_h gradients and the formation of an electrolytic corrosion cell within a single microcolony. The image shown in the right window was visualized using carboxyfluorescein as a pH-dependent fluorescent probe (fluorescence intensity reduced at low pH). The image shown in the left window was visualized using resorufin as an E_h-dependent probe (fluorescent when oxidized, nonfluorescent when reduced). Red–blue anaglyph projection of serial laser micrographs (to be viewed with red/blue 3-D glasses).

A

B

Figure 30. Digital imaging of biofilm communities colonizing the surface of two-dimensional steady-state diffusion gradients. (A) A gradient of two test dyes, safranine (bottom edge) and crystal violet (right edge) to illustrate the concept of perpendicular steady-state diffusion gradients. (B) The sulphureta and nitroeta which form on the gradients of ammonium sulfate (left edge) and thiosulfate (bottom edge). (C) The banded rainbow pseudocolor map which is used to define contour bands when the biofilm image is too complex to produce meaningful contour lines. (D) The same biofilm using a standard rainbow pseudocolor map with labeled contour lines and labeled pseudocolor legend.

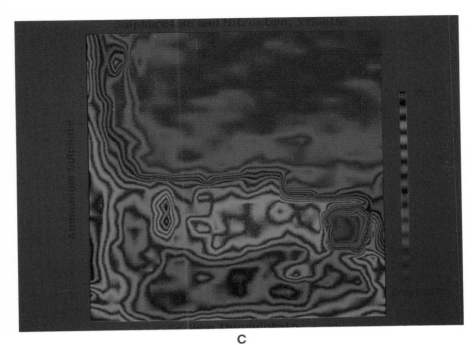

C

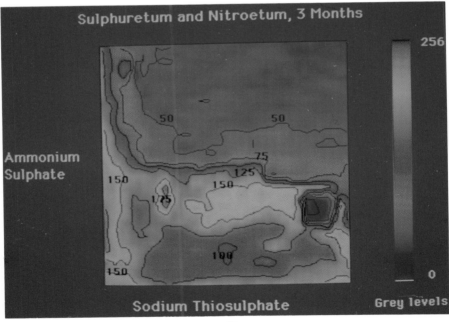

D

Figure 30 *(Continued)*

system and using it to create an optical transfer function necessary to deconvolve 3-D digital image data (Shaw and Rawlins, 1991). This approach can be applied either to traditional optical microscopy or confocal laser microscopy. The simplest example is the nearest neighbor deconvolution (NND). The PSF is determined by focusing on a point light source (0.04 μm fluorescent beads). The 3-D image of the source consists primarily of stray light and is normally egg-shaped rather than spherical, due to low axial resolution as compared to lateral resolution. The NND uses three adjacent optodigital thin sections to predict where stray light from objects in the upper and lower sections enters the middle section. This stray light is then digitally subtracted from the middle section. Deconvolution procedures may eventually increase the resolution of light microscopes beyond the current theoretical resolution of diffraction-limited lens systems. They also offer the possibility of obtaining confocal quality images using epifluorescence or phase microscopy (Kesterson and Richardson, 1991). This is particularly important due to the limited number of excitation wavelengths available in laser microscopy as opposed to epifluorescence microscopy. This is only possible under ideal conditions where objects are not too densely packed, however, and cannot approach the quality of confocal laser images that have been deconvolved (Shaw and Rawlins, 1991). Commercial deconvolution software (Micro-Tome) is available from VayTek, Inc. (Fairfield, Iowa) and runs on Macintosh II computers and IBM AT clones.

3. Confocal Laser Microscopy

3.1. Strengths and Weaknesses of Confocal Laser Imaging

In conventional light microscopy, all light passing through the specimen is imaged directly and simultaneously. The resulting image is formed instantly and can be viewed directly. However, these conventional images lack clarity and fail to accurately represent 3-D objects. Stray light from above, below, and beside an object interferes with formation of the object's image. In CLM, the confocal pinholes at the laser and at the detector eliminate these sources of interference. Because light from above and below the plane of focus is not included when the image is formed, the image can be considered an optodigital thin section with a thickness approaching the theoretical resolution of the light microscope (~ 0.2 μm) depending on the lenses used and the size of the confocal pinhole. Light emitted from a fluorescent molecular probe can be measured analytically, as though it were contained in an optodigital spectrofluorometer cuvette with a well-defined volume. Consequently, the 2-D image formed using CLM is a more accurate representation of the specimen and can be used for precise analytical measurements of molecular concentrations as well as morphology.

The laser microscope not only produces a more accurate 2-D image but can also be used to produce 3-D images. This is done by digitizing a sequential series of 2-D (x–y) images obtained while focusing through the specimen in the third (z) dimension. This series of images, sometimes referred to as a z-series, is used to create a 3-D reconstruction of the specimen. The objects in this reconstruction may be rendered in various colors, as though illuminated from various directions by multiple sources of light, or made translucent to visualize objects within objects. They can also be viewed as a stereo pair (with the aid of a stereoscope), a red–green pair (with the aid of red–green stereo glasses), a rotating video animation (using a VCR), or as objects floating in space (using a multiplanar display system; Emmett, 1991).

However, there are several pitfalls involved in applying CLM to microbiological specimens. A fluorescent stain (fluorescent molecular probe) is normally used to visualize objects or the chemistry associated with objects. This may lead to difficulties during the analyses of environmental samples which autofluoresce. In addition, laser microscopes tend to be more restricted in the number of filter combinations available as compared to those used in epifluorescence microscopy. An additional concern is that the scanning action of the laser beam takes time. The better the image, the more time is required. Thus, construction of a 3-D image can be a slow process. It requires that a series of 2-D images (optodigital thin sections) be digitized. Each image or section is constructed by scanning several times and averaging to create a composite image which contains less electronic noise (snow) and fewer vibration artifacts than the individual scans. However, the process of averaging results in a loss of contrast and resolution if noise and vibration are excessive. Consequently, if good results are to be obtained at high magnifications, care must be taken to minimize artifacts.

During the construction of a 3-D image the laser beam passes repeatedly through points both above and below the focal plane, which are not currently being imaged, but which are subjected to repeated photobleaching. However, because the detector is a highly light-sensitive photomultiplier, fading is not severe. Another problem due to the scanning beam is that objects which are opaque to the laser beam and which occur above and below the specimen can sometimes cause shadows to appear on objects in the focal plane (see Section 3.8).

Slow scan rates make it difficult to focus on the specimen and pinpoint a location of interest. In addition, there is no out-of-focus image which gradually becomes clearer as the specimen comes into focus. The combination of a slow scan rate and the lack of an out-of-focus image, often make it difficult to find an extremely thin specimen. Epifluorescence microscopy may be used to focus in on and scan a specimen while the laser is used only when a 3-D reconstruction or optical section is required. When using epifluorescence to focus or search across a field, severe photobleaching can occur and an ISIT or similar light-sensitive television camera is required to avoid damaging the specimen. Similarly, it is equally important to use a programmable motorized stage so that several fluorescent objects, to be observed over a time course, can be relocated without having to repeatedly search and realign each field.

3.2. CLM versus Conventional Light Microscopy

The strength of CLM is that it precisely analyzes 3-D specimens in 3-D rather than assuming that they are 2-D and collapsing them into a 2-D image. For example, with epifluorescence, phase, or brightfield microscopy, stray light from above and below the focal plane interferes with the object being viewed in the focal plane. These out-of-focus images obscure the object of interest. In addition, stray light originating from other objects in the same focal plane can also reduce clarity. Consequently, a digitized phase or brightfield image cannot readily be discriminated (thresholded) by computer image analysis. However, with CLM the optodigital thin section greatly reduces out-of-focus cell material and more accurately defines cell boundaries as well as the chemistry associated with cells. Therefore, it is possible to nondestructively analyze and quantify a 3-D assemblage of microbial cells in a biofilm or bioaggregate using CLM but not using conventional light microscopy. This provides the ability to quantify microorganisms as they occur *in situ* in 3-D associations with one another or in association with plant, animal, and mineral surfaces. It also provides an optodigital cuvette in which fluorescence can be quantified and used to create pseudocolor images identifying organisms, proteins, enzymatic activity, metabolism, etc. It should also be possible to visualize gene expression by using the photon-counting mode when viewing organisms with lux insertions in the promoter region of specific genetic sequences.

3.3 CLM versus Electron Microscopy (SEM and TEM)

The $x-y$ resolution of the CLM is not significantly improved over the conventional light microscope, the limiting constraint being the wavelength of light used and the design of the lenses. The electron microscope greatly improves resolution but normally requires that the sample be dehydrated, embedded in plastic, or shadowed with a metal coating. This frequently produces artifacts. With CLM, living material can be examined over a time course without altering the growth and metabolism of living cells. A photomultiplier is used as the detector of fluorescence emission during laser microscopy. Consequently, a very low-intensity, nondestructive laser beam can be used to scan the specimen. This nondestructive approach is invaluable in observing relations between microbial cells and their ambient microenvironment and in observing *in situ* time courses. For example, it allows periodic scanning of individual bacterial cells in continuous-flow slide culture to follow the time course of cell division (Lawrence and Caldwell, 1990; Caldwell *et al.*, 1992). However, the laser is generally too inhibitory to allow continual scanning and observation of living prokaryotic cells, as in the case of phase microscopy using ISIT television systems (see Section 2.2, Figs. 2 and 3). Although eukaryotic cells can often be continuously scanned without any adverse effects, prokaryotic cells require higher magnification and consequently a higher-intensity laser beam to produce an acceptable image.

Although it is possible to produce serial sections and a 3-D reconstruction using TEM, the process requires that the specimen be embedded in plastic, thin sectioned with a diamond knife, and then observed. With CLM, a reconstruction based on optical sections can be applied to living tissue, nondestructively in a matter of minutes. However, the production of serial sections from a plastic block, using a diamond knife, requires days for embedding and dehydration and may involve numerous attempts before a set of usable sections are obtained. These must then be mounted, viewed, photographed, digitized, and used to reconstruct the original object.

3.4. CLM versus Scanning Probe Microscopy

Scanning probe microscopy includes scanning tunneling electron microscopy, atomic force microscopy (Drake *et al.*, 1989), scanning ion-conductance microscopy (Hansma *et al.*, 1989a), scanning tunneling microscopy (Hansma *et al.*, 1989b; Martin *et al.*, 1988), and related imaging methods. These techniques normally involve a probe which serves as a sensor and scans the surface topography of cells and materials. While this approach provides atomic resolution of living material, it provides only a surface view (as opposed to a complete internal 3-D volumetric reconstruction) of the objects being studied. In addition, it cannot utilize fluorescent molecular probes to visualize internal structure and chemistry.

3.5. Spectral Emission of Confocal Lasers

Argon lasers emit primarily blue light and are most commonly used in laser micro-scopes. They are relatively inexpensive and reliable, with lifetimes ranging from 5000 to 10,000 hr (Gratton and vandeVen, 1990). They produce primary emission peaks at 488 and 514 nm, and also a number of other smaller peaks from 274 to 528 nm. The wavelengths available depend upon the optical elements used in laser construction and the number of useful peaks available from an argon or from other types of gas lasers depend to some extent upon the manufacturer's design.

The argon laser is considered optimal for fluorescein and its derivatives (excitation maximum of approximately 490 nm) but suboptimal for rhodamine and other fluors which require a longer wavelength both for efficient excitation and for more effective separation in dual labeling experiments. Krypton/argon lasers have been introduced and these have major peaks at 586 and 647 nm, as well as the shorter blue wavelengths. This allows optimal excitation of rhodamine and Texas red, respectively. UV lasers are available but prohibitively expensive.

The selection of lasers is most critical in dual-labeling experiments when the requirement for narrow bandpass filters greatly decreases the amount of laser light available unless the laser selected has a major excitation peak at both of the desired excitation wavelengths. Using the BioRad MRC 600 microscope, we and others (Harris, 1991) have found that FITC fades. Harris (1991) suggests using various antifade agents including *p*-phenylenediamine and FITC-Guard (from TESTOG, Inc., Department 476, 2271 North Lincoln Ave., Chicago Ill. 60614, USA). We have found that RITC is less susceptible and use it as an alternative. Both we and Harris (1991) have found that FITC is difficult to separate from RITC in dual-labeling experiments. Harris (1991) suggests the use of Texas red as an alternative to rhodamine in dual-labeling experiments.

3.6. Objective Lenses

CLM places new demands on objective lens systems. The 3-D images which are formed require that the axial (vertical) resolution of these lenses be considered as well as their traditional lateral resolution. In theory, the axial resolution of an objective lens is approximately one-half of the lateral resolution for the same lens, the 3-D image of a diffraction-limited point light source being football-shaped (Linfoot and Wolfe, 1953; Inoué, 1990). While focusing through a sample to obtain the third dimension of a 3-D image, the distance traveled through the coverslip and suspension medium varies depending upon how deeply the focal point of the lens penetrates the specimen. This can result in further axial distortion of the image. Due to these and other effects, 3-D reconstruction of a 1.0- to 0.2-μm latex sphere (a point light source) normally results in an oval-shaped object. These limitations are particularly important when studying bacteria, which are near the limits of resolution.

The depth of 3-D reconstructions depends upon the working distance of the objective. Long-working-distance refractive lenses are available from several manufacturers. In addition, extremely long-working-distance reflective objectives (based on the principle of the reflecting telescope) are also available but have not yet been tried. Long-working-distance lenses usually have a lower numerical aperture, however, and consequently lower resolution.

3.7. Optical Transfer Efficiency

One of the most important factors in CLM is the optical transfer efficiency. If the object is to be viewed nondestructively, then the fluorescence emission must be efficiently collected to minimize the exposure of the specimen to the laser beam. The fluorescence optical transfer efficiency is defined by Wells *et al.* (1990) as "the fraction of the fluorescence light emitted by fluorophores within the focal volume at the object plane that is detected by the photomultiplier tube." The optical transfer efficiency of the mirror system used in the MRC-500 CLM (the first confocal laser microscope commercially available) was 0.32 (32%). In the MRC-600 this was improved to 0.70.

3.8. Reflections, Shadows, and Quenching of the Scanning Laser Beam

If objects in the sample shade one another from the scanning laser beam, the resulting image will appear distorted. Consequently, it is important that the scan beam be intense enough to saturate the fluorescence emission of the fluorescent molecular probe at the maximum depth being imaged. This is particularly important when the specimen is flooded with a fluor, as opposed to using a fluor to stain specific structures. Flooding is sometimes necessary to visualize nonfluorescent objects by negatively staining them. It is also necessary when fluorescent probes are used to visualize the pH or E_h within the ambient microenvironment of microbial cells (also see Section 7.2). Under these circumstances, if the concentration of fluor is too high, the laser beam may be completely or partially quenched before it reaches cells embedded deeply within the sample. If it is too low, the fluorescent emission may not be detected. Consequently, the optimal concentration should be determined in preliminary experiments.

If quenching does occur or if opaque objects are present outside the focal plane and not accounted for, shadows can easily be misinterpreted as objects, distort the shape of objects, or result in errors in measuring concentration by fluorescence. It is important to remember that fluorescent objects outside the focal plane are likely to quench the scanning laser beam to some extent and that internal reflection of the beam near glass and other reflective surfaces, may result in additional artifacts. Additional information concerning artifacts and other aspects of CLM, as applied to biological specimens, is available in the *Handbook of Biological Confocal Microscopy* (Pawley, 1990) and other publications (White *et al.*, 1987; Brakenhoff *et al.*, 1988; Shotton, 1989; Boyde, 1990).

4. Enumeration and Morphometry

The most frequent application of image analysis techniques in microbiology has been the enumeration of microorganisms on surfaces, or in environmental samples. These applications were prompted by the desire to reduce tedium, while increasing subjectivity, precision, accuracy, and sampling intensity. In addition, the same images may be used to generate estimates of bacterial biovolume and biomass. Although image analysis techniques were available for at least 30 years, it has been during the last 10 that rapid progress was achieved in the application of these techniques to enumeration and biovolume estimates. Early applications of this type in microbiology include Bradbury (1979) and Pettipher and Rodrigues (1982), the latter using epifluorescence and image analysis techniques to enumerate bacteria in milk samples. Application of these techniques to aquatic and marine samples (Fry and Davies, 1985; Sieracki *et al.*, 1985, 1989; Sieracki and Webb, 1986; Bjornsen, 1986; Getliff and Fry, 1989), soil (Wynn-Williams, 1988a,b), and food and fermentations (Costello and Monk, 1985; Fernandes *et al.*, 1988) are now routinely made in many laboratories. Further, Verran and Rocliffe (1986) utilized light microscopy and automatic image analysis to measure dental plaque *in situ*. Image analysis has frequently been applied in conjunction with epifluorescence images but may be effectively applied with phase (Escher and Characklis, 1988) or low-magnification darkfield images (Sjollema *et al.*, 1989; Lawrence *et al.*, 1989a; Korber *et al.*, 1990). All of these studies utilized image analysis techniques to study the attachment kinetics of bacteria to surfaces in flow cells. Biovolume estimates are typically calculated from the measured mean cell areas determined by image analyses, using the appropriate assumptions of spherical cells, spheroid cells (length-to-width ratio of 2), or cylindrical cells. These estimates may also be made for individual cells utilizing data such as area, perimeter, minimum diameter, maximum diameter, and circularity to more accurately define the cell's dimensions or to more accurately classify the cell (Sieracki *et al.*, 1985; Bjornsen, 1986; Krambeck *et al.*, 1990).

Morphometric analyses have been used to correct for clumping of cells during enumeration (Sjollema *et al.*, 1989) and to simultaneously determine the numbers of ciliates and bacterial microcolonies in a marine microcosm (Lawrence *et al.*, 1989a). During the latter study, ciliates were discriminated from bacteria based on their movement and size, showing that bacterial biofilm formation occurred uniformly over time while ciliate numbers increased after 15–20 hr (Fig. 7). Some investigators have also utilized morphometric distributions (length, curvature, chord length, etc.) of bacterial cells to characterize and distinguish different species of bacteria (Meijer *et al.*, 1990). The application in this instance was to carry out automated detection of variations in intestinal microflora. Sjollema *et al.* (1990a) used image analysis to determine the

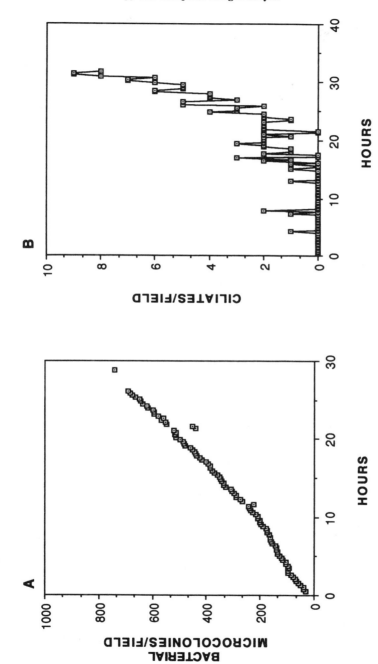

Figure 7. Use of darkfield computer-enhanced microscopy to detect and enumerate grazing ciliates within a marine biofilm consisting primarily of bacteria. Continuous-flow slide cultures were continuously irrigated with water from a marine aquarium. Bacterial attachment and growth occurred at a uniform rate over 30 hr (A), whereas ciliate immigration occurred only after 15–20 hr of bacterial colonization (B). (From Lawrence *et al.*, 1989a, *J. Microbiol. Methods* **10:**123–138, reprinted with permission.)

positions of two species of oral streptococci colonizing a parallel plate flow cell and calculated radial and angular pair distributions of these cells. The results of these calculations showed that there were cooperative effects in the adhesion of these streptococci. Other quantitative uses of image analysis techniques in microbiology include automatic plate counting, monitoring fungal hyphal development, studies of microcolony development, and studies of microbial growth in response to physical chemical gradients (Peters, 1990).

In summary, image analysis techniques have been successfully applied to problems of identification, enumeration, and calculation of biovolumes, and have reduced the tedium associated with these tasks.

5. Analysis of Growth, Metabolism, and Viability

5.1. Direct Measurement of Growth and Viability

Singh *et al.* (1990) combined the procedure for determining viable but noncultureable bacteria with computer image analysis. The method is based upon the use of specific inhibitors (DNA gyrase) to allow growth but not cell division. In the presence of the inhibitor, growing cells become elongated but are unable to undergo binary fission. By applying image analysis, the number of elongated cells was determined and compared to control samples incubated in the absence of the inhibitor. This procedure might also be used to determine the rate of bacterial growth.

One of the first attempts to measure the growth rate of individual cells within a population was Staley's use of an immersed microscope and water immersion lens to measure the interdivision time for algal cells growing in a forest pond (Staley, 1971). By using computer-based image analysis, the growth rate of individual cells can be determined more accurately and over time intervals which are much shorter than a single division cycle. The accuracy of these measurements has been evaluated by comparing them to growth rates calculated from interdivision times and plots of cell number versus time (Caldwell and Lawrence, 1986).

Measurement of microbial growth rates by image analysis involves stereological assumptions inherent in analyzing 3-D objects using 2-D image analysis. In 2-D images, the growth of microorganisms is seen as changes in cell area. Cell area is the area occupied by the projection of a 3-D cell on a 2-D surface. If bacterial cells are growing as a monolayer on a glass or mineral surface, this method can be used to calculate both the actual growth rates (rate of increase in cell area) and specific growth rates (instantaneous fractional rate of increase in cell area) (Caldwell and Germida, 1985; Caldwell and Lawrence, 1986). However, if cells are growing in 3-D aggregates, 2-D image analysis cannot be used to analyze their rate of growth. The projections of cells positioned above and below one another overlap, resulting in underestimation of growth rates. Under these conditions, CLM could be used to construct a 3-D image of the aggregation and directly determine cell volumes as described in Section 2.5.6. This latter approach has not yet been applied in microbial ecology.

5.2. Difference Imaging of Growth

Bacterial growth has been directly visualized by using difference imagery (Caldwell and Germida, 1985). This method can be used to discriminate growing cells from dead cells, fine sand, clay particles, and other debris to obtain a more accurate direct viable count and to calculate the rate of cell growth. The image of bacterial cells is digitized at time zero and after a short time interval. By subtracting the first image from the second, a difference image is constructed showing only the differences between the two original images, and removing any objects which remain unchanged. Consequently, only growing or moving cells are visible in the difference image. Areas of cell growth appear as dark objects. Areas where cells have moved from one location to another produce a light area where the cells were originally positioned and a dark area where they have relocated. By subtracting the light areas from the corresponding dark areas, calculations of growth rate can be corrected for cell movement. In the analysis of 3-D images the same principle would apply but the light and dark areas would be replaced by light and dark volumes. However, difference imaging has not yet been applied to 3-D volumetric images.

5.3. Visualization of Microbial Activity and Viability using Fluorescent Molecular Probes

Fluorescent molecular probes have also been used to image bacterial metabolic activity. One example is the use of resorufin as an E_h probe to determine the redox potential of bacterial cells. Resorufin is colorless and nonfluorescent in its reduced state but fluoresces red when it becomes oxidized. It is nontoxic and widely used as a redox indicator in microbiological culture media. When it penetrates bacterial cells, it provides an indication of the metabolic state for facultatively anaerobic organisms. In actively metabolizing cells, growing under aerobic but oxygen-limited conditions, the cytoplasm becomes reducing and resorufin is nonfluorescent. However, in cells that are dead or inactive, resorufin remains oxidized and fluoresces. This has been used to distinguish living cells from dead (Caldwell and Lawrence, 1989). Several factors can complicate the interpretation of these results. One is the rate of penetration of cells by resorufin. Slow penetration of some cells and rapid penetration of others can give confusing results. In addition, the fluorescence of resorufin is pH-dependent as well as E_h-dependent. However, internal pH is generally constant and if not, dual labeling with carboxy fluorescein or other pH-dependent probes could be used to correct for pH effects.

Another approach is to use fluorogenic substrates (Soderstrom, 1977, 1979). Fluorescein diacetate has been used to detect esterase activity and confirm that cells are metabolically active. In its native form it is nonfluorescent, but when cleaved by an esterase it releases fluorescein which causes metabolically active cells to fluoresce. This method has been used to detect viable versus nonviable fungi. It is equally useful in bacteria but the fluorescent emission is too weak to be seen without an extremely low-light ISIT television camera or laser microscope. As in the case of resorufin, the degree and rate of penetration of the probe can make it difficult to accurately determine rates of enzyme activity if the concentration of substrate is continually changing. However, if dual labeling were used to calibrate the rate of cell penetration by a fluorescent marker, then the effect of changing concentration could be corrected.

5.4. Effects of Periodic Environmental Stresses

Computer image analysis has been used to observe the effects of periodic environmental stress on bacterial populations colonizing the walls of continuous-flow slide

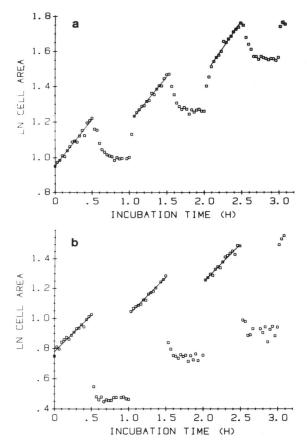

Figure 8. Response of *Pseudomonas fluorescens* colonizing the wall of a flow cell to repeated salt stress at half-hour intervals. Continuous-flow slide cultures were inoculated at time zero and subsequently irrigated with sterile medium. (a) Results with 0.35 M magnesium sulfate; (b) results with 1.5 M magnesium sulfate. Salt stress was imposed at 0.5, 1.5, and 2.5 hr. Salt stress was relieved at 1.0, 2.0, amd 3.0 hr. Upon exposure to salt stress the cells became plasmolyzed, the rate of plasmolysis being dependent upon the salt concentration. When the salt stress was relieved, the protoplasts returned to their original size by refilling the peptidoglycan sacculus, and resumed exponential growth without a lag. This recovery was nearly instantaneous regardless of the salt concentration used.

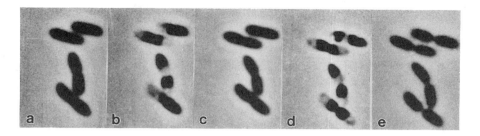

Figure 9. Response of attached cells of *Pseudomonas fluorescens* to salt stress at half-hour intervals. Continuous-flow slide cultures were inoculated at time zero and subsequently irrigated with sterile medium. Phase micrographs of the cells corresponding to data shown in Fig. 8b are presented. Exponentially growing cells in the absence of salt stress are shown in a, cells exposed to the first salt stress are shown in b, relief of first salt stress in shown in c, second salt stress in d, relief of second salt stress in e. (From Caldwell and Lawrence, 1989, *Binary* **1:**147–150, reprinted with permission.) (Phase contrast photomicrographs, width of each field is 3 μm.)

cultures (Caldwell and Lawrence, 1986, 1989). This was done by adjusting conditions in the irrigation solution, which changed conditions within the microenvironment of the cell population colonizing the walls of the flow cell. The response of the population was studied either by continuous on-line image analysis or by analyzing video recordings. In addition to determining the resistance of individuals and populations to environmental stress, their resilience (ability to recover) was also analyzed.

P. fluorescens recovered rapidly when exposed to periodic salt stress at 0.5-hr intervals (Caldwell and Lawrence, 1989). As shown in Figs. 8 and 9, exposure to 0.35 M magnesium sulfate at 0.5-hr intervals resulted in the gradual plasmolysis of individual bacterial cells. When salt stress was relieved the cells recovered immediately, swelling to their original size and resuming growth at their original rate without a lag period. When the salt concentration used was increased to 1.5 M, the recovery was also complete but plasmolysis occurred immediately.

In the case of hypochlorite stress (Caldwell and Lawrence, 1989), recovery was highly dependent upon the concentration used, as shown in Figure 10. Exposure to 0.5 ppm hypochlorite for a period of 1 hr gradually inhibited and stopped growth. After the stress was relieved, the cells recovered and resumed growth following a lag period. At a concentration of 5 ppm, cell growth stopped immediately and did not resume following removal of hypochlorite. However, at 50 ppm not only was growth inhibited, but the exopolymer binding the cells to the surface was dissolved and the cells gradually detached from the surface at a constant rate. When the stress was relieved, the remaining cells were unable to resume growth and no longer detached.

5.5. Effects of Laminar Flow and Substrate Concentration on Microbial Growth

Studies of bacterial populations colonizing the walls of continuous-flow slide cultures have shown that their rate of growth is more likely to be dependent upon laminar

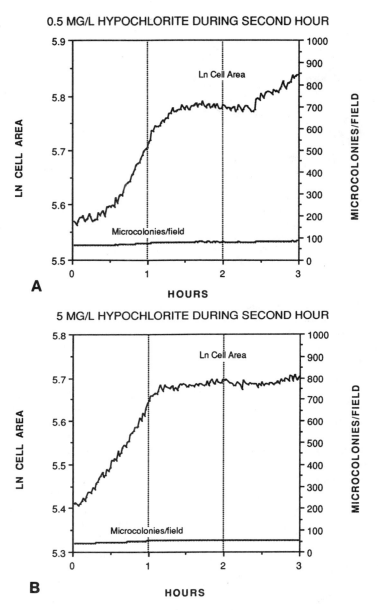

Figure 10. Response of *Pseudomonas fluorescens* colonizing the wall of a flow cell to hypochlorite in three experiments with 0.5 (A), 5.0 (B), and 50 (C) mg/liter of hypochlorite, respectively, during the second hour of incubation but not during the first or third hours. Continuous-flow slide cultures were inoculated at time zero and subsequently irrigated with sterile medium. On exposure to 0.5 mg/liter hypochlorite (A) in the irrigation solution, growth was inhibited and gradually stopped. When the stress was relieved the cells recovered and resumed growth after a lag period. When 5.0 mg/liter hypochlorite (B) was applied in the irrigation solution, the cells immediately stopped growing and did not recover after the hypochlorite stress was relieved. The 50 mg/liter treatment (C) resulted in both the cessation of growth (ln cell area declined) and the detachment of individual cells and microcolonies (ln microcolonies per field declined). Relief of the stress did not allow growth to resume but did stop cell detachment. (From Caldwell and Lawrence, 1989, *Binary* **1**:147–150, reprinted with permission.)

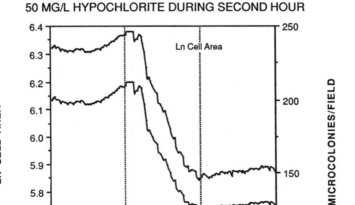

50 MG/L HYPOCHLORITE DURING SECOND HOUR

Ln Cell Area

Microcolonies/field

C

HOURS

Figure 10. *(Continued)*

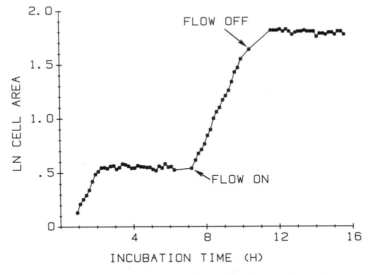

FLOW OFF

FLOW ON

INCUBATION TIME (H)

Figure 11. Effect of laminar flow velocity on the growth rate of *Pseudomonas fluorescens* microcolonies at a glucose concentration of 100 mg/liter. A continuous-flow slide culture was inoculated at time zero and subsequently irrigated with sterile medium. Although there was no flow initially, the cells grew exponentially at a specific growth rate of 0.32 h^{-1} (correlation coefficient = 0.988, cell doubling time of 2.2 hr) for 2.2 hr. At 2.2 hr the surface microenvironment was depleted of substrate and the growth rate decreased to zero until a laminar flow velocity of 10 cm/sec was established at 7.2 hr. This replenished the supply of substrate within the microenvironment and the specific growth rate increased to 0.36h^{-1} (correlation coefficient = 0.997, doubling time of 1.9 hr) until the flow was again reduced to zero at 9.92 hr. Then the surface microenvironment once again became substrate depleted and the growth rate decreased to zero. Data shown are for the mean of eight microcolonies. (From Caldwell and Lawrence, 1986, *Microb. Ecol.* **12:**299–312, reprinted with permission.)

flow velocities than substrate concentration (Caldwell and Lawrence, 1986). At concentrations exceeding 100 ppm glucose, *P. fluorescens* populations grew at their maximum rate independent of flow rate. However, at concentrations below 100 ppm, growth gradually stopped when flow stopped, and resumed again when flow resumed (Fig. 11). This suggested that cells growing within bioaggregates and biofilms easily become diffusion limited. Other studies have shown that a brief pulse of substrate resulted in the resumption of growth by starving cells after a 1-hr lag period (Caldwell, 1987). This was attributed to an unknown mechanism for sieving substrate molecules from flowing solutions.

6. Analysis of Surface Behavior

The behavior and activity of surface-associated microorganisms has most frequently been studied by direct observation and documented using photomicrographs (Marshall *et al.*, 1971; Kjelleberg *et al.*, 1982; Lawrence and Caldwell, 1987). More recently, image analysis has been utilized to study the positioning behavior of bacteria within surface microenvironments. It provides the advantages of rapid, precise analysis and quantitative data collection. While the majority of these studies were directed at the enumeration of cells present or being deposited on the surface of glass slides (Sieracki *et al.*, 1985; Sjollema *et al.*, 1988, 1989; Busscher *et al.*, 1990a; Korber *et al.*, 1990), computer-enhanced microscopy (CEM) has also been applied to the analysis of surface growth and positioning behavior during surface colonization (Caldwell and Lawrence, 1986, 1989; Lawrence *et al.*, 1987; Marshall, 1988; Korber *et al.*, 1989a; Sjollema *et al.*, 1990a).

6.1. Motility

The importance of motility in flowing waters has been questioned (Bott and Brock, 1970; Brock, 1971). However, subsequent image analysis studies have shown that motility is crucial in the attachment of cells moving from the bulk phase, through the surface hydrodynamic boundary layers, and to the surface (Korber *et al.*, 1989a). Analysis of cell motility using microscopy is problematic, in that motile cells move through three dimensions. Thus, the majority of studies involving cell motility have been conducted within the confines of flow cells or have been limited to the analysis of cells near solid–liquid interfaces. A study by Berg and Brown (1972) represents one attempt to follow bacterial movement three-dimensionally. The authors used a computer-assisted tracking microscope to follow individual wild-type and chemotactic mutant *Escherichia coli* cells responding to a chemotactic gradient, with the computer functioning to store and output the tridimensional coordinates of the bacteria. The movement of cells through various test solutions was described in terms of the length of motile runs, the speed of runs, the length of time for intervening "twiddles" (tumbling behavior), and the intervals between changes in cell direction. This technique was limited in that only single cells could be tracked (reducing the scope of the analysis), and that rapidly moving cells (greater than 20 μm/sec) could not effectively be followed.

Two-dimensional motion analyses of microbial behavior have been more common and usually involve the construction and measurement of microbial "motility tracks" for cells confined to a slide chamber or flow cell system (Davenport, 1973; Gualtieri *et al.*, 1985, 1988; Donovan *et al.*, 1987; Buskey and Stoecker, 1989; Korber *et al.*, 1989b). Davenport (1973) was among the first to utilize video-computer x–y position analysis to quantitate the motility responses of either individual flagellates or flagellate populations exposed to various stimuli. A unique preprocessing interface (named the "Bug-watcher") was used to selectively limit the flow of information to an IBM 1800 computer, thereby facilitating rapid analysis. Motility tracks could be stored at various intervals (from 60 frames/sec to 1 frame/min), depending on the rate of flagellate movement, subsequently allowing computer determination of cell mass movement, changes in linear velocity, and changes in direction. Others have subsequently applied similar techniques to the analysis of microbe motion. Gualtieri *et al.* (1988) used automated off-line image analysis to track the motion of free-swimming *Euglena gracilis*, measuring cell-path displacement, path direction, and instantaneous and average rates of cell movement at motility rates up to 100 μm/sec. A thresholding function (structured to segment a three-mode gray level histogram into a binary image) allowed a series of cell baricenters to be determined during a frame-by-frame video playback of microbial motion. A user-defined "equivalence" function then joined object baricenters if they were either adjacent or if paths of connected pixels existed between them. Crossing motility tracks were evaluated using an algorithm which statistically determined "ownership" of over-lapping pixels.

While the majority of motion analysis techniques involve x–y analysis during track reconstruction, Korber *et al.* (1989b) evaluated the rates and direction of movement of *Amphora coffeaeformis* cells in response to mannose gradients using image subtraction and summation. Difference imagery was used to identify changes in cell position at defined intervals, eliminating nonmoving diatoms, uneven illumination, time–date information, and debris. The resultant series of difference images were then enhanced before logically summing binary images using the Boolean "OR" function, resulting in a composite image displayed as a motility track. Figure 12 illustrates the various image processing steps utilized during the compilation of motility tracks from individual images collected over time. Computer analysis of the diatom motility tracks thus allowed the determination of individual and population chemotactic responses (population response shown in Fig. 13).

6.2. Phases of Surface Colonization

The colonization behaviors seen in many studies are species-specific and can be grouped into various maneuvers or strategies for bacterial reproductive success. Each maneuver can in turn be subdivided into a series of phases or steps in the colonization process (Marshall et al., 1971; Marshall, 1988; Lawrence *et al.*, 1987). For example, in some bacterial species colonization involved the formation of surface microcolonies prior to the formation of a confluent biofilm. In this case colonization often began with a motile attachment phase during which cells attached but were able to move laterally

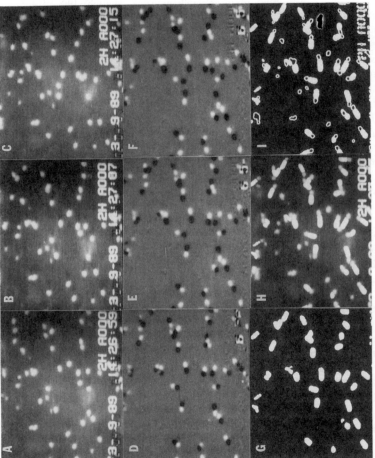

Figure 12. Image processing steps involved in the formation of a diatom motility track. Originally, nine gray level images were digitized in succession (of which image 1, 5, and 9 are shown as A, B, and C). Image 1 was then subtracted from images 2–9, resulting in eight difference images (D, E, and F shown here), displaying diatom movement over time. These images were then enhanced using a low-pass filter, eliminating electronic and videotape noise, and digitized. The digital images were then summed, using the Boolean operator (OR), forming a motility track, G. Overlaying a gray level image on the diatoms' original position (H) on the binary motility track provided a composite image showing the diatoms' direction of movement (I). (From Korber *et al.*, 1989, *Binary*, **1:**155–169, reprinted with permission.) (Computer processing of digitized video images.)

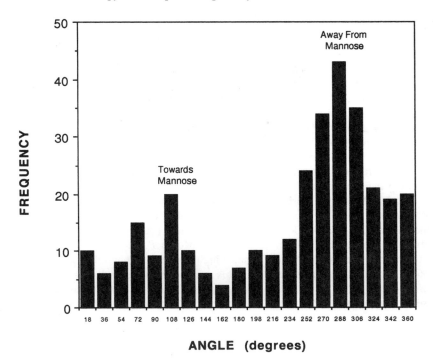

Figure 13. Frequency of diatom movement in specific directions over a 20-min period in a mannose concentration gradient. The majority of diatoms moved directly away from mannose (see "away from mannose" peak at 285°) showing negative chemotaxis, whereas a minority headed directly toward the mannose (see "towards mannose peak" at 105°) being unable to respond to the gradient while aligned perpendicular to it. (From Korber *et al.*, 1989, *Binary* **1**:155–169, reprinted with permission.)

across the surface to reposition themselves without being swept away by the current. This was often followed by a reversible attachment phase (cells became temporarily immobile while attached) an irreversible attachment phase (cells became permanently immobile while attached), the growth phase (cells within microcolonies grew and divided with little or no emigration from the colonies), and finally the recolonization phase (cells detached from developing microcolonies and redistributed themselves over the surface prior to the formation of a new set of microcolonies). These phases are normally preceded or accompanied by the mass transport of cells from the bulk aqueous phase to the surface hydrodynamic boundary layers, where attachment, growth, and development take place. This particular series of maneuvers was the most common observed for bacterial stream communities (Lawrence and Caldwell, 1987).

6.2.1. Motile Attachment

When exhibiting motile attachment behavior, bacteria travel rapidly upstream or cross-stream against flow velocities exceeding the maximum rate of cell motility (Lawrence *et al.*, 1987) by attaching to the surface while moving across it. Power and Marshall (1988) used time-lapse video analysis to study the colonization behavior of starved *Pseudomonas* sp., and ascertained that cells did not become irreversibly attached to surfaces coated with fatty acids. Rather, the bacteria were observed to grow and divide, with each newly formed daughter cell moving away from the others at slow rates (0.04–0.19 μm/min). It was hypothesized that this behavior was the result of sluggish flagellar rotation while the cell remained attached. The motile attachment behavior observed by Lawrence *et al.* (1987), following observations of flow-independent motility behavior by *P. fluorescens* on surfaces where the laminar flow velocity was 200 μm/sec, was much more rapid, as was the motile attachment observed by Malone (1988), who reported that various *Rhizobium* spp. traveled upstream against flow rates exceeding their maximum reported rates of motility.

In a CEM study by Korber *et al.* (1989a), the ability of polarly flagellated, motile and nonmotile *P. fluorescens* strains to move against the direction of flow was determined under high and low flow conditions (120 and 8 μm/sec in the microenvironment within 0.2 μm of the surface, respectively). Motile *P. fluorescens* actively moved upstream from the biofilm "front" against high flow even though the maximum rate of motility for this strain was 85 μm/sec. This resulted in backgrowth (upstream colonization) exceeding that which could have occurred from growth alone, as confirmed by observing a nonmotile *P. fluorescens* mutant which was unable to backgrow (Fig. 14). Thus, motile attachment due to flagellar rotation is responsible, in part, for bacterial positioning within flowing systems. The role of the quiescent hydrodynamic boundary layers in allowing bacterial positioning at high laminar flow velocities by flagellar motility may not be as significant.

6.2.2. Reversible/Irreversible Attachment

Observations have shown that the initial attachment of bacteria to surfaces occurs in two stages: the reversible attachment phase and irreversible attachment phase (Marshall *et al.*, 1971; Lawrence *et al.*, 1987; Marshall, 1988). Reports have indicated that various species of bacteria attach to surfaces by a portion of the cell or flagellum while continuing to revolve (Meadows, 1971; Lawrence *et al.*, 1987; Malone, 1988; Marshall, 1988). Silverman and Simon (1974) used high-speed video analysis to study the rotational behavior of motile *E. coli* tethered to surfaces by antiflagellum antibodies. They found that the speed of rotation of individual cells varied from two to nine revolutions per second, and that cells primarily spun in a counterclockwise direction (although direction reversals were observed). Also, cells possessed the capacity to vary the speed of rotation, as well as the frequency of stopping and restarting flagellar rotation. Marshall *et al.* (1971) demonstrated that cells became irreversibly attached to surfaces only after a period of unstable attachment, during which time cells revolved around the axis of attachment and frequently emigrated from the attachment site rather than becoming irreversibly attached. One possible explanation for spinning behavior might be the function of a chemosensory mechanism whereby the cells "determine" the suitability of potential colonization sites by binding, rotating, and sensing the ambient conditions

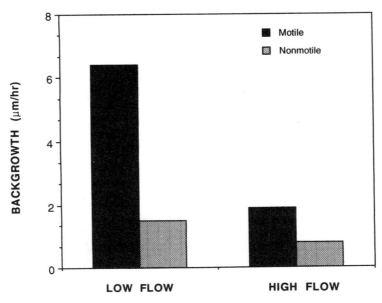

Figure 14. The effect of high and low laminar flow velocities (120 and 8 μm/sec respectively, above and below the maximum rate of flagellar motility) on the backgrowth (lateral colonization for the lower surface of a flow cell against the direction of flow) and consequent reproductive success of mot+ and mot− *Pseudomonas fluorescens* during extended (35 hr) continuous-flow slide cultures inoculated at time zero and subsequently irrigated with sterile medium. At low flow the mot+ strain backgrew at 6.4 μm/sec compared with only 1.5 μm/sec for the mot+ strain. At high flow the rates of backgrowth decreased for both strains. The mot+ strain backgrew at 1.9 μm/sec whereas the mot− strain backgrew at 0.8 μm/sec under these conditions. Thus, in this instance, laminar flow impeded bacterial colonization of upstream surfaces, and flagellar motility was effective as an adaptive mechanism to overcome this environmental stress even when the rate of flow greatly exceeded the cell's maximum rate of motility, suggesting that the cells may be able to use flagellar motility to move across the surface while remaining attached. (From Korber *et al.*, 1989a, *Microb. Ecol.* **18**:1–19, reprinted with permission.)

through chemoreceptors (Lawrence *et al.*, 1987), a process which might be referred to as chemoadherence as opposed to chemotaxis.

It has previously been hypothesized that the absence of a functional flagellum would limit the reversible attachment phase as well as overall attachment success (Lawrence *et al.*, 1987). These hypotheses were confirmed by Korber *et al.* (1989a, 1990) following CEM analyses of motile and nonmotile *P. fluorescens* in flowing environments. It was determined that the motile strain exhibited a variable period of reversible attachment before becoming irreversibly attached, whereas the nonmotile strain either attached irreversibly instantaneously, or detached and washed away. As a result, the magnitude of cell attachment at high and low flow velocities varied with the presence or absence of a functional flagellum (Fig. 15).

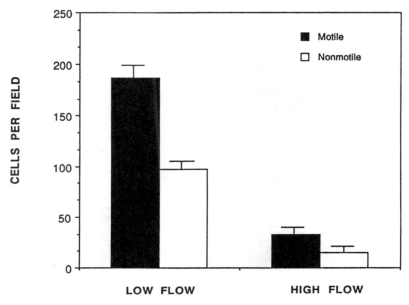

Figure 15. Effect of high and low flow (120 and 8 μm/sec) on the attachment of mot+ and mot− *Pseudomonas fluorescens* to the lower surface of a flow cell during a 5-min attachment period. One milliliter standardized inoculum (0.1 O.D.660, diluted 10-fold) was injected through the slide chamber inlet tube and cells allowed to attach. mot+ cells reattached to surface sites 2–3 times more rapidly than the mot− cells at high and low flow rates. Thus, in this instance, laminar flow impeded bacterial attachment to surfaces, and flagellar motility was effective as an adaptive mechanism to overcome this environmental stress even when the rate of flow greatly exceeded the cell's maximum rate of motility. (From Korber *et al.*, 1989a, *Microb. Ecol.* **18**:1–19, reprinted with permission.)

6.2.3. Accumulation and Orientation of Cells on Surfaces

Image analysis has also been used to measure the accumulation of cells on surfaces. The majority of these studies emphasize the importance of laminar flow (Sjollema *et al.*, 1989) and surface thermodynamic properties during sorption events (Absolom *et al.*, 1983; Busscher *et al.*, 1990b; Sjollema *et al.*, 1990b). Attachment behavior has been studied using nonmotile mutants of *P. fluorescens* (Korber *et al.*, 1990), *Vibrio parahaemolyticus* (unpublished data), and *Caulobacter crescentus* (Fig. 16). *P. fluorescens*, *V. parahaemolyticus*, and *C. crescentus* attached to the upper and lower surfaces of flow cells at equivalent rates. Nonmotile mutants attached much less rapidly to the upper surface; however, cell settling and gravitational force facilitated cell attachment to lower surfaces (Fig. 16). Nonmotile organisms were also unable to control their final attachment orientation once irreversible attachment occurred, aligning longitudinally with the direction of flow, presumably due to the presence of an adhesive region located at one

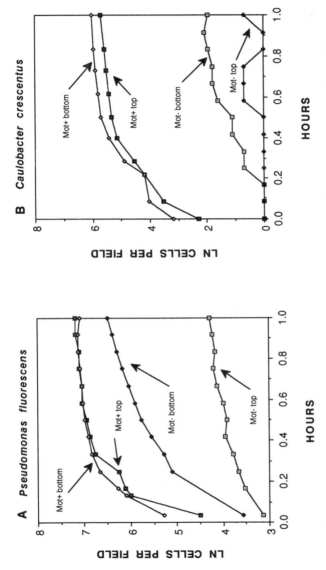

Figure 16. Attachment of mot− and mot+ *Pseudomonas fluorescens* to the walls of a glass flow cell at a laminar flow velocity of 40 μm/sec (A). Comparison of attachment to the upper versus the lower surface revealed differences due to the effect of gravitational force. Data were obtained using computer image analysis of darkfield video images and expressed as the natural logarithm of the number of cells present per field (502 × 502 μm) versus time. Gravity affected the attachment of the mot− strain, where 32 cells per field attached to the upper surface and 389 cells per field attached to the lower surface (i.e., 12-fold greater attachment on the lower surfaces). mot+ *P. fluorescens* attached independent of gravity, as indicated by final cell densities of approximately 2500 cells per field on upper and lower surfaces. Attachment by mot− cells to the upper surface was 1% that observed for mot+ cells on the same surface (32 versus 2505 cells per field). Similar motility-dependent data were also observed for mot+ (strain CB2a) and mot− (strain CB2KR2) *Caulobacter crescentus*, shown in B. (From Korber *et al.*, 1990, *Biofouling* **2:**335–350, reprinted in part with permission.)

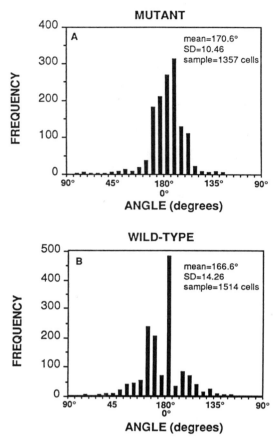

Figure 17. Effect of flow direction on the orientation of mot⁻ (A) and mot⁺ (B) *Pseudomonas fluorescens* during attachment to the lower surface of a glass flow cell. Attachment angles were expressed as the angle measured counter-clockwise from the *x* axis to the longest cell diameter, as determined using CEM. Using this system, angles from 0 to 180° could be obtained; therefore, a cell with an angle of 170° was indistinguishable from one which had a reciprocal attachment angle of 350°. Note that the peak for the motile cells is broader (100°) as opposed to the peak for the non-motile cells (50°), indicating that flagellated cells are less likely to attach with their longitudinal axis parallel to the direction of flow (180°). (From Korber *et al.*, 1990, *Biofouling* **2**:335–350, reprinted with permission.)

pole (Marshall and Cruickshank, 1973). Motile cells attached more randomly with respect to the direction of flow (Fig. 17).

6.2.4. Growth and Recolonization

Following the irreversible attachment of bacteria to surfaces, cells often undergo growth and development, forming microcolonies and eventually confluent biological films. Computer analyses have shown that behavioral patterns of microcolony development are frequently species-specific, and may also be influenced by a number of factors (flow rates, viscosity, nutrient status, light intensity, etc.) (Lawrence and Caldwell, 1987; Marshall, 1988; Caldwell and Lawrence, 1989; Korber *et al.*, 1989a). Lawrence and Caldwell (1987) described a number of colonization maneuvers exhibited by indigenous stream microorganisms, establishing that cells exhibited packing, spreading, shedding, and rolling surface colonization maneuvers (Fig. 18) and do not necessarily form discrete microcolonies during biofilm formation. In pure culture studies *P. fluorescens* exhibited a behavior pattern that generally included adsorption of single cells and the formation of microcolonies consisting of a monolayer of between 8 and 16 cells (following 4–5 hr surface growth) (Lawrence *et al.*, 1987). Following the 8- to 16-cell stage, additional growth resulted in the release of some colony members into the aqueous phase, those detached bacteria being termed "recolonizing cells." Recolonizing cells frequently reattached to vacant sites, thereby raising the number of microcolonies per field, and increasing the number of motile cells per field (Fig. 19). Growth rates remained constant throughout this process (Fig. 20). Motility plays a significant role during these events (Korber *et al.*, 1989a). Nearest-neighbor analysis of recolonizing motile and nonmotile *P. fluorescens* showed that motile cells attached randomly to available surface sites during recolonization (mean distance to nearest neighbor = 47 μm, S.D. = 28.5), whereas nonmotile cells recolonized sites located immediately downstream from the parent microcolony (mean distance to nearest neighbor = 14.2 μm, S.D. = 6.2), presumably facilitated by vortex currents. This led to distinctive microcolony morphologies for motile versus nonmotile *P. fluorescens* strains throughout biofilm development (Fig. 21). This was particularly evident at the leading edges of the developing biofilms. After 8 hr, recolonization resulted in the formation of a confluent biofilm.

Kjelleberg *et al.* (1982) and Power and Marshall (1988) used time-lapse video microscopy during the study of two *Vibrio* spp. and one *Pseudomonas* sp., all of which displayed unique surface colonization behaviors. During the study of attached *Vibrio* DW1 grown in either oligotrophic or nutrient-rich media, the authors observed that the interdivision times doubled when the cells were grown under nutrient limiting conditions (from 28 to 57 min). Although the timing of division was variable, colonization mechanisms remained constant: perpendicularly oriented mother cells released motile daughter cells into the bulk aqueous phase.

Other *Pseudomonas* spp. exhibit different paths of microcolony development and timing of recolonization contrasting that of *P. fluorescens*. Lawrence *et al.* (1990) observed that *P. fragi* microcolonies displayed a high degree of internal structure and organization. Colonies developed via a packing maneuver, resulting in a monolayer of regular, circular colonies. However, after approximately 8 hr development, secondary structure developed with some polarly attached cells subsequently maturing into a pallisade layer extending vertically from the surface upwards. After 7 hr, recolonization of motile cells occurred, marked by an increase in the number of microcolonies per field and also by an increase in the number of motile cells present in the surface boundary layer. Alternately, *P. syringae* cells which had been adsorbed to flow cell surfaces in

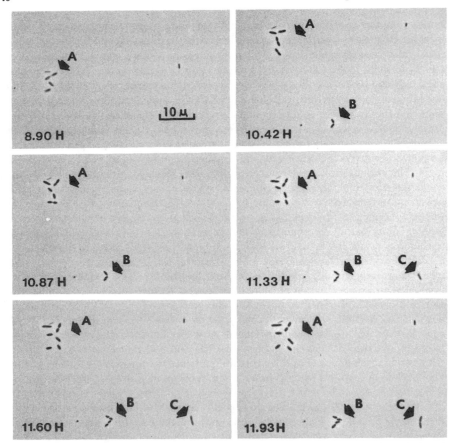

Figure 18. Time course of surface colonization by bacterial stream communities pumped continuously through a glass flow cell, showing the three most common behavioral maneuvers associated with bacterial surface colonization. These include the spreading (colony A, cells drift apart at an imperceptible rate as they divide), packing (colony B, cells form a tightly packed microcolony and eventually disperse by detaching and reattaching to the surface at new locations), and shedding maneuvers (colony C, each daughter cell detaches from the mother cell which is perpendicular to the surface) within a single microscopic field. The cells evident as blurred areas at 14.1 hr exhibit a tumbling or rolling maneuver and never become firmly attached to the surface. They appear out of focus due to their rapid movement. These maneuvers are adaptive mechanisms which allow the cells to simultaneously grow and remain attached without becoming density limited due to nutrient depletion or waste product accumulation within surface microcolonies. (From Lawrence and Caldwell, 1987, *Microb. Ecol.* **14:**15–27, reprinted with permission.) (Phase contrast photomicrographs.)

minimal medium continuously detached for extended periods without exhibiting any tendency to form microcolonies, resulting in continuously declining counts, cell areas per field, and motility.

Unique paths of microcolony development have also been observed and quantitated for a number of different microbial strains including *Rhizobium* spp., *V. para-*

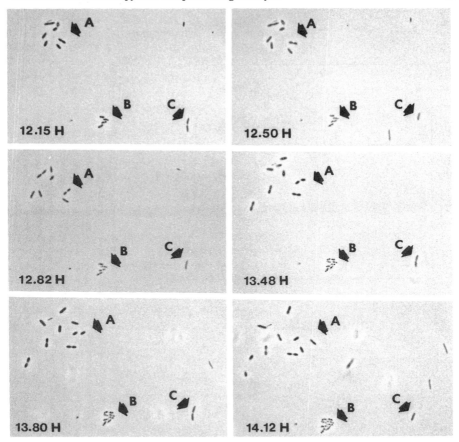

Figure 18. *(Continued)*

haemolyticus, Pedomicrobium spp., and *C. crescentus. Rhizobium* spp. grew exponentially and increased in size by three-fold following attachment, after which motile daughter cells were released into the aqueous phase (Malone, 1988). During growth, *Rhizobium* spp. continuously recolonized, releasing daughter cells into the bulk phase (shedding) resulting in a diffuse film of polarly attached cells bearing daughter cells on their apical tips as described by Marshall *et al.* (1975). *Caulobacter* spp. also continuously release daughter cells during surface colonization. Single colonizing cells attached to surfaces via adherent stalks, with the body of the cell held off the surface. Cells developed and increased in size, forming daughter cells as buds on the apical portion of the mother cell. Progeny were then released, with these cells remaining actively motile until they settled on available surface sites via adhesive material, after which the cells then developed stalks of their own. Thus, a diffuse biofilm was formed with no tendency for cells to form 3-D aggregates.

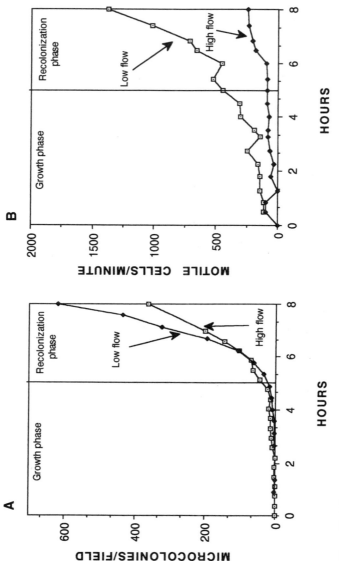

Figure 19. Effect of high and low laminar flow velocities (120 and 8 μm/sec above and below the maximum rate of flagellar motility) on the colonization of surfaces by *Pseudomonas fluorescens* in continuous-flow slide culture inoculated at time zero and subsequently irrigated with sterile medium. Data were reported as the percent increase in microcolony count (initial cell densities were 47 and 40 cells/field for mot+ cells at low and high flow, respectively) to account for differences in initial field densities (A). The number of microcolonies per field remained constant during the growth phase, the increase due to recolonization at 5 hr being flow dependent. The initial cell density did not affect the timing or magnitude of recolonization during these experiments. The effect of high and low flow on the number of mot+ cells (motile cells/field per min) is shown in B. No cell movement was detected by difference imaging during the first 5 hr of incubation for either treatment. After 5 hr, an increase in motility occurred during the low flow treatment. High flow rate experiments showed only slight increases in motility after 5 hr (From Korber *et al.*, 1989a, *Microb. Ecol.* **18:**1–19, reprinted with permission.)

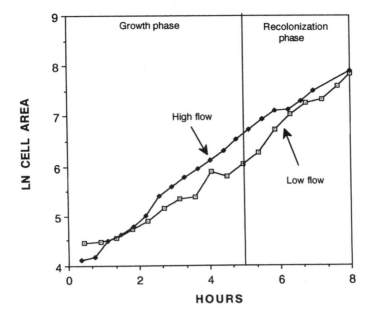

Figure 20. Effect of high and low flow on mot+ *Pseudomonas fluorescens* microcolony cell area (μm²). Continuous-flow slide cultures were inoculated at time zero and subsequently irrigated with sterile medium. The specific growth rate remained constant during both growth and recolonization phases (μ = 0.47, r = 0.99), regardless of the flow rate or the number of cells which reattached. (From Korber *et al.*, 1989a, *Microb. Ecol.* **18**:1–19, reprinted with permission.)

CEM was used to determine the kinetics of surface colonization by motile *C. crescentus* and showed that cell counts increased periodically (Fig. 22A), corresponding to the period required for the attached mother cells to release motile daughter cells. This cyclic pattern of the count parameter resulted from the use of filtered *C. crescentus* cells (sterile, 1-μm filter), a procedure which eliminated rosettes and largely confined the analysis to attached unicells at similar stages of development. The natural log of cell area increased steadily over the 18-hr incubation period at a rate of 0.14 hr^{-1} (Fig. 22b), despite fluctuations in the number of cells present per analysis field due to cell repositioning.

The growth and behavior of *Pedomicrobium* spp. was also studied using CEM. Hirsch (1974) established that budding bacteria also go through discrete phases of surface colonization. Initially, attached cells initiate hyphal elongation, with one to four branching hyphae arising from the central mother cell. Hyphal elongation continues with the initiation of bud formation and subsequent bud growth preceding release of daughter cells. Lawrence *et al.* (1989b) used computer-enhanced image analysis to quantitate the surface growth and behavior of *Pedomicrobium* spp. present within a mixed marine

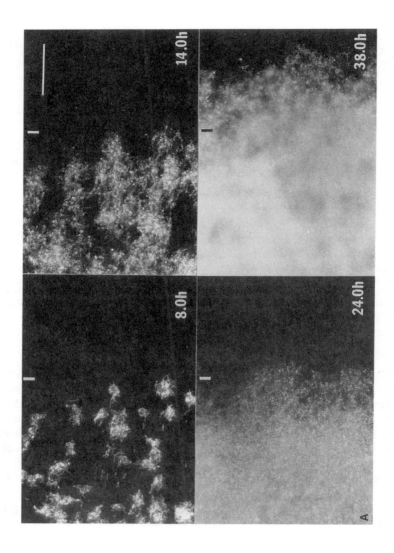

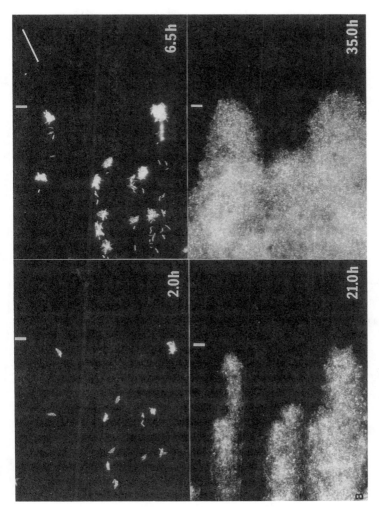

Figure 21. Darkfield photomicrographs of mot⁺ (A) and mot⁻ (B) *Pseudomonas fluorescens* backgrowth (lateral colonization against the direction of flow) at low flow (8 μm/sec, from right to left). Continuous-flow slide cultures were inoculated at time zero and subsequently irrigated with sterile medium. The mot⁺ strain backgrew at a rate of 6.4 μm/sec, progressed 250 μm over a 38-hr period, and is shown 8, 14, 24, and 38 hr after inoculation, whereas the mot⁻ strain backgrew at 1.5 μm/sec over 35 h (shown at 2, 6.5, 21, and 35 h). The vertical bar positioned near the top central region of each photograph represents the initial position of the bacterial "front" for each time period. (From Korber *et al.*, 1989a, *Microb. Ecol.* **18:**1–19, reprinted with permission.) (Darkfield photomicrograph, horizontal bar shown at upper right equals 100 μm).

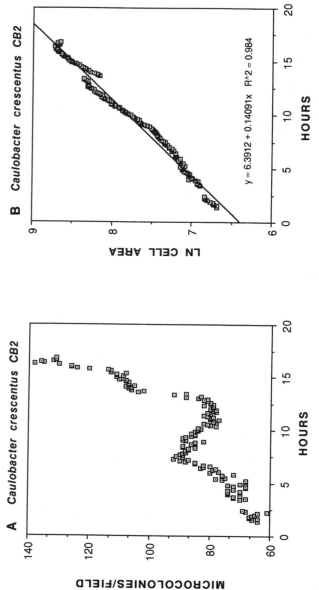

Figure 22. Surface colonization by *Caulobacter crescentus* CB2 in slide cultures as measured using image analysis. Continuous-flow slide cultures were inoculated at time zero and subsequently irrigated with sterile medium. Changes in microcolony count (A) indicated the rate of cell attachment. The rate of increase in the natural logarithm of cell area was used to measure growth (B).

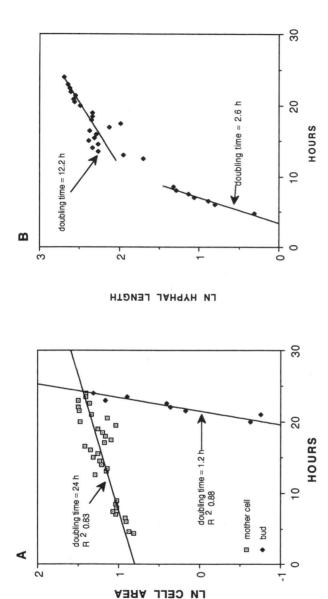

Figure 23. Natural logarithm of cell area versus time comparing the specific growth rates of the mother and daughter cells of *Pedomicrobium* sp. in a marine community. Computer image enhancement was used to digitally increase depth of field prior to image analysis of growth rate for the mother and daughter cells respectively (A). The mother cell exhibited a slow growth rate (doubling time = 24 hr) whereas the bud developed rapidly (doubling time = 1.2 hr). The natural logarithm of hyphal length versus time (B) was used to calculate specific elongation rates of *Pedomicrobium* sp. hyphae (corresponding to specific growth rates) during surface colonization. Note the decrease in rates of hyphal elongation following the transition from hyphal growth to bud development. (From Lawrence *et al.*, 1989b, *Binary* **1**:181–185, reprinted by permission.)

microcosm and cultured using continuous-flow slide culture. Behavior similar to that reported by Hirsch was observed, with cells attaching and developing hyphae, and later bearing daughter cells on their apical tips. The hyphae extended along the surface and also into the surrounding medium away from the surface plane. Image analysis was used to increase the workable depth of field by summing images obtained from different focal planes, allowing the determination of cell area, hyphal length, and the growth rates of mother and daughter cells (Fig. 23). Hyphae doubled in length at 2.6-hr intervals until the onset of bud formation, following which only slight extension of hyphae occurred (time to double in length, 12.2 hr). Daughters were released into the bulk phase and eventually recolonized vacant sites within the flow cell system, resulting in the formation of a network of hyphae and cells.

Overall, the phases of surface attachment represent a complicated series of behaviors which may vary significantly between different bacterial species and which represent bacterial adaptations necessary to optimize reproductive success. The use of image processing during the analysis of these behaviors provides a unique opportunity to quantitatively delineate the effects of natural and induced stresses on their relative colonization success.

7. Biofilm Architecture and Chemistry

There is a continuing need for nondestructive procedures to study the chemistry and microstructure of undisturbed microcolonies and biofilms on surfaces. Epifluorescence techniques are commonly used in studies of biological systems and the introduction of a broad range of fluorescent compounds (i.e., concentration-sensitive fluorophores for calcium, pH, fluorescently labeled dextrans, proteins, and lipids, as well as fluorescent RNA probes) provides the potential for the development of new methods (Luby-Phelps *et al.*, 1988; Haugland, 1989; Tsien and Waggoner, 1990). However, the major disadvantage of fluorescence techniques (and other light microscopy methods) is degradation of the image by out-of-focus information (White *et al.*, 1987). The development of CLM systems has extended light microscopy beyond the limitations of traditional phase, darkfield or fluorescence. CLM allows removal of out-of-focus haze, horizontal and vertical optical sectioning (as fine as 0.2 μm), the determination of 3-D relationships between cells, and 3-D computer reconstruction and analysis from optical thin sections (Agard *et al.*, 1989a,b; Carlsson and Lileborg, 1989; Carlsson *et al.*, 1989; Shotton, 1989; Shotton and White, 1989). In addition, the images acquired can be quantitatively analyzed using image processing techniques (Caldwell and Germida, 1985; Caldwell and Lawrence, 1986, 1989). However, these approaches have not been as widely applied to microbiological studies as in other biological research areas (Brakenhoff *et al.*, 1988; Shotton, 1989; Carlsson *et al.*, 1989; Pawley, 1990).

Attached bacterial cells, microcolonies, and biofilms can be effectively studied using negative fluorescent staining or fluorescence exclusion in conjunction with CLM (Caldwell *et al.*, 1992). Use of low-molecular-weight fluorescent compounds (e.g., fluorescein, resazurin) provided definition of the cell boundary suitable for quantitative image analysis of cell size and shape. The nontoxic nature of these compounds at low concentrations also allowed time courses of microcolony development to be obtained using the CLM system. In addition, the fluorophores effectively penetrated thick biofilms (> 20 μm) allowing xy or xz optical sectioning of biofilms at 0.2-μm intervals. Structural studies of microbial biofilms have previously involved examination of thin-sectioned and freeze-fractured specimens using scanning and transmission electron microscopy as the basis for development of conceptual models (Costerton et al., 1987). Scanning CLM and negative staining techniques offer the promise of detailed visualization of thick microbiological samples nondestructively during in situ time courses.

7.1. Biofilm Architecture

Biofilms are organized multicellular ecosystems with structural/functional features which influence metabolic processes, response to nutrients, resistance to antimicrobial agents, predation, and other factors. The spatial arrangement of the cells, extracellular polysaccharide (EPS), and open areas may be referred to as its architecture. This arrangement of cells within a biofilm likely optimizes nutrient and waste flux to and from the biofilm while contributing to the maintenance of a suitable growth environment for the cells. Over time, this arrangement would be expected to change as the biofilm progressed from initial to mature stages. The objective of architectural analysis is to identify the significant components of biofilm structure and facilitate quantitative analysis and investigation. CLM allows this type of approach and should provide for quantitative analyses of structure and the influence of environmental or induced factors.

In Lawrence et al. (1991) these techniques were used to elucidate the structure of microbial biofilms. Figure 24A shows a series of optical thin (xy) sections through a negatively stained biofilm of the bacterium P. fluorescens. Figure 24B represents a sagittal (xz) section taken through the same biofilm, showing individual microcolonies in cross section. In this preparation, quenching of the excitation beam by the 0.1% fluorescein solution (negative stain) and shading by the microcolonies caused darkened areas in the bottom half of both the lower (high magnification) and upper (low magnification) images. Studies of this type have shown that biofilms of V. parahaemolyticus, P. aeruginosa, and P. fluorescens exhibit distinctive species-specific arrangements of the major biofilm components. The pseudomonads exhibited highest cell densities at the attachment surface, whereas the vibrio had the lowest cell density at the surface (Table I). The optical thin sections obtained using CLM may also be compiled to form a 3-D image displayed as a stereo pair or as shown in Fig. 25 (see color insert), a red–green anaglyph projection, allowing the reader to visualize the entire data set.

7.2. Micro-physicochemical Environment

The microstructure of microcolonies and biofilms may be probed using size-fractionated fluorescein derivatives of dextran, ficoll, or other inert tracer particles in conjunction with CLM. These techniques can be used to examine penetration and distribution of defined probes within biofilms and bioaggregates, demonstrating the

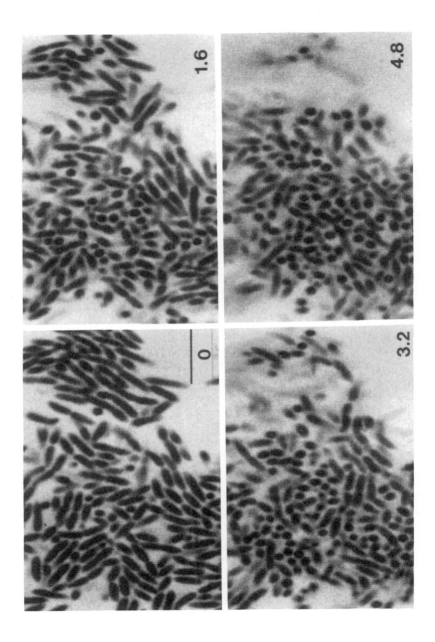

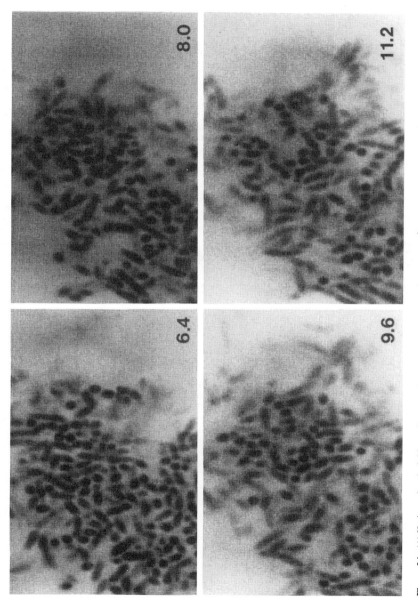

Figure 24. (A) Horizontal optical thin section (xy), shown at 1.6-μm intervals, of a *Pseudomonas fluorescens* biofilm negatively stained with a 0.1% fluorescein solution and growing within a glass flow cell. Continuous-flow slide cultures were inoculated at time zero and subsequently irrigated with sterile medium. The distance intervals shown give the distance of the optical thin section from the glass surface in micrometers. (Laser micrograph of a horizontal optodigital section showing living cells, *in situ*, and obtained using fluorescein as a fluorescent negative stain; bar equals 10 μm).

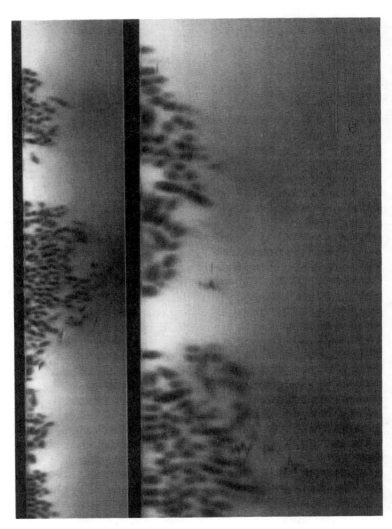

Figure 24. (B) Vertical (sagittal) sections (xz) of the same biofilm shown in (A) as horizontal sections. The upper and lower images show the same field of view at low (upper) and high (lower) magnifications. The surface on which the biofilm formed is the black band at the top of both images. The scanning laser beam entered from above, through the upper surface of the flow cell. The lower portion of the image is darkened slightly due to quenching of the beam by the 0.1% fluorescein solution used as the negative fluorescent stain. Note that the biofilm is not yet confluent. Laser penetration is best in open areas with no cells, indicating additional quenching of the beam by unstained cells. (Laser micrograph of a vertical optodigital section using fluorescein as a fluorescent negative stain; bars equal 10μm.)

Table I. Computer Image Analysis of Horizontal Optodigital Sections of Biofilms

Depth (μm)	Cell area (μm^2)		
	P. aeruginosa	V. parahaemolyticus	P. fluorescens
0	267.0	76.3	168.8
0.2	372.6	110.2	123.8
0.4	404.3	79.6	123.5
0.6	281.1	54.9	130.7
0.8	297.0	174.2	18.9
1.0	196.4	225.5	32.2
1.2	140.4	0	27.5
1.4	108.6	0	0
1.6	151.0	170.1	0
1.8	122.9	229.9	0
2.0	132.7	0	0
2.2	125.9	0	0
2.4	153.4	198.1	0
2.6	142.6	192.9	0

existence of channeling and sieving in microbial biofilms. Dextrans of 35,600 Da or less migrate freely through biofilms of *V. parahaemolyticus*. Figure 26 (see color insert) shows the penetration of 35,600- and 487,000-Da FITC-conjugated dextrans to the base of a 10-μm-thick biofilm of *V. parahaemolyticus*. Note that there appears to be hindered diffusion of the higher-molecular-weight dextran indicating some sieving potential for the EPS component of the biofilm.

Techniques such as fluorescence recovery after photobleaching (FRAP) may be used to measure diffusion and mobility of defined fluorescently labeled materials within natural systems such as biofilms. Photobleaching is a problem in all types of fluorescence microscopy; however, it is also environmentally sensitive and therefore can be extremely useful in conjunction with CLM, allowing application of microspectrofluorometry (Kohen and Hirschberg, 1989) to microbial ecology. During photobleaching studies, the treatment areas may consist of either a spot, a linear pattern, or a 3-D sphere in which a high-intensity beam is focused to degrade the active fluorescent agent. After photobleaching, the recovery of fluorescence intensity is monitored (Luby-Phelps *et al.*, 1988). Diffusion and flow rates may then be determined using appropriate calculations. Thus, FRAP and quantitative fluorescence microscopy may be used to probe the structure and effective viscosity of the microbial colony or biofilm and to examine the spatial and temporal variation of these properties and their response to environmental stress. These procedures have been applied extensively in biophysical studies but not in microbiological systems.

Fluorescent conjugated lectins or antibodies may be used to define the chemistry of exopolymers produced by microcolonies and biofilms. We have used FITC-conjugated UEA gorse lectin (fucose sensitive) to visualize lectin binding sites within exopolymers

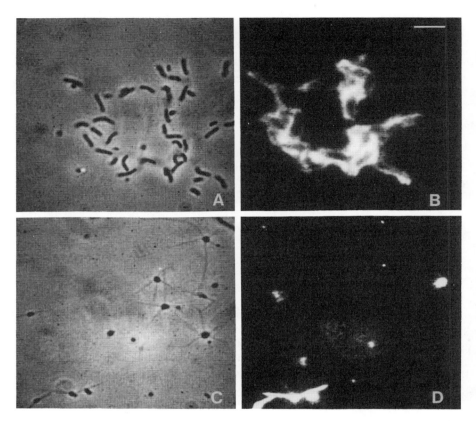

Figure 27. Exopolymer distribution during colonization of continuous-flow slide cultures by communities of marine bacteria. Panels A and B show phase-contrast and epifluorescence photomicrographs of a microcolony consisting of an unidentified bacillus. Panels C and D show phase-contrast and epifluorescence photomicrographs of *Hyphomicrobium* (lower right) and *Pedomicrobium* spp. (upper left) microcolonies. The fluorescence of FITC-conjugated lectin was used to visualize exopolymers. Note that the cells and hyphae of the *Hyphomicrobium* spp. are encased in exopolymer while the cells and hyphae of the *Pedomicrobium* spp. are not. (Phase contrast and epifluorescence photomicrographs; bar at upper right equals 5μm.)

in marine biofilms. Figure 27 shows microcolonies of *Hyphomicrobium* spp. growing in a mixed-species marine biofilm. Some individuals bound UEA lectin while others did not, illustrating the heterogeneous surface chemistry within biofilms among bacteria which appear to be very similar morphologically.

It is clear from the extensive number of electron microscope studies of biofilm structure, and recent CLM studies (Lawrence *et al.*, 1991) that a marked degree of structural heterogeneity exists in cellular and noncellular components (Eighmy *et al.*, 1983; Kinner *et al.*, 1983; Robinson *et al.*, 1984; Costerton *et al.*, 1987; Costerton, 1988). It can also be inferred from the corrosive effects of biofilms on metal surfaces that these temporal/spatial heterogeneities are also reflected in the physicochemical environment within the biofilm. Biofilm-induced corrosion is only one major example (Lappin-Scott and Costerton, 1990).

The effective pH of the periplasmic space of a gram-negative bacterium may differ by more than two units from that in the extracellular environment (Cheng et al., 1970). Consequently, the periplasmic space may cause sharp changes in pH at the cell boundary (Costerton et al., 1974). However, this is inferred indirectly and the possibility of acidic gradients around aerobic bacterial cells has been questioned (van Loosdrecht et al., 1990).

CLM, when used in conjunction with fluorescent molecular probes, allows exploration of the microenvironment in which cells live. A range of ratiometric pH indicators are available, many based on modifications to fluorescein, which have pH-sensitive and -insensitive wavelengths (Haugland, 1989; Tsien, 1989; Tsien and Waggoner, 1990) and are suitable for microecological applications. Other ion-sensitive probes (e.g., calcium, sodium) are available from a variety of sources (Haugland, 1989; Tsien, 1989; Tsien and Waggoner, 1990). The application of pH-dependent molecular probes such as 5- and 6-carboxyfluorescein has allowed the visualization of pH gradients within microbial biofilms. We have utilized CLM in conjunction with fluorescent pH-sensitive probes to noninvasively visualize the vertical and horizontal pH gradients within fully hydrated biofilms of V. parahaemolyticus. Figure 28 (see color insert) shows a series of pseudocolor images of pH gradients within optical thin sections digitized at approximately 3-μm vertical increments. These images show changes in the intensity of fluorescence in contours associated with the bacterial cells and microcolonies within the biofilm. A sagittal thin section taken through a P. fluorescens microcolony (Fig. 1) shows the change in fluorescence intensity of the pH probe at a glass surface where a bacterial microcolony has formed, allowing visualization of the microenvironment associated with the surface and the microcolony.

These results indicate that an acidic pH gradient forms within the microenvironment of cells and microcolonies of V. parahaemolyticus, which carries out a mixed-acid fermentation under anaerobic conditions. However, no acidic gradients were detected for P. fluorescens, an obligate aerobe which does not produce fermentative end products. This suggests that the hypothesis put forth by Ellwood et al. (1982), that the formation of cell microcolonies or films results in the sharing of proton (pH) gradients within attached communities, applies to anaerobes but is not significant in the case of aerobes. It also confirms the conclusion of van Loosdrecht et al. (1990) that there is no significant leakage of protons from aerobic organisms during the generation of ATP via hydrogen ion gradients across the cell membrane, and consequently no potential benefits via this mechanism due to microbial surface attachment. This is in contrast to Ellwood et al. (1982) who proposed that the sharing of leaked protons in microcolonies and biofilms might account for more rapid growth of both aerobic and anaerobic bacteria that grow attached to surfaces as opposed to growing in suspension.

We have also used environmentally sensitive probes to visualize changes in the microenvironment surrounding V. parahaemolyticus cells within corrosion pits in mild steel. Stereo projections of these images (Fig. 29; see color insert) show gradients of fluorescence from the surface and outer edge of the pit to the center, suggesting the formation of an electrolytic corrosion cell within a single microcolony due to pH and E_h gradients.

At this point in the application of fluorescent environmental probes to microbial systems, the possibility of artifacts has not been eliminated. Changes in fluorescence can be due to (1) shadows caused by opaque particles, (2) the reflection of the laser beam from glass or other surfaces, (3) differential penetration and concentration of the probe, (4) inhibition of fluorescence due to interaction of the probe with proteins or other molecules, or (5) differential quenching (absorption) of the fluorescence emission or the excitation beam by fluor located outside the region of confocality (focal plane). Consequently, the use of microelectrodes, comparison of results for acid-producing and non-acid-producing cells, and other control experiments, are important to ensure correct interpretation of laser micrographs. Read *et al.* (1992) have used fluorescence ratio imaging and confocal microscopy to analyze calcium in filamentous fungi. Ratio imaging corrects for variable concentration of the molecular probe by relating the ratio of two emission peaks to concentration as opposed to measuring the brightness of a single emission peak. However, it does not resolve the other problems associated with interfering molecules, etc.

8. Analysis of Microstat Biofilms

The microstat produces a two-dimensional steady-state diffusion gradient within a gel which is irrigated with medium and colonized by microorganisms. It provides a highly defined environment necessary for the isolation, maintenance, and subculture of well-defined biofilm communities. The microenvironments within the gradient are constant in terms of both the flux and concentration of test molecules. Consequently, it is termed a "microstat" and functions somewhat like a solid-state chemostat, providing defined steady-state microenvironments for the isolation and subculture of steady-state microecosystems, biofilm communities, and consortia (Wolfaardt *et al.*, 1992). When this steady-state gradient approach was originally developed (Caldwell and Hirsch, 1973), there was a lack of adequate analytical methodology for quantifying the information generated during the colonization of even a single, two-dimensional diffusion gradient. Microscopic observations were made and recorded manually, a process that was too tedious for routine analytical work. Consequently, detailed analysis of two-dimensional gradient systems awaited the development of 2-D digital imaging methods (Peters 1990, Peters *et al.*, 1991) and 3-D confocal laser microscopy (Wolfaardt *et al.*, 1992).

Two-dimensional gradients represent an environmental continuum or test grid in which all concentrations and proportions of the two test compounds or factors are represented (Caldwell *et al.* 1973, Wimpenny *et al.* 1988, Peters *et al.* 1991). Quantitative gradients are defined in that both the steady-state chemical concentrations and fluxes are known and constant at any point in the gradient. By incubating the microstat chamber in a stream, the two-dimensional environmental gradient is superimposed on (equilibrated with) *in situ* physicochemical conditions. The system was initially used as a technique for microbial enrichment and isolation (Caldwell and Hirsch, 1973) and later to define the habitat domain of microbial communities and populations containing species which could not be grown in pure culture (Caldwell *et al.*, 1973, 1975). This approach has several advantages over traditional bacterial plating methods that date back more than a century (Wimpenny *et al.*, 1988). It provides: a) a range of physicochemical environments for microbial growth, rather than constraining organisms to a single growth condition; b) a physical pathway for the development of communities which could not form directly at high concentrations of a toxicant or antibiotic; c) a steady-state microenvironment for the culture and subculture of steady-state microecosystems so that toxic intermediates do not accumulate sequentially as they would in a batch culture system.

Figure 30a (see color insert) shows a two-dimensional gradient that has been removed from the microstat diffusion chamber. It was formed using two stains, safranine (bottom edge) and crystal violet (left edge), to illustrate the concept of perpendicular steady-state environmental gradients. Figure 30b (see color insert) shows the biofilm which formed on the surface of a two-dimensional steady-state diffusion gradient of ammonium sulfate (left edge) versus thiosulfate (bottom edge), irrigated with surface water from the South Saskatchewan River. The upper left corner of the gel contains an ammonia-oxidizing community (nitroetum). The lower right corner contains a sulfur-oxidizing community (sulphuretum). The lower left corner contains the ectone or transitional community between the two extremes. By digitizing the biofilm and converting it to a gray-scale map, contour lines (isopleths) and pseudocolor maps can be generated and used as a guide in sampling the biofilm or to reveal multiple levels of spatial organization.

Pseudocolor maps (Fig. 30c; see color insert) and contours (Fig. 30d; see color insert) are created by digitizing the analog image obtained using a television camera. Alternatively, the biofilm can be photographed and the 35 mm slide digitized using a slide scanner. This produces a much higher resolution image, revealing fine details. The digital image is then rendered using pseudocolor or contour mapping. This can be done using Spyglass Transform (Macintosh software, Spyglass Inc., Champaign, Ill.). Contour and 3-D gray-level maps have traditionally been used to analyze this type of image data. In addition, continuous-tone pseudocolor legends and maps provide quantitative image information not only along contour lines but also between contour lines (Fig. 30d; see color insert). One of the more useful and universal pseudocolor legends is "rainbow." The sequence of colors in the visible spectrum (rainbow) is universal, ranging from the short blue wavelengths (representing low values) to the longer red wavelengths (representing high values). The color order is violet, blue, green, yellow, orange, and red.

In high-resolution biofilm images, contour lines can become too complex to understand visually and tend to obscure relationships which occur on a larger spatial scale. Consequently, a banded-rainbow pseudocolor legend is preferable (Fig. 30c; see color insert). It darkens bands of the rainbow at uniform intervals to provide broad contour bands as opposed to contour lines. The degree of detail in a complex image can also be controlled by using Adobe Photoshop (Adobe Systems Inc., Mountain View, Calif.) to create a series of images varying in resolution (size). By rendering a low-resolution (Fig.

30d; see color insert) as opposed to a high-resolution image (Fig. 30c; see color insert), the complexity of the contours can be controlled and the biofilm viewed at several different levels of spatial organization. Viewing at low resolution may reveal relationships not seen at high resolution and vice versa. This helps to avoid "seeing the trees and missing the forest."

Contour maps are useful to provide contour lines along which to sample the biofilm. For example, five replicate plugs taken from a gel might be collected along a contour to determine the bacterial count or for scintillation counting of a radioisotope. Data from several contours can then be used to produce a standard curve relating gray level to counts, isotope assimilation, etc. The rainbow legend can then be transformed mathematically to represent the specific parameter of interest. Potential future applications include use of a fluorescent molecular probe such as resazurin to visualize the rate of metabolism over the entire surface of the gel. In this case, the rate at which the fluor fades is related to the rate of microbial respiration (oxygen depletion and reduction of the probe). Thus, control biofilms (with no gradients) would be used to produce a standard curve relating metabolic rate to gray-level and physical sampling along biofilm contours would not be required.

9. Terms and Abbreviations

2-D Image. A two-dimensional image normally displayed on the surface of a computer monitor.

2-D Image Analysis. Morphometric analysis of objects in a two-dimensional image. For example, the length and width of a cell in a two-dimensional image might be measured by locating the center of gravity for the cell, drawing 32 lines through this point (from one side of the cell to the other) at $10°$ increments, and then recording the longest line as the cell length and the shortest line as the cell width. The software for 2-D image analysis is inexpensive when compared to 3-D image analysis and provides a wide variety of morphological measurements.

3-D Image Analysis. Morphometric analysis of objects in a three-dimensional volumetric, space-filling, image. For example, the length and width of a cell in a three-dimensional image might be measured by locating the center of gravity for the cell, drawing 32^2 (1024) lines through this point (from one edge of the cell to the other) in all three dimensions at $10°$ intervals, and then recording the longest line as the cell length and the shortest line as the cell width. Volumes can be determined directly by 3-D image analysis (calculated from the number and size of voxels within each object) but not by 2-D image analysis. The software necessary for 3-D image analysis is still being developed and the parameters which can be measured using commercially available software are still very rudimentary.

3-D Volumetric Image. A three-dimensional space-filling computer reconstruction of an object or set of objects.

Axial Resolution. The resolution of an objective lens in the z dimension of a 3-D volumetric image, as compared to its resolution in the $x–y$ (lateral) dimension of a 2-D image. The axial resolution is approximately one-half of the lateral resolution.

Binary Image (*see also* **Gray Level Image**). A digital image in which each of the pixels is either white (gray level of 255) or black (gray level of 0). The black pixels are normally defined as being within objects of interest and the white pixels are considered as part of the background. The formation of a binary image by thresholding is necessary to define the boundaries between the objects and their background prior to image analysis and morphometry.

CCD Camera. Television camera using a charge-coupled device (light-sensitive silicone chip) in place of a pick-up tube.

Cell Area. The area occupied by the projection (shadow) of a 3-D cell on a 2-D surface.

CEM. Computer-enhanced microscopy.

CLM. Confocal laser microscopy (confocal scanning laser microscopy).

Color Look-up Table. A table which is used to replace the gray level of each pixel with a color value. The lookup table defines which color will be substituted for each gray level.

CRT. Cathode ray tube (monitor).

Deconvolution. A digital process whereby the haze due to diffraction in diffraction-limited lens systems can be removed from an optodigital thin section.

DIC microscopy. Differential interference contrast microscopy.

Discrimination (*see* **Thresholding**)

Difference Image. An image resulting from the subtraction of one image from another to reveal only the differences between the two images.

EPS. Extracellular polysaccharide

FRAP. Fluorescence recovery after photobleaching.

FITC. Fluorescein isothiocyanate.

Gray Level (gray value). The brightness of a pixel, normally any one of 256 levels of gray (making most effective use of one computer byte which consists of 2^8 or 256 bits).

Gray Level Histogram. A histogram showing the frequency distribution for pixels of various brightness (gray levels) which occur within a digital image. The frequency (number of pixels) is shown on the y axis and the brightness of the pixels (normally 0 to 255) is shown on the x axis. This histogram is frequently used as an aid in thresholding images.

Gray Level Image (*see also* **Binary Image**). An image in which each pixel has any gray level between 0 and 255.

Gray Level Transformation. Reassignment of gray level value for each pixel. For example, the gray level value for each of the pixels in an image might be redefined such that the relationship between the number and brightness of the pixels follows a normalized distribution.

Imaging. The process of creating a digital 2-D or 3-D image. Image digitization.

ISIT Camera. A television camera utilizing an intensified silicone intensification target tube to produce an analog television signal.

NND. Nearest-neighbor deconvolution.

Optodigital Spectrofluorimeter Cuvette. One or more voxels, the brightness of which is directly related to the fluorescence emission of a fluorescent molecular probe.

Optodigital Thin Section. A digital 2-D image consisting of pixels, which may be part of a series used to create a 3-D digital reconstruction of a specimen.

PC. Personal computer.

Pixel. The smallest picture element (pixel) in a digitized 2-D image (an individual point of light on the computer screen).

Point-Spread Function. A description of the dispersion pattern for stray light originating from a point light source. It is used for the deconvolution of optodigital thin sections.

Pseudocolor Map (*see also* **Color Look-up Table**). An image in which differences in gray level between pixels have been redefined as color differences to improve image contrast. Pseudocolor maps are often used in combination with a color legend to define the pH, E_h, or concentrations of fluorescent probes within images.

RAM. Random access memory.

Rendering (*see* **Volume Rendering**). The process whereby a 2-D or 3-D array of digital image data is displayed as an understandable image on the computer monitor. This is often done by using pseudocolor look-up tables to transfer 2-D data sets.

Ratio Imaging. Corrects for variable concentration (penetration) of fluorescent molecular probes by creating an image using the ratio of two emission peaks as opposed to the brightness of a single emission. (Read *et al.*, 1992).

RITC. Rhodamine Isothiocyanate.

Segmentation (*see* **Thresholding**).

Shading Correction. Subtraction of a background image from an image containing a specimen to correct for uneven microscope illumination.

SIT Camera. A television camera utilizing a silicone intensification target tube used to produce an analog television signal.

Thresholding (object recognition, segmentation, discrimination). The most common procedure by which objects are recognized through computer image analysis of digital images. In the simplest case, pixels above a specified brightness are set to white and those below a specified brightness are set to black creating a binary image, generally with either white objects on a black background or black objects on a white background.

TRITC. Texas Red Isothiocyanate

VCR. Videocassette recorder, video tape recorder.

VTR. Video tape recorder.

Volume Rendering. The process by which a 3-D array of data, representing the reconstruction of an object in 3-D space, is transformed into a 2-D image which gives the illusion of a 3-D image and can be viewed on a computer screen. This is often accomplished by rotating the object in a video animation or by projecting a hypothetical source of illumination from one or more angles to highlight surface contours.

Volumetric Image. A digital 3-D image consisting of a volume-filling, 3-D reconstruction.

Voxel. The smallest volume element (voxel) in a digitized 3-D image. Each voxel is a hypothetical cubic or rectangular polyhedron with a defined length, depth, width, and volume.

ACKNOWLEDGMENTS. The Natural Sciences and Engineering Research Council (NSERC) and the U.S. Office of Naval Research (ONR) are gratefully acknowledged for financial support. John Smit is acknowledged for providing the *Caulobacter* strains. We also acknowledge the National Aeronautics and Space Administration's program in Planetary Biology and Microbial Ecology (PBME), organized and directed by Lynn Margulis and Ken Nealson. Our efforts to apply remote sensing principles in microbial ecology began as a result of the NASA PBME programs held in Santa Clara (Calif.) during 1980, and in San Jose during 1984.

References

Absolom, D. R., Lamberti, F. V., Policova, Z., Zingg, W., van Oss, C. J., and Neumann, A. W., 1983, Surface thermodynamics of bacterial adhesion, *Appl. Environ. Microbiol.* **46:**90–97.

Agard, D. A., Hiraoka, Y., Shaw, P. J., and Sedat, J. W., 1989, Fluorescence microscopy in three dimensions, *Methods Cell Biol.* **30:**353–377.

Anwar, H. M., Dasgupta, Lam, K., and Costerton, J. W., 1989, Tobramycin resistance of mucoid *Pseudomonas aeruginosa* biofilm grown under iron limitation, *J. Antimicrob. Chemother.* **24:**647–655.

Berg, H. C., 1985, Physics of bacterial chemotaxis, in: *Sensory Perception and Transduction in Aneural Organisms* (G. Colombetti, F. Linci, and P.-S. Song, eds.), Plenum Press, New York, pp. 19–30.

Berg, H. C., and Brown, D. A., 1972, Chemotaxis in *Escherichia coli* analyzed by three-dimensional tracking, *Nature* **239:**500–504.

Bjornsen, P. K., 1986, Automatic determination of bacterioplankton biomass by means of image analysis, *Appl. Environ. Microbiol.* **51:**1199–1204.

Bott, T. L., and Brock, T. D., 1970, Growth and metabolism of periphytic bacteria: Methodology, *Limnol. Oceanogr.* **15:**333–342.

Boyde, A., 1990, Confocal optical microscopy, in: *Modern Microscopies: Techniques and Applications* (P. J. Duke and A. G. Michette, eds.), Plenum Press, New York, pp. 185–204.

Bradbury, S., 1979, Microscopical image analysis: Problems and approaches, *J. Microsc.* **115:**137–150.

Brakenhoff, G. J., van der Voort, H. T. M., Baarslag, M. W., Mans, B., Oud, J. L., Zwart, R., and van Driel, R., 1988, Visualization and analysis techniques for three dimensional information acquired by confocal microscopy, *Scanning Microsc.* **2:**1831–1838.

Brock, T. D., 1971, Microbial growth rates in nature, *Bacteriol. Rev.* **35:**39–58.

Buskey, E. J., and Stoecker, D. K., 1989, Behavioral responses of the marine tintinnid *Favella* sp. to phytoplankton: Influence of chemical, mechanical and photic stimuli, *J. Exp. Mar. Biol. Ecol.* **132:**1–16.

Busscher, H. J., Bellon-Fontaine, M.-N., Mozes, N., van der Mei, H. C., Sjollema, J., and Rouxhet, P. G., 1990a, Deposition of *Leuconostoc mesenteroides* and *Streptococcus thermophilus* to solid substrata in a parallel plate flow cell, *Biofouling* **2:**55–63.

Busscher, H. J., Sjollema, J., and van der Mei, H. C., 1990b, Relative importance of surface free energy as a measure of hydrophobicity in bacterial adhesion to solid surfaces, in: *Microbial Cell Surface Hydrophobicity* (R. J. Doyle and M. Rosenberg, eds.), ASM, Washington, D.C., pp. 335–359.

Caldwell, D. E., 1985, New developments in computer-enhanced microscopy, *J. Microbiol. Methods* **4:**117–125.

Caldwell, D. E., 1987, Microbial colonization of solid–liquid interfaces, *Ann. N.Y. Acad. Sci.* **506:**274–280.

Caldwell, D. E., and Caldwell, S. J., 1978, A *Zoogloea* sp. associated with blooms of *Anabaena flos-aquae, Can J. Microbiol.* **24:**922–931.

Caldwell, D. E., and Germida, J. J., 1985, Evaluation of difference imagery for visualizing and quantitating microbial growth, *Can J. Microbiol.* **31:**35–44.

Caldwell, D. E., and Hirsh, P., 1973, Growth of microorganisms in two-dimensional steady-state diffusion gradients, *Can. J. Microbiol.* **19:**53–58.

Caldwell, D. E., and Lawrence, J. R., 1986, Growth kinetics of *Pseudomonas fluorescens* microcolonies within the hydrodynamic boundary layers of surface microenvironments, *Microb. Ecol.* **12:**299–312.

Caldwell, D. E., and Lawrence, J. R., 1988, Study of attached cells in continuous-flow slide culture, in: *CRC Handbook of Laboratory Model Systems for Microbial Ecosystems* (J. W. T. Wimpenny, ed.), CRC Press, Boca Raton, pp. 117–138.

Caldwell, D. E., and Lawrence, J. R., 1989, Microbial growth and behavior within surface microenvironments, in: *Proceedings of ISME-5* (T. Hattori, Y. Ishida, Y. Maruyama, R. Y. Morita, and A. Uchida, eds.), JSS Press, Tokyo, pp. 140–145.

Caldwell, D. E., and Tiedje, J. M., 1975a, The structure of anaerobic bacterial communities in the hypolimnion of several Michigan lakes, *Can. J. Microbiol.* **21:**377–385.

Caldwell, D. E., and Tiedje, J. M., 1975b, A morphological study of anaerobic bacteria from the hypolimnion of two Michigan lakes, *Can. J. Microbiol.* **21:**362–376.

Caldwell, D. E., Lai, S. H., and Tiedje, J. M., 1973, A two-dimensional steady-state diffusion gradient for ecological studies, *Bull. Ecol. Res. Commun.* **17:**151–158.

Caldwell, D. E., Caldwell, S. J., and Tiedje, J. M., 1975, An ecological study of the sulfur-oxidizing bacteria from the littoral zone of a Michigan lake and a sulfur spring in Florida, *Plant Soil* **43:**101–114.

Caldwell, D. E., Korber, D. R., and Lawrence, J. R., 1992, Imaging of bacterial cells by fluorescence exclusion using scanning confocal laser microscopy, *J. Microbiol. Methods* **15:**249–261.

Carlsson, K., and Lileborg, A., 1989, A confocal laser microscope scanner for digital recording of optical serial sections, *J. Microsc.* **153:**171–180.

Carlsson, K., Wallen, P., and Brodin, L., 1989, Three-dimensional imaging of neurons by confocal fluorescence microscopy, *J. Microsc.* **155:**15–26.

Casida, L. E., 1969, Observation of microorganisms in soil and other natural habitats, *Appl. Microbiol.* **18:**1065–1071.

Casida, L. E., 1972, Interval scanning photomicrography of microbial cell populations, *Appl. Microbiol.* **23:**190–192.

Casida, L. E., 1975, Infrared color photomicrography of soil microorganisms, *Can. J. Microbiol.* **21:**1892–1893.

Casida, L. E., 1976, Continuously variable amplitude contrast microscopy for the detection and study of microorganisms in soil, *Appl. Environ. Microbiol.* **31:**605–608.

Cheng, K.-J., Ingram, J. M., and Costerton, J. W., 1970, Alkaline phosphatase localization and spheroplast formation of *Pseudomonas aeruginosa, Can J. Microbiol.* **16:**1319–1324.

Cooksey, B., and Cooksey, K. E., 1988, Chemical signal-response in diatoms of the genus *Amphora, J. Cell Sci.* **91:**523–529.

Costello, P. J., and Monk, P. R., 1985, Image analysis method for the rapid counting of *Saccharomyces cerevisiae* cells, *Appl. Environ. Microbiol.* **49:**863–866.

Costerton, J. W., 1988, Structure and plasticity at various organization levels in the bacterial cell, *Can. J. Microbiol.* **34**:513–521.

Costerton, J. W., Ingram, J. M., and Cheng, K.-J., 1974, Structure and function of the cell envelope of gram-negative bacteria, *Bacteriol. Rev.* **38**:87–110.

Costerton, J. W., Cheng, K.-J., Geesey, G. G., Ladd, T., Nickel, J. C., Dasgupta, M., and Marrie, T. J., 1987, Bacterial biofilms in nature and disease, *Annu. Rev. Microbiol.* **41**:435–464.

Davenport, D., 1973, Studies of the behavior of microorganisms by computerized television, in: *Behavior of Micro-organisms* (A. Perez-Miravete, ed.), Proceedings of the 10th International Congress, Plenum Press, New York.

DeYoung, H. G., 1988, Microscopy and image analysis, *Bio/Technology* **6**:78–79.

Donovan, R. M., Goldstein, E., Kim, Y., Lippert, W., Kailath, E., Aoki, K. T., Cheung, A. T. W., Miller, M. E., and Chang, D. P., 1987, A computer-assisted image-analysis system for analyzing polymorphonuclear leukocyte chemotaxis in patients with Diabetes mellitus, *J. Infect. Dis.* **155**:737–741.

Drake, B., Prater, C. B., Weisenhorn, A. L., Gould, S. A. C., Albrecht, T. R., Quate, C. F., Cannell, D. S., Hansma, H. G., and Hansma, P. K., 1989, Imaging crystals, polymers, and processes in water with the atomic force microscope, *Science* **241**:1586–1589.

Edgar, L. A., 1979, Diatom locomotion: Computer-assisted analysis of cine film, *Br. Phycol. J.* **14**:83–101.

Eighmy, T. T., Maratea, D., and Bishop, P. L., 1983, Electron microscopic examination of wastewater biofilm formation and structural components, *Appl. Environ. Microbiol.* **45**:1921–1931.

Ellwood, D. C., Keevil, C. W., Marsh, P. D., Brown, C. M., and Wardell, J. N., 1982, Surface-associated growth, *Philos. Trans. R. Soc. London Ser. B* **297**:517–532.

Emmett, A., 1991, In search of the miracle hologram: Spatial image researchers strive to achieve stereoscopic reality, *Comput. Graphics World* **14**:44–52.

Escher, A. R., and Characklis, W. G., 1988, Microbial colonization of a smooth substratum: A kinetic analysis using image analysis, *Water Sci. Technol.* **20**:45–51.

Fernandes, M. A., Jackman, P. J., Clark, S. A., and Gunard, S. R., 1988, Detection and quantification of microorganisms in a heterogenous foodstuff by image analysis, *Comput. Appl. Biosci.* **4**:291–295.

Friedhoff, R. M., 1991, Microvisualization, *Comput. Graphics World* **14**:38–44.

Fry, J. C., 1988, Determination of biomass, in: *Methods in Aquatic Bacteriology* (B. Austin, ed.), Wiley, New York, pp. 27–72.

Fry, J. C., and Davies, A. R., 1985, An assessment of methods for measuring volumes of planktonic bacteria, with particular reference to television image analysis, *J. Appl. Bacteriol.* **58**:105–112.

Gaju, N., Guerrero, R., and Pedros-Alio, C., 1989, Measurement of cell volume of phototrophic bacteria in pure cultures and natural samples: Phase contrast, epifluorescence and particle sizing, *FEMS Microbiol. Ecol.* **62**:295–302.

Geesey, G. C., Mutch, R., and Costerton, J. W., 1978, Sessile bacteria: An important component of the microbial population in small mountain streams, *Limnol. Oceanogr.* **23**:1214–1223.

Getliff, J. M., and Fry, J. C., 1989, Using the solitaire plus image analyser for direct estimates of bacterial volume, *Binary* **1**:93–100.

Gonzalez, R. C., and Wintz, P., 1977, *Digital Image Processing*. Addison–Wesley, Reading, Mass.

Gratton, E., and van deVen, M. J., 1990, Laser sources for confocal microscopy, in *Handbook of Biological Confocal Microscopy* (J. B. Pawley, ed.), Plenum Press, New York, pp. 53–67.

Gualtieri, P., Colombetti, G., and Lenci, F. 1985, Automatic analysis of the motion of microorganisms, *J. Microsc.* **139**:57–62.

Gualtieri, P., Francesco, G., Passarelli, V., and Barsanti, L., 1988, Microorganism track reconstruction: An image processing approach, *Comput. Biol. Med.* **18**:57–63.

Hansma, P. K., Drake, B., Mari, O., Gould, S. A. C., and Prater, C. B., 1989a, The scanning ion-conductance microscope, *Science* **243**:641–643.

Hansma, P. K., Elings, V. B., Mari, O., and Bracker, C. E., 1989b, Scanning tunneling microscopy and atomic force microscopy: Application to biology and technology, *Science* **241**:209–216.

Harris, R., 1991, Confocal microscopy, *Microsc. Soc. Can. Bull.* **19**:33–35.

Haugland, R. P., 1989, *Handbook of Fluorescent Probes and Research Chemicals,* Molecular Probes Inc., Eugene, Oreg.

Henrici, A. T., and Johnson, D. E., 1935, Studies of freshwater bacteria. II. Stalked bacteria, a new order of Schizomycetes, *J. Bacteriol.* **30**:61–93.

Hirsch, P., 1974, Budding bacteria, *Annu. Rev. Microbiol.* **28**:391–433.

Hirsch, P., 1977, Distribution and pure culture studies of morphologically distinct solar lake microorganisms, in: *Hypersaline Brines and Evaporitic Environments* (A. Nissenbaum, ed.), Elsevier, Amsterdam, pp. 41–60.

Hirsch, P., 1980, Some thoughts on and examples of microbial interactions in the natural environment, in: *Aquatic Microbial Ecology* (R. R. Colwell and A. J. Foster, eds.), University of Maryland, pp. 36–54.

Inoué, S., 1986, *Video Microscopy,* Plenum Press, New York, pp. 263–307.

Inoué, S., 1990, Foundations of confocal scanned imaging in light microscopy, in: *Handbook of Confocal Laser Microscopy* (J. B. Pawley, ed.), Plenum Press, New York, pp. 1–14.

Jenkinson, D. S., Powlson, D. S., and Wedderburn, R. M. W., 1976, The effects of biocidal treatments on metabolism in soil. III. The relationship between soil biovolume, measured by optical microscopy and the flush of decomposition cause by fumigation, *Soil Biol. Biochem.* **8**:189–202.

Kesterson, J., and Richardson, M., 1991, Confocal microscope capability with desktop affordability, *Advanced Imaging* **6**:23–25.

Kinner, N. E., Balkwill, D. L., and Bishop, P. L., 1983, Light and electron microscopic studies of microorganisms growing in rotating biological contactor biofilms, *Appl. Environ. Microbiol.* **45**:1659–1669.

Kjelleberg, S., Humphrey, B., and Marshall, K. C., 1982, The effect of interfaces on small starved marine bacteria, *Appl. Environ. Microbiol.* **43**:1166–1172.

Kohen, E., and Hirschberg, J. G., 1989, Cell Structure and Function by Microspectrofluorometry, Academic Press, New York.

Korber, D. R., Lawrence, J. R., Sutton, B., and Caldwell, D. E., 1989a, Effect of laminar flow velocity on the kinetics of surface recolonization by mot$^+$ and mot$^-$ *Pseudomonas fluorescens, Microb. Ecol.* **18**:1–19.

Korber, D. R., Lawrence, J. R., Cooksey, K. E., Cooksey, B., and Caldwell, D. E., 1989b, Computer image analysis of diatom chemotaxis, *Binary* **2**:335–350.

Korber, D. R., Lawrence, J. R., Zhang, L., and Caldwell, D. E., 1990, Effect of gravity on bacterial deposition and orientation in laminar flow environments, *Biofouling* **2**:335–350.

Krambeck, C., Krambeck, H. J., Schroder, D., and Newell, S. Y., 1990, Sizing bacterioplankton: A juxtaposition of bias due to shrinkage, halos, subjectivity in image interpretation and asymmetric distributions, *Binary* **2**:5–14.

Kuhn, D. A., and Starr, M. P., 1970, Effects of microscope illumination on bacterial development, *Arch. Mikrobiol.* **74**:292–300.

Labeda, D. P., Liu, K., and Casida, L. E., 1976, Colonization of soil by Arthrobacter and Pseudomonas under varying conditions of water and nutrient availability as studied by plate counts and transmission electron microscopy, *Appl. Environ. Microbiol.* **31**:551–561.

Lappin-Scott, H. M., and Costerton, J. W., 1990, Bacterial biofilms and surface fouling, *Biofouling* **1**:323–342.

Lawrence, J. R., and Caldwell, D. E., 1987, Behavior of bacterial stream populations within the hydrodynamic boundary layers of surface microenvironments, *Microb. Ecol.* **14**:15–27.

Lawrence, J. R., and Caldwell, D. E., 1990, Scanning confocal laser microscopy of biofilms, *Can. Lab.* **2**:12.

Lawrence, J. R., Delaquis, P. J., Korber, D. R., and Caldwell, D. E., 1987, Behavior of *Pseudomonas fluorescens* within the hydrodynamic boundary layers of surface microenvironments, *Microb. Ecol.* **14:**1–14.

Lawrence, J. R., Korber, D. R., and Caldwell, D. E., 1989a, Computer-enhanced darkfield microscopy for the quantitative analysis of bacterial growth and behavior on surfaces, *J. Microbiol. Methods* **10:**123–138.

Lawrence, J. R., Malone, J. A., Korber, D. R., and Caldwell, D. E., 1989b, Computer image enhancement to increase depth of field in phase contrast microscopy, *Binary* **1:**181–185.

Lawrence, J. R., Delaquis, P. J., Zanyk, B. N., Korber, D. R., and Caldwell, D. E., 1990, Computer-enhanced microscopy study of *Pseudomonas fragi* biofilm development, Abstracts of the ASM Conference on Multicellular Behavior of Bacteria in Nature, Industry, and the Laboratory, Woods Hole Marine Biological Laboratory.

Lawrence, J. R., Korber, D. R., Hoyle, B. D., Costerton, J. W., and Caldwell, D. E., 1991, Optical sectioning of microbial biofilms, *J. Bacteriol.* **173:**6558–6567.

Linfoot, E. H., and Wolfe, E., 1953, Diffraction images in systems with an annular aperture, *Proc. Phys. Soc. B* **66:**145–149.

Luby-Phelps, K., Lanni, F., and Taylor, D. L., 1988, The submicroscopic properties of cytoplasm as a determinant of cellular function, *Annu. Rev. Biophys. Chem.* **17:**369–396.

McLean, R. J. C., Lawrence, J. R., Korber, D. R., and Caldwell, D. E., 1991, *Proteus mirabilis* biofilm protection against struvite crystal dissolution and its implications in struvite urolithiasis, *J. Urol.* **146:**1130–1142.

Malone, J. A., 1988, Colonization of surface microenvironments by *Rhizobium* spp., M.Sc. thesis, University of Sask.

Marshall, K. C., 1986, Microscopic methods for the study of bacterial behavior at inert surfaces, *J. Microbiol. Methods* **4:**217–227.

Marshall, K. C., 1988, Adhesion and growth of bacteria at surfaces in oligotrophic habitats, *Can J. Microbiol.* **34:**503–506.

Marshall, K. C., and Cruickshank, R. H., 1973, Cell surface hydrophobicity and the orientation of certain bacteria at interfaces, *Arch. Mikrobiol.* **91:**29–40.

Marshall, K. C., Stout, R., and Mitchell, R., 1971, Mechanisms of the initial events in the sorption of marine bacteria to solid surfaces, *J. Gen. Microbiol.* **68:**337–348.

Marshall, K. C., Cruikshank, R. H., and Bushby, H. V. A., 1975, The orientation of certain root-nodule bacteria at interfaces, including legume root-hair surfaces, *J. Gen. Microbiol.* **91:**198–200.

Martin, Y., Williams, C. C., and Wickramasinghe, H. K., 1988, Tip techniques for microcharacterization of materials, *Scanning Microsc.* **2:**3–8.

Meadows, P. S., 1971, The attachment of bacteria to solid surfaces, *Arch. Mikrobiol.* **75:**374–381.

Meijer, B. C., Kootstra, G. J., and Wilkinson, M. H. F., 1990, A theoretical and practical investigation into the characterization of bacterial species by image analysis, *Binary* **2:**21–31.

Pawley, J. B. (ed.), 1990, *Handbook of Biological Confocal Microscopy,* Plenum Press, New York.

Perfil'ev, B. V., and Gabe, D. R., 1969, *Capillary Methods of Investigating Microorganisms* (J. M. Shewan, trans.), University of Toronto Press, Toronto.

Peters, A. C., 1990, Using image analysis to map bacterial growth on solid media. *Binary* **2:**73–75.

Peters, A. C., Wimpenny, J. W. T., Thomas, L. V., and Griffiths, J., 1991, Mapping bacterial growth on gradient plates using image analysis, *Binary* **3:**147–154.

Pettipher, G. L., and Rodrigues, U. M., 1982, Semi-automated counting of bacteria and somatic cells in milk using epifluorescence microscopy and television image analysis, *J. Appl. Bacteriol.* **53:**323–329.

Power, K., and Marshall, K. C., 1988, Cellular growth and reproduction of marine bacteria on surface-bound substrate, *Biofouling* **1:**163–174.

Read, N. D., Knight, H., and Trewas, A. J., 1992, Fluorescence ratio imaging and confocal microscopy in filamentous fungi, *Binary* **4**:50–52.

Robinson, R. W., Akin, D. E., Nordstedt, R. A., Thomas, M. V., and Aldrich, H. C., 1984, Light and electron microscopic examinations of methane-producing biofilms from anaerobic fixed-bed reactors, *Appl. Environ. Microbiol.* **48**:127–136.

Russ, J. C., 1990, *Computer-Assisted Microscopy: The Measurement and Analysis of Images,* Plenum Press, New York.

Shaw, P. J., and Rawlins, P. J., 1991, The point-spread function of a confocal microscope: Its measurement and use in deconvolution of 3-D data, *J. Micros.* **163**:151–165.

Shotton, D. M., 1989, Confocal scanning optical microscopy and its applications for biological specimens, *J. Cell Sci.* **94**:175–206.

Shotton, D., and White, N., 1989, Confocal scanning microscopy: Three dimensional biological imaging, *Trends Biochem. Sci.* **14**:435–438.

Sieracki, M. E., and Webb, K. L., 1986, A color video image analysis system for studying pico- and nanoplanktonic bacteria, *EOS Trans. Am. Geophys. Union* **66**:1298.

Sieracki, M. E., Johnson, P. W., and Sieburth, J. M., 1985, Detection, enumeration, and sizing of planktonic bacteria by image-analzyed epifluorescence microscopy, *Appl. Environ. Microbiol.* **49**:799–810.

Sieracki, M. E., Reichenback, S. E., and Webb, K. L., 1989, Evaluation of automated threshold selection methods for accurately sizing microscopic fluorescent cells by image analysis, *Appl. Environ. Microbiol.* **55**:2762–2772.

Silverman, M., and Simon, M., 1974, Flagellar rotation and the mechanism of bacterial motility, *Nature* **249**:73–74.

Singh, A., Yu, F.-P., and McFeters, G. A., 1990, Rapid detection of chlorine-induced bacterial injury by the direct viable count method using image analysis, *Appl. Environ. Microbiol.* **56**:389–394.

Sjollema, J., Busscher, H. J., and Weerkamp, A. H., 1988, Deposition of oral streptococci and polystyrene lattices onto glass in a parallel plate flow cell, *Biofouling* **1**:101–112.

Sjollema, J., Busscher, H. J., and Weerkamp, A. H., 1989, Real-time enumeration of adhering microorganisms in a parallel plate flow cell using automated image analysis, *J. Microbiol. Methods* **9**:73–78.

Sjollema, J., van der Mei, H. M., and Busscher, H. J., 1990a, Direct observations of cooperative effects in oral streptococcal adhesion to glass by analysis of the spatial arrangement of adhering bacteria, *FEMS Microbiol. Ecol. Lett.* **69**:263–270.

Sjollema, J., van der Mei, H. M., and Busscher, H. J., 1990b, The influence of collector and bacterial cell surface properties on the deposition of oral streptococci in a parallel plate flow cell. *J. Adhesion Sci. Technol.* **4**:765–777.

Soderstrom, B., 1977, Vital staining of fungi in pure cultures and in soil with fluorescein diacetate, *Soil Biol. Biochem.* **9**:59–63.

Soderstrom, B. E., 1979, Some problems in assessing the fluorescein diacetate-active fungal biomass in the soil, *Soil Biol. Biochem.* **11**:147–148.

Staley, J. T., 1971, Growth rates of algae determined *in situ* using an immersed microscope, *J. Phytol.* **7**:13–17.

Tsien, R. Y., 1989, Fluorescent indicators of ion concentrations, *Methods Cell Biol.* **30**:127–156.

Tsien, R. Y., and Waggoner, A., 1990, Fluorophores for confocal microscopy: Photophysics and photochemistry, in: *Handbook of Confocal Microscopy* (J. B. Pawley, ed.), Plenum Press, New York, pp. 169–178.

Vaitzus, Z., and Doetsch, R. N., 1969, Motility tracks: Technique for quantitative study of bacterial movement, *Appl. Environ. Microbiol.* **17**:584–588.

van Loosdrecht, M. C. W., Lyklema, J., Norde, W., and Zehnder, A. J. B., 1990, Influence of interfaces on microbial activity, *Microbiol. Rev.* **54**:75–87.

van Veen, J., and Paul, E. A., 1979, Conversion of biovolume measurements of soil organisms, grown under various moisture tensions, to biomass and their nutrient content, *Appl. Environ. Microbiol.* **37**:686–692.

Verran, J., and Rocliffe, M. D., 1986, Feasibility of using automatic image analysis for measuring dental plaque *in situ, J. Dent.,* **14**:11–13.

Wells, K. S., Sandison, D. R., Strickler, J., and Webb, W. W., 1990, Imaging with laser scanning confocal microscopy, in: *Handbook of Biological Confocal Microscopy* (J. B. Pawley, ed.), Plenum Press, New York, pp. 27–39.

White, J. G., Amos, W. B., and Fordham, M., 1987, An evaluation of confocal versus conventional imaging of biological structure by fluorescence light microscopy, *J. Cell Biol.* **105**:41–48.

Wimpenny, J. W. T., Waters, P., and Peters, A. C., 1988, Gel-plate methods in microbiology, in: Handbook of Laboratory Model Systems for Microbial Ecosystems, Vol. 1 (J. W. T. Wimpenny, ed.), CRC Press, Boca Raton, pp. 229–251.

Wolfaardt, G. M., Lawrence, J. R., Hendry, M. J., Roberts, R. D., and Caldwell, D. E., 1992, The use of model diffusion gradients for the isolation of degradative microbial consortia, Abstracts of the Annual Meeting of the Canadian Society of Microbiologists.

Wynn-Williams, D. D., 1988a, Television image analysis of microbial communities in Antarctic fell-fields, *Polarforschung* **58**:239–249.

Wynn-Williams, D. D., 1988b, Microbial colonization processes in Antarctic fellfield soils—An experimental overview, in: Proceedings of the NIPR Symposium on Polar Biology, National Institute of Polar Research, Tokyo, Vol. 3, pp. 164–178.

Zanyk, B. N., Korber, D. R., Lawrence, J. R., and Caldwell, D. E., 1991, 4-D visualization of biofilm development by *Pseudomonas fragi, Binary* **3**:24–29.

2

Microbial Biosynthesis of Ethylene and Its Influence on Plant Growth

MUHAMMAD ARSHAD and W. T. FRANKENBERGER, JR.

1. Introduction

Ethylene (C_2H_4) is a plant hormone that is involved in the regulation of many physiological processes. It is the simplest unsaturated carbon compound in nature which is a gas under physiological conditions of temperature and pressure, and exerts a major influence on many aspects of plant growth and development. Ethylene is produced by all higher plants and many soil microorganisms. In trace amounts, it interacts with the other plant hormones, particularly auxins.

Ethylene is a common constituent of the soil atmosphere under both aerobic and anaerobic conditions and its concentrations are often high enough to influence plant growth (Smith, 1976a). Soil C_2H_4 is of microbial origin since its production is eliminated by steam sterilization (Smith and Restall, 1971; Smith and Cook, 1974) but considerable dispute exists concerning the identity of responsible microorganisms. According to Primrose (1979), C_2H_4 is synthesized by many species of bacteria and fungi but is oxidized only by a limited group of the microbiota.

Pratt and Goeschl (1969) speculated that microbial production of C_2H_4 could have agronomic ramifications. Similarly, Primrose (1979) indicated that C_2H_4 concentrations as low as 10 ppb can evoke a plant response. Our own study (Arshad and Frankenberger, 1988) provided direct proof of these speculations as etiolated pea seedlings exhibited the classical "triple" response [reduction in elongation, swelling of the hypocotyl, and a change in the direction of growth (horizontal)] when exposed to microbially produced C_2H_4. Although there are several reviews on C_2H_4 (Burg, 1962; Pratt and Goeschl, 1969; Abeles, 1972; Smith, 1976a; Lieberman, 1979; Primrose, 1979; Yang and Hoffman, 1984; Jackson, 1985; Arshad and Frankenberger, 1992), the main focus of this review is on microbially produced C_2H_4 in soil and its possible impact on plant growth.

MUHAMMAD ARSHAD • Department of Soil Science, University of Agriculture, Faisalabad, Pakistan. W. T. FRANKENBERGER, JR. • Department of Soil and Environmental Sciences, University of California, Riverside, California 92521.
Advances in Microbial Ecology, Vol. 12, edited by K.C. Marshall. Plenum Press, New York, 1992.

2. History

Historically, only the auxins predate the discovery of C_2H_4. The Russian botanist Neljubow (1901) is believed to have been the first to recognize the regulatory properties of this gas. He reported that C_2H_4 was the agent in illuminating gas which most effectively caused the "triple" response in dark-grown pea seedlings. Later, Crocker and Knight (1908) reported that C_2H_4 was capable of causing floral epinasty, abscission, intumescences, and inhibition of plant growth even at levels as low as 0.1 μl/liter. Cousins (1910) noted the ability of gases produced by oranges to ripen banana, and later Denny (1924) reported that C_2H_4 accelerated the ripening and respiration of lemons. Regeimbal and Harvey (1927) found that C_2H_4 treatment enhanced invertase and protease activity of pineapple and suggested that synthesis of these enzymes might be controlled through C_2H_4 action. The first chemical proof that C_2H_4 was a natural plant product was demonstrated by Gane (1934). Crocker et al. (1935) proposed that C_2H_4 was a fruit-ripening hormone and also acted as a regulator in vegetative plant organs. Zimmerman and Wilcoxon (1935) postulated the concept that auxin increased C_2H_4 production and that the C_2H_4 so produced might play a role in auxin action. Lieberman and Mapson (1964) were the first to show that methionine was a precursor of C_2H_4 biosynthesis in plants.

It was not until the use of gas chromatography (GC) for C_2H_4 detection that Burg and Stolwijk (1959) and Burg and Thimann (1959) elucidated the role of C_2H_4 in fruit ripening. GC analyses rapidly advanced the field of C_2H_4 research in plant sciences and by the mid-1960s, C_2H_4 had been clearly identified as an endogenous regulator of plants. With the resurgence of interest that followed, C_2H_4 rapidly gained in hormonal stature.

The first report of C_2H_4 production by fungi was by Gane (1934) who found that growth of pea seedlings was inhibited by an atmospheric metabolite produced by a fungal culture grown aerobically on baker's yeast. The metabolite resembled C_2H_4 since it could be removed by absorption in bromine water. Later, Miller et al. (1940) showed that Penicillium digitatum growing on potato dextrose agar produced a gas causing epinasty of tomato leaves. Simultaneously, Biale (1940) reported that emanation of a gas from P. digitatum promoted degreening of citrus fruit. Biale and Shepherd (1941) confirmed that P. digitatum released a gas which caused epinasty of test plants and Young et al. (1951) proved conclusively that this gas was C_2H_4. The first report on C_2H_4 production by a bacterium, Pseudomonas solanacearum, was provided by Freebairn and Buddenhagen (1964). Following the initial observations by Smith and Russell (1969), several investigators have shown that soil is a potential source of C_2H_4. Field studies (Dowdell et al., 1972) revealed that C_2H_4 accumulates in the soil atmosphere.

3. Methodology

As a simple gaseous hydrocarbon, C_2H_4 can be separated and quantified by GC analysis and detected at concentrations as low as 0.01 μl/liter. The analysis is quick and easy to perform once the operating conditions have been established and its reliability, accuracy, and precision are superior to bioassays used by earlier workers.

3.1. Bioassays

The development and use of bioassays were intimately linked to the discovery and characterization of the major classes of plant hormones. For example, the classical "triple" response of etiolated pea seedlings to exogenously applied C_2H_4 was the basis for its discovery as a plant hormone (Neljubow, 1901). Since C_2H_4 causes a number of physiological and morphological changes in the exposed plant tissues, a variety of bioassays have been developed (Yopp et al., 1986). The majority of these bioassays exhibit log-linear dose–response curves. However, C_2H_4 bioactivity may be dependent on many factors including a hormonal balance, inhibitors, and environmental parameters.

3.2. Gas Chromatography

Abeles (1973) summarized the earlier chemical methods used for quantifying C_2H_4 but many of these are now inferior to GC. Being a gas, C_2H_4 requires no extensive extraction techniques and it can be easily quantified to μg/liter levels using a GC equipped with a flame ionization detector (FID) (McKeon and Yang, 1987). No elaborate accessories are needed. The solid supports that can be used as a stationary phase include alumina or Porapak columns. Details of other considerations for the GC analysis of C_2H_4 have been well documented by Ward et al. (1978b).

3.3. High-Performance Liquid Chromatography

In contrast to the biosynthesis of C_2H_4 by higher plants, where methionine is the sole precursor, the pathway for microbial biosynthesis is not well established and several amino acids have been proposed as possible precursors. Reverse-phase high-performance liquid chromatography (HPLC) for analysis of amino acids by precolumn derivatization (McClung and Frankenberger, 1988) may be applicable for detecting these compounds as substrates or intermediates.

3.4. Units Dilemma of Ethylene

Currently, many soil scientists and plant physiologists studying the impact of exogenous C_2H_4 on plant growth and development have used the following units to express C_2H_4 concentrations: μl/liter, mg/liter, mg/kg, kg/ha, and moles (pico, nano, micro, milli)/liter. These units are extensively used in the literature to indicate the concentrations of C_2H_4 often without mentioning the physical parameters such as temperature (T) and pressure (P). Being a gas, C_2H_4 obeys gas laws, so it is very confusing for the reader to know precisely the actual concentrations of C_2H_4 used or produced in a particular experiment. For instance, if it is given that C_2H_2 was applied at a rate of 1 μl/liter, it would be impossible to repeat the same experiment without knowing the physical conditions in which the study was conducted. According to Charles's or Gay Lussac's law, the volume of a gas is proportional to its temperature (K) provided that pressure remains constant. A given mass of a gas will increase in volume by 1/273rd of its volume at 0°C for every 1°C rise in temperature (Morris, 1968). A mixture of C_2H_4 in air at 1 μl/liter composition at a low temperature would have more C_2H_4 compared to a mixture of the same ratio under constant pressure and a higher temperature. The plant response would also be different when exposed to these two conditions.

Usually C_2H_4 concentrations (applied or produced) are quite small. The concentration unit, "mole," gives the best indication of C_2H_4 concentration. The term *mole* is synonymous with *gram-molecules* and is the mass of a substance in grams equal numerically to its molecular weight. Given P and T, one can repeat the experiment with almost 100% accuracy, knowing the C_2H_4 concentration is expressed in moles since the numerical value can be calculated using the following relationship:

$$PV = nRT$$

where

P = pressure in atmospheres
V = volume in cm³ (ml) or liters
n = number of moles of gas
R = gas constant in cm³-atm/K-mole or liters-atm/K-mole
T = temperature in K

The numerical value of the gas constant, R, depends on the units in which pressure and volume are reported assuming that only the absolute, or Kelvin, temperature scale is used. The most commonly used values of R are 82.0575 cm³-atm/K-mole and 0.0820575 liter-atm/K-mole.

The ideal gas law can be employed to determine n, given the standard conditions of P, V, and T. One may argue that the behavior of real gases is not always in accordance with that predicted by the ideal gas equation and modifications (such as the van der Waals equation of state) are sometimes employed. However, most gases, including C_2H_4, do obey the ideal gas equation at low pressures.

The use of moles to express C_2H_4 concentration fulfills all of the requirements of a standard unit. Results reported in derived units of moles along with the physical parameters (e.g., P, V, and T) do not cause confusion or misunderstanding and indicate the precise concentrations of C_2H_4 used or produced.

4. Physiological Aspects of Ethylene in Plants

4.1. Endogenous Ethylene Production

Ethylene is produced by essentially all organs of higher plants (Abeles, 1973). Beyer *et al.* (1985) reported that the rate of C_2H_4 production varies with both the type of tissue and its stage of development. The meristematic tissue and nodal regions are the most vigorous sites of C_2H_4 production; high rates of C_2H_4 synthesis also occur during seed germination and at the initial stages of fading in flowering. Biale and Young (1981) demonstrated that of all plant tissues considered, C_2H_4 production in fruits is best characterized. In climacteric fruits, a low rate of C_2H_4 is produced during the preclimacteric stage, and later followed by a sudden increase in C_2H_4 production and respiration in the ripening stage.

4.2. Plant Response

In recent years, it has become apparent that C_2H_4 has a much greater physiological role than its influence in fruit ripening alone. Many effects previously considered to be induced directly by auxins are now known to be mediated by an intervening step in which auxin leads to an increase in the synthesis of ethylene. Zimmerman and Wilcoxon (1935) were the first to suggest a hormonal interaction between C_2H_4 and auxin. Morgan and Hall (1962, 1964) clearly showed the influence of superoptimal levels of auxins (10^{-5} to 10^{-3} M) on C_2H_4 production, which was later confirmed by Abeles (1966) and Burg and Burg (1966). Chadwick and Burg (1967) and Burg and Burg (1967) attributed the inhibitory effects of superoptimal concentrations of auxin on plant growth to auxin-induced C_2H_4. Similarly, control of cell shape and size by the interaction of auxin and C_2H_4 was suggested (Sargent et al., 1973; Hanson and Kende, 1976; Osborne, 1976).

Studies indicate that auxin stimulates C_2H_4 production by enhancing the conversion of S-adenosylmethionine (SAM) to 1-aminocyclopropane-1-carboxylic acid (ACC) (Beyer et al., 1985). The ability of auxin and C_2H_4 to cause a number of similar responses suggests that the effects previously attributed to auxin might be due to C_2H_4 produced in response to the auxin treatment.

Some effects of C_2H_4 on plants are positive, such as growth promotion and flower initiation, whereas others appear to be negative including growth inhibition and abscission (Table I). Ethylene influences many phases of plant development from seed germination to senescence and growth in all parts of the plant from roots to the shoot tips; hence, C_2H_4 must be viewed as a substance with broad regulatory activity. However, any one process is presumably influenced by the balance of other plant hormones (Beyer et al., 1985).

4.3. Biochemistry

Many compounds were once proposed as precursors of C_2H_4 synthesis in plants including linolenic acid, propanal, ethanol, acrylic acid, β-alanine, β-hydroxypropionic acid, fumaric acid, and methionine. Methionine, the only confirmed precursor in plants, was first proposed by Lieberman and Mapson (1964). Later, Lieberman et al. (1966) demonstrated in vivo conversion of ^{14}C-labeled methionine to [14]C_2H_4 in apple tissues. It is now well established that methionine serves as a precursor of C_2H_4 in all higher plant tissues.

Table I. Plant Response to Ethylene[a]

Growth inhibition[b]	Flower initiation[b]
Growth promotion	Flower sex shifts[b]
Geotropism modification[b]	Fruit growth stimulation[b]
Tissue proliferation[b]	Fruit degreening
Root and root hair initiation[b]	Fruit ripening[b]
Aerenchyma development	Respiratory changes
Leaf epinasty[b]	Storage product hydrolysis
Leaf movement inhibition[b]	Latex and gum exudation promotion[b]
Formative growth	Protein synthesis promotion
Hook formation	RNA synthesis promotion
Chlorophyll destruction	Abscission and dehiscence promotion[b]
Anthocyanin synthesis promotion	Seed and bud dormancy release
Anthocyanin synthesis inhibition	Apical dominance release

[a] Adapted from Morgan (1976). Under suitable conditions, most of the responses can be induced by auxin as well as ethylene. However, the last three, abscission, seed dormancy, and apical dominance, are usually affected differently.
[b] Indicates early literature, where the plant response was originally attributed to the action of auxin.

Tracer studies conducted by Lieberman (1979) with [^{14}C]methionine revealed that carbon atoms 3 and 4 of methionine were the atoms converted to C_2H_4. Methionine and ethionine were the only amino acids which evolved significant amounts of C_2H_4, whereas methionine sulfoxide and methionine sulfone were inactive, suggesting the necessity for an unencumbered sulfur atom that could be converted to a sulfonium ion. The inhibition of C_2H_4 formation from methionine by an oxidative phosphorylation inhibitor, 2,4-dinitrophenol, indicated involvement of an energy (ATP)-dependent step in C_2H_4 biosynthesis. This led to the discovery of SAM as an intermediate which was later confirmed by Adams and Yang (1977) while working with labeled [^{35}S]methionine and [^{3}H-*methyl*]methionine.

Adams and Yang (1979) identified ACC, 5'-methylthioadenosine (MTA), and 5-methylthioribose (MTR) as labeled products which accumulated when L-[U-^{14}C]methionine was incubated with apple tissues under anaerobic conditions. Further incubation in air resulted in the production of labeled C_2H_4 from the accumulated labeled ACC. Lürssen *et al.* (1979) found that ACC dramatically stimulated C_2H_4 in plant tissues and they speculated that ACC was derived from SAM. Finally, Yung *et al.* (1982) proposed the complete pathway of C_2H_4 biosynthesis in higher plants which is illustrated in Fig. 1.

The sulfur atom of methionine is recycled to maintain a steady rate of C_2H_4 production (Adams and Yang, 1977). More recently, Yung *et al.* (1982) and Wang *et al.* (1982) showed that the ribose moiety of MTR is directly incorporated into the 2-aminobutyrate moiety of methionine along with the CH_3S unit. Thus, the overall result of this cycle is that the CH_3S group is conserved for the continued synthesis of methionine while the 3,4-carbon moiety from which the C_2H_4 molecule is derived is ultimately replenished from the ribose moiety of ATP. Hence a very small amount of methionine is quite effective in producing C_2H_4.

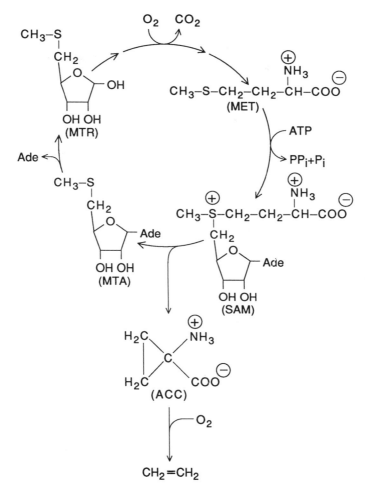

Figure 1. Methionine cycle in relation to the biosynthesis of C_2H_4 in apple tissue. From Yung *et al.* (1982) with permission.

The enzymes involved in the biosynthesis and regulation of ethylene include ACC synthase and the C_2H_4-forming enzyme (EFE).

4.3.1. ACC Synthase

ACC synthase, which catalyzes the conversion of SAM to ACC, plays a key role in regulating C_2H_4 production. It has been partially purified in tomato fruit slices and characterized (Yu *et al.*, 1979; Boller *et al.*, 1979). Factors such as changes in growth environments, hormonal levels, and physiological and developmental events influence the levels of ACC synthase (Yang and Hoffman, 1984). The enzyme requires pyridoxal phosphate for activity; hence, it is sensitive to pyridoxal phosphate inhibitors, especially aminoethoxyvinylglycine (AVG) (K_i = 0.2 μm) and aminooxyacetic acid (AOA) (K_i = 0.8 μm).

4.3.2. C_2H_4-Forming Enzyme

EFE catalyzes the conversion of ACC to C_2H_4 through an oxidative process. The activity of EFE was first described by Adams and Yang (1979) who trapped ACC in apple tissues, incubated in a nitrogen atmosphere, and demonstrated its conversion to C_2H_4 under aerobic conditions. Efforts to obtain cell-free EFE have not succeeded. All characterization of EFE has been done *in vivo*.

EFE in plant tissues has a high affinity for ACC as a substrate (McKeon and Yang, 1984). A number of inhibitors of EFE have been reported, including cobaltous ion (Lürssen *et al.*, 1979; Yu and Yang, 1979), α-aminoisobutyric acid (Satoh and Esashi, 1980), and free radical scavengers (Yang and Hoffman, 1984).

5. Ethylene Production by Soil Microorganisms

5.1. Pathogen–Host Interactions and Ethylene

There appears to be a definite relationship between pathogenesis and C_2H_4 synthesis. Several reports indicate that infection with pathogens triggers C_2H_4 production which coincides with or precedes the development of disease symptoms and subsequent physiological changes in plants (Table II).

The pathogen–host relationship is very complex, and it is difficult to be conclusive about the origin of this increased C_2H_4 generation in the case of the infected host, i.e., either a host metabolite or a pathogen product. Coleman and Hodges (1984) suggested that the pathogen may stimulate C_2H_4 production from the host tissue early in pathogenesis but the pathogen may also directly contribute C_2H_4 and ACC later during infection. Similarly, Achilea *et al.* (1985a) indicated that a relatively low rate of C_2H_4 production in infected grapefruit seems to be mostly from the fruit tissues while a later and higher rate of C_2H_4 synthesis originates mostly from the fungus, *Penicillium digitatum*. Achilea *et al.* (1985b) later used radiolabeled precursors to study the source of C_2H_4 in *P. digitatum*-infected grapefruit and found that C_2H_4 produced by healthy portions of the fruit originated from methionine, whereas C_2H_4 produced by the infected fruit was derived mostly from glutamic acid. Furthermore, C_2H_4 production from the healthy fruit was markedly enhanced by ACC and to a lesser extent by $CuSO_4$, but inhibited by AVG. In contrast, the production of C_2H_4 by the infected peel (*P. digitatum*) was not affected by ACC, but was markedly inhibited by $CuSO_4$, and to a lesser extent by AVG. Based upon these observations, they suggested that C_2H_4 production in the healthy fruit was of plant origin, whereas markedly enhanced production of C_2H_4 by the *P. digitatum*-infected region was mostly or entirely of fungal origin. Similarly, Coleman and Hodges (1986) found that the addition of ACC to leaf blade infusion media of the host (*Poa pratensis*) resulted in low C_2H_4 production compared with that produced when infected by the pathogen *Bipolaris sorokiniana* with the addition of methionine. They concluded that the pathogen did not convert ACC to C_2H_4 efficiently and C_2H_4 may be produced via more than one pathway.

On the other hand, studies have shown indirectly that increased C_2H_4 release from infected tissue may involve a plant metabolite with infection stimulating this process. Lund and Mapson (1970) observed a marked increase in the rate of C_2H_4 production by cauliflower florets infected by *Erwinia carotovora* and these increases were directly correlated with bacterial numbers. They were of the view that, although bacterial infection resulted in enhanced C_2H_4 production, the C_2H_4 was most likely a plant metabolite since the pure culture of *E. carotovora* failed to produce C_2H_4 when cultivated on either pectate medium or cauliflower extract supplemented with methionine. Toppan *et al.* (1982) revealed that enhanced C_2H_4 in melon infected by *Colletotrichum lagenarium* was suppressed by specific inhibitors of the plant C_2H_4 biosynthetic pathway, namely L-canaline and AVG, implying that C_2H_4 biosynthesis was a plant metabolic product. Similarly, several studies have shown that high rates of C_2H_4 production triggered by infection were suppressed by AVG in pea pods infected by *Fusarium solani* f. sp. *pisi* (Mauch *et al.*, 1984); in parsley cells infected by *Phytophthora megasperma* (Chappell *et al.*, 1984); and melon seedlings treated with *Colletotrichum lagenarium* (Roby *et al.*, 1985, 1986). These studies further support the hypothesis that C_2H_4 production in the infected host is the result of a plant metabolite, since AVG inhibits the conversion of SAM to ACC.

5.2. Soil Isolates

Ilag and Curtis (1968), in a comprehensive survey on C_2H_4 production by soil fungi, examined 228 species belonging to 81 different genera. Twenty-six percent of the cultures isolated on corn-steep liquor produced C_2H_4. They also observed that 20 unidentified actinomycetes produced C_2H_4. El-Sharouny (1984) tested 80 fungal species isolated from diseased roots in Egypt, for C_2H_4 production and found that 31% of the isolates produced C_2H_4 concentrations varying from 0.4 to over 380 ppm. Lynch (1975) reported that relatively high amounts of C_2H_4 were released by *Mucor hiemalis* and two soil yeasts, *Candida vartiovaarai* and *Trichosporon cutaneum*, when glucose and methionine were provided. Recently, Arshad and Frankenberger (1989) revealed that corn rhizosphere is quite rich with microbiota capable of producing C_2H_4 from L-methionine at rates comparable to that produced by *Mucor hiemalis* and *Candida vartiovaarai*. Among these isolates, fungi were the most dominant. We concluded that corn rhizosphere contains an appreciable number of microorganisms which can synthesize C_2H_4 to concentrations which could affect plant growth. Primrose (1976b) examined 497 soil and water bacterial isolates for C_2H_4 production and concluded that C_2H_4-producing bacteria are ubiquitous in the soil environment. Dasilva *et al.* (1974) proposed that C_2H_4 production is of widespread occurrence in both eukaryotic and prokaryotic forms. It is

Table II. Ethylene Production in Response to Host–Pathogen Infection

Pathogen	Host	Specific response to infection	Reference
Agrobacterium sp.	Carrot disks	Infection resulted in production of elevated levels of C_2H_4 continuously	Goodman *et al.* (1986)
Agrobacterium tumefasciens	*Nicotiana* and *Lycopersicon*	Synthesis of ACC and the conversion of ACC to C_2H_4 were influenced by crown gall transformation	Miller and Pengelly (1984)
Alternaria and *Glocosporium* spp.	Navel orange	C_2H_4 and fungal infection were associated with blossom-end yellowing of navel orange	Southwick *et al.* (1982)
Bipolaris sorokiniana	*Poa pratensis* leaves	Enhanced C_2H_4 was responsible for much of the chlorophyll loss	Hodges and Coleman (1984)
	Poa pratensis leaves	Stimulated ACC synthase activity and C_2H_4 production during pathogenesis	Coleman and Hodges (1984)
Cercospora arachidicola	Peanut leaves	Increase in C_2H_4 production coincided with disease symptoms, i.e., defoliation and abscission	Ketring and Melouk (1982)
Colletotrichum lagenarium	Melon seedlings	C_2H_4 and cell wall hydroxyproline-rich glycoprotein biosynthesis was greatly enhanced	Toppan *et al.* (1982)
	Melon tissue	Infection led to an early stimulation of C_2H_4	Toppan and Esquerre-Tugaye (1984)
	Melon hypocotyl	Infection triggered C_2H_4 production, may be involved in hydroxyproline-rich glycoprotein (HRGP) synthesis	Roby et al. (1985)
	Melon leaves or seedlings	Increased in chitinase activity with a simultaneous increase in C_2H_4 production	Roby *et al.* (1986)
Fusarium sp.	Tomato	Increased C_2H_4 production; reached peak within 9–10 days, coincident with marked foliar wilting and basal leaf abscission	Gentile and Matta (1975)
Fusarium spp. pathogenic to tulips	Tulip bulb	Produced 2000 times more C_2H_4 than other nonpathogenic *Fusarium*	Swart and Kamerbeek (1976)
Fusarium oxysporum f. sp. *tulepae*	Tulip bulb	Increased C_2H_4 production, caused gummosis and bud necrosis	de Munk (1971)

Organism	Plant/tissue	Effect	Reference
Fusarium solani f. sp. *phaseoli* (nonpathogenic) f. sp. *pisi* (pathogenic)	Pea pods	Fungal infection strongly increased C_2H_4 production, but C_2H_4 and fungal infection were independent signals for the induction of chitinase and β-1,3-glucanase	Mauch *et al.* (1984)
Mycorrhizal fungi and *Fusarium*	Douglas fir	Enhancement of C_2H_4 formation coinciding with development of mycorrhizae and stimulating lateral root development. *Fusarium*-infected seedlings produced more C_2H_4	Graham and Linderman (1980)
Mycosphaerella citri	Rough lemon and grapefruit leaves	Infection induced C_2H_4 production and caused leaf chlorosis and abscission	Graham *et al.* (1984)
Penicillium digitatum	Grapefruit	Fungal invasion was associated with increase in both ACC and C_2H_4 production but ability of tissue to convert ACC to C_2H_4 decreased with the development of infection	Achilea *et al.* (1985a)
Penicillium italicum	Orange fruit	Fungal inoculation increased C_2H_4 production. Treatment with C_2H_4 (1000 μl/liter) and inoculation enhanced respiration rates of fruit	El-Kazzaz *et al.* (1983)
Peronospora tabacina Adam.	Tobacco	Induced increase in C_2H_4 release, causing growth retardation and accumulation of scopoletin in upper stem	Reuveni and Cohen (1978)
Phytophthora citrophthora	Citrus	C_2H_4 production by the infected stem tissues was a direct factor influencing duct development	Gedalovich and Fahn (1985)
Phytophthora megasperma var. *sojae*	Soybean cotyledons	Increased C_2H_4 formation, phenylalanine ammonia lyase (PAL) activity, and glyceollin accumulation	Paradies *et al.* (1980)
Phytophthora megasperma	Parsley cells	Peak of ACC synthase activity preceded maximal (PAL) activity	Chappell *et al.* (1984)
Pyricularia oryza	Rice	Considerable increase in C_2H_4 evolution, creating stunting of blast	Kozaka and Teraoka (1978)
Rhizopus stonolifer	Nonripening tomato mutants	Infection markedly stimulated C_2H_4 production followed by accelerated climacteric-like patterns of respiration	Barkai-Golan and Kopeliovitch (1983)

(continued)

Table II. (*Continued*)

Pathogen	Host	Specific response to infection	Reference
Uromyces phaseoli	Beans	Outburst of C_2H_4 caused differentiation of uredosori and large, brown necrotic spots	Montalbini and Elstner (1977)
Ustilago maydis	Maize seedlings	Reduction in elongation growth of leaves and shoots, increase in basal diameter, and decrease in weight are preceded by a 4-fold increase in C_2H_4 synthesis	Andrews *et al.* (1981)
Verticillium dahliae Kleh.	Cotton	Accelerated C_2H_4 production in defoliating plants	Tzeng and DeVay (1985)
Xanthomonas campestris pv. *Vesicatoria*	Pepper leaves	Chlorotic zone surrounding necrotic lesion of bacterial spot associated with increased C_2H_4 synthesis in diseased leaves	Stall and Hall (1984)
Xanthomonas citri	Citrus leaves	Development of disease symptoms directly related to increase in C_2H_4 production. Rate of defoliation was directly related to rate of C_2H_4 production	Goto *et al.* (1980)

now well documented that C_2H_4 is produced by many soil-inhabiting microorganisms. A comprehensive list of C_2H_4-producing fungi and bacteria is given in Tables III and IV, respectively.

5.3. Ethylene Production by Nonpathogens and Their Impact on Plant Growth

Ethylene has been identified as a common constituent of the soil atmosphere and under certain conditions has been shown to reach concentrations sufficiently high enough to influence plant growth and development (Smith and Restall, 1971; Smith and Robertson, 1971; Yoshida and Suzuki, 1975). Ethylene concentrations as low as 10 ppb can evoke plant responses while 25 ppb results in decreased fruit and flower development (Primrose, 1979). Jackson and Campbell (1975) were the first to reveal the probable significance of C_2H_4 produced in soil influencing plant growth. They demonstrated a rapid movement of radiolabeled $^{14}C_2H_4$ when applied to roots in nutrient solution from the roots to shoots of tomato plants producing a specific epinastic response.

Little direct evidence is available in the existing literature on the microbial effect of C_2H_4 production on plant growth. Recently, Arshad and Frankenberger (1988) demonstrated the influence of microbially derived C_2H_4 on etiolated pea seedlings by observing the classical "triple" response (including reduction in elongation, swelling of the hypocotyl, and a change in the direction of growth), the same observations made in the discovery of C_2H_4 as a plant hormone. We showed that etiolated pea seedlings exhibited the classical "triple" response to C_2H_4 derived from an inoculum, *Acremonium falciforme* (Figs. 2 and 3) and the soil indigenous microbiota (Table V) in utilization of L-methionine. A similar response was observed when seedlings were exposed to C_2H_4 gas directly applied (Fig. 4). Likewise, Neljubow (1901), Goschl et al. (1966), and Beyer (1976) reported the classical "triple" response of etiolated pea seedlings in response to direct application of C_2H_4.

Arshad and Frankenberger (1990a) tested the effects of two C_2H_4 precursors, L-methionine and L-ethionine, applied to soil on the growth of corn (*Zea mays*) and tomato (*Lycopersicon esculentum*), respectively. L-Methionine applied at 1.85 mg/kg soil was the most effective in promoting shoot height, shoot fresh weight, and stem diameter of two corn cultivars (Table VI). In one cultivar (Kandy Korn), the resistance to stem breaking (stem strength) was improved, whereas in the other (Miracle), resistance was reduced upon treatment with L-methionine. A significant epinastic response (typical for C_2H_4) was observed in the second and third leaves of tomato plants, when soil was treated with L-ethionine. An L-ethionine treatment of 0.2 mg/kg soil resulted in maximum fresh fruit yield, whereas 2 mg/kg soil gave the highest average fresh fruit weight (Table VI). Soil treatment with L-ethionine also caused early fruit formation and ripening compared to the untreated control. Three possible mechanisms were proposed: (1) substrate-dependent C_2H_4 production by the soil indigenous microorganisms, (2) uptake directly by plant roots followed by metabolism within the tissues, and/or (3) a change in the balance of rhizosphere microorganisms affecting plant growth.

The effects of exogenous C_2H_4, applied as a gas or compounds releasing C_2H_4

Table III. Ethylene-Evolving Fungi

Species	Reference
Acremonium falciforme	Arshad and Frankenberger (1989)
Agaricus bisporus	Lockard and Kneebone (1962); Wood and Hammond (1977), Ward *et al.* (1978a)
Alternaria solani	Ilag and Curtis (1968)
Ascochyta imperfecti	Ilag and Curtis (1968)
Aspergillus sp.	Dasilva *et al.* (1974), Babiker and Pepper (1984)
Aspergillus candidus	Ilag and Curtis (1968)
Aspergillus clavatus	Ilag and Curtis (1968)
Aspergillus flavus	Ilag and Curtis (1968)
Aspergillus niger	El-Sharouny (1984)
Aspergillus ustus	El-Sharouny (1984), Ilag and Curtis (1968)
Aspergillus variecolor	Ilag and Curtis (1968)
Blastomyces dermatitidis	Nickerson (1948)
Botrytis spectabilis	Ilag and Curtis (1968)
Candida vartiovaarai	Lynch (1975), Arshad and Frankenberger (1989)
Cenococcum geophilum	Graham and Linderman (1980)
Cephalosporum gramineum	Ilag and Curtis (1968)
Chaetomium chlamaloides	Ilag and Curtis (1968)
Currularia sp.	Babiker and Pepper (1984)
Dematium pullulans	Ilag and Curtis (1968)
Fusarium eguiseti	El-Sharouny (1984)
Fusarium moniliforme	El-Sharouny (1984)
Fusarium oxysporum	El-Sharouny (1984)
Fusarium solani	El-Sharouny (1984)
Hansenula subpelticulosa	Ilag and Curtis (1968)
Hebeloma crustuliniforme	Graham and Linderman (1980)
Laccaria laccata	Graham and Linderman (1980)
Mucor sp.	Dasilva *et al.* (1974)
Mucor hiemalis	Lynch (1972), Arshad and Frankenberger (1989)
Mucor silvaticus	Lindberg *et al.* (1979)
Myrothecium roridum	Ilag and Curtis (1968)
Neurospora crassa	Ilag and Curtis (1968)
Penicillium sp.	Babiker and Pepper (1984)
Penicillium corylophilum	Ilag and Curtis (1968)
Penicillium crustosum	Considine *et al.* (1977), El-Sharouny (1984)
Penicillium cyclopium	Considine *et al.* (1977), El-Sharouny (1984)
Penicillium digitatum	Biale (1940), and many others
Penicillium luteum	Ilag and Curtis (1968)
Penicillium notatum	Ilag and Curtis (1968)
Penicillium patulum	Ilag and Curtis (1968)
Penicillium stecki	El-Sharouny (1984)
Phythium butleri	El-Sharouny (1984)
Pythium ultimum	El-Sharouny (1984)
Rhizoctonia solani	El-Sharouny (1984)
Rhizopus sp.	Babiker and Pepper (1984)
Schizophyllum commune	Ilag and Curtis (1968)

Table III. (*Continued*)

Species	Reference
Sclerotinia laxa	Ilag and Curtis (1968)
Scopulariopsis brevcaulis	Ilag and Curtis (1968)
Thamnidium elegans	Ilag and Curtis (1968)
Thielavia alata	Ilag and Curtis (1968)
Trichosporon cutaneum	Lynch (1975)
Fusarium sp.	Babiker and Pepper (1984)
Mortierella sp.	Babiker and Pepper (1984)
Geotrichum sp.	Babiker and Pepper (1984)
Rhizopus nigrican	Babiker and Pepper (1984)

nonbiologically, on plant growth support the view that C_2H_4 of microbial origin could play a vital role in plant physiology, growth, and development.

5.4. Exogenous Application of Ethylene and Plant Growth

To support the view that C_2H_4 of microbial origin could have a pronounced impact on plant growth, the response of different crops to exogenously applied C_2H_4 gas and

Table IV. Ethylene-Evolving Bacteria

Species	Reference
Aeromonas hydrophila	Primrose (1976b)
Arthrobacter spp.	Primrose (1976b)
Citrobacter spp.	Primrose (1976b)
Clostridium butyricum	Pazout et al. (1981)
Enterobacter cloacae	Primrose (1976b)
Erwinia herbicola	Primrose (1976b)
Escherichia coli	Primrose (1976b)
Klebsiella ozaenae oxytoca	Primrose (1976b)
Klebsiella ozaenae	Primrose (1976b)
Klebsiella pneumoniae	Primrose (1976b)
Pseudomonas spp.	Primrose (1976b)
Pseudomonas fluorescens	Pazout et al. (1981)
Pseudomonas inigofera	Primrose (1976b)
Pseudomonas putida	Pazout et al. (1981)
Pseudomonas solanacearum	Bonn et al. (1975), Freebairn and Buddenhagen (1964)
Serratia liquefaciens	Primrose (1976b)
Streptomyces spp.	Dasilva et al. (1974), Ilag and Curtis (1968)

Figure 2. Response of etiolated pea seedlings to exogenous L-methionine-derived C_2H_4 produced by *A. falciforme* (Arshad and Frankenberger, 1988).

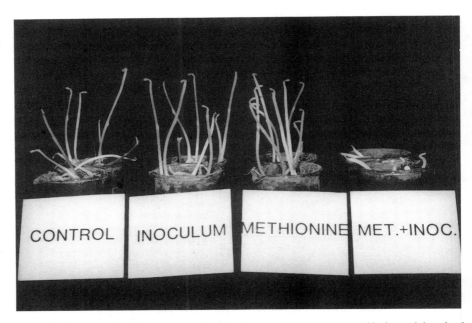

Figure 3. Response of etiolated pea seedlings to the interaction between L-methionine and inoculated *A. falciforme* in sterile soil (Arshad and Frankenberger, 1988).

Table V. Influence of L-Methionine-Derived C_2H_4 Produced by
Indigenous Soil Microbiota on Etiolated Pea Seedlings[a]

Treatment	Seedling length (cm)[b]	Seedling diameter (mm)[b]
Control[c]	6.56b	1.87a
AgNO$_3$ (240 mg/liter)[d]	13.50d	1.93ab
L-Methionine (5mM) + AgNO$_3$ (240 mg/liter)	11.10c	2.06ab
L-Methionine (10 mM)	3.90a	2.75d
L-Methionine (10mM) + AgNO$_3$ (240 mg/liter)	10.10c	2.11b

[a]Modified from Arshad and Frankenberger (1988).
[b]Values followed by the same letters were not significantly different at the $P < 0.05$ level according to the Duncan multiple range test.
[c]Control received equivalent volume of 240 mg/liter NaNO$_3$ solution.
[d]AgNO$_3$ inhibits C_2H_4 action. Samples that did not receive AgNO$_3$ received NaNO$_3$ (240 mg/liter).

nonenzymatically C_2H_4-releasing compounds has been compiled in Table VII. The exact mechanism through which exogenous C_2H_4 influences plant growth is still not clear. The general mode of action of exogenous hormones on crop productivity has been suggested by Bruinisma (1980) to be on endogenous hormones—stimulating their mode of action or interacting with their biosynthesis, translocation, and/or inactivation.

5.5. Biochemistry of Microbial Ethylene Production

As indicated earlier, L-methionine serves as a C_2H_4 precursor in higher plants. In contrast, controversy still exists in the case of microorganisms, regarding the common precursor of C_2H_4. Although methionine has been shown to stimulate C_2H_4 production in bacteria (Primrose, 1976b; Primrose and Dilworth, 1976; Swanson et al., 1979) and many fungal species (Lynch, 1974; Chalutz et al., 1977), several Krebs cycle intermediates also act as substrates for the citrus mold, *Penicillium digitatum* (Chou and Yang, 1973; Owens et al., 1971). Primrose (1976a) tested C_2H_4 formation by *Escherichia coli* with a number of methionine analogues [L-ethionine, N-formylmethionine, L-methionine methyl ester, DL-methionine (hydroxy analogue), and L-norleucine] and other compounds (L-cysteine, 2-keto-4-methyl-mercaptobutyric acid, L-homocysteine, α-ketobutyric acid, 2-aminobutyric acid, α-ketoglutaric acid) serving as substrates and found that all of these compounds except the last four were relatively effective. Phenolic compounds of a humic nature provide a source of carbon for an C_2H_4-producing *Penicillium* species isolated from peat (Considine and Patching, 1975). Chalutz and Lieberman (1978) found that static cultures of *P. digitatum* utilized glutamate and α-ketoglutarate as C_2H_4 precursors.

Arshad and Frankenberger (1989) also tested a number of compounds (Table VIII) as C_2H_4 precursors for *Acremonium falciforme*, a fungal isolate producing C_2H_4 from L-methionine, and found that ethionine, homocysteine, and homoserine also served as

Figure 4. Response of etiolated pea seedlings to C_2H_4 gas. (Arshad and Frankenberger, 1988).

substrates for C_2H_4 production. This may give an indication of the metabolic pathway in the fungal generation of C_2H_4. Carbon sources such as serine, malate, alanine, ethanol, and some sugars promote C_2H_4 production by *P. digitatum*. Some workers reported that glucose serves as a substrate for C_2H_4 production by some microbial isolates (Dasilva *et al.*, 1974; Swart and Kamerbeek, 1977), while others believe that glucose stimulates C_2H_4 generation from methionine by serving as an energy source (Lynch and Harper, 1974a; Chalutz *et al.*, 1977; Arshad and Frankenberger, 1989).

Although L-methionine is the common precursor of C_2H_4 biosynthesis by microorganisms, there is little indication that microbial C_2H_4 biosynthesis follows the same pathway as that of higher plants (MET $\rightarrow$ SAM $\rightarrow$ ACC $\rightarrow$ C_2H_4). Thomas and Spencer (1977) reported that *Saccharomyces cerevisiae* was unable to use SAM for C_2H_4 production. Arshad and Frankenberger (1989) also found that *A. falciforme* released high amounts of C_2H_4 from L-methionine and grew well on ACC, but could not produce C_2H_4 from the latter substrate. Nor could *A. falciforme* use SAM as a source for growth. Yet, Frankenberger and Phelan (1985a) reported that ACC is converted into C_2H_4 in soil under nonsterile conditions and at negligible rates under sterile conditions indicating a biotic transformation. Perhaps ACC is transformed into C_2H_4 in soil through co-metabolism and the soil microbiota are unable to derive energy or C from this substrate.

Recently, we have found that the majority of amino acids, organic acids, and carbohydrates, typically reported in the rhizosphere stimulate C_2H_4 production in soil (Arshad and Frankenberger, 1990b). Since heterotrophic microorganisms can use a

Table VI. Influence of L-Methionine (MET) and L-Ethionine (ETH) as Ethylene Precursors on Plant Growth[a]

Corn

L-MET (mg/kg soil)	Shoot height (cm)		Shoot fresh weight (g)		Shoot dry weight (g)		Stem diameter (mm)		Resistance to stem breaking (relative unit)	
	Kandy Korn	Miracle	Kandy Korn	Miracle	Kandy Korn	Miracle	Kandy Korn	Miracle	Kandy Korn	Miracle
Control	134a[b]	121a	159a	221a	26.1a	33.2a	15.4a	18.6a	3.41a	5.30b
0.0185	159b	134b	185a	226a	28.7ab	30.4a	16.7ab	18.4a	3.67ab	3.41a
0.185	160b	137b	206b	230a	31.8ab	30.5a	17.0ab	19.1a	3.66ab	3.43a
1.85	173b	140b	231b	258b	34.5b	32.3a	17.4b	20.1b	4.35b	4.35ab

Tomato

L-ETH (mg/kg soil)	Fresh fruit yield (g)	Av. wt. of fresh fruit (g)	Total No. of ripe fruit	Epinastic movement (degrees) 72 hr after treatment
Control	261a[b]	37.3a	11a	4.8a
0.2	477b	55.0ab	15ab	9.0b
2.0	445b	62.1b	16ab	9.8b
20	351ab	50.1ab	19b	12.3c

[a]Modified from Arshad and Frankenberger (1990a).
[b]Values sharing the same letter(s) do not differ significantly at the P <0.05 level according to the Duncan's multiple range test.

Muhammad Arshad and W. T. Frankenberger, Jr.

Table VII. Plant Response to Exogenously Applied Ethylene

Crop	Source	Concentration	Plant response	Reference
Rice	Gas	<0.5 ppm	Increased growth rate of coleoptile	Ku et al. (1970)
Rice	Gas	<1 ppm	Promoted elongation of coleoptile	Imaseki and Pjon (1970)
Barley	Gas	<1 ppm	Inhibited extension of root axis	Smith and Robertson (1971)
Rice and rye	Gas	<1 ppm	Increased root extension	Smith and Robertson (1971)
		10 ppm	Reduced root extension up to 25% in rice and 40% in rye	Smith and Robertson (1971)
Cotton	Gas	Up to 3.92 kg/ha	Increased yield up to 25%	Freytag et al. (1972)
Sorghum	Gas	Up to 3.14 kg/ha	Increased yield up to 13%	Freytag et al. (1972)
Tomato	Gas	>2 ppm	Developed petiole epinasty Promoted adventitious rooting	Jackson and Campbell (1975)
Barley	Gas	n.s.[a]	Inhibited seminal root extension Stimulated lateral root growth Did not affect ion uptake	Crossett and Campbell (1975)
Witchweed	Gas	<1.1 kg/ha	Stimulated seed germination	Eplee (1975)
Pea and white clover	Gas	<10 ppm	Inhibited root extension Reduced shoot dry weight Reduced nodulation and nitrogenase activity	Goodlass and Smith (1979)
Pea	Ethrel	>2 ppm	Inhibited nodulation	Drennan and Norton (1972)
Wheat and oats	Ethrel	2.24 kg/ha 0.56 kg/ha	Effectively reduced lodging Increased yield significantly (15.8% in wheat, 7.8% in oats)	Brown and Earley (1973)
Tomato	Ethephon	3×792 ppm	Reduced stem growth and leaf chlorophyll content	Kuo and Chen (1980)
Wheat, barley, and triticale	Ethephon	0.55 kg/ha	Reduced lodging and increased yield	Dahnous et al. (1982)
Maize	Ethephon	140 g/ha	Increased yield by 700 kg/ha	Langan and Oplinger (1987)

Table VIII. Utilization of Various Substrates in C_2H_4 Formation by *A. falciforme*[a]

Substrate	Structure	% efficiency relative to L-methionine
L-Methionine	CH_3—S—CH_2—CH—COOH | NH_2	100.0
L-Ethionine	CH_3—CH_2—S—CH_2—CH_2—CH—COOH | NH_2	14.8
L-Cysteine	HS—CH_2—CH—COOH | NH_2	0
L-Homocysteine	HS—CH_2—CH_2—CH—COOH | NH_2	4.1
L-Homoserine	CH_2OH—CH_2—CH—COOH | NH_2	2.7
L-Glutamic acid	COOH—CH_2—CH_2—CH—COOH | NH_2	0
β-Alanine	NH_2—CH_2—CH_2—COOH	0
Fumaric acid	COOH—CH=CH—COOH	0
L-Malic acid	COOH—CH_2—CHOH—COOH	0
L-Lactic acid	CH_3—CHOH—COOH	
Pyruvic acid	CH_3—CO—COOH	0
Succinic acid	COOH—CH_2—CH_2—COOH	0
α-Ketoglutaric acid	COOH—CH_2—CH_2—CO—COOH	0
Acrylic acid	CH_2=CH—COOH	0
Acetic acid	CH_3COOH	0

[a]From Arshad and Frankenberger (1989).

variety of compounds as substrates of C_2H_4 biosynthesis, it is likely that more than one pathway exists. Primrose (1977) proposed that 2-keto-4-methylthiobutyric acid (KMBA) served as an intermediate in the synthesis of C_2H_4 with the requirement of flavin in the presence of light or peroxidase in the absence of light. Fukuda *et al.* (1989) also reported accumulation of KMBA, a deaminated product of MET, in culture filtrates of *Cryptococcus albidus* and partially purified the cell-free C_2H_4-forming enzyme. However, while working with *Penicillium digitatum*, Fukuda *et al.* (1986) reported that the cell free extracts of this fungus did not utilize MET to produce C_2H_4. A C_2H_4 forming system was isolated which utilized ketoglutaric acid as an immediate precursor when the reaction mixture was incubated on a shaker (Fukuda *et al.*, 1986). Since many microbial isolates produce C_2H_4 from methionine, efforts should first be made to determine the pathway through which microorganisms derive C_2H_4 from methionine. The use of radiolabeled ^{14}C precursors, proposed labeled intermediates, and application of specific inhibitors would elucidate the microbial pathways for C_2H_4 generation.

6. Factors Affecting Ethylene Production

A number of factors influence C_2H_4 biosynthesis in plants, both in axenic cultures and in soil. An understanding of these factors may be useful in controlling C_2H_4 synthesis and ultimately affect the crop response.

6.1. Plants

6.1.1. Other Plant Hormones

It is thought that many of the plant responses which were initially attributed to auxin, are in fact the result of C_2H_4 stimulated by auxin. Other plant hormones such as cytokinins, abscisic acid, and C_2H_4 itself can influence C_2H_4 synthesis (Abeles, 1973). Similarly, auxin synthesis (Valdovinos et al., 1967), transport (Beyer and Morgan, 1969, 1970, 1971), and concentrations (Burg et al., 1971) in plant tissues are influenced by C_2H_4.

6.1.2. Stress

The tendency of stress in promoting the production of C_2H_4 by plant tissues has proven to be universal among plants. These include the exposure to chemicals, chilling temperature, drought, flooding, radiation, insect damage, disease, and mechanical wounding (Abeles, 1973). Stress C_2H_4 is of metabolic origin which tends to accelerate senescence and abscission (Beyer et al., 1985). The most thoroughly investigated stress factor is flooding. Bradford and Yang (1980) studied the regulation of C_2H_4 biosynthesis in waterlogged tomato plants. They found that ACC is synthesized in anaerobic roots in response to flooding and is then translocated to the shoot where it is converted aerobically to C_2H_4. Yang (1980) concluded that ACC synthase, which converts SAM to ACC, is the main site of control. Various factors affecting the pathway and regulation of C_2H_4 biosynthesis in plants are illustrated in Fig. 5.

The synthesis of the enzyme ACC synthase accompanies certain developmental events such as fruit ripening and senescence and is induced by external factors, including the application of auxin or C_2H_4, physical wounding, chemical injury, root anaerobiosis, drought, and chilling injury.

6.2. Microbial Isolates

Factors including substrate concentration, carbon and nitrogen content, pH, temperature, aeration, and cofactors have been studied to evaluate their influence on C_2H_4 production by microbial isolates.

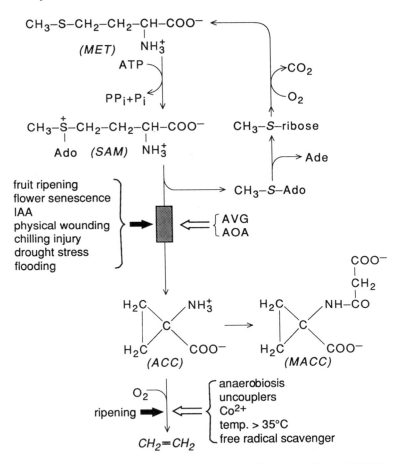

Figure 5. Regulation of ethylene biosynthesis including induction of enzyme synthesis and inhibition of each reaction. Ado, Ade, AVG, and AOA represent adenosine, adenine, aminoethoxyvinylglycine, and aminooxyacetic acid, respectively. From Yang (1980) with permission.

6.2.1. Substrate Concentration

As mentioned previously, microorganisms are capable of deriving C_2H_4 from various compounds including Krebs cycle intermediates, phenolic acids, organic acids, carbohydrates and amino acids. However, in most of cases, methionine has been found to be the most favorable substrate, hence many workers have studied methionine-dependent C_2H_4 production by various microbial isolates. The optimum methionine concentrations for microbial C_2H_4 production are indicated in Table IX. However, it should be noted that substrate concentration optima in pure cultures may not be optimal when added to soil.

Table IX. L-Methionine-Dependent C_2H_4 Production by Microbial Isolates

Isolate	Medium	[MET] for optimum C_2H_4 production	Reference
Acremonium falciforme	Basal salt	1.0 mM	Arshad and Frankenberger (1989)
Cenococcum geophilum	Modified Melin–Norkrans	2.5 mM	Graham and Linderman (1980)
Cylindrocladium floridanum	Pratt's	6.0 mM	Axelrod-McCarthy and Linderman (1981)
Cylindrocladium scoparium	Pratt's	8.0 mM	Axelrod-McCarthy and Linderman (1981)
Escherichia coli	Mineral salts, thiamine-HCl, Ca-pantothenate, biotin	12.0 mM	Primrose (1976a)
Hebeloma crustaliniforme	Modified Melin–Norkrans	7.5 mM	Graham and Linderman (1980)
Laccaria laccata	Modified Melin–Norkrans	7.5 mM	Graham and Linderman (1980)
Mucor hiemalis	Mineral salt	6.7 mM	Lynch and Harper (1974a)
Penicillium digitatum	Modified Pratt's	7.0 mM	Chalutz *et al.* (1977)
Pseudomonas solanacearum	Basal salt	1.0 mM	Swanson *et al.* (1979)
Saccharomyces cerevisiae	Lactate	5.0 mM	Thomas and Spencer (1977)

6.2.2. Carbon Requirements

The addition of carbohydrates along with C_2H_4 precursors often stimulates the production of C_2H_4. The glucose concentrations employed by various workers resulting in enhanced C_2H_4 generation by microbial isolates are given in Table X. A critical issue here is whether or not glucose can be used by microorganisms as an C_2H_4 precursor. Several workers (Lynch and Harper, 1974a; Chalutz *et al.*, 1977; Arshad and Frankenberger, 1989) believe that glucose stimulates microbial methionine-derived C_2H_4 as an energy source and does not directly serve as an C_2H_4 substrate.

On the other hand, Dasilva *et al.* (1974) claimed that *Aspergillus* sp. and *Mucor* sp. were capable of deriving C_2H_4 from glucose. However, the combination of glucose and methionine stimulated C_2H_4 evolution even more so. They did not test methionine alone as an C_2H_4 precursor. Similarly, glucose addition to a lactate medium enhanced C_2H_4 production by *Saccharomyces cerevisiae* (Thomas and Spencer, 1977, 1978). Considine *et al.* (1977) showed that *Penicillium cyclopium* and *Penicillium crustosum* produced

Table X. Influence of Glucose on C_2H_4 Production by Microbial Isolates

Isolates	Possible substrate	[Glucose]	Increase in C_2H_4 production over C_2H_4 substrate	Comment	Reference
Acremonium falciforme	Methionine	0.25%	25-fold over methionine alone	Glucose did not serve as a substrate	Arshad and Frankenberger (1989)
Aspergillus sp.	Methionine and glucose	1%	30.8% over glucose alone	Glucose also served as a substrate; methionine alone was not tested	Dasilva et al. (1974)
Mucor sp.	Methionine and glucose	1%	6.3-fold over glucose alone	Methionine alone was not tested	Dasilva et al. (1974)
Mucor hiemalis	Methionine	0.5%	3.9-fold over methionine alone	Glucose did not serve as a substrate	Lynch and Harper (1974a)
Penicillium sp.	Vanillic acid	1.3%	26.7% over vanillic acid alone	Production of C_2H_4 from glucose was not detected	Considine and Patching (1975)
Penicillium sp.	Syringic acid	1.3%	100.0% over syringic acid alone	Production of C_2H_4 from glucose was not detected	Considine and Patching (1975)
Penicillium digitatum	Methionine	1.26%	3.6-fold over methionine alone	Glucose did not serve as a substrate	Chalutz et al. (1977)

higher amounts of C_2H_4 from glucose. Similar findings were reported by Pazout *et al.* (1981) in that glucose was a suitable substrate for C_2H_4 formation by *Pseudomonas putida,* especially in cultures with limited aeration. Combined applications of glucose and methionine resulted in lower levels of C_2H_4 evolution.

6.2.3. Nitrogen Requirements

There is little information on the influence of added nitrogen on C_2H_4 biosynthesis by microbial isolates. Arshad and Frankenberger (1989) found a negative relationship between nitrogen addition and C_2H_4 biosynthesis by *A. falciforme* when methionine was added to a basal salt medium. It was speculated that this might be due to the preference of the fungus to use N from the added NH_4NO_3 rather than N of the precursor, L-methionine.

6.2.4. pH

The majority of microbial culture studies on C_2H_4 production have been carried out in the pH range of 6 to 7. Primrose (1976b) reported pH 6 as the optimum for C_2H_4 biosynthesis by *Escherichia coli* in the presence of methionine. Similar results were observed for *A. falciforme* utilizing L-methionine (Arshad and Frankenberger, 1989).

6.2.5. Temperature

Mattoo *et al.* (1977) reported that 23°C was optimal for C_2H_4 production by *P. digitatum* whereas Primrose (1976b) found 30°C to be most suitable for C_2H_4 generation by *E. coli.* Arshad and Frankenberger (1989) reported 30°C to be optimal for C_2H_4 biosynthesis by *A. falciforme.*

6.2.6. Aeration

Shake versus static studies reveal that shaking often enhances C_2H_4 production in pure cultures. Chalutz *et al.* (1977) reported higher rates of methionine-dependent C_2H_4 production by *P. digitatum* in shaken cultures versus static systems. Glucose-stimulated C_2H_4 production by *S. cerevisiae* in lactate medium was enhanced by oxygen transfer (Thomas and Spencer, 1978). Arshad and Frankenberger (1989) observed a greater than sevenfold increase in C_2H_4 production by *A. falciforme* with shaking over static incubation. Oxygen also promoted the growth and thus C_2H_4 production per unit weight of *Mucor hiemalis* (Lynch and Harper, 1974a). Among the bacteria, glucose-dependent C_2H_4 production by *Pseudomonas putida* and *P. fluorescens* was enhanced by limited aeration (Pazout *et al.,* 1981).

6.3. Soil

Ethylene has been identified as a common constituent of the soil atmosphere. It is well known that this gas is a result of microbial activity and concentrations can be high enough to affect plant growth (Arshad and Frankenberger, 1990d, 1992). It has been suggested that C_2H_4 produced outside the soil could move rapidly unchanged from roots to shoots and could cause physiological changes in plants (Jackson and Campbell, 1975). The first report of C_2H_4 production in soil came from geochemical studies (Smith and Ellis, 1963) and later it was reported to be a common constituent in waterlogged anaerobic soils (Smith and Russell, 1969; Smith and Restall, 1971; Smith and Jackson, 1974). Field studies have revealed that C_2H_4 concentrations within the soil atmosphere can typically range from 0.36 to 530 mmole/m³ (Dowdell *et al.*, 1972; Smith and Dowdell, 1974), with accumulation in the upper range usually occurring under water-logged conditions. Recently, Arshad and Frankenberger (1991) assessed 19 California soils maintained at field capacity, for C_2H_4 production and reported that these soils varied greatly in their potential to generate C_2H_4 ranging from 1.1 to 348.4 nmole C_2H_4/kg soil. As little as 5 nmole/liter of an exogenous application of C_2H_4 can cause a dramatic physiological response in plants (Arshad and Frankenberger, 1988, 1990d). Ethylene production in soil is governed by many factors which will be discussed in detail.

6.3.1. Substrates

Soil microorganisms can produce C_2H_4 from a variety of substrates in addition to methionine, the sole physiological precursor of C_2H_4 in plants. Various amino acids, organic acids, carbohydrates, alcohols, and proteins stimulate C_2H_4 production in soil (Arshad and Frankenberger, 1990b). However, these compounds may or may not be true precursors for microbial C_2H_4 synthesis. Organic amendments may maintain the activity of the microflora capable of generating C_2H_4 from the native humic materials of soil by providing a carbon and energy source for their proliferation. Generally, the combination of methionine as a precursor and glucose as an energy source was found to yield the greatest quantity of C_2H_4 gas. This was demonstrated with C_2H_4 production by mucoraceous fungi and yeasts (Lynch, 1972, 1974; Lynch and Harper, 1974a,b). Later, Lynch and Harper (1980) and Arshad and Frankenberger (1990c, 1991) showed that the combination of methionine and glucose effectively promoted C_2H_4 production in soil. However, Hunt *et al.* (1980) demonstrated that methionine stimulated C_2H_4 production only under aerobic conditions and not when oxygen levels declined below 10%. Arshad and Frankenberger (1990c) found that methionine is more effective in stimulating C_2H_4 production in soil maintained at field capacity than under waterlogged conditions while glucose was equally effective in promoting C_2H_4 synthesis under both the moisture regimes. Babiker and Pepper (1984) also observed that the addition of methionine to soil significantly stimulated C_2H_4 production.

6.3.2. Organic Matter

There appears to be a direct relationship between the rate of C_2H_4 production in soil and the level of soil organic matter content. Ethylene released from soils rich in organic matter is usually high (Van Cleemput *et al.*, 1983; Goodlass and Smith, 1978a; Babiker and Pepper, 1984). A study conducted by Babiker and Pepper (1984) revealed a high correlation between the organic matter content of soil and C_2H_4 production ($r^2 = 0.85$).

Table XI. Effect of Organic Amendments on C₂H₄ Production in Soil

Soil	Organic amendment	Soil conditions	Effect on C_2H_4 production	Reference
Grassland	Animal excreta	20% moisture content	Stimulated C_2H_4 production	Burford (1975)
Six different soils	Glucose	Anaerobic	Doubled the rate of C_2H_4 formation	Smith and Restall (1971)
n.s.[a]	Peptone	Anaerobic	No effect	
	Chitin	25% moisture	Stimulated C_2H_4 production	Wainwright and Kowalenko (1977)
	Cellulose	25% moisture	Stimulated C_2H_4 production	
	Urea	25% moisture	Stimulated C_2H_4 production	Wainwright and Kowalenko (1977)
	Barley straw	25% moisture	Stimulated C_2H_4 production	
Macmerry sandy loam	Wheat straw	Anaerobic	3.5-fold enhancement	Goodlass and Smith (1978b)
	Barley straw	Anaerobic	2.6-fold enhancement	
	Hay	Anaerobic	No effect	
Plano silt loam	Rhizomes of quack grass	Unsaturated Saturated	No effect 14.3-fold enhancement	Harvey and Linscott (1978)

Sandy loam	Crop residues	Anaerobic	Stimulated C_2H_4 production	Lynch and Harper (1980)
Coastal plain soil	Bermuda grass	28% moisture	Stimulated C_2H_4 production	Hunt et al. (1980)
Saline sodic desert soil	Glycerol Ethanol Methionine	Field capacity	Stimulated C_2H_4 production	Babiker (1983)
Hanford soil	Carbohydrates, organic acids, alcohols, amino acids, proteins	Field capacity	Stimulated C_2H_4 production (up to 2400-fold)	Arshad and Frankenberger (1990b)
Hanford soil	Methionine, glucose, methionine + glucose	(1) Field capacity (2) Waterlogged	Stimulated C_2H_4 production	Arshad and Frankenberger (1990c)
Nineteen California soils	Methionine, glucose, methionine + glucose	Field capacity	Stimulated C_2H_4 prduction	Arshad and Frankenberger (1991)

[a]n.s., not specified.

Similarly, Goodlass and Smith (1978a) reported that the amount of C_2H_4 released correlates with organic matter in grassland and arable soils of both the topsoil and subsoil. The importance of crop residues on C_2H_4 production was investigated by Lynch and Harper (1980) who found a highly significant correlation ($r = 0.63$, $P < 0.001$). However, no correlation between C_2H_4 production and the amount of humus present in soil was observed (Lynch and Harper, 1980). Frankenberger and Phelan (1985b) reported no correlation between C_2H_4 generation and organic matter content in ACC-amended soils. Similarly, Arshad and Frankenberger (1991) observed no correlation between the organic matter content of unamended, methionine-, glucose-, and methionine plus glucose-amended California soils and the amount of C_2H_4 released.

Amendments of soils with organic materials often stimulates C_2H_4 evolution (Table XI). Ethylene production is a function of not only the type and amount of amendment applied but also the soil condition with respect to aeration. Some amendments stimulate C_2H_4 generation under anaerobic conditions, while others enhance production in an aerobic environment.

6.3.3. Soil Reaction

Soil pH can affect C_2H_4 evolution by influencing the activity of microorganisms responsible for generation of this gas. Goodlass and Smith (1978a) found a significant correlation between C_2H_4 production and soil pH ranging from 5.0 to 7.3 in arable soils. Frankenberger and Phelan (1985a) reported a direct relationship between soil pH of 20 unbuffered surface soils and ACC-enhanced C_2H_4 production with the optimum being pH 9. Similarly, increased C_2H_4 production in soil amended with lime ($CaCO_3$) was observed by Wainwright and Kowalenko (1977). However, Arshad and Frankenberger (1990a) found a significant negative linear correlation ($P = 0.05$) between soil pH and the amounts of C_2H_4 released in 19 California unamended ($r = 0.54$) and methionine-amended ($r = 0.53$) soils.

6.3.4. Nitrogen Amendment

Microbial biosynthesis of C_2H_4 is markedly influenced by the NO_3^- content in soil, but there are conflicting results as apparent from Table XII. In general, higher levels of NO_3^- suppress C_2H_4 generation in soil, although an interaction of many factors may be involved, including soil organic matter, redox potential, and pH. According to Hunt et al. (1982), soils consisting of low organic matter content accumulate more C_2H_4 with lower pH values, and generally increase in C_2H_4 with increasing NO_3^- content; on the other hand, soils of higher organic matter content (2.5 to 3.5%) tend to increase in C_2H_4 with increasing pH and lower NO_3^- content. Hunt et al. (1980) proposed that the NO_3^- effect on C_2H_4 evolution could be related to the physiochemical differences among soils involving pH, E_h, Fe, and Mn.

Many workers (Smith, 1976b; Hunt et al., 1980; Smith and Cook, 1974) are of the view that the presence of NO_3^- in soil influences the redox potential, since NO_3^- serves as an alternate terminal electron acceptor for facultative anaerobic bacteria in the absence of oxygen, and thus reduces or delays C_2H_4 accumulation in soil. However, Goodlass and Smith (1978a) have indicated that the indigenous levels of NO_3^- in soil

Table XII. Effect of Nitrate Content on C_2H_4 Production in Soil

NO_3-N ($\mu g/g$ soil)	Impact on C_2H_4 generation	Reference
100	Almost no influence on C_2H_4 production	Van Cleemput et al. (1983)
300	Markedly reduced C_2H_4 production	Van Cleemput et al. (1983)
25–100	Suppressed C_2H_4 accumulation during the first week but as denitrification proceeded, the NO_3^- effect diminished	Hunt et al. (1980)
20–200	C_2H_4 production was observed only after a period of denitrification or not at all	Smith and Cook (1974), Smith (1976b)
50 and 100	A transient effect on the evolution of C_2H_4 occurred, maximum levels were delayed by 1 and 2 days	Goodlass and Smith (1978a)
500, 1000, and 2000	Reduced the total C_2H_4 evolved by 69, 77, and 85%, respectively	Goodlass and Smith (1978a)
2000 and 10,000	Greatly reduced the rate of C_2H_4 production, but never suppressed it completely	Smith and Restall (1971)
10–20 and 10,000	Methionine amendment enhanced C_2H_4 production in soils low in NO_3^- (10–20 $\mu g/g$ soil) compared to a high nitrate content (10,000 $\mu g/g$ soil)	Kapulnik et al. (1985)

and N fertilizers at normal agricultural rates would have little impact on C_2H_4 production. Arshad and Frankenberger (unpublished) have found that the addition of NH_4NO_3 up to 500 mg/kg soil had no effect on methionine-derived C_2H_4 production in soil.

6.3.5. Temperature

The influence of temperature on C_2H_4 production in soil has not been thoroughly investigated. Smith and Restall (1971) indicated that temperatures below 10°C resulted in considerably lower rates of C_2H_4 evolution and high temperatures (30–35°C) promoted a 1.6- to 2.0-fold increase. Frankenberger and Phelan (1985a) observed that ACC-dependent formation of C_2H_4 in soil was maximal at 50°C being 2.3- to 3.8-fold greater than under ambient conditions. They also detected C_2H_4 at temperatures as low as 5°C, whereas Lindberg et al. (1979) were unable to detect C_2H_4 in coniferous forest soils at or below 10°C. Smith and Dowdell (1974) reported that concentrations of C_2H_4 increased with soil temperature, over the range of 4 to 11°C.

6.3.6. Waterlogging

It is important to understand the behavior of waterlogged soils in C_2H_4 formation and their influence on C_2H_4 synthesis in higher plants. This subject has been extensively reviewed by Jackson (1985). The rapid development of epinastic (downward) growth of petioles is a characteristic response of tomato plants to waterlogged soil conditions. Turkova (1944) was the first to recognize the close similarity between this response and the effect of applying C_2H_4, but it was not until 1956 that the role of C_2H_4 in the epinastic growth of waterlogged plants was first reported (Jackson, 1956). There are many other characteristic features displayed by the shoots of plants growing in waterlogged conditions, being similar to the symptoms caused by direct application of C_2H_4, including aerenchyma development, root extension and orientation, hypertrophy and adventitious rooting, inhibition of stem extension, leaf expansion, and promotion of senescence and abscission.

There is ample evidence that C_2H_4 can occur in waterlogged soils at concentrations in excess of those known to affect plant growth (Smith and Russell, 1969; Kays, 1971; Smith and Dowdell, 1974). Jackson and Campbell (1974) found that epinastic growth by petioles of tomato was stimulated by waterlogging the soil and the responding leaves and other shoot parts contained higher concentrations of C_2H_4 than those of nonwaterlogged plants. In later studies, Jackson and Campbell (1975) studied the movement of ^{14}C-labeled C_2H_4 in plants under waterlogged conditions and found that the gas could move rapidly, unchanged from the roots to the shoots. They proposed that an increase in soil C_2H_4 and movement of the gas to the shoot are factors contributing to the development of epinasty and other responses of the shoots to waterlogging. Bradford and Yang (1980) proposed that enhanced C_2H_4 production by plant organs grown in waterlogged soils might be the result of increased synthesis of the immediate precursor of C_2H_4, ACC. ACC in waterlogged roots is exported in the transpiration stream to the shoot, and rapidly converted to C_2H_4. Cook and Smith (1977) reported maximal C_2H_4 production in water-saturated soils and minimal C_2H_4 production in soils maintained at -5 bars.

Factors that could contribute to the excess accumulation of C_2H_4 in waterlogged soils may include immobilization in water [its diffusion coefficient in water ranges from 9.0×10^{-4} to 20.0×10^{-3} mm^2/sec at a temperature range of 20 to 25°C (Baird and Davidson, 1962; Unver and Himmelblau, 1964; Huq and Wood, 1968)] and enhanced stability. Under well-aerated conditions, C_2H_4 is metabolized by gram-positive mycobacteria but not under anoxia (Abeles et al., 1971; Cornforth, 1975; deBont, 1975). Jackson (1985) suggested that during the early stages of waterlogging, aerobic microorganisms form C_2H_4 while oxygen is still available but with time C_2H_4 becomes trapped in water into a subsequent anoxic phase and is preserved by slow rates of degradation. Arshad and Frankenberger (1990c) studied the production and stability of C_2H_4 in soil under saturated (waterlogged, anaerobic) versus unsaturated (field capacity, aerobic) conditions. They concluded that C_2H_4 production under these two extremes is dependent on the nature of organic amendments added to soil. Methionine was a better stimulator of C_2H_4 production in soil maintained at field capacity than waterlogged conditions while glucose was equally effective under both moisture regimes. It is the greater stability of C_2H_4 under waterlogged conditions which results in accumulation of high concentrations of C_2H_4 in such soils. Ethylene is catabolized at a much greater rate (9.8-fold) under aerobic conditions than waterlogged conditions (Arshad and Frankenberger, 1990c). This increased stability under reducing conditions could be due to a less optimal environment for C_2H_4-decomposing microorganisms, because only aerobic bacteria have been reported to be capable of degrading C_2H_4.

6.3.7. Soil Aeration

There are conflicting reports regarding C_2H_4 synthesis with respect to aerobic versus anaerobic conditions in soil. This may be related to the availability of C_2H_4 precursors and to the stability of C_2H_4. Lynch (1975) suggested that an interactive oxidative–reductive process may be involved where anaerobic microsites are conducive for the synthesis of C_2H_4 substrates while aerobic conditions enhance C_2H_4 production. Hunt *et al.* (1982) proposed that C_2H_4 can accumulate under both oxidative and reduced conditions being a function of both production and consumption, while Smith (1976b) postulated that C_2H_4 production is regulated by the oxygen supply in soil. Smith (1976b) proposed a self-regulated C_2H_4 cycle based on the presence of anaerobic microsites in well-aerated soils. Anaerobes proliferate in these microsites especially near a rich organic source and produce C_2H_4 which diffuses through the soil. Sensitive aerobes are suppressed in growth by the C_2H_4 and as the oxygen demand diminishes, oxygen diffuses into the microsites regulating C_2H_4 production. The anaerobes partially depend on the aerobic production of substrates for C_2H_4 synthesis. Thus, prolonged and maximum production requires microsites of an aerobic–anaerobic interface. However, this hypothesis has been criticized by Primrose (1979) on the grounds that C_2H_4 is readily oxidized by aerobic bacteria (deBont, 1976; Heyer, 1976); high rates of C_2H_4 are produced by aerobic microorganisms (Primrose, 1976a; Lynch and Harper, 1974a); and there is little effect of high levels of C_2H_4 on aerobic metabolic activity regardless of the organic status of soil (Smith, 1978). Further research is needed to demonstrate clearly how aeration affects C_2H_4 production in soil.

Ethylene production in soil occurs under both reducing and aerobic conditions (Arshad and Frankenberger, 1990c). However, the magnitude of C_2H_4 released is dependent on the nature of the added organic amendment. Ethylene persists longer under reducing conditions and is subjected to rapid catabolism under aerobic conditions. Since the net amount of C_2H_4 present in a soil system represents the net balance of production minus decomposition, it is the greater stability of C_2H_4 under anaerobic conditions which leads to accumulation of C_2H_4 in higher amounts in waterlogged soil, and not more production favored by anaerobic conditions. It is highly likely that the involvement of any specific heterotroph in generating C_2H_4 may be controlled by the nature of organic material available as carbon and energy source or as a possible precursor and by the soil environment (Arshad and Frankenberger, 1990b,c).

6.3.8. Trace Elements

Little information is available on the interaction of trace elements with microbial biosynthesis of C_2H_4. Some elements such as Fe, Cu, Mn, and Co have concentration-dependent effects on C_2H_4 synthesis in soil and pure cultures.

Lynch (1974) found that Fe(II) (200 mg/liter) was more effective (8.6 times) than Fe(III) in stimulating C_2H_4 production by an extracellular preparation from *Mucor hiemalis*, while Cu(II) (20 mg/liter) and Mn(II) (200 mg/liter) had negative effects. Smith *et al.* (1978) reported that Fe(II) at 100–1000 mg/kg in soil solution markedly stimulated C_2H_4 production via a strictly chemical reaction while Mn(II), Co(III), and Ni(II) did not promote C_2H_4 production. Hunt *et al.* (1980) proposed that Fe and Mn affected C_2H_4 synthesis by altering the E_h of the soil. Treating soil with a 5 mM solution of Co(II) significantly increased ACC-dependent C_2H_4 production (Frankenberger and Phelan, 1985a). The addition of Co(II) to a culture medium at 1 μM also stimulated C_2H_4 generation from L-methionine by *Acremonium falciforme*, but concentrations > 1 μm strongly inhibited C_2H_4 synthesis (Arshad and Frankenberger, 1989).The cobaltous ion (Co^{2+}) is highly effective in inhibiting the activity of EFE in plant tissues when applied in the range of 10 to 100 μM (Lürssen *et al.*, 1979; Yu and Yang, 1979). Treatment with $CuSO_4$ (20 mM) markedly decreased C_2H_4 production from grapefruit peel infected with *Penicillium digitatum* and from *P. digitatum* cultures alone, but increased production from a healthy peel (Achilea *et al.*, 1985a).

Arshad and Frankenberger (1991) conducted a comprehensive study showing the effects of various transitional metals and metalloids on C_2H_4 generation in soil. The concentration-dependent effects of trace elements on methionine-derived C_2H_4 accumulation in soil varied considerably. Six trace elements [Ag(I), Cu(II), Fe(II), Mg(II), Zn(II), Al(III)] significantly stimulated C_2H_4 synthesis when applied at low concentrations ($\leq$ 1.0 mg/kg soil) but inhibited the reaction at concentrations $\geq$ 100 mg/kg soil. The addition of Ni(II) up to 10 mg/kg soil also significantly enhanced methionine-dependent C_2H_4 production in soil. The most effective trace elements in promoting synthesis of C_2H_4 were Co(II) and As(III) when added at 100 mg/kg soil. Ethylene generation was inhibited in the presence of Hg(II), Fe(III), and Mo(VI) at $\geq$ 10 mg/kg soil. The application of Fe(II) at $\geq$ 100 mg/kg soil promoted the abiotic production of C_2H_4 in soil. This confirmed the findings of Smith (1976a); however, at low concentrations (0.5 mg/kg soil) Fe(II) stimulates the biological production of C_2H_4. The influence of trace elements on C_2H_4 production in soil may be related to their effects on redox potential (E_h), the catalytic activity (cofactors versus inhibitors), and toxicity to the microflora.

In addition to these briefly described factors, other parameters such as salinity, soil texture, soil depth, application of fungicides, herbicides, bactericides, and insecticides, also affect microbial biosynthesis of C_2H_4 (Babiker and Pepper, 1984; Campbell and Moreau, 1979; Wainwright and Kowalenko, 1977).

7. Concluding Remarks

Soils are usually rich with substances which can serve as precursors for the microbial biosynthesis of C_2H_4, particularly in the rhizosphere. Plant roots excrete organic compounds (including amino acids, organic acids, and carbohydrates) that have been demonstrated to enhance C_2H_4 production. Moreover, C_2H_4 produced in this zone has been shown to directly diffuse to the roots and bring about a corresponding change in plant growth and development.

How can the generation of microbially produced C_2H_4 as a natural resource be used to influence crop production? The effects of exogenous hormones on plant growth have been well demonstrated, with both stimulatory and inhibitory effects being observed depending on the concentration of the hormones, microbial diversity, uptake by plants, and the stage of plant development. The plant response will be governed by the rate of hormone uptake, the active concentration in the rhizosphere, and modification of the plant's own pool of hormones as a result of the exogenous supply (Frankenberger and Fitzpatrick, 1984). It is well established that different crops and cultivars can show a different response to C_2H_4 depending on the plant's genetic makeup, the concentration of C_2H_4, and prevailing environmental factors.

Our own work (Arshad and Frankenberger, 1988) clearly demonstrates the potential of microbially produced C_2H_4 influencing plant growth. This study also reveals the importance of substrate–inoculum interactions. Further work is needed to screen potential economical precursors of C_2H_4 with its release as a metabolite from the soil indigenous microbiota or by a specific microbe used as an inoculum. Further studies are needed to investigate factors affecting production of C_2H_4 and its distribution and stability in soil. An understanding of the substrate–inoculum–plant response may prove to be very fruitful in sustaining high crop productivity.

References

Abeles, F. B., 1966, Auxin stimulation of ethylene evolution, *Plant Physiol.* **41**:585–588.

Abeles, F. B., 1972, Biosynthesis and mechanisms of action of ethylene, *Annu. Rev. Plant Physiol.* **23**:259–292.

Abeles, F. B., 1973, *Ethylene in Plant Biology,* Academic Press, New York.

Abeles, F. B., Craker, L. E., Forrence, L. E., and Leather, G. R., 1971, Fate of air pollutant: Removal of ethylene, sulfur dioxide and nitrogen dioxide by soil, *Science* **173**:914–916.

Achilea, O., Chalutz, E., Fuchs, Y., and Rot, I., 1985a, Ethylene biosynthesis and related physiological changes in *Penicillium digitatum*-infected grapefruit (*Citrus paradisi*), *Physiol. Plant Pathol.* **26**:125–134.

Achilea, O., Fuchs, Y., Chalutz, E., and Rot, I., 1985b, The contribution of host and pathogen to ethylene biosynthesis in *Penicillium digitatum*-infected citrus fruit, *Physiol. Plant Pathol.* **27**:55–63.

Adams, D. O., and Yang, S. F., 1977, Methionine metabolism in apple tissue: Implication of S-adenosylmethionine as an intermediate in the conversion of methionine to ethylene, *Plant Physiol.* **60**:892–896.

Adams, D. O., and Yang, S. F., 1979, Ethylene biosynthesis: Identification of 1-aminocyclopropane-1-carboxylic acid as an intermediate in the conversion of methionine to ethylene, *Proc. Natl. Acad. Sci. USA* **76**:170–174.

Andrews, E., Hanowski, C., and Beiderbeck, R., 1981, Growth changes of maize seedlings after attack by haploid lines of corn smut *Ustilago maydis, Phytopathology* **102**:10–20.

Arshad, M., and Frankenberger, W. T., Jr., 1988, Influence of ethylene produced by soil microorganisms on etiolated pea seedlings, *Appl. Environ. Microbiol.* **54**:2728–2732.

Arshad, M., and Frankenberger, W. T., Jr., 1989, Biosynthesis of ethylene by *Acremonium falciforme*, *Soil Biol. Biochem.* **21**:633–638.

Arshad, M., and Frankenberger, W. T., Jr., 1990a, Response of *Zea mays* L. and *Lycopersicon esculentum* to the ethylene precursors, L-methionine and L-ethinoine, applied to soil, *Plant Soil* **22**:219–227.

Arshad, M., and Frankenberger, W. T., Jr., 1990b, Ethylene accumulation in soil in response to organic amendments, *Soil Sci. Soc. Am. J.* **54**:1026–1031.

Arshad, M., and Frankenberger, W. T., Jr., 1990c, Production and stability of ethylene in soil, *Biol. Fert. Soils* **10**:29–34.

Arshad, M., and Frankenberger, W. T., Jr., 1990d, Microbial production of plant hormones, in: *The Rhizosphere and Plant Growth* (D. L. Kessler and P. B. Gregan, eds.), Kluwer Academic Publ., Dordrecht, pp. 327–334.

Arshad, M., and Frankenberger, W. T., Jr., 1991, Effects of soil properties and trace elements on ethylene production in soils, *Soil Sci.* **151**:377–387.

Arshad, M., and Frankenberger, W. T., Jr., 1992, Microbial production of plant growth regulators, in: *Soil Microbial Ecology* (B. Metting, ed.), Dekker Inc., New York, pp. 307–347.

Axelrod-McCarthy, P. E., and Linderman, R. G., 1981, Ethylene production by cultures of *Cylindrocladium floridanum* and *C. scoparium, Phytopathology* **71**:825–830.

Babiker, H. M., 1983, Microbial production of ethylene in desert soils, Ph.D. thesis, University of Arizona, Tucson.

Babiker, H. M., and Pepper, I. L., 1984, Microbial production of ethylene in desert soils, *Soil Biol. Biochem.* **16**:559–564.

Baird, M. H. I., and Davidson, J. F., 1962, Annualar jets—11. Gas absorption, *Chem. Eng. Sci.* **17**:472–480.

Barkai-Golan, R., and Kopeliovitch, E., 1983, Induced ethylene evolution and climacteric-like respiration in *Rhizopus*-infected *rin* and *nor* tomato mutants, *Physiol. Plant Pathol.* **22**:357–362.

Beyer, E. M., Jr., 1976, A potent inhibitor of ethylene action in plants, *Plant Physiol.* **58**:268–271.

Beyer, E. M., Jr., and Morgan, P. W., 1969, Time sequence of the effect of ethylene on transport, uptake and decarboxylation of auxins, *Plant Cell Physiol.* **10**:787–799.

Beyer, E. M., Jr., and Morgan, P. W., 1970, Effect of ethylene on the uptake, distribution, and metabolism of indole-acetic acid-1-^{14}C and -2-^{14}C and naphthaleneacetic acid-1-^{14}C, *Plant Physiol.* **46**:157–162.

Beyer, E. M., Jr., and Morgan, P. W., 1971, Abscission, the role of ethylene modification of auxin transport, *Plant Physiol.* **48**:208–212.

Beyer, E. M., Jr., Morgan, P. W., and Yang, S. F., 1985, Ethylene, in: *Advanced Plant Physiology* (M. B. Wilkins, ed.), Pitman Publ., London, pp. 111–126.

Biale, J. B., 1940, Effect of emanations from several species of fungi on respiration and color development of citrus fruits, *Science* **91**:458–459.

Biale, J. B., and Shepherd, A. D., 1941, Respiration of citrus fruits in relation to metabolism of fungi. Effects of emanations of *Penicillium digitatum* Sacc. on lemons, *Am. J. Bot.* **28**:263–270.

Biale, J. B., and Young, R. E., 1981, Respiration and ripening of fruits—Retrospect and prospect, in: *Recent Advances in the Biochemistry of Fruits and Vegetables* (J. Friend and M. J. C. Rhoades, eds.), Academic Press, London, pp. 1–39.

Boller, T., Herner, R. C., and Kende, H., 1979, Assay for and enzymatic formation of an ethylene precursor, 1-aminocyclopropane-1-carboxylic acid, *Planta* **145**:293–303.

Bonn, W. G., Sequira, L., and Upper, C. D., 1975, Technique for the determination of the rate of ethylene production by *Pseudomonas solanacearum, Plant Physiol.* **56**:688–691.

Bradford, K. J., and Yang, S. F., 1980, Xylem transport of 1-amino-cyclopropane-1-carboxylic acid, an ethylene precursor, in waterlogged tomato plants, *Plant Physiol.* **65**:323–326.

Brown, C. M., and Earley, E. B., 1973, Response of one winter wheat and two spring oat varieties to foliar application of 2-chloroethyl phosphonic acid (Ethrel), *Agron. J.* **65**:829–832.

Bruinisma, J., 1980, The endogenous pattern and its interference by exogenous plant growth regulators, in: *Physiological Aspects of Crop Productivity*, 15th Colloq. Int. Potash Inst., Bern, Switzerland, pp. 117–124.

Burford, J. R., 1975, Ethylene in grassland soil treated with animal excreta, *J. Environ. Qual.* **4:**55–57.

Burg, S. P., 1962, The physiology of ethylene formation, *Annu. Rev. Plant Physiol.* **13:**265–302.

Burg, S. P., and Burg, E. A., 1966, The interaction between auxin and ethylene and its role in plant growth, *Proc. Natl. Acad. Sci. USA* **55:**262–269.

Burg, S. P., and Burg, E. A., 1967, Inhibition of polar auxin transport of ethylene, *Plant Physiol.* **42:**1224–1228.

Burg, S. P., and Stolwijk, J. A. A., 1959, A highly sensitive katharometer and its application to the measurement of ethylene and other gases of biological importance, *J. Biochem. Microbiol. Technol. Eng.* **1:**245–259.

Burg, S. P., and Thimann, K. V., 1959, The physiology of ethylene formation in apples, *Proc. Natl. Acad. Sci. USA* **45:**335–344.

Burg, S. P., Apelbaum, A., Eisinger, W., and Kang, B. G., 1971, Physiology and mode of action of ethylene, *HortScience* **6:**359–364.

Campbell, R. B., and Moreau, R. A., 1979, Ethylene in compacted field soil and its effect on growth, tuber quality and yield of potatoes, *Am. Potato J.* **56:**199–210.

Chadwick, A. V., and Burg, S. P., 1967, An explanation of the inhibition of root growth caused by indole-3-acetic acid, *Plant Physiol.* **42:**415–420.

Chalutz, E., and Lieberman, M., 1978, Inhibition of ethylene production in *Penicillium digitatum*, *Plant Physiol.* **61:**111–114.

Chalutz, E., Lieberman, M., and Sisler, H. D., 1977, Methionine induced ethylene production by *Penicillium digitatum*, *Plant Physiol.* **60:**402–406.

Chappell, J., Hahlbrock, K., and Boller, T., 1984, Rapid induction of ethylene biosynthesis in cultured parsley cells by fungal elicitor and its relationship to the induction of phenylalanine ammonialyase, *Planta* **161:**475–480.

Chou, T. W., and Yang, S. F., 1973, The biogenesis of ethylene in *Penicillium digitatum*, *Arch. Biochem. Biophys.* **157:**73–82.

Coleman, L. W., and Hodges, C. F., 1984, Ethylene biosynthesis in leaves of *Poa pratensis* and injury in response to infection by *Bipolaris sorokiniana*, *Plant Physiol.* **75:**462–465.

Coleman, L. W., and Hodges, C. F., 1986, The effect of methionine on ethylene and 1-aminocyclopropane-1-carboxylic acid production by *Bipolaris sorokiniana*, *Phytopathology* **76:**851–855.

Considine, P. J., and Patching, J. W., 1975, Ethylene production by microorganisms grown on phenolic acids, *Ann. Appl. Biol.* **81:**115–119.

Considine, P. J., Flynn, N., and Patching, J. W., 1977, Ethylene production by soil microorganisms, *Appl. Environ. Microbiol.* **33:**977–979.

Cook, R. J., and Smith, A. M., 1977, Influence of water potential on production of ethylene in soil, *Can. J. Microbiol.* **23:**811–817.

Cornforth, I. S., 1975, The persistence of ethylene in aerobic soils, *Plant Soil* **42:**85–96.

Cousins, H. H., 1910, *Annual Report of the Jamaican Department of Agriculture* **7:**15.

Crocker, W., and Knight, L. I., 1908, Effect of illuminating gas and ethylene upon flowering carnations, *Bot. Gaz.* **46:**259–276.

Crocker, W., Hitchock, A. E., and Zimmerman, P. W., 1935, Similarities in the effects of ethylene and plant auxins, *Contrib. Boyce Thompson Inst.* **7:**231–248.

Crossett, R. N., and Campbell, D. J., 1975, The effects of ethylene in the root environment upon the development of barley, *Plant Soil* **42:**453–464.

Dahnous, K., Vigue, G. T., Law, A. G., Konzak, C. F., and Miller, D. G., 1982, Height and yield response of selected wheat, barley and triticale cultivars to ethephon, *Agron J.* **74:**580–582.

Dasilva, E. J., Henriksson, E., and Henriksson, L. E., 1974, Ethylene production by fungi, *Plant Sci. Lett.* **2:**63–66.

deBont, J. M. M., 1975, Oxidation of ethylene by bacteria, *Ann. Appl. Biol.* **81:**119–121.

deBont, J. A. M., 1976, Oxidation of ethylene by soil bacteria, *Antonie van Leeuwenhoek J. Microbiol. Serol.* **42:**73–80.

deMunk, W. J., 1971, Bud necrosis, a storage disease of tulips. II. Analysis of disease-promoting storage conditions, *Neth. J. Plant Pathol.* **77:**177–186.

Denny, F. E., 1924, Hastening the coloration of lemons, *J. Agric. Res.* **27:**757–769.

Dowdell, R. J., Smith, K. A., Crees, R., and Restall, S. W. F., 1972, Field studies of ethylene in the soil atmosphere—Equipment and preliminary results, *Soil Biol. Biochem.* **4:**325–331.

Drennan, D. S. H., and Norton, C., 1972, The effect of ethrel on nodulation in *Pisum sativum* L., *Plant Soil* **36:**53–57.

El-Kazzaz, M. K., Chordas, A., and Kader, A. A., 1983, Physiological and compositional changes in orange fruit in relation to modification of their susceptibility to *Penicillium italicum* by ethylene treatment, *J. Am. Soc. Hortic. Sci.* **108:**618–621.

El-Sharouny, H. M., 1984, Screening of ethylene producing root infecting fungi in Egyptian soil, *Mycopathologia* **85:**13–15.

Eplee, R. E., 1975, Ethylene, a witchweed seed germination stimulant, *Weed Sci.* **23:**433–436.

Frankenberger, W. T., Jr., and Fitzpatrick, K. L., 1984, Exogenous hormone production in soil–root systems, in: *Improving Efficiencies in Crop Production Systems*, Proc. Calif. Plant Soil Conf., Am. Soc. Agron., pp. 58–61.

Frankenberger, W. T., Jr., and Phelan, P. J., 1985a, Ethylene biosynthesis in soil. I. Method of assay in conversion of 1-aminocyclopropane-1-carboxylic acid to ethylene, *Soil Sci. Soc. Am. J.* **49:**1418–1422.

Frankenberger, W. T., Jr., and Phelan, P. J., 1985b, Ethylene biosynthesis in soil. II. Kinetics and thermodynamics in the conversion of 1-aminocyclopropane-1-carboyxlic acid to ethylene, *Soil Sci. Soc. Am. J.* **49:**1422–1426.

Freebairn, H. T., and Buddenhagen, I. W., 1964, Ethylene production by *Pseudomonas solanaceanum, Nature* **202:**313–314.

Freytag, A. H., Wendt, C. W., and Lira, E. P., 1972, Effects of soil-injected ethylene on yields of cotton and sorghum, *Agron. J.* **64:**524–526.

Fukuda, H., Fujii, T., and Ogawa, T., 1986, Preparation of a cell-free ethylene-forming system from *Penicillium digitatum, Agric. Biol. Chem.* **50:**977–981.

Fukuda, H., Takahasi, M., Fujii, T., and Ogawa, T., 1989, Ethylene production from L-methionine by *Crytococcus albidus, J. Ferment. and Bioeng.* **67:**173–175.

Gane, R., 1934, Production of ethylene by some ripening fruits, *Nature* **134:**1008.

Gedalovich, E., and Fahn, A., 1985, Ethylene and gum duct formation in citrus, *Ann. Bot.* **56:**571–577.

Gentile, I. A., and Matta, A., 1975, Production of and some effects of ethylene in relation to *Fusarium* wilt of tomato, *Physiol. Plant Pathol.* **5:**27–35.

Goodlass, G., and Smith, K. A., 1978a, Effect of pH, organic matter content and nitrate on the evolution of ethylene from soils, *Soil Biol. Biochem.* **10:**193–199.

Goodlass, G., and Smith, K.A., 1978b, Effects of organic amendments on evolution of ethylene and other hydrocarbons from soil, *Soil Biol. Biochem.* **10:**201–205.

Goodlass, G., and Smith, K. A., 1979, Effects of ethylene on root extension and nodulation of pea (*Pisum sativum* L.) and white clover (*Trifolium repens* L.), *Plant Soil* **51:**387–395.

Goodman, T. C., Montoya, A. L., Williams, S., and Chilton, M. D., 1986, Sustained ethylene production in *Agrobacterium*-transformed carrot disks caused by expression of the T-DNA *tms* gene products, *J. Bacteriol.* **167:**387–388.

Goschl, J. D., Rappaport, L., and Pratt, H. K., 1966, Ethylene as a factor regulating the growth of pea epicotyls subjected to physical stress, *Plant Physiol.* **41:**877–884.

Goto, M., Yaguchi, Y., and Hyodo, H., 1980, Ethylene production in citrus leaves infected with *Xanthomonas citri* and its relation to defoliation, *Physiol. Plant Pathol.* **16:**343–350.

Graham, J. H., and Linderman, R. G., 1980, Ethylene production by ectomycorrhizal fungi, *Fusarium oxysporum* f. sp. *pisi,* and by aseptically synthesized ectomycorrhizae and *Fusarium*-infected Douglas fir roots, *Can. J. Microbiol.* **26:**1340–1347.

Graham, J. H., Whiteside, J. O., and Barmore, C. R., 1984, Ethylene production by *Mycospharella citri* and greasy spot-infected citrus leaves, *Phytopathology* **74:**817.

Hanson, A. C., and Kende, H., 1976, Methionine metabolism and ethylene biosynthesis in senescent flower tissue of morning-glory, *Plant Physiol.* **57:**528–537.

Harvey, R. G., and Linscott, J. J., 1978, Ethylene production in soil containing quackgrass rhizomes and other plant materials, *Soil Sci. Soc. Am. J.* **42:**721–724.

Heyer, J., 1976, Mikrobielle verwetung von äthylen, *Z. Allg. Mikrobiol.* **16:**633–637.

Hodges, C. F., and Coleman, L. W., 1984, Ethylene-induced chlorosis in the pathogenesis of *Bipolaris sorokiniana* leaf spot of *Poa pratensis, Plant Physiol.* **75:**462–465.

Hunt, P. G., Campbell, R. B., and Moreau, R. A., 1980, Factors affecting ethylene accumulation in a Norfolk sandy loam soil, *Soil Sci.* **129:**22–27.

Hunt, P. G., Matheny, T. A., Campbell, R. B., and Parsons, J. E., 1982, Ethylene accumulation in southeastern coastal plain soils: Soil characteristics and oxidative–reductive involvement. *Commun. Soil Sci. Plant Anal.* **13**(4):267–278.

Huq, A., and Wood, T., 1968, Diffusion coefficient of ethylene gas in water, *J. Chem. Eng. Data* **13:**256–259.

Ilag, L., and Curtis, R. W., 1968, Production of ethylene by fungi, *Science* **159:**1357–1358.

Imaseki, H., and Pjon, C. J., 1970, The effect of ethylene on auxin-induced growth of excised rice coleoptile segments, *Plant Cell Physiol.* **11:**827–829.

Jackson, M. B., 1985, Ethylene and responses of plants to soil waterlogging and submergence, *Annu. Rev. Plant Physiol.* **36:**145–174.

Jackson, M. B., and Campbell, D. J., 1974, Ethylene and the epinastic response of tomato plants to waterlogging, *Agricultural Research Council Letcombe Laboratory Annual Report,* Her Majesty's Stationery Office, London, pp. 23–26.

Jackson, M. B., and Campbell, D. J., 1975, Movement of ethylene from roots to shoots, a factor in the responses of tomato plants to waterlogged conditions, *New Phytol.* **74:**397–406.

Jackson, W. T., 1956, The relative importance of factors causing injury to shoots of flooded tomato plants, *Am. J. Bot.* **43:**637–639.

Kapulnik, E., Quick, J., and DeVay, J. E., 1985, Germination of propagules of *Verticillium dahliae* in soil treated with methionine and other substances affecting ethylene production, *Phytopathology* **75:**1348.

Kays, S. J., 1971, Plant competition, root growth and ethylene evolution, Ph.D. thesis, Michigan State University, MI.

Ketring, D. L., and Melouk, H. A., 1982, Ethylene production and leaflet abscission of three peanut genotypes infected with *Cercospora arachidicola* Hori, *Plant Physiol.* **69:**789–792.

Kozaka, T., and Teraoka, T., 1978, Ethylene evolution by rice plants infected with *Pyricularia oryzae* in relation to the stunting of diseased plants, *Ann. Phytopathol. Soc. Jpn.* **43:**549–556.

Ku, H. S., Suge, H., Rappaport, L., and Pratt, H. K., 1970, Stimulation of rice coleoptile growth by ethylene, *Planta* **90:**333–339.

Kuo, G. G., and Chen, B. W., 1980, Physiological responses of tomato cultivars to flooding, *J. Am. Soc. Hortic. Sci.* **105:**751–755.

Langan, T. D., and Oplinger, E. S., 1987, Growth and yield of ethephon treated maize, *Agron. J.* **79:**130–134.

Lieberman, M., 1979, Biosynthesis and action of ethylene, *Annu. Rev. Plant Physiol.* **30:**533–591.

Lieberman, M., and Mapson, L. W., 1964, Genesis and biogenesis of ethylene, *Nature* **204:**343–345.

Lieberman, M., Kunishi, A. T., Mapson, L. W., and Wardale, D. A., 1966, Stimulation of ethylene production in apple tissue slices by methionine, *Plant Physiol.* **41:**376–382.

Lindberg, T., Granhall, U., and Berg, B., 1979, Ethylene formation in some coniferous forest soils, *Soil Biol. Biochem.* **11:**637–643.

Lockard, J. E., and Kneebone, O. R., 1962, Investigation of the metabolic gases produced by *Agaricus biporus* (Large) Sing, *Mushroom Sci.* **5**:281–299.

Lund, B. M., and Mapson, L. W., 1970, Stimulation of *Erwinia carotovora* of the synthesis of ethylene in cauliflower tissue, *Biochem. J.* **119**:251–263.

Lürssen, K., Naumann, K., and Schröder, R., 1979, 1-Aminocyclopropane-1-carboxylic acid—An intermediate of the ethylene biosynthesis in higher plants, *Z. Pflanzenphysiol.* **92**:285–294.

Lynch, J. M., 1972, Identification of substrates and isolation of microorganisms responsible for ethylene production in soil, *Nature* **240**:45–46.

Lynch, J. M., 1974, Mode of ethylene formation by *Mucor hiemalis, J. Gen. Microbiol.* **83**:407–411.

Lynch, J. M., 1975, Ethylene formation by soil microorganisms, *Ann. Appl. Biol.* **81**:114–115.

Lynch, J. M., and Harper, S. H. T., 1974a, Formation of ethylene by a soil fungus, *J. Gen. Microbiol.* **80**:187–195.

Lynch, J. M., and Harper, S. H. T., 1974b, Fungal growth rate and formation of ethylene in soil, *J. Gen. Microbiol.* **85**:91–96.

Lynch, J. M., and Harper, S. H. T., 1980, Role of substrates and anoxia in the accumulation of soil ethylene, *Soil Biol. Biochem.* **12**:363–368.

McClung, G., and Frankenberger, W. T., Jr., 1988, Comparison of reverse-phase high performance liquid chromotographic methods for precolumn-derivatized amino acids, *J. Liquid Chromatogr.* **11**:613–646.

McKeon, T. A., and Yang, S. F., 1984, A comparison of the conversion of 1-amino-2-ethylcyclopropane-1-carboxylic acid stereoisomers to 1-butene by pea epicotyls and by a cell-free system, *Planta* **160**:84–87.

McKeon, T. A., and Yang, S. F., 1987, Biosynthesis and metabolism of ethylene, in: *Plant Hormones and Their Role in Plant Growth and Development* (P. J. Davies, ed.), Nijhoff, The Hague, pp. 94–112.

Mattoo, A. K., Baker, J. E., Chalutz, E., and Lieberman, M., 1977, Effect of temperature on the ethylene-synthesizing systems in apple, tomato, and in *Penicillium digitatum, Plant Cell Physiol.* **18**:715–719.

Mauch, F., Hadwiger, L. A., and Boller, T., 1984, Ethylene: Symptoms, not signal for the induction of chitinase and β-1,3-glucanase in pea pods by pathogen and elicitors, *Plant Physiol.* **76**:607–611.

Miller, A. R., and Pengelly, L., 1984, Ethylene production by shoot-forming and unorganized crown-gall tumor tissues of *Nicotiana* and *Lycopersicon* cultured in vitro, *Planta* **161**:418–424.

Miller, E. V., Winston, J. R., and Fisher, D. F., 1940, Production of epinasty by emanation from normal and decaying citrus fruits and from *Penicillium digitatum, J. Agric. Res.* **60**:269–277.

Montalbini, P., and Elstner, E. F., 1977, Ethylene evolution by rust-infected, detached bean (*Phaseolus vulgaris* L.) leaves susceptible and hypersensitive to *Uromyces phaseoli* (Pers.) Wint., *Planta* **135**:301–306.

Morgan, P. W., 1976, Effects on ethylene physiology, in: *Herbicide: Physiology, Biochemistry, Ecology,* 2nd ed. (L. J. Audus, ed.), Academic Press, New York, Vol. 1, pp. 255–280.

Morgan, P. W., and Hall, W. C., 1962, Effect of 2,4-D on the production of ethylene by cotton and grain sorghum, *Physiol. Plant.* **15**:420–427.

Morgan, P. W., and Hall, W. C., 1964, Accelerated release of ethylene by cotton following application of indolyl-3-acetic acid, *Nature* **201**:91.

Morris, J. G., 1968, *A Biologist's Physical Chemistry,* Addison–Wesley, Reading, Mass.

Neljubow, D., Über die horizontale Nutation der Stengel von *Pisum sativum* und einiger Anderer, *Pflanzen. Beih. Bot. Zentralbl.* **10**:128–138.

Nickerson, W. J., 1948, Ethylene as a metabolic product of the pathogenic fungus, *Blastomyces dermatitidis, Arch. Biochem.* **17**:225–233.

Osborne, D. J., 1976, Control of cell shape and cell size by dual regulation of auxin and ethylene, in: *Perspectives in Experimental Biology* (N. Sunderland, ed.), Pergamon Press, Oxford, United Kingdom, Vol. 2, pp. 89–102.

Owens, L. D., Lieberman, M., and Kunishi, A., 1971, Inhibition of ethylene production by rhizobitoxine, *Plant Physiol.* **48**:1–4.

Paradies, I., Konze, J. R., and Elstner, E. F., 1980, Ethylene: Indicator but not inducer of phytoalexin synthesis in soybean, *Plant Physiol.* **66**:1106–1109.

Pazout, J., Wurst, M., and Vancura, V., 1981, Effect of aeration on ethylene production by soil bacteria and soil samples cultivated in a closed system, *Plant Soil* **62**:431–438.

Pratt, H. K., and Goeschl, J. D., 1969, Physiological roles of ethylene in plants, *Annu. Rev. Plant Physiol.* **20**:541–584.

Primrose, S. B., 1976a, Formation of ethylene by *Escherichia coli*, *J. Gen. Microbiol.* **95**:159–165.

Primrose, S. B., 1976b, Ethylene-forming bacteria from soil and water, *J. Gen. Microbiol.* **97**:343–346.

Primrose, S. B., 1977, Evaluation of the role of methional, 2-keto-4-methyl-thiobutyric acid and peroxiadase in ethylene-formation by *Escherichia coli*, *J. Gen. Microbiol.* **98**:519–528.

Primrose, S. B., 1979, A review, ethylene and agriculture: The role of microbes, *J. Appl. Bacteriol.* **46**:1–25.

Primrose, S. B., and Dilworth, M. J., 1976, Ethylene production by bacteria, *J. Gen. Microbiol.* **93**:177–181.

Regeimbal, L. O., and Harvey, R. B., 1927, The effect of ethylene on the enzymes of pineapple, *J. Am. Chem. Soc.* **49**:1117–1118.

Reuveni, M., and Cohen, Y., 1978, Growth retardation and changes in phenolic compounds, with special reference to scopoletin, in mildewed and ethylene-treated tobacco plants, *Physiol. Plant Pathol.* **12**:179–189.

Roby, D., Toppan, A., and Esquerre-Tugaye, M. T., 1985, Cell surfaces in plant–microorganism interactions. V. Elicitors of fungal and of plant origin trigger the synthesis of ethylene and of cell wall hydroxyproline-rich glycoprotein in plants, *Plant Physiol.* **77**:700–704.

Roby, D., Toppan, A., and Esquerre-Tugaye, M. T., 1986, Cell surfaces in plant–microorganism interactions. VI. Elicitors of ethylene from *Colletotrichum lagenarium* trigger chitinase activity in melon plants, *Plant Physiol.* **81**:228–233.

Sargent, J. A., Stack, A. V., and Osborne, D. J., 1973, Orientation of cell growth in the etiolated pea stem. Effect of ethylene and auxin on cell wall deposition, *Planta* **109**:185–192.

Satoh, S., and Esashi, Y., 1980, α-Aminoisobutyric acid: A probable competitive inhibitor of conversion of 1-aminocyclopropane-1-carboxylic acid to ethylene, *Plant Cell Physiol.* **21**:939–949.

Smith, A. M., 1976a, Ethylene in soil biology, *Annu. Rev. Phytopathol.* **14**:53–73.

Smith, A. M., 1976b, Ethylene production by bacteria in reduced microsites in soil and some implications to agriculture, *Soil Biol. Biochem.* **8**:239–298.

Smith, A. M., and Cook, R. J., 1974, Implication of ethylene production by bacteria for biological balance of soil, *Nature* **252**:703–705.

Smith, A. M., Milham, P. J., and Morrison, W. L., 1978, Soil ethylene production specifically triggered by ferrous iron, in: *Microbial Ecology* (M. W. Loutit and J. A. R. Mites, eds.), Springer-Verlag, Berlin, pp. 329–336.

Smith, G. H., and Ellis, M. M., 1963, Chromatographic analysis of gases from soils and vegetation, related to geochemical prospecting for petroleum, *Bull. Am. Assoc. Pet. Geol.* **47**:1897–1903.

Smith, K. A., 1978, Ineffectiveness of ethylene as a regulator of soil microbial activity, *Soil Biol. Biochem.* **10**:269–272.

Smith, K. A., and Dowdell, R. J., 1974, Field studies of the soil atmosphere. I. Relationship between ethylene, oxygen, soil moisture content and temperature, *J. Soil Sci.* **25**:217–230.

Smith, K. A., and Jackson, M. B., 1974, Ethylene, waterlogging and plant growth, *ARC Letcombe Lab. Annu. Rep.* **1973**:60–75.

Smith, K. A., and Restall, S. W. F., 1971, The occurrence of ethylene in anaerobic soil, *J. Soil Sci.* **22**:430–443.

Smith, K. A., and Robertson, P. D., 1971, Effect of ethylene on root extension of cereals, *Nature* **234**:148–149.

Smith, K. A., and Russell, R. S., 1969, Occurrence of ethylene and its significance in anaerobic soil, *Nature* **222**:769–771.

Southwick, S. M., Davies, F. S., El-Gholl, N. E., and Schoulties, C. L., 1982. Ethylene, fungi and summer fruit drop of navel orange, *J. Am. Soc. Hortic. Sci.* **107**:800–804.

Stall, R. E., and Hall. C. B., 1984, Chlorosis and ethylene production in pepper leaves infected by *Xanthomonas compestris* pv. *vesicatoria, Phytopathology* **74**:373–375.

Swanson, B. T., Wilkins, H. F., and Kennedy, B. W., 1979, Factors affecting ethylene production by some plant pathogenic bacteria, *Plant Soil* **51**:19–26.

Swart, A., and Kamerbeek, G. A., 1976, Different ethylene production *in vitro* by several species and formae speciales of *Fusarium, Neth. J. Plant Pathol.* **82**:81–84.

Swart, A., and Kamerbeek, G. A., 1977, Ethylene production and mycelium growth of the tulip strain of *Fusarium oxysporum* as influenced by shaking of and oxygen supply to the culture medium, *Physiol. Plant.* **39**:38–44.

Thomas, K. C., and Spencer, M., 1977, L-Methionine as an ethylene precursor in *Saccharomyces cerevisiae, Can. J. Microbiol.* **23**:1669–1674.

Thomas, K. C., and Spencer, M., 1978, Evolution of ethylene by *Saccharomyces cerevisiae* as influenced by the carbon source for growth and the presence of air, *Can. J. Microbiol.* **24**:637–642.

Toppan, A., and Esquerre-Tugaye, M. T., 1984, Cell surfaces in plant–microorganism interaction. IV. Fungal glycopeptides which elicit the synthesis of ethylene in plants, *Plant Physiol.* **75**:1133–1138.

Toppan, A., Roby, D., and Esquerre-Tugaye, M. T., 1982, Cell surfaces in plant–microorganism interactions. III. *In vivo* effect of ethylene on hydroxyproline-rich glycoprotein accumulation in the cell wall of diseased plants, *Plant Physiol.* **70**:82–86.

Turkova, N. S., 1944, Growth reactions in plants under excessive watering, *C.R. (Dokl.) Acad. Sci. USSR* **42**:87–90.

Tzeng, D. D., and DeVay, J. E., 1985, Physiological responses of *Gossypium hirsutum* L. to infection by defoliating and nondefoliating pathotypes of *Verticillium dahliae* Kleb., *Physiol. Plant Pathol.* **26**:57–72.

Unver, A. A., and Himmelblau, D. M., 1964, Diffusion coefficients of CO_2, C_2H_4, C_3H_6 and C_4H_8 in water from 60 to 65°C, *J. Chem. Eng. Data* **9**:428–431.

Valdovinos, J. G., Ernest, L. C., and Henry, E. W., 1967, Effects of ethylene and gibberellic acid on auxin synthesis in plant tissue, *Plant Physiol.* **42**:1803–1806.

Van Cleemput, O., El-Sebaay, A. S., and Baert, L., 1983, Evolution of gaseous hydrocarbons from soil, effect of moisture content and nitrate level, *Soil Biol. Biochem.* **15**:519–524.

Wainwright, M., and Kowalenko, C. G., 1977, Effects of pesticides, lime and other amendments on soil ethylene, *Plant Soil* **48**:253–258.

Wang, S. Y., Adams, D. O., and Lieberman, M., 1982, Recycling of 5′-methylthioadenosine-ribose carbon atoms into methionine in tomato tissue in relation to ethylene production, *Plant Physiol.* **70**:117–121.

Ward, T., Turner, E. M., and Osborne, D. J., 1978a, Evidence for the production of ethylene by the mycelium of *Agaricus bisporus* and its relationship to sporocarp development, *J. Gen. Microbiol.* **104**:23–30.

Ward, T. M., Wright, M., Robert, J. A., Self, R., and Osborne, D. J., 1978b, Analytical procedures for the assay and identification of ethylene, in: *Isolation of Plant Growth Regulators* (J. R. Hillman, ed.), Cambridge University Press, London, p. 135.

Wood, D. A., and Hammond, J. B. W., 1977, Ethylene production by axenic fruiting cultures of *Agaricus bisporus, Appl. Environ. Microbiol.* **34**:228–229.

Yang, S. F., 1980, Regulation of ethylene biosynthesis, *HortScience* **15**:238–243.

Yang, S. F., and Hoffman, N. E., 1984, Ethylene biosynthesis and its regulation in higher plants, *Annu. Rev. Plant Physiol.* **35**:155–189.

Yopp, J. H., Aung, L. H., and Steffans, G. L., 1986, *Bioassays and Other Special Techniques for Plant Hormones and Plant Growth Regulators,* Plant Growth Regulator Society of America, pp. 105–122.

Yoshida, T., and Suzuki, T., 1975, Formation and degradation of ethylene in submerged rice soil, *Soil Sci. Plant Nutr. (Tokyo)* **21**:129–135.

Young, R. E., Pratt, H. K., and Biale, J. B., 1951, Identification of ethylene as a volatile product of the fungus *Penicillium digitatum, Plant Physiol.* **26**:304–310.

Yu, Y. B., and Yang, S. F., 1979, Auxin-induced ethylene production and its inhibition by aminoethoxyvinylglycine and cobalt ion, *Plant Physiol.* **64**:1074–1077.

Yu, Y. B., Adams, D. O., and Yang, S. F., 1979, 1-Aminocyclopropane-carboxylate synthase, a key enzyme in ethylene biosynthesis, *Arch. Biochem. Biophys.* **178**:280–286.

Yung, K. H., Yang, S. F., and Schlenk, F., 1982, Methionine synthesis from 5-methylthioribose in apple tissue, *Biochem. Biophys. Res. Commun.* **104**:771–777.

Zimmerman, P. W., and Wilcoxon, F., 1935, Several chemical growth substances which cause initiation of roots and other responses in plants, *Contrib. Boyce Thompson Inst.* **7**:209–229.

3

Oceanic Bacterial Production

HUGH W. DUCKLOW and CRAIG A. CARLSON

1. Introduction

There has been an explosion of research on marine microbial foodweb processes in the past decade. Today it is widely accepted that about 50% of the primary production in marine and fresh water is processed by bacteria each day (Williams, 1981; Cole *et al.*, 1988). This striking finding was stimulated, as others have noted, by the introduction of convenient methods for the estimation of microbial biomass and activities in natural waters. Hobbie *et al.* (1977) and Watson *et al.* (1977) demonstrated conclusively that bacterial populations in the sea were large. By 1980, in addition to the pioneering and prescient work by Sorokin (e.g., Sorokin, 1971, 1973), reports of bacterial production measurements had begun to emerge (Sieburth *et al.*, 1977; Karl, 1979; Larsson and Hagstrom, 1979; Fuhrman and Azam, 1980). Brock (1971) and Sieburth (1977) wrote early reviews on the subject, and Pomeroy (1974) introduced the importance of marine microbial processes to a large audience. In this chapter we review recent research on bacterial production in the ocean. The emphasis is on the open sea, but we will also discuss other marine habitats, partly because there are still few comprehensive studies of oceanic bacterial production. There is an equally large and rapidly growing literature on bacterial production in fresh waters (Cole *et al.*, 1988; Currie, 1990) which deserves a review of its own, as well as comparison with the marine findings (Hobbie, 1988). We will not review related work in sediments, nor for the most part, related work on bacteriovores.

1.1. Previous Reviews

This is not a review of methods, which have been treated comprehensively by Karl (1986). Other reviews emphasizing bacterial production measurement techniques include Karl (1980), Azam and Fuhrman (1984), Karl and Winn (1984), Moriarty (1984, 1985), and Riemann and Bell (1990). van Es and Meyer-Reil (1982) and Joint and

HUGH W. DUCKLOW and CRAIG A. CARLSON • Horn Point Environmental Laboratories, University of Maryland–CEES, Cambridge, Maryland 21613.
Advances in Microbial Ecology, Vol. 12, edited by K.C. Marshall. Plenum Press, New York, 1992.

Morris (1982) reviewed bacterioplankton processes during the 1970s, a period dominated by measurements of heterotrophic uptake of ^{14}C-labeled substrates, and early attempts to survey biomass and production. Wright (1984) and Button (1985) addressed the kinetics of organic matter utilization. Williams (1981, 1984), Azam et al. (1983), and Ducklow (1983, 1984) surveyed aspects of the trophic roles played by bacterioplankton. Fenchel and Jorgensen (1977) and Newell (1984) treated the problem of detritus decomposition by bacteria and protozoans. Azam and Cho (1987) made a penetrating ecological interpretation of physiological adaptations of bacterioplankton for capturing low concentrations of organic matter in a dilute environment. Lee and Wakeham (1988) surveyed the field from the point of view of organic geochemists. Recently, Longhurst and Harrison (1989) included a section on bacterioplankton in their exhaustive synthesis of information on the vertical organization of plankton communities.

1.2. A Trophic Viewpoint

Prior to the mid-1970s, again excepting the Russian data which most Western investigators discounted, there seemed little role for bacterioplankton in marine plankton foodwebs. Bacterial populations revealed by the culture-based techniques still predominant seemed too small to have much impact on nutrient cycling or to serve as food for animals (Steele, 1974). Pomeroy (1974, 1979), Williams (1981), and Joint and Morris (1982) argued on the basis of emerging studies for a new view in which bacteria could be fitted into the plankton paradigm first articulated by Steele:

> The present exercise points out very clearly that if one wishes to understand the dynamics of the food web, it is necessary to establish the fate of the "microbial production." [Williams, 1981, p. 22]

Pomeroy (1979), Sorokin (1981), and Williams (1981) presented early models of material flows through a plankton food web which included microheterotrophs (bacterioplankton and protozoans), dissolved organic matter, fecal particles, and diverse alternative pathways. Azam and Cho (1987) discussed bacterial physiology in the context of the microenvironment experienced by bacteria. In our review we will point out research findings which have expanded on this view. First, we review published estimates of bacterial production in marine habitats. Then, we will analyze data pertaining to the regulation of bacterial populations. Finally, we discuss new views about the origins and fluxes of organic matter which sustain bacterial production.

2. Bacterial Production in Marine Ecosystems

Our survey of published estimates of bacterial production is summarized in Tables I–IV. Some of the reports cited in Table I are exhaustive, containing tens to hundreds of individual estimates of bacterial production as a function of depth in the water column, time of day or year, geographic location, and so forth. In order to portray the range of work which has been reported, we have tabulated average values from these works, breaking down the data by habitat, and in a few cases by season. Besides employing a diverse array of methods, researchers have reported bacterial production in many different units, using a wide range of conversion factors. We have recalculated the published estimates using conversion factors given in each report in all instances where the information to make the conversion was supplied. In a few cases we used a pair of "standard" factors (20 fgC cell^{-1} and 2×10^{18} cells mole^{-1} of thymidine incorporated) to convert to our standard units. The resulting data range over seven orders of magnitude, from 0.0004 mgC m^{-3} day^{-1} in McMurdo Sound, Antarctica (Fuhrman and Azam, 1980) to over 2000 mgC m^{-3} day^{-1} in a eutrophic bay in the Ivory Coast (Torréton et al., 1989). Billen et al. (1990) report a similar range in a graph from which it was difficult to extract ranges for our table. In spite of the large dynamic range, however, average estimates cover a surprisingly narrow range, from 2 to 119 mgC m^{-3} day^{-1} (Table I, habitat averages). Below, these data will be used to derive global estimates of bacterial production in the euphotic zones of each habitat, and a global total.

2.1. Methods and Conversion Factors

Estimates derived from different methods differ little (Table II), a conclusion also reached by Cole et al. (1988). Estimates from seawater cultures gave higher values than the other techniques, reflecting the restricted range of habitats in which the method has been employed, or perhaps stimulation of growth after 12–24 hr of incubation in bottles. The most striking aspect, though, is the extent to which the thymidine method has been adopted by workers worldwide for work in all habitats. Well over half of all published estimates have been derived from this method. In spite of its popularity, the method remains somewhat controversial. Several complex processes affect the accuracy of estimates from this method. These have been discussed in a number of publications and have been reviewed again recently by Riemann and Bell (1990).

One approach toward addressing the variability inherent in the thymidine method was developed by Kirchman et al. (1982) and first employed by Ducklow and Kirchman (1983). This involves empirical derivation of the conversion factors for translating thymidine uptake rates (usually pmoles liter^{-1} hr^{-1}) into cell- or carbon-based rates (cells liter^{-1} hr^{-1} or μgC liter^{-1} hr^{-1}). Kirchman et al. (1982) argued that experimental determination of the pertinent factor provided an alternative to measuring all of the individual terms needed to make the conversion. These include cellular DNA content, isotope dilution, integrity of de novo synthesis, and nonspecific incorporation, and have been addressed by other investigators (Fuhrman and Azam, 1982; Moriarty, 1985; Robarts et al., 1986; Hollibaugh, 1988; Chrzanowski, 1988; Jeffrey and Paul, 1988). There have been a number of comprehensive studies of thymidine conversion factors (TCF; Ducklow and Hill, 1985b; Riemann et al., 1987; Rivkin et al., 1989) and as a consequence, a wide range of factors has been employed (Table III). Bell (1990) has demonstrated that the variability in conversion factors can be reduced simply by using higher final concentrations of [^{3}H] thymidine, though he warns that the same concentration must be used in the individual assays. Ducklow and Kirchman (1983) had pointed this out earlier, stating that the high conversion factor they derived was needed to compensate for a lack of uptake saturation at the 5 nM levels used in their study.

Table I. Estimates of Bacterial Production in Marine Waters, 1974–1991[a]

Location	Method[b]	Reported bacterial production	BACTPROD ($mgC\ m^{-3}\ d^{-1}$)	BP:PP (%)	Reference
Salt marshes					
Sippewissett, MA	TDR	$14\text{–}37 \times 10^7$ cells $l^{-1}\ h^{-1}$	67–177[c]	—	Kirchman et al. (1982)
	SWCULT	8.6 kgC marsh$^{-1}\ d^{-1}$	252	<5	Kirchman et al. (1984)
So. Carolina	TDR	8–13 mgC m$^{-3}\ d^{-1}$	8–13	10	Chrzanowski and Zingmark (1989)
Sapelo open estuary	TDR	37 µgC l$^{-1}\ d^{-1}$	37	—	Sherr et al. (1989)
Sapelo tidal creek	TDR	131 µgC l$^{-1}\ d^{-1}$	131	—	Sherr et al. (1989)
Sapelo estuary	TDR	150 pmole l$^{-1}\ d^{-1}$	85	—	Griffith et al. (1990)
		average	97–116		
Estuaries					
Kiel Bight	SWCULT	10–520 µC l$^{-1}\ d^{-1}$	10–520	15–30	Meyer-Reil (1977)
Port Hacking, Australia	14CREL	0.1 mgC m^{-1} 3h^{-1}	2.4		Wiebe and Smith (1977)
Baltic Sea	14CREL	29 gC m^{-2} season^{-1}	4.7	26	Larsson and Hagstrom (1979)
York River, VA	TDR	7–75 µgC l$^{-1}\ d^{-1}$	7–75	—	Ducklow (1982)
Buzzards Bay, MA	TDR	$10\text{–}20 \times 10^7$ cells l$^{-1}\ h^{-1}$	48–96[c]	—	Kirchman et al. (1982)
Himmerfjorden	FDC	50.9 gC m$^{-2}\ y^{-1}$	4.6	24	Larsson and Hagstrom (1982)
Open Baltic Sea	FDC	38.3 gC m$^{-2}\ y^{-1}$	3	24	Larsson and Hagstrom (1982)
Kiel Fjord	14CREL	1–70 µgC l$^{-1}\ d^{-1}$	1–70	10–30	Wolter (1982)
Randers Fjord	14CREL	19–24 µgC l$^{-1}\ d^{-1}$	19–24	3–30	Jensen (1983)
Narragansett	TDR	7×10^5 cells l$^{-1}\ h^{-1}$	336	—	Hobbie and Cole (1984)

Location	Method	Value		%	Reference
Limfjord, Oct.	FDC	9–15 mgC m^{-3} d^{-1}	8.5–14.5	—	Riemann et al. (1984)
	DARKCO2	11 mgC m^{-3} d^{-1}	11	—	Riemann et al. (1984)
	TDR	3.8–10.6 mgC m^{-3} d^{-1}	3.8–10.6	—	Riemann et al. (1984)
Limfjord, Sept.	FDC	2.6–7.0 mgC m^{-3} d^{-1}	2.6–7.0	—	Riemann et al. (1984)
	DARKCO2	17 mgC m^{-3} d^{-1}	17	—	Riemann et al. (1984)
	TDR	6.1–23.9 mgC m^{-3} d^{-1}	6.1–23.9	—	Riemann et al. (1984)
Ems–Dollard	TDR	9 gC m^{-3} y^{-1}	24.6	12	Admiraal et al. (1985)
Tampa Bay	TDR	73–322 pmole l^{-1} h^{-1}	70–309[c]	—	Paul et al. (1985)
Chesapeake Bay	TDR	52–680 mgC m^{-2} d^{-1}	2.6–34	25	Malone et al. (1986)
Delaware Bay	CYCLHX	9.53–44.9 µgC l^{-1} d^{-1}	9.53–44.9	23	Coffin and Sharp (1987)
Chesapeake Bay	LEU	6.9 × 10^7 cells l^{-1} h^{-1}	33.12	—	Chin-Leo and Kirchman (1988)
	TDR	8.5 × 10^7 cells l^{-1} h^{-1}	40.5	—	Chin-Leo and Kirchman (1988)
Delaware Bay	TDR, LEU	10–80 cells l^{-1} h^{-1}	4.8–38[c]	30	Kirchman and Hoch (1988)

[a] Values from the literature were averaged and grouped by season and location. All units were converted to mgC m^{-3} d^{-1} using conversion factors given in reports or using standard factors of 20 fgC cell^{-1} and 2 × 10^{18} cells mole^{-1} if factor values were missing. Average production values for each habitat were derived from minimum–maximum values in Table. No integration over days or seasons was made. Cited estimates of bacterial production ratio given as % of primary production.

[b] TDR: thymidine incorporation; SWCULT: changes in cell numbers during incubation; 14CREL: incorporation of ^{14}C-DOC released by phytoplankton; FDC: frequency of dividing cells; DARKCO2: anapleurotic CO$_2$ uptake; CYCLHEX: changes in cell numbers after treatment with antibiotic; LEU: leucine incorporation; SACCHAR: changes in dissolved monosaccharides; DIELATP: changes in < 1 µM ATP; ADENINE: adenine incorporation.

[c] Assumed standard conversion factors for carbon-based estimates.

(continued)

Table I. (*Continued*)

Location	Method[b]	Reported bacterial production	BACTPROD ($mgC\ m^{-3}\ d^{-1}$)	BP:PP (%)	Reference
Tampa Bay	TDR	20–275 pmole $l^{-1}\ h^{-1}$	19–264[c]	—	Paul *et al.* (1988)
Finland spring	TDR	5.58 gC m^{-2} 62 d^{-1}	4.5	11.7	Kuosa and Kivi (1989)
Finland summer	TDR	5.05 gC m^{-2} 86 d^{-1}	2.93	22.4	Kuosa and Kivi (1989)
Finland fall	TDR	1.41 gC m^{-2} 110 d^{-1}	0.52	16.5	Kuosa and Kivi (1989)
Finland winter	TDR	0.45 gC m^{-2} 59 d^{-1}	0.51	13.9	Kuosa and Kivi (1989)
Sapelo I.	TDR	9.3 μgC $l^{-1}\ h^{-1}$	223.2	—	Pedros-Alio and Newell (1989)
Chesapeake Bay spring	TDR	1–4 × 10⁹ cells $l^{-1}\ d^{-1}$	52[c]	—	Jonas and Tuttle (1990)
Chesapeake Bay summer	TDR	4–9 × 10⁹ cells $l^{-1}\ d^{-1}$	132[c]	—	Jonas and Tuttle (1990)
Baltic mesocosm	TDR	4–8 cells $ml^{-1}\ h^{-1}$	21–38	—	Kuppo-Leinikki (1990)
Baltic Sea	TDR	12.1 gC $m^{-2}\ y^{-1}$	33.1	14.4	Lignell (1990)
	DARKCO2	38.4 gC $m^{-2}\ y^{-1}$	105	45.6	Lignell (1990)
Roskilde Fjord	TDR	3.7 mgC $m^{-3}\ h^{-1}$	88	5	Sand-Jensen (1990)
Finnish Bay	TDR	1.4 × 10⁴ cells $ml^{-1}\ h^{-1}$	9.1	—	Wikner *et al.* (1990)
Bothnian Sea	TDR	2.1 × 10⁴ cells $ml^{-1}\ h^{-1}$	13.6	—	Wikner *et al.* (1990)
		average	50–73		
Coastal plumes					
Hudson River	TDR	6.5 × 10⁷ cells $l^{-1}\ h^{-1}$	31.2[c]	—	Kirchman *et al.* (1982)
	TDR	83–157 pmole $l^{-1}\ d^{-1}$	6.8–10.2	23–35	Ducklow and Kirchman (1983)

Location	Method	Rate			Reference
Rhone River	TDR	20–280 µgC l⁻¹ h⁻¹	<0.0067		Kirchman et al. (1989b)
Chesapeake Bay, Feb.	TDR	4 µgC l⁻¹ d⁻¹	4	13	Malone and Ducklow (1990)
Chesapeake Bay, Apr.	TDR	22 µgC l⁻¹ d⁻¹	22	19	Malone and Ducklow (1990)
Chesapeake Bay, June	TDR	41 µgC l⁻¹ d⁻¹	41	10	Malone and Ducklow (1990)
Chesapeake Bay, Aug.	TDR	50 µgC l⁻¹ d⁻¹	50	13	Malone and Ducklow (1990)
			average 50–73		
Fjords					
Saanich Inlet	TDR	7.2–71 µgC l⁻¹ d⁻¹	7.2–71	10	Fuhrman and Azam (1980)
Howe Sound, B.C.	TDR	0–36.9 mgC m⁻³ d⁻¹	0–36.9	9–189	Albright and McCrae (1987)
	FDC	0–13 mgC m⁻³ d⁻¹	0–13	4–190	Albright and McCrae (1987)
			average 2–40		
Coastal ocean					
English Channel	14CREL	14–59 µgC l⁻¹ d⁻¹	14–59	2–33	Derenbach and Williams (1974)
Scripps Pier	TDR	1–53 µgC l⁻¹ d⁻¹	0.7–53	>10	Fuhrman et al. (1980)
	SWCULT	10–34 µgC l⁻¹ d⁻¹	10–34	9–17	Fuhrman et al. (1980)
Nearshore Georgia Bight	FDC	1–7 mgC m⁻³ h⁻¹	19–177	—	Newell and Christian (1981)
Georgia Bight	TDR	0.1–4 × 10⁸ cells l⁻¹ h⁻¹	5–192[c]	25	Newell and Fallon (1982)

(continued)

Table I. (*Continued*)

Location	Method[b]	Reported bacterial production	BACTPROD ($mgC\ m^{-3}\ d^{-1}$)	BP:PP (%)	Reference
North Sea	TDR	$12\text{--}54 \times 10^{-3}$ nmole l^{-1} h^{-1}	12–52	44–68	Lancelot and Billen (1984)
English Channel	TDR	1.5×10^{-3} nmole l^{-1} h^{-1}	1.44	44–68	Lancelot and Billon (1984)
So. Calif. Bight	14CREL	1–5 μgC l^{-1} 8 h^{-1}	4–16	5–19	Ward (1984)
So. Calif. Bight, Oct.	TDR	$4\text{--}8 \times 10^{8}$ cells l^{-1} h^{-1}	4–8	20–25	Fuhrman et al. (1985)
So. Calif. Bight, May	TDR	$2\text{--}6 \times 10^{8}$ cells l^{-1} h^{-1}	2–6	20–25	Fuhrman et al. (1985)
Oosterschelde	TDR	0.5–7 μgC l^{-1} d^{-1}	0.5–7	5	Laanbroek et al. (1985)
Gulf of Mexico	TDR	39–55 pmole l^{-1} h^{-1}	37–53^c	—	Paul et al. (1985)
Irish Sea	FDC	3–13 μgC l^{-1} d^{-1}	3–13	—	Turley and Lochte (1985)
Oosterschelde	TDR	15–90 μgC l^{-1} d^{-1}	15–90	—	Laanbroek and Verplanke (1986)
Newfoundland	TDR	17–45 pmole l^{-1} d^{-1}	0.7–1.8	—	Pomeroy and Deibel (1986)
Belgium	TDR	8 gC m^{-2} 66d^{-1}	6.73	—	Billen and Fontigny (1987)
Nova Scotia	TDR	0.8–0.84 μgC l^{-1} d^{-1}	0.8	2	Douglas et al. (1987)
Santa Monica Basin	TDR	253 mgC m^{-2} d^{-1}	0.33	—	Cho and Azam (1988)
SE Bight USA	TDR	0.4–5 mgC m^{-3} d^{-1}	0.5–6	2–17	Hanson et al. (1988)
Mediterranean	TDR	0.2×10^{9} cells l^{-1} h^{-1}	96^c	—	Vives-Rego et al. (1988)
Concepción Bay, Chile	TDR	$0.3\text{--}3 \times 10^{6}$ cells ml^{-1} h^{-1}	5–50^c	—	Pantoja et al. (1989)

Location	Method	Rate			Reference
Bietri Ivory Coast	TDR	11–91 μgC l⁻¹ h⁻¹	264–2184	80	Torréton et al. (1989)
Georgia Bight	TDR	3 pmole l⁻¹ h⁻¹	1.7	—	Griffith et al. (1990)
So. Calif. Bight	TDR	40–240 ngC l⁻¹ h⁻¹	1–5.6	—	Simon and Azam (1989)
Georgia, USA	LEU	9–181 ngC l⁻¹ h⁻¹	0.2–4.3	—	Simon and Azam (1989)
Georgia, USA	TDR	3 pmole TdR l⁻¹ h⁻¹	1.7	—	Griffith et al. (1990)
Spanish Med. Sea	TDR	1.55 ngC ml⁻¹ h⁻¹	37.2	—	Iriberri et al. (1990)
North Sea	TDR	160–356 mgC m⁻² d⁻¹	5.3–11.9	—	Rosenberg et al. (1990)
			average 25–119		
Coastal upwelling zones					
Peru	14CREL	0–12 μgC l⁻¹ d⁻¹	0–12	9	Sellner (1981)
	SACCHAR	85 μgC l⁻¹ d⁻¹	85	85	Sellner (1981)
Ria de Arosa, Spain	TDR	0.8–3.8 mgC m⁻³ d⁻¹	0.8–3.8	2–10	Hanson et al. (1986a)
Benguela, S. Afr.	SWCULT		32–83	14–98	Lucas et al. (1986)
	TDR		42–75	14–98	Lucas et al. (1986)
Chile	TDR	0.13–1.4 μgC l⁻¹ h⁻¹	3.12–33.6	5	McManus and Peterson (1988)
Benguela microcosm	SWCULT	0.34–2.4 μgC l⁻¹ h⁻¹	0.8–58	—	Painting et al. (1989)
Peru	TDR	0.013–1.25 μgC l⁻¹ h⁻¹	0.3–30	—	Painting et al. (1989)
	DARKCO2	1.2–6.4 gC m⁻¹ d⁻¹	6–32	—	Sorokin and Mamaeva (1991)
			average 19–46		

(continued)

Table I. (*Continued*)

Location	Method[b]	Reported bacterial production	BACTPROD ($mgC\ m^{-3}\ d^{-1}$)	BP:PP (%)	Reference
Continental shelf waters					
New York Bight shelf	TDR	5.8×10^7 cells $l^{-1}\ h^{-1}$	27.8^c	—	Kirchman *et al.* (1982)
Georgia Bight Shelf	TDR	$1\text{--}9 \times 10^7$ cells $l^{-1}\ h^{-1}$	$5\text{--}43^c$	25	Newell and Fallon (1982)
Celtic Sea, Aug.	TDR	$0.04\text{--}0.18$ mgC $m^{-3}\ d^{-1}$	$0.04\text{--}0.2$	—	Joint and Pomroy (1983)
Celtic Sea, Apr.–Aug.	TDR	$5\text{--}24$ mgC $m^{-2}\ d^{-1}$	$0.02\text{--}0.5$	<6	Joint and Pomroy (1987)
Celtic Sea, Sep.–Dec.	TDR	$0.8\text{--}6$ mgC $m^{-2}\ d^{-1}$	$0.02\text{--}0.12$	<6	Joint and Pomroy (1987)
Georgia midshelf	TDR	$0.48\text{--}2.7$ mgC $m^{-3}\ d^{-1}$	$0.5\text{--}2.7$	2–12	Hanson *et al.* (1988)
North Sea	TDR	$0.3\text{--}66$ mgC $m^{-3}\ d^{-1}$	$0.27\text{--}66$		Van Duyl *et al.* (1990)
			average 4–18		
Coral reefs					
Lizard Is. open water	TDR	11 μgC $l^{-1}\ d^{-1}$	11	—	Moriarty *et al.* (1985)
Lizard Is. reef front	TDR	26 μgC $l^{-1}\ d^{-1}$	26	—	Moriarty *et al.* (1985)
Lizard Is. reef flat	TDR	$28\text{--}56$ μgC $l^{-1}\ d^{-1}$	$28\text{--}56$	—	Moriarty *et al.* (1985)
Lizard Is. lagoon	TDR	18 μgC $l^{-1}\ d^{-1}$	18	—	Moriarty *et al.* (1985)
One Tree Is.	FDC	$0.87\text{--}147$ mgC $m^{-3}\ d^{-1}$	$0.87\text{--}147$	25	Linley and Koop (1986)
Davies Reef	TDR	$6\text{--}180$ mgC $m^{-2}\ d^{-1}$	$1.2\text{--}12$	—	Ducklow (1990)
			average 15–52		

Open ocean					
Azores	DIELATP	122 µgC l⁻¹ d⁻¹	122	—	Sieburth et al. (1977)
	SACCHAR	118 µgC l⁻¹ d⁻¹	118	—	Sieburth et al. (1977)
N. Atlantic	SACCHAR	29–50 µgC l⁻¹ d⁻¹	29–50		Burney et al. (1982)
Caribbean	ADENINE	2–6 µgC l⁻¹ d⁻¹	2–6		Karl (1979)
So. Calif. Bight	TDR	11 × 10⁻¹¹ mole l⁻¹ d⁻¹	4.32		Fuhrman and Azam (1980)
South Pacific	FDC	0.6–4 µgC l⁻¹ d⁻¹	0.62–4.1	15–45	Hanson and Lowery (1983)
Gulf of Mexico	DFAA	0.3–4.6 µgC l⁻¹ d⁻¹	0.3–4.6	7	Ferguson and Sunda (1984)
Warm core ring 82B	SWCULT	0.01–0.68 µgC l⁻¹ h⁻¹	0.2–6	10	Ducklow and Hill (1985a)
Coral Sea, Australia	TDR	11 µgC l⁻¹ d⁻¹	11	—	Moriarty et al. (1985)
Gulf of Mexico	TDR	0.01–40 pmole l⁻¹ h⁻¹	0.01–38ᶜ	—	Paul et al. (1985)
So. Calif. Bight	TDR	2–8 × 10⁸ cells l⁻¹ d⁻¹	2.4–8.3	20–25	Fuhrman et al. (1985)
Warm core ring 82B	TDR	44–499 mgC m⁻² d⁻¹	2.6–7.79	12	Ducklow (1986)
Warm core ring Gulf St.	TDR	57–291 pmole l⁻¹ d⁻¹	2.7–14ᶜ	—	Peele et al. (1984)
Cold core ring Gulf St.	TDR	0.12–1.41 µgC l⁻¹ d⁻¹	0.12–1.41	—	Hanson et al. (1986b)
Warm core ring Gulf St.	TDR	2 µgC l⁻¹ d⁻¹	2	23	Douglas et al. (1987)
Nova Scotia Slope	TDR	1.42–2.73 µgC l⁻¹ d⁻¹	1.42–2.73	2–33	Douglas et al. (1987)
Cold core ring NE Atl.	FDC	1.9–2.3 mgC m⁻³ d⁻¹	1.9–2.3	—	Lochte and Pfannkuche (1987)

(continued)

Table I. (*Continued*)

Location	Method[b]	Reported bacterial production	BACTPROD ($mgC\ m^{-3}\ d^{-1}$)	BP:PP (%)	Reference
NE Atlantic	FDC	1.4–3.1 $mgC\ m^{-3}\ d^{-1}$	1.4–3.1	—	Lochte and Pfannkuche (1987)
No. Pacific gyre	TDR	39 $mgC\ m^{-2}\ d^{-1}$	0.044	—	Cho and Azam (1988)
Meddit. Oligo	TDR	5.2 $\mu gC\ l^{-1}\ d^{-1}$	5.2	37	Hagstrom *et al.* (1988)
Sargasso Sea	TDR	0.8–6.19 $\mu gC\ l^{-1}\ d^{-1}$	0.8–6.19	—	Fuhrman *et al.* (1989)
Gulf of Aden	CYCLHEX	0.29–1.08 $gC\ m^{-2}\ d^{-1}$	5–18.6	—	Weisse (1989)
Red Sea	CYCLHEX	0.50–1.86 $gC\ m^{-2}\ d^{-1}$	6–7	—	Weisse (1989)
No. Atlantic 59N	TDR	6–7 $mgC\ m^{-3}\ d^{-1}$		—	Carlson (unpublished)
Gulf Stream front	TDR	79–129 $mg\ m^{-2}\ d^{-1}$	0.7–16	—	Borsheim (1990)
Subarctic Pacific	TDR	56 $mgC\ m^{-2}\ d^{-1}$	0.7	11	Kirchman *et al.* (1992)
Tropical Pacific	DARKCO2	0.8–4.9 $gC\ m^{-2}\ d^{-1}$	3–25	—	Sorokin and Mamaeva (1991)
Equatorial Pacific	DARKCO2	1–4 $gC\ m^{-2}\ d^{-1}$	6–18	—	Sorokin and Mamaeva (1991)
			average 12–15		
Antarctic					
McMurdo Sound	TDR	0.0004–2.9 $\mu gC\ l^{-1}\ d^{-1}$	0.0004–2.9	10	Fuhrman and Azam (1980)
Drake Passage	FDC	3–17 $\mu gC\ l^{-1}\ d^{-1}$	2.6–17.1	15–45	Hanson and Lowery (1983)
	TDR	84 $mgC\ m^{-2}\ d^{-1}$	0.42	17	Bailiff *et al.* (1990)

Gerlache Strait	TDR	564 mgC m^{-2} d^{-1}	2.82	70	Bailiff et al. (1990)
Adélie Land	SWCULT	0.17–1.21 µg l^{-1} h^{-1}	4.08–29	—	Delille et al. (1988)
McMurdo Sound, Oct.	TDR	91–112 mgC m^{-2} d^{-1}	0.9–1.1		Rivkin et al. (1989)
Weddell marginal ice	TDR	0.2–1.3 mgC m^{-3} d^{-1}	0.2–1.3	76	Cota et al. (1990)
McMurdo Sound, early Sept.	TDR	30–40 mgC m^{-2} d^{-1}	0.3–0.4	2500	Rivkin (1990)
McMurdo Sound, mid-Sept.	TDR	40–60 mgC m^{-2} d^{-1}	0.4–0.6	2500	Rivkin (1990)
McMurdo Sound, mid-Oct.	TDR	70–90 mgC m^{-2} d^{-1}	0.7–0.9	3000	Rivkin (1990)
McMurdo Sound, mid-Nov.	TDR	0.9–2.4 mgC m^{-2} d^{-1}	0.02	2	Rivkin (1990)
McMurdo Sound, mid-Dec.	TDR	3–19 mgC m^{-2} d^{-1}	0.03–0.2	1–4	Rivkin (1990)
Weddell open sea	TDR	1.2 mgC m^{-3} d^{-1}	1.2	11	Sullivan et al. (1990)
Weddell open sea-west	TDR	17.3 mgC m^{-3} d^{-1}	17.3	11	Sullivan et al. (1990)
Weddell marginal ice	TDR	0.3 mg m^{-3} d^{-1}	0.3	11	Sullivan et al. (1990)
McMurdo under sea ice	SWCULT	0.1–1 doublings d^{-1}	0.03–1.3	—	Anderson et al. (1991)
McMurdo ice transect	TDR	0.02–0.35 pmole l^{-1} h^{-1}	0.01–1.4	—	Gustafson et al. (1991)
			average 2–4		

**Table II. Bacterial Production Estimates Grouped by
Measurement Technique[a]**

Method	Mean mgC m^{-3} d^{-1}	No. of studies
Thymidine	26–54	103
Frequency of dividing cells	4–31	13
Dark CO_2 fixation	20–26	9
Seawater culture	73–155	8
^{14}C release	6–27	7
Other methods[b]	42–52	9

[a]Data abstracted from Table I.
[b]Leucine, adenine, cycloheximide, V_{max}, diel ATP, and monosaccharide changes.

To derive carbon-based estimates from thymidine and most other assays, it is also necessary to use a carbon conversion factor (CCF) for translating cell-based estimates into carbon biomass units. The correct value for the CCF is also controversial, and a wide range of values has been determined and used (Watson *et al.*, 1977; Bratbak and Dundas, 1984; Bratbak, 1985; Nagata, 1986; Lee and Fuhrman, 1987; Nagata and Watanabe, 1990). Simon and Azam (1989) suggest that the leucine incorporation method developed by Kirchman *et al.* (1985) does not require a CCF because the ratio of protein to carbon in bacterial biomass is very constant, and protein synthesis rates can be converted using a single value. However, a factor is still required to convert leucine incorporation into protein synthesis.

In Table III, we summarize the thymidine-based estimates from Table I and include the ranges of TCF and CCF which were employed to generate carbon-based production estimates. Empirically determined TCF range from 1×10^{17} (Kuuppo-Leinikki, 1990) to 60×10^{18} cells mole^{-1} (Ducklow and Kirchman, 1983) with a median value of 2×10^{18} cells mole^{-1} (Fig. 1A). CCF values range from 2 (Joint and Pomroy, 1987) to ca. 28 fgC cell^{-1} (Bratbak, 1985; Laanbroek and Verplanke, 1986; Coffin and Sharp, 1987; Chrzanowski and Zingmark, 1989), with a median value of 11 (Fig. 1B). Together, these factors yield a combined factor with units of μgC pmole^{-1}, which ranges from 0.0012 (Fuhrman and Azam, 1980) to 0.3 (Ducklow and Kirchman, 1983) with a median value of 0.023 (Fig. 1C). It is clear that choice of conversion factors and their combination may have a great impact on the levels of bacterial production calculated in any given study. To get some idea of this effect, we calculated the combined factor values from TCF and CCF reported in the literature and compared them to the median value of 0.023. The calculated ratios range from 0.03 to over 3. If we assume that all of these values are "correct," that is, accurately reflecting intrinsic properties of bacterial growth in the environment of each study, the ratios indicate that reliance on standard conversion factor values is likely to overestimate the "true" rates. This is probably not a good assumption, however, because very few studies use empirically derived CCF, and in most cases TCF from just a few samples are applied to full data sets. Therefore, we might more safely regard estimates with ratios closer to 1.0 as more accurate until better

Table III. Bacterial Production Estimates from [³H]-Thymidine Incorporation, Demonstrating Ranges of Conversion Factors Employed[a]

Reference	Location	BACTPROD (mgC m⁻³ d⁻¹)	TCF (10¹⁸ cells mole⁻¹)	CCF (fgC cell⁻¹)	CCF (fgC μm⁻³)	COMBFAC[b] (μgC pmole⁻¹)	RATIO
Salt marshes							
Kirchman et al. (1982)	Sippewissett, MA	67.2–177.6	3.3–9	—	—	—	—
Chrzanowski and Zingmark (1989)	So. Carolina	8–13	0.4–3	—	560	0.01	0.49
Sherr et al. (1989)	Sapelo Is.	37–131	1.1	—	350	0.02	0.84
Griffith et al. (1990)	Sapelo estuary	84.9	1.18	20	—	0.02	1.03
Estuaries							
Ducklow (1982)	York River, VA	7–75	3.5	—	110	0.02	0.84
Kirchman et al. (1982)	Buzzards Bay	48–96	1.9–3.7	—	—	—	—
Hobbie and Cole (1984)	Narragansett mesocosm	336	1.4	—	—	—	—
Riemann et al. (1984)	Limfjord, Oct.	3.8–24	—	—	121	—	—
Admiraal et al. (1985)	Ems–Dollard	24.6	1.7	—	—	—	—
Paul et al. (1985)	Tampa Bay	70–309	—	—	—	—	—
Malone et al. (1986)	Chesapeake Bay	2.6–34	2	20	—	0.04	1.74
Chin-Leo and Kirchman (1988)	Chesapeake Bay	40.5	2.83	20	—	0.06	2.46
Paul and et al. (1988)	Tampa Bay	19–264	—	—	—	—	0.65
Kuosa and Kivi (1989)	Gulf of Finland	0.51–4.5	1.1	—	270	0.01	—
Pedros-Alio and Newell (1989)	Sapelo Is. brackish	223.2	1.1	—	—	—	—
Jonas and Tuttle (1990)	Chesapeake Bay	52–132	2	—	—	—	—
Kuuppo-Leinikki (1990)	Baltic mesocosm	20.6–37.9	0.1	—	—	—	—
Lignell (1990)	Baltic Sea	33.1	1.1	—	270	0.01	0.65
Sand-Jensen et al. (1990)	Roskilde Fjord	88.32	1.1	—	350	0.02	0.84

[a]TCF: thymidine conversion factor; CCF: bacterial cell : biomass factor; COMBFAC: combined factor derived from TCF × CCF. RATIO: quotient of COMBFAC and product of median values of TCF and CCF (see text). Table entries abstracted from Table I.
[b]Only lowest value of range listed.
[c]Water column depth not given.

(continued)

Table III. (*Continued*)

Reference	Location	BACTPROD (mgC m⁻³ d⁻¹)	TCF (10¹⁸ cells mole⁻¹)	CCF (fgC cell⁻¹)	CCF (fgC μm⁻³)	COMBFAC[b] (μgC pmole⁻¹)	RATIO
Wikner et al. (1990)	Bothnian Sea	9–14	1.7	27	—	0.05	2.00
Plumes							
Firchman et al. (1982)	Hudson	31.2	17	—	—	—	—
Ducklow and Kirchman (1983)	Hudson	6.8–10.2	17	5	—	0.09	3.70
Kirchman et al. (1989)	Rhone	0.0005–0.007	2	20	—	0.04	1.74
Malone and Ducklow (1990)	Chesapeake	4–50	2	20	—	0.04	1.74
Fjords							
Fuhrman and Azam (1980a)	Saanich Inlet	7.2–71	0.2–1.3	—	120	0.0012	0.05
Albright and McCrae (1987)	Howe Sound, Can.	0–36.9	1.2	—	117	0.01	0.31
Coastal							
Fuhrman and Azam (1980)	Scripps Pier	0.7–53	0.2–1.3	—	120	0.0012	0.05
Fuhrman et al. (1980)	So. Calif. Bight	4.32	—	—	—	—	—
Newell and Fallon (1982)	Georgia, USA	96–192	1.3	—	—	—	—
Lancelot and Billen (1984)	North Sea	1.4–52	2	20	—	0.04	1.74
Fuhrman et al. (1985)	So. Calif. Bight	2.4–8.3	2.3	10	—	0.02	1.00
Laanbroek et al. (1985)	Oosterschelde Basin	0.5–7	2.1	—	121	0.01	0.55
Paul et al. (1985)	Gulf of Mexico	37–53	—	—	—	—	—
Laanbroek and Verplanke (1986)	Oosterschelde Basin	15–90	2.1	—	560	0.06	2.56
Pomeroy and Deibel (1986)	Newfoundland	0.7–1.82	—	—	—	—	—
Billen and Fontigny (1987)	Belgian coastal	6.73	1.7	—	120	0.01	0.44
Douglas et al. (1987)	Nova Scotia coastal	0.8–0.84	2	—	120	0.01	0.52
Cho and Azam (1988)	Santa Monica Basin	0.33	1.18	—	—	—	—
Hanson et al. (1988)	Georgia nearshore	0.68–4.9	2	20	—	0.04	1.74

Vives-Rego et al. (1988)	Mediterranean coastal	96	1.4–2.4	—	—	—	—
Pantoja et al. (1989)	Concepción Bay, Chile	5.4–50	—	—	—	—	—
Torréton et al. (1989)	Bietri Ivory Coast	264–2184	0.75	20	106	0.004	0.17
Griffith et al. (1990)	Georgia Bight	1.7	1.18	—	—	0.02	1.03
Iriberri et al. (1990)	Coastal Spain (beach)	37.2	1.3	—	220	0.01	0.62
Rosenberg et al. (1990)	North Sea	5.3–11.9	1.1	13.2	—	0.01	0.62
Upwelling							
Hanson et al. (1986a)	Ria de Arosa, Spain	0.76–3.82	4	5	—	0.02	0.87
Lucas et al. (1986)	Benguela upwelling	41.5–74.6	0.2	—	—	—	—
McManus and Peterson (1988)	Chile upwelling	3.12–33.6	2	20	—	0.04	1.74
Painting et al. (1989)	Benguela (microcosm)	0.31–30	1.7	—	121	0.01	0.45
Shelf							
Kirchman et al. (1982)	New York Bight shelf	27.8	60	—	—	—	—
Newell and Fallon (1982)	Georgia, USA	4.8–43.2	1.3	1.7	—	0.003	0.15
Joint and Pomroy (1983)	Celtic Sea, Aug.	0.04–0.19	1.7	2	—	0.01	0.35
Joint and Pomroy (1987)	Celtic Sea	0.02–0.49	4	20	—	0.04	1.74
Hanson et al. (1988)	Georgia midshelf	0.48–2.7	2	—	—	—	—
Van Duyl et al. (1990)	North Sea	0.27–66	1.7	—	220	0.02	0.81
Coral reefs							
Moriarty et al. (1985)	Lizard Is.	26–56	2	15	—	0.03	1.30
Ducklow (1990)	Davies Reef	1.2–12	—	10	—	—	—
Moriarty et al. (1990)	Gulf Carpenteria	11–100[c]	0.5	40	220	0.02	0.87
Open ocean							
Fuhrman and Azam (1980)	So. Calif. Bight offshore	4.3	0.2–1.3	—	120	0.0012	0.05
Moriarty et al. (1985)	Coral Sea Australia	11	2	15	—	0.03	1.30
Paul et al. (1985)	Gulf of Mexico	0.01–38	—	—	—	—	—
Peele et al. (1984)	Warm core ring	2.7–14	2.4	—	—	—	—

(continued)

Table III. (*Continued*)

Reference	Location	BACTPROD (mgC m^{-3} d^{-1})	TCF (10^{18} cells mole^{-1})	CCF (fgC cell^{-1})	CCF (fgC μm^{-3})	COMBFAC[b] (μgC pmole^{-1})	RATIO
Ducklow (1986)	Warm core ring 82B	2.6–7.79	4	—	242	0.05	2.10
Hanson et al. (1986b)	Cold core ring	0.12–1.41	2	5	—	0.01	0.43
Douglas et al. (1987)	Warm core ring	2	2	—	120	0.01	0.52
Cho and Azam (1988)	North Pacific gyre	0.044	1.18	—	—	—	—
Hagstrom et al. (1988)	Oligotr. Mediterranean	5.2	1.7	8.3	—	0.01	0.61
Fuhrman et al. (1989)	Sargasso Sea	0.8–6.19	4	20	—	0.08	3.48
Carlson (unpublished)	NE Atl.59N, 20W July	5.8	2	20	—	0.04	1.74
Borsheim (1990)	Gulf Stream front	0.71–16.1	4	—	350	0.07	3.04
Kirchman et al. (1992)	Subarctic Pacific	0.69	1.74	20	—	0.03	1.51
Antarctica							
Fuhrman and Azam (1980a)	McMurdo Sound	0.0004–2.9	0.2–1.3	—	120	0.001	0.05
Bailiff et al. (1990)	Coastal areas	0.4–2.8	1.1	—	220–560	0.01	—
Rivkin (1990)	McMurdo Sound	0.51–1.12	2.2	8.3	—	0.02	0.79
Cota et al. (1990)	Weddell Sea marg. ice	0.2–1.3	2.05	2.2	—	0.0045	0.20
Rivkin (1990)	McMurdo Sound	0.009–0.6	0.8	8.3	—	0.007	0.03
Sullivan et al. (1990)	Weddell Sea	1.2–17	2.05	—	220	0.02	0.98
Gustafson et al. (1991)	McMurdo ice transect	0.006–1.37	—	8.3	—	—	—

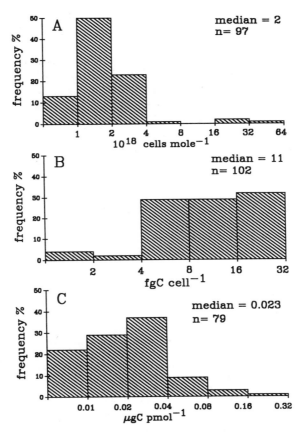

Figure 1. Frequency distributions for conversion factor values. (A) Thymidine to cell production conversion factor; (B) cell to carbon biomass factor; (C) combined thymidine to carbon biomass production factor (i.e., factor A times factor B).

data on biomass conversions are available. This has the effect of raising many of the production estimates by a factor of ca. 2. We find it ironic that so much attention has been focused on factors governing thymidine incorporation when choices about carbon conversion seem to be made almost arbitrarily.

In the following sections we discuss some aspects of bacterial production in the coastal and open ocean. Bacterial productivity in coral reefs has been reviewed elsewhere (Ducklow, 1990), and production in estuaries and marshes requires a separate review (Ducklow and Shiah, 1992).

2.2. Bacterial Production in Coastal and Shelf Regions

Most studies of bacterioplankton dynamics have been conducted in inner shelf regions in coastal waters (e.g., Ferguson and Rublee, 1976; Jacobsen *et al.*, 1983;

Pomeroy *et al.*, 1983; Lancelot and Billen, 1984; Billen and Fontigny, 1987), in or near estuarine plumes (Ducklow and Kirchman, 1983; Kirchman *et al.*, 1989b; Malone and Ducklow, 1990) or upwelling regimes (Hanson *et al.*, 1986a; McManus and Peterson, 1988). Bacterial dynamics associated with intrusions of nutrient-laden Gulf Stream water have also been studied (Pomeroy *et al.*, 1983). Ferguson and Palumbo (1979) and Ducklow and Kirchman (1983) observed offshore gradients in abundance along cross-shelf transects of the New York Bight, though in each case, midshelf surface maxima were observed. Although Malone and Ducklow (1990) reported instances where bacterial biomass equaled phytoplankton biomass, most of these observations are in line with the Cole *et al.* (1988) synthesis, showing that bacterial biomass was usually $< 20\%$ of phytoplankton biomass. Levels of bacterial abundance and activity are highest near the coast in low-salinity, high-nutrient waters, mostly as a consequence of estuarine output. Enhanced bacterial levels are also observed above intrusions of nutrient-rich water from offshore, probably as a response to increased production and grazing. The general implication of these studies is that nutrient inputs somehow lead to enhanced levels of bacterial abundance or activity, over and above the ambient levels of ca. $10^8 - 10^9$ cells liter^{-1} characteristic of midshelf waters. The mechanisms must involve trophic responses to increased primary production which has been stimulated by new nutrients (e.g., Billen and Fontigny, 1987). As Pomeroy *et al.* (1983, p. 18) stated in their discussion of Gulf Stream intrusions over the southeastern USA continental shelf,

> . . . the present data show that there is a major input of nitrate by intrusions, and that the input has a marked effect on phytoplankton on the outer continental shelf. . . . Over six years of observations we have repeatedly found heterotroph-dominated water above intrusions in an otherwise autotroph-dominated, oligotrophic outer shelf. The only biological indication at the water surface of the intrusion and its associated phytoplankton bloom is the increase in bacteria and their dominance of the biomass.

The work of Joint and Pomroy (1983, 1987) in the Celtic Sea provides a provocative example of bacterial production in coastal waters. In most studies, evidence has been presented for strong couplings between phytoplankton and bacteria, with bacterial production usually being a substantial fraction of the primary production. Joint and Pomroy (1983) were mainly concerned with estimating the amount of primary production by picoplankton < 1 μm in diameter, and correctly recognized that carbon flow from phytoplankton (of any size) to bacteria would appear in their estimates as picoplankton primary carbon fixation. They measured bacterial production independently with thymidine to correct their estimates, and found that bacterial production was ca. 1–17% of the picoplankton production, or just 0.2–6% of total primary production (Joint and Pomroy, 1987). Originally, Joint and Pomroy (1983) used very low conversion factors of 1.7×10^{18} cells mole^{-1} and 1.7 fgC cell^{-1}. Later, defending their approach, Joint and Pomroy (1987) showed that thymidine incorporation rates were never closely correlated with chlorophyll *a* or primary production and concluded that bacteria in the Celtic Sea were simply not well coupled with primary production processes. They used higher conversion factor values to illustrate the problem, but argued that CCF values of 20 fgC cell^{-1} were physiologically impossible. This critical approach should be followed by others. The question of whether the Celtic Sea is different from other coastal seas where bacterial–Chl correlations are better remains unanswered.

2.3. Bacterial Production in the Open Sea

2.3.1. Frontal Regimes

Although there has been little research conducted in the open sea, especially in oligotrophic areas, there have been a number of studies conducted in oceanic eddies and rings and near other frontal regions. Locally elevated abundances of bacteria have commonly been observed near fronts in coastal, shelf, and open ocean regions. The classic observations of Fischer (1894) showed that cultivable bacteria were numerous in "ocean streams" or at watermass boundaries. Floodgate *et al.* (1981), Holligan *et al.* (1984), and Lochte and Turley (1985) all found accumulations of bacteria in the tidal fronts in Liverpool Bay and the English Channel. Peele *et al.* (1984) and Ducklow (1986) found high levels of bacterial biomass near the frontal regions of warm-core Gulf Stream Rings, whereas Lochte and Pfannkuche (1987) found the highest levels in the center of a cold-core eddy near the Polar Front in the eastern North Atlantic. Hanson *et al.* (1986b) found no differences in bacterial abundance across a cold-core Gulf Stream Ring. Lochte and Pfannkuche (1987) attributed these differences to the "successional stages" of nutrient input and phytoplankton response observed in each location. In most of these studies, bacterial biomass and production were on the order of 20% of the respective phytoplankton parameters, as phytoplankton were stimulated by physically driven nutrient inputs (Nelson *et al.*, 1989). The few observations which have been made at the shelf-break front off the eastern USA coast show indications of cross-frontal gradients, with the higher levels on the shelf side (Ferguson and Palumbo, 1979; Ducklow and Kirchman, 1983). Analogous concentrations of microbial biomass and activity have been observed on density interfaces in the oceanic midwater column (Karl, 1982).

2.3.2. The Open Sea

Relatively few studies have been conducted in the open sea outside of eddies and away from frontal zones (one might wonder if this is really possible), with the notable exception of the many stations reported by Sorokin (reviewed in Sorokin, 1971, 1981) and Cho and Azam (1990). Here we address some of the more recent reports using similar techniques and conversion factors. The most interesting finding concerns the relative amounts of plankton biomass in the bacteria in oceanic waters. Whereas in nearshore waters bacterial biomass tends to make up < 20% of the phytoplankton biomass and the total POC (but see Malone and Ducklow, 1990), Fuhrman *et al.* (1989) made the surprising observation that bacterial biomass *dominated* the total plankton biomass off Bermuda. Bacterial biovolume exceeded the combined biovolume of the cyanobacteria, nanophytoplankton, and microflagellates at all depths from 0 to 150 m between July and November. Cho and Azam (1990) showed that bacterial carbon biomass exceeded phytoplankton carbon biomass (Chl $\times$ 50) by up to a factor of 8 in the North Pacific gyre when Chl was < ca. 0.3 μg liter^{-1}. These observations bear out predictions made from the Chl–bacteria regression calculated by Cole *et al.* (1988; Fig. 2A). Using a CCF value of 2×10^{-14} gC cell^{-1}, their regression implies that bacterial carbon will exceed phytoplankton when Chl < ca. 0.1–1, depending on the C : Chl ratio

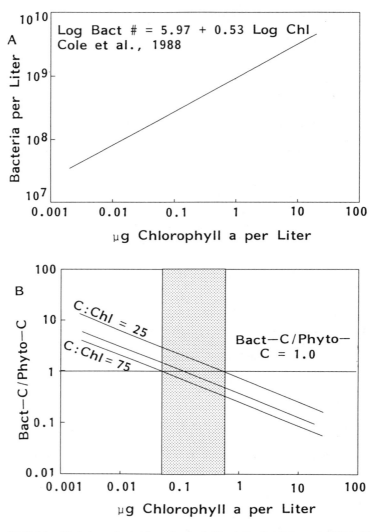

Figure 2. (A) Relationship between bacterial numbers and chlorphyll, after Cole *et al.* (1988). (B) ratio of bacterial to phytoplankton biomass assuming 20 fgC cell^{-1} and a range of carbon to chlorophyll ratios. The two biomasses are equal at Chl levels of ca. 0.1–1 μg Chl liter^{-1}.

(Fig. 2B). It is also interesting to note that the dynamic range of bacterial biomass is only about 10% of that for Chl (Cho and Azam, 1990).

Some other observations are summarized in Table IV. Warm Core Ring (WCR) 82H was a very large ring > 200 km in diameter which was sampled during its formation in September–October 1982. The center of this ring was unmodified Sargasso Sea water

Table IV. Some Recent Estimates of Bacterial and Phytoplankton Biomass (Ba-C and Ph-C; $mgC\ m^{-2}$) and Production (BP and PP; $mgC\ m^{-2}\ d^{-1}$) in the Oceanic Euphotic Zone

Region[a] and dates[b]	Ph-C	Ba-C	%[c]	PP	BP	%
WCR 82H 29/Sept	650	190	29	466	214	46
WCR 82H 01/Oct	1050	111	11	691	104	15
WCR 82H 03/Oct	—	—	—	315	101	32
WCR 82H 07/Oct	750	265	35	453	155	34
WCR 82H 12/Oct	700	351	50	572	54	09
WCR 82H 14/Oct	1750	424	24	443	—	—
Sargasso 08/87	360	1270	353	—	—	—
N. Pacific 05/88	1116	1108	99	529	65	12
N. Pacific 06/87	1575	1127	72	816	41	05
N. Pacific 08/88	1151	1132	98	544	62	11
N. Pacific 09/87	1252	1200	96	627	57	09
Indian ON	—	1274	>100?	413–533	493	92
Indian 8N	—	2099	>100?	236–364	150	42
Indian 14N	—	2566	>100?	421–511	160	30
Indian 21N	—	1692	>100?	449	133	30
Gulf of Oman	—	2485	>100?	726	308	42

[a]Sources: Warm Core Ring (WCR) 82H (39N, 65W), Ducklow (unpublished observations); N. Pacific (50N, 145W), Kirchman et al. (1992); Indian Ocean (on 67E), Ducklow (1992); Sargasso, Fuhrman et al. (1989).
[b]Day/month or month/year.
[c]% = percentage of phytoplankton levels.

(euphotic zone and nitracline > 80 m). Ducklow (1986) originally calculated bacterial biomass in WCR using a very conservative volume-dependent factor. The 82H data given in Table IV were recalculated using the 2×10^{-14} factor to facilitate comparison with the other reports. Euphotic zone Chl averaged just 0.2 µg liter^{-1} but bacterial abundance was very low, averaging only $0.5–2.5 \times 10^8$ cells liter^{-1}, so bacterial biomass was 11–50% of the phytoplankton. We observed the same relative pattern during a study in the eastern North Atlantic (47N, 20W) in May 1989, when bacterial abundance was $0.5-3 \times 10^9$ cells liter^{-1} but composed just 10–30% of the total POC in the spring bloom dominated by phytoplankton biomass (Ducklow *et al.*, 1992). Kirchman *et al.* (1992) observed that bacteria and phytoplankton biomass were equal during the spring–summer period in the North Pacific (Table IV). Ducklow (1992) observed very high bacterial biomass in the NW Arabian Sea. Pigment values would need to average 0.4–0.9 μg liter^{-1} (C:Chl = 50) to equal the bacterial biomass. This seems unlikely in this oligotrophic region. Ducklow (1992) suggested that the dominance of bacterioplankton on that cruise (September 86) may have been due to the decay of the phytoplankton bloom driven by the summer monsoon (Banse, 1987).

These observations, drawn from just a few reports, clearly indicate that bacterial biomass can exceed phytoplankton biomass. It is not yet possible to conclude that bacterial biomass dominates as a general rule in oceanic waters, except perhaps in the minimally seasonal and persistently oligotrophic waters studied by Cho and Azam (1990) and Sorokin (1971). Even there, such dominance is only possible as a steady condition when, as Fuhrman *et al.* (1989) point out, the bacterial turnover time is substantially longer than that of the phytoplankton, or when some sources of carbon not derived from photosynthesis and grazing on short time scales are available. The data shown in Table V support this view: when Bact-C/Phyto-C is high, Bact-T > Phyto-T and vice versa.

Except for the oligotrophic North Pacific gyre (Cho and Azam, 1990), all of these studies were carried out in markedly seasonal environments characterized by strong annual variations in primary production. As Fasham *et al.* (1990) showed for Bermuda,

Table V. Bacterial and Phytoplankton Turnover Times (T) in Oceanic Areas[a]

Region	Bact T days	Phyto T days	Bact biomass (% of Phyto)
WCR 82H 29/Sept	0.9	1.4	29
WCR 82H 1/Oct	1.1	1.5	11
WCR 82H 7/Oct	1.7	1.7	35
WCR 82H 12/Oct	6.5	1.2	50
WCR 82H 14/Oct	—	4.0	24
N. Pacific 05/88	17	2.1	99
N. Pacific 06/87	27	1.9	72
N. Pacific 08/88	18	2.1	98
N. Pacific 09/87	21	2.0	96
Indian ON	2.5	—	>100?
Indian 8N	14	—	>100?
Indian 14N	16	—	>100?
Indian 21N	12	—	>100?
Gulf of Oman	8	—	>100?

[a]Sources: Warm Core Ring 82H (39N, 65W), Ducklow (unpublished observations); N. Pacific (50N, 145 W), Kirchman *et al.* (1992); Indian ocean (on 67E), Ducklow (1992).

bacterial biomass can exceed phytoplankton biomass simply by utilizing the production of phytoplankton growth (particularly phytodetritus) with a delay of weeks to months. The excursions of the biomass ratio around 1.0 may be a feature of seasonally varying plankton systems (Malone and Ducklow, 1990). In the context of these speculations, the equatorial region presents an interesting stage for hypothesis testing: it is minimally seasonal like the oligotrophic gyres, but persistently nutrient-rich with high production, like the area studied by Kirchman *et al.* (1992). Both characteristics suggest that bacteria should be important agents of carbon cycling in equatorial waters.

2.3.3. Bacterial Production in Equatorial Waters

Sorokin has made numerous measurements of bacterial and primary production in tropical waters of the world ocean, including several stations at or near the equator. A north–south transect at 142E, 2–14N in the oligotrophic warm pool region consistently showed bacterial production about equal to primary production (Sorokin, 1973). These are among the stations from which Sorokin concluded that bacteria oxidized DOC upwelled from subsurface waters, a view criticized by Banse (1974). Equatorial stations farther east at 180 and ca. 160W had more conventional levels of bacterial production 20–30% of primary production in the surface, but integrated bacterial production in the euphotic zone was equal to primary production. Comparative biomass levels were not presented. It is hard to know how to regard these observations for Sorokin used the Romanenko "dark CO_2 fixation" method to measure bacterial production with a constant conversion factor of 5%, when in fact the ratio of CO_2 assimilation to biomass production varies and may at times be much less (e.g., Li, 1982). Ducklow (1992) observed high bacterial production equaling 92% of primary production at one station on the equator at 65W in the Indian Ocean (Table IV). Clearly more work on the role of bacterial production at the equator should be performed.

2.4. Global Bacterial Production

After more than a decade of research, there exist bacterial production estimates for a reasonably comprehensive selection of marine habitats (Table I). In a manner analogous to the many global estimates of primary production (Berger *et al.,* 1987), we use these data to derive an estimate of annual bacterial production in the euphotic zone (Table VI). The simple mean values for each habitat in Table I were used to derive annual areal estimates by assuming nominal euphotic zone depths and taking total global habitat areas from Walsh (1984). A few high values were excluded from the analysis, yielding similar ranges of integrated bacterial productivity (gC m^{-2} year^{-1}) in all habitats, with values for the open sea being slightly lower, as expected. The global totals are strongly influenced by the large oceanic area, so that 84% of the total bacterial production is oceanic. The total bacterial production is estimated to be 54–110% of the global primary production estimate. This is certainly too high unless much of the bacterial production is sustained by terrestrial inputs which are converted to biomass at high efficiency. Both possibilities seem unlikely.

Table VI. Global Estimates of Bacterioplankton Production in the Euphotic Zones of Major Marine Habitats[a]

System	AREA (10^{12} m²)	BACTPROD1 (mgC m^{-3} d^{-1})	DEPTH (m)	BACTPROD2 (gC m^{-2} y^{-1})	BACTPROD3 (gtC y^{-1})	PRIPROD1 (gtC y^{-1})	PRIPROD2 (gC m^{-2} y^{-})	BP/PP (%)
Marsh	0.35	97–116	5	177–212	0.1	0.49	172	13–15
Estuary	1.4	44–79	10	161–288	0.2–0.4	0.92	657	24–44
Coastal/shelf[b]	27	12–34	25	110–310	3–8.4	5.4	200	55–155
Reef	0.11	14–45	25	128–411	0.1–0.3	0.3	2727	5–15
Ocean[c]	290	4–11	50	73–201	21–58	38	131	56–153
So. ocean	44	2–4	50	37–73	1.6–3.2	4.2	95	38–76
Total/av					26–70	49.31	53–143	

[a]Habitat averages (BACTPROD1) from Table I. Global habitat area totals and mean primary production estimates (PRIPROD1) from Walsh (1984), Berger et al. (1987), and Martin et al. (1987). Nominal mean euphotic zone depths taken from the reports in Table I. BACTPROD2 = BACTPROD1 × DEPTH × 365 days. BACTPROD3 = BACTPROD2 × AREA. PRIPROD2 = PRIPROD1/AREA. BP/PP = 100 × BACTPROD3/PRIPROD1.

[b]Average BACTPROD1 does not include estimates of Torréton et al. (1989). Data pooled from plumes, coastal, upwelling, and shelf waters.

[c]Average does not include estimates of Sieburth et al. (1977).

Several factors might contribute to these high estimates. It seems improbable that high conversion factor values are the main culprit (Joint and Pomroy, 1987), because study-specific estimates of BP : PP are not similarly high (Table I). The main problem is that the open seas have been poorly studied and grossly undersampled. Most bacterial production work has been carried out in nutrient-enriched eddy systems, in summer when production is high, and away from the central gyres. These latter areas have low primary production but large area, so the BP : PP ratio reported here is derived from dissimilar data sets. Nonetheless, the two estimates are not greatly disparate. The ratio BP : PP is neither 1% nor 1000%, or even 5–500%, suggesting that the bacterial productivity data set cannot be grossly in error. A better integration, partitioning the studies between seasons, using correct euphotic zone depths and so on, may yield a better value. We should not discard the possibility that global BP : PP is high, but if it is, bacterial conversion efficiency must also be high, or unrecognized sources of organic matter must be available. These possibilities are addressed in a later section.

3. Regulation of Bacterioplankton Biomass and Production

With the veritable explosion of studies on bacterial trophodynamics in the 1980s (Table I), microbial ecologists have begun to mobilize the techniques and information needed to answer the question, "What controls bacterioplankton populations in the sea?" This of course is one aspect of the most fundamental question of ecology, which is "What factors control the abundance of individuals and species in nature?" Recently, several new concepts of population regulation have been introduced into plankton research. Below, we will introduce the concept of cascading trophic interactions and then review some of the observations supporting different mechanisms controlling bacterial populations in marine environments.

3.1. Trophic Control of Plankton Populations

There are two opposing views regarding most kinds of populations of organisms: (1) that they are controlled by the availability of resources for maintenance and growth requirements (e.g., Hairston *et al.*, 1960) or (2) that they are controlled by predation (e.g., Murdoch, 1966). For bacterial populations, the question is whether population size is limited by the fluxes of dissolved and particulate organic matter (or perhaps of dissolved inorganic nitrogen) or whether it is limited by bacteriovores and other loss mechanisms. Recent theoretical work has refined the debate regarding the relative importance of these opposing "bottom-up" or resource-limiting and "top-down" or predator-limiting regulatory mechanisms in plankton systems (Fig. 3 and Carpenter *et al.*, 1985). This theory states that maximum, or potential biomass of a given population is determined by resource availability (bottom-up control), but that the actual or realized biomass at any given time is set by consumers (top-down control). The strength of these controls are dependent on trophic level (McQueen *et al.*, 1986). That is, bottom-up controls are strongest and most predictable near the base of food webs, whereas near the top of food webs, the strength and predictability of bottom-up control by prey availabili-

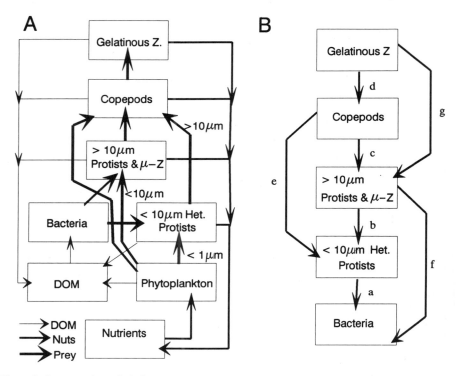

Figure 3. Representations of plankton community structure and elemental fluxes among the compartments, showing (A) bottom-up control or regulation of biomass by food supply; and (B) top-down control, or control by predation. B also shows the linearization of the food web and the "bypasses" which appear with increasing enrichment (Bjornsen *et al.*, 1988).

ty is replaced by top-down controls arising from predator pressure. Bottom-up control can be demonstrated by regressions of consumer biomass (dependent variable) on producer biomass (independent variable, McQueen *et al.*, 1986).

Some reflection on food-web structure suggests that the biomass at any given trophic level will not merely be dependent on the levels immediately above and below, but on more distant trophic levels as well. This gives rise to the concept of the "trophic cascade" (Carpenter *et al.*, 1985), which can work in two ways. The direct effects of increased resources at the base of the food web should propagate up the food web, though with decreasing impact at higher trophic levels. McQueen *et al.* (1986) showed that in a series of lake enclosures, a 10-fold increase in total phosphorus produced a similar increase in chlorophyll, but just a 4-fold increase in zooplankton biomass and a 1.5-fold increase in carnivore biomass. Top-down effects cascade in a different way: increases in a consumer population cause decreases in the prey population directly below, but increases in the prey at the next level down, and so on.

These concepts demonstrate that we need to view the bacteria in the context of the plankton community and consider the entire food-web structure, not just the immediate substrates or bacteriovores acting directly on the bacterioplankton.

3.2. Factors Controlling Bacterioplankton

The prediction of trophic cascade theory can be applied to bacterial observations. First, however, it is necessary to define the trophic level for bacteria. Bacteria generally might be considered at or near the base of most food webs because they utilize dissolved nutrients for growth. Because most of the resources available to bacteria are released by "higher" organisms, however, bacteria tend to be located beside, not in the main axis of food chain models (e.g., Scavia, 1988). Bacteria reside at trophic level 2 (directly above the producer level) following mathematical decomposition of food chain structure into simple Lindeman-type "spines" (Fig. 3; Ulanowicz, 1986; Ducklow *et al.*, 1989). Thus, one may predict that bacteria will be controlled more closely by resource availability than by predation, because they are closer to the base of planktonic food webs.

3.2.1. Control by Resource Supply

Testing the hypothesis that bacteria are controlled by resource availability is not straightforward because it is still not possible to determine the concentrations and fluxes of all of the resources bacteria are using in the environment. However, several investigators have examined the dependence of bacterial abundance and production on primary production and phytoplankton biomass, reasoning that resources for bacteria are ultimately derived from primary producers. This hypothesis will be most applicable to the open sea, remote from allochthonous supplies of organic matter, and less applicable in coastal and estuarine areas where terrestrial runoff and benthic fluxes may also support bacteria (Ducklow *et al.*, 1988). Another problem with this test of resource utilization is that bacteria may depend on limiting nutrients which are not direct products of primary producers. As Wheeler and Kirchman (1986), Goldman *et al.* (1987) and others have shown, ammonium, a product of grazers and perhaps also bacteria themselves (Tupas and Koike, 1990), can be limiting for bacteria in oceanic situations.

In spite of these pitfalls, many investigators have observed significant correlations between bacteria and Chl at a variety of scales (Ducklow, 1984) and concluded that bacterial biomass is regulated by primary producers. Fuhrman and Azam (1980) may have been the first to report such correlations, though a significant relationship is clearly suggested but not calculated in Hagstrom *et al.* (1979). Bird and Kalff (1984) presented some data on bacterial abundance–Chl regressions from marine samples. Cole *et al.* (1988) collected data from the literature and presented "global" regressions of both bacterial numbers and production on Chl, and of bacterial production on primary production. Information on published regressions is compiled in Table VII, and an example of these relationships is presented in Fig. 4. There is also considerable information from lakes (e.g., Bird and Kalff, 1984; Currie, 1990) which is beyond the scope of this review.

Bacterial abundance and, in some cases, bacterial production are statistically correlated with phytoplankton biomass (as Chl). Recognizing the caveats arising from the use

Table VII. "Bottom-Up" Regressions between Bacterial and Phytoplankton Parameters

Slope	Intcpt	r^2	n	Scale[a]	Reference
		1. Y = Bacterial abundance; X = Chlorophyll			
0.71	3.38	0.88, $p<0.001$	9	local	Linley et al. (1983)[c]
1.05	0.79	0.94, $p<0.001$	12	local	Linley et al. (1983)[d]
0.68	2.81	0.84, $p<0.01$	9	local	Linley et al. (1983)[e]
−0.32	3.03	0.10, ns	9	local	Linley et al. (1983)[f]
0.44	2.31	0.62, $p<0.001$	28	local	Linley et al. (1983)[g]
0.82	2.34	0.87, $p<0.001$	84	local	Linley et al. (1983)[h]
0.74	5.84[b]	0.79, $p<0.001$	19	local	Bird and Kalff (1984)
0.45	6.52[b]	0.91, $p<0.05$	160	week	Malone et al. (1986)[i]
0.23	6.64[b]	0.65, $p<0.05$	158	week	Malone et al. (1986)[j]
0.62	2.34	0.71, $p<0.05$	11	local	Hanson et al. (1986a)
0.53	2.81	0.60, $p<0.05$	15	local	Hanson et al. (1986a)
0.52	5.96[b]	0.75, $p<0.001$	35	global	Cole et al. (1988)
0.39	11.02	0.53, $p<0.001$	219	1983	Cota et al. (1990)
0.11	11.2	0.02, $p<0.05$	264	1986	Cota et al. (1990)
—	—	0.56, $p<0.001$	<39	region	Fuhrman et al. (1980)
—	—	0.12, $p<0.01$	59	season	Hobbie and Cole (1984)
—	—	0.85, —	—	local	Paul et al. (1985)
—	—	0.19, $p<0.001$	1188	season	Joint and Pomroy (1987)
—	—	0.49, $p<0.01$	35	annual	Paul et al. (1988)
—	—	0.35, $p<0.05$	36	local	Torréton et al. (1989)
—	—	0.74, $p<0.001$	36	local	Torréton et al. (1989)
—	—	−0.06, $p<0.01$	172	season	Rivkin et al. (1989)
—	—	0.52, $p<0.001$	228	season	Rivkin et al. (1989)
—	—	0.38, $p<0.05$	—	local	Sullivan et al. (1990)
—	—	−0.58, $p<0.05$	—	week	Jonas and Tuttle (1990)
—	—	0.10, ns	29	local	van Duyl et al. (1990)
		2. Y = Bacterial abundance, X = Primary production			
—	—	0.05–0.23, ns	—	region	Ducklow and Kirchman (1983)
—	—	0.11, ns	<39	region	Fuhrman et al. (1980)
—	—	0.50, $p<0.01$	35	annual	Paul et al. (1988)
—	—	0.26, $p<0.05$	—	local	Sullivan et al. (1990)
—	—	0.56, $p<0.01$	29	local	van Duyl et al. (1990)
		3. Y = Bacterial production, X = Chlorophyll			
—	—	0.74, $p<0.001$	<39	region	Fuhrman et al. (1980)
—	—	0.34–0.38, ns	—	region	Ducklow and Kirchman (1983)
—	—	0.11 ns?	—	local	Paul et al. (1985)
3.8	69	0.33, $p<0.1$	34	season	Hanson et al. (1986a)
16	15	0.70, $p<0.05$	9	local	Hanson et al. (1986a)
—	—	0.07, $p<0.001$	1188	season	Joint and Pomroy (1987)

Table VII. (*Continued*)

Slope	Intcpt	r^2	n	Scale[a]	Reference
—	—	—, $p<$???	—	region	Hanson *et al.* (1988)
—	—	0.43, $p<0.05$	35	annual	Paul *et al.* (1988)
—	—	0.37, $p<0.05$	—	local	Sullivan *et al.* (1990)
—	—	0.34, $p<0.10$	25	annual	Lignell (1990)

4. Y = Bacterial production, X = Primary production

Slope	Intcpt	r^2	n	Scale[a]	Reference
—	—	0.55, ns?	<39	region	Fuhrman *et al.* (1980)
4.0	64.4	0.65, $p<0.001$	36	season	Hanson *et al.* (1986a)
—	—	0.06, ns	126	season	Joint and Pomroy (1987)
0.07	0.07	0.72, $p<0.01$	26	season	Malone and Ducklow (1990)
0.37	−0.66	0.12, $p<0.01$	271	1983	Cota *et al.* (1990)
0.18	−0.43	0.03, $p<0.10$	133	1986	Cota *et al.* (1990)
—	—	0.44, $p<$?	—	local	Sullivan *et al.* (1990)
—	—	0.55, $p<0.01$	35	annual	Paul *et al.* (1988)
—	—	0.50, $p<0.01$	25	annual	Lignell (1990)

[a]Scale refers to the time and space domain of the observations.
[b]Log-transformed data.
[c]English Channel frontal station.
[d]So. Benguela upwelling, So. Africa.
[e]Celtic Sea.
[f]English Channel, mixed water column.
[g]English Channel, nearshore.
[h]All data, notes *c–g*.
[i]July–Aug.
[j]Sept.–Oct.

of Chl as an index of resource availability, the available relationships suggest that over 50% of the variability in bacterial abundance is usually explained by resource availability at local to annual scales. Where regression equations were supplied by the authors, the slopes were < 1, suggesting that bacterial responses to increased resource availability tend to be strongly attenuated, perhaps by top-down pressure.

Positive correlations between bacteria and Chl suggest that, if phytoplankton are also controlled by bottom-up forces, bacteria should respond to increases in phytoplankton nutrients (e.g., Model 1 of Currie, 1990). Hobbie and Cole (1984) demonstrated this effect by adding increasing amounts of nitrogen and phosphorus to a series of flow-through enclosures. Bacterial production was slightly better correlated with primary production ($r^2 = 0.89$) than with nutrient loading ($r^2 = 0.82$) over a 6-month study, suggesting an indirect response, modulated by the phytoplankton response. Bjornsen *et al.* (1988) also added nutrients (NO_3^- and PO_4) to estuarine microcosms and observed increases of bacterial biomass and production over levels in control enclosures.

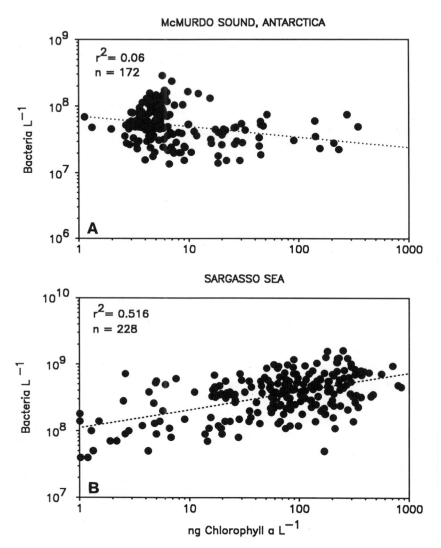

Figure 4. Bottom-up regressions of bacterial numbers on chlorophyll. In A, from McMurdo Sound, Antarctica, the negative relationship implies a lack of bottom-up control, whereas in B, from the Sargasso Sea, bacterial abundance may be regulated by the supply of organic matter indicated by chlorophyll stocks. (Data and figure courtesy of Richard Rivkin, Memorial University, Newfoundland.)

3.2.2. Control by Predation

There is abundant evidence to show that bacteriovores, the majority of which are heterotrophic microflagellates (Fenchel, 1984) and small ciliates (E. B. Sherr et al., 1986; Sherr and Sherr, 1987), are capable of ingesting large fractions of bacterial production over scales of hours to weeks (Ducklow and Hill, 1985a; Coffin and Sharp, 1987; Weisse, 1989; Wikner et al., 1990) although some reports also indicate that flagellate populations are not large enough to control bacteria in some places (e.g., McManus and Peterson, 1988). Rassoulzadegan and Sheldon (1986b, p. 1011) state that "nanoplankton populations seem to exert total control over the development of bacterial populations in the sea." If bacterial populations are controlled by top-down forces acting via bacteriovore ingestion, bacterioplankton abundance should be inversely correlated with bacteriovore abundance or biomass, according to trophic theory. In spite of the attention devoted to bacterivory in recent years, there have been remarkably few reports from which the top-down regressions of bacteria on bacteriovore abundance can be obtained (Table VIII). The data are inconclusive, but do not support strong top-down control. There is a single report of an inverse correlation from an enclosed laboratory tank experiment in which population parameters were followed in illuminated upwelled water over several weeks (Painting et al., 1989). Field data show direct relationships or no relationship at all. These observations suggest that the top-down control exerted by bacteriovores is usually obscured by bottom-up forcing of the bacteriovores by their bacterial prey. This conclusion is consistent with the predictions made by McQueen et al. (1986) that bottom-up controls predominate near the base of food webs.

3.2.3. Cascading Responses

If bacteria constitute an important food resource for protozoans, as the data in Table VIII suggest, and if bacteriovores are preyed upon by larger grazers, it should also be possible to look for indirect linkages in food webs. Since bacterial carbon does not

Table VIII. "Top-Down" Regressions of Bacterial Abundance (Y) on Microflagellate Abundance (X)

Slope	Intcpt	r^2	n	Scale[a]	Reference
0.49	0.84	0.35, $p<0.05$	15	regional	Linley et al. (1983)
−0.34	11.9	0.39, $p<0.05$	15	tank	Painting et al. (1989)
−0.13	1.94	0.08, ns	9	seasonal	B. F. Sherr et al. (1986)
0.36	0.87	0.01, ns	7	plume–Feb	McManus and Fuhrman (1988)
0.81	4.84	0.61, $p<0.01$	10	plume–Jun	McManus and Fuhrman (1988)
—	—	—, $p<0.001$	32	regional	Davis et al. (1985)
—	—	—, ns	160	seasonal	McManus and Fuhrman (1990)
—	—	0.51, $p<0.01$	29	local	van Duyl et al. (1990)
—	—	0.64, $p<0.01$	23	local	van Duyl et al. (1990)
—	—	0.05, ns	23	local	van Duyl et al. (1990)

appear to contribute significantly to zooplankton > 100 μm (Ducklow *et al.*, 1986; Hagstrom *et al.*, 1988; Pomeroy, 1990), positive regressions between bacterial abundance and zooplankton biomass cannot be interpreted simply as examples of bottom-up control by bacteria on large consumers. However, there is evidence to suggest that top-down control cascades from zooplankton to bacteria through the intermediate micro-zooplankton trophic levels. Rassoulzadegan and Sheldon (1986a) conducted a series of prescreening experiments to remove different-sized members from a ciliate–microflagel-late–bacteria food web. They suggested that removal of the > 10 μm size fraction released grazing pressure on bacteriovores and in turn retarded development of the bacteria. Roman *et al.* (1988) conducted tank experiments in which either phytoplankton (*Thalassiosira weissflogii*) or copepods (*Acartia tonsa*) or both were added to estuarine water containing natural populations of bacterioplankton and microflagellates. Bacterial abundance and production were greatest in tanks with copepod additions, in part because the copepods consumed microflagellates. The stimulatory effect on bacteria could also be a consequence of dissolved organic matter release by the copepods (Riemann *et al.*, 1986; Williams and Poulet, 1986) which complicates the interpretation of these cascading effects.

McManus and Fuhrman (1990) observed that heterotrophic microflagellate biomass was largest in the Chesapeake Plume relative to bacteria in winter, when copepod populations were lowest. In spring and summer, bacterial populations were an order of magnitude greater (Malone and Ducklow, 1990), in part because microflagellate populations had not grown (McManus and Fuhrman, 1990) and were not able to balance bacterial production. This effect was attributed to grazing pressure on the bacteriovores by copepods. Riemann *et al.* (1990), reporting on the same study as Bjornsen *et al.* (1988), showed that mussels (*Mytilus edulis*) added to estuarine enclosures effectively controlled zooplankton > 20 μm, which led to increases in heterotrophic nanoflagellates and corresponding decreases in bacterial biomass. These mesocosm studies suggest the functioning of top-down cascading responses affecting the dynamics and yields of bacterioplankton in estuarine waters, even though the evidence for direct top-down control is less clear. Perhaps the greatest value of such studies is that they afford insight into particular trophic linkages (pathways) and mechanisms of predator–prey interaction which place bacterioplankton squarely into generic trophodynamic models.

Another approach to the question of bacterial population regulation has been suggested by Billen *et al.* (1990). They noted the difficulty of testing the bottom-up hypothesis due to the analytical problem of specifying the stocks and fluxes of bacterial substrates. They assumed that at or near steady state, the substrate supply rate should be balanced by bacterial production. Accordingly, bacterial production rates could be used as proxies for substrate fluxes in a bottom-up regression of bacterial biomass on production. Data collated from measurements in a range of oligotrophic and eutrophic habitats showed a good correlation ($r^2 = 0.91$, $n = 288$) of bacterial biomass with production over 5 orders of magnitude. Billen *et al.* (1990) concluded from this analysis and a simple analytical model that bacterial biomass was more tightly controlled by resources than by predation in agreement with the studies cited above.

This is a powerful approach because the supporting data are available from so many previous studies (Table I) but there are some difficulties as well. Chief among these is the adequacy of the assumption that bacterial production balances the resource supply at scales other than the "global" scale invoked by Billen *et al.* (1990). It seems plausible that when ultraoligotrophic systems (the Parisian water supply) are compared with hypereutrophic regions like the Scheldt estuary, this assumption is a good one. But what about the smaller scales at which questions about control mechanisms are more meaningful?

A regression of bacterial biomass on production for pooled data from the mesohaline region of Chesapeake Bay collected during 1985–1989 (Fig. 5A) is significant ($r^2 = 0.47$, $n = 1228$, $p < 0.01$) and, following Billen *et al.* (1990), suggests that bacterial biomass is controlled by resource supply in Chesapeake Bay. The same data grouped according to water temperatures < 10, 10–20, and $> 20°C$, respectively, are presented in Fig. 5B–D. It is evident that the annual regression is forced by the extremes of the individual seasonal regressions. The relationships between bacterial biomass and pro-

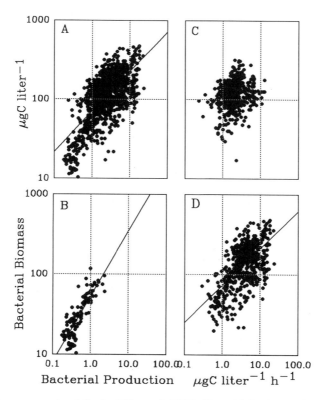

Figure 5. Bottom-up regressions following Billen *et al.* (1990) of bacterial abundance on bacterial production in Chesapeake Bay, 1985–1989. (A) All data. (B–D) Data from ambient water temperatures < 10, 10–20, and $> 20°$ C, respectively (Ducklow *et al.*, 1988, unpublished data).

duction (i.e., resources) are significant for temperatures < 10 and $> 20°C$, but in the intermediate range 10–20°C, there is no relationship (slope $= 0.16$, $r^2 = 0.06$, $n = 505$, $p > 0.05$). One interpretation of these relationships is that bacterial biomass in mid-Chesapeake Bay is regulated by bottom-up forces in winter, spring, and autumn, but that top-down forces are more important in summer. These observations also suggest that bacterial biomass is regulated by different factors at different times, and that the agents of control can be scale-dependent.

Most of the evidence used in support of the bottom-up and top-down hypotheses has been obtained from estuarine or coastal systems. There are few data to suggest the mechanisms or processes of population regulation in continental shelf, open ocean, and other marine habitats. The approach of Billen *et al.* (1990) should be extended to oceanic data sets. Additional experimental tests and field observations are needed to refine our understanding of resource supply and predation as controls on the bacteria. But most of all, better operational definitions and analytical methods for assessing bacteria resources are required for advancing our understanding by direct measurement of the fluxes. This topic is examined in the following section.

4. Resources for Bacterial Production

One of the most fundamental problems facing marine bacteriologists has been the difficulty in specifying the identity and fluxes of organic compounds to bacterioplankton. There is a large literature on uptake and metabolism of individual simple compounds like amino acids and monosaccharides determined by heterotrophic uptake assays of ^{14}C- and ^{3}H-labeled substrates (Joint and Morris, 1982; Wright, 1984). More recently, the isotope dilution methodology using high-specific-activity ^{3}H-labeled tracers has been applied to determine the rates of supply and uptake of individual amino acids simultaneously (Fuhrman, 1987, 1990). The main drawback of these techniques is that they only reveal the dynamics of the target compounds, not the complete array of substrates actually being used at any given moment. Lee and Wakeham (1988) state that it is now possible to identify hundreds of thousands of compounds in the environment. One attraction of the various methods for estimating bacterial production is that the resulting data provide an integration of the total utilization of various substrates, even as these change in time and space. Heterotrophic uptake and other assays provide selective, exact information of bacterioplankton metabolism of individual, defined compounds. Bacterial production assays give a better estimate of the output resulting from metabolism of undefined substrates. These approaches are complementary and both are required to provide a complete view allowing some attempts at budgeting of C and N flows. But better descriptions of the sources supporting bacterial production are still needed.

Over the past five years or so, our vista of the nature of the carbon and nitrogen pools available to bacterioplankton has widened considerably. Results from organic chemistry, animal physiology, particle studies, new instrumentation, and modeling have all revealed new, and in some cases unexpected, sources of nutrition for bacteria.

Addressing these new substrate pools represents a challenge to marine ecologists and microbiologists to develop new approaches and ask new questions in future studies.

As usual in the history of science, most of the new observations about bacterial substrates have their roots in previous studies. For example, Sorokin (1971 and other citations reviewed in Sorokin, 1981) observed that bacterial production was in excess of observed primary production in many areas of the tropical ocean euphotic zone. He postulated that the excess bacterial production was supported by allochthonous dissolved organic carbon (DOC) supplied by upwelling and horizontal advection into warm surface waters. Thus, bacterial oxidation in surface waters was seen as the major sink for oceanic DOC. Banse (1974) reviewed data on hydrography and DOC distribution in the tropics to refute this hypothesis and concluded that Sorokin's estimates of bacterial production were an order of magnitude too high. But Banse also stated that it was not possible with the extant data to choose between the deep sea and warm surface waters as the major potential sinks for deep-water DOC.

This controversy was revisited by Sieburth et al. (1977), who again observed very high bacterial production and also high rates of DOC release in oceanic waters. Sieburth (1977) argued from these and other observations not that allochthonous sources of DOC were required, but instead that conventional estimates of primary production were too low. At about the same time, Sieburth (1976) called attention to the great diversity of sources, types, and sizes of POC in the ocean. He argued that much of the oceanic POC and DOC arose from ingestion and defecation by the myriad members of oceanic food webs, and implicated these "fecal–sestonic ecosystems" as sources of bacterial production. Sorokin and Sieburth's results, together with other observations, resulted in reconsideration of techniques and concepts of primary and bacterial production. After a further decade of observations with increasingly sophisticated approaches, some of the earlier questions remain unanswered, and new ones have been posed.

4.1. Dissolved Organic Matter (DOM)

4.1.1. Sources of DOM and NH_4^+

In estuaries and in the coastal zone, some DOM may be of terrestrial or benthic origin. For example, kelps and other seaweeds apparently release large amounts of polysaccharides, sugars, and sugar alcohols which support high bacterial production and associated protozoan grazers (Laycock, 1974; Lucas et al., 1981; Koop et al., 1982). The high C:N ratios of such material (Newell and Field, 1983) probably necessitate supplements of NH_4^+ for complete utilization. In estuaries and salt marshes, bacterial production may be a large proportion of phytoplankton production (Ducklow et al., 1988), implying allochthonous DOM sources. Coffin et al. (1989, 1990) addressed this issue by determining the natural abundance of stable carbon isotopes of the cellular contents and extracted nucleic acids of bacterioplankton concentrated from estuarine sites or grown in filtered estuarine water. Like other organisms, bacteria have $\delta^{13}C$ values similar to their food. The bacteria have ^{13}C abundances ranging from -31.9 to -20.5 (-27.9 to -20.2 in extracted nucleic acids), indicating that a diversity of carbon sources were assimilated. In general, the $\delta^{13}C$ values were quite similar to phytoplankton (-16.6 to -21) at some stations and higher at others. High values are consistent with utilization of leachates from *Spartina* and other grasses in addition to phytoplankton. This approach shows great potential for resolving the paradox of high bacterial production in near-shore areas.

   4.1.1a. Phytoplankton Exudation. Outside the immediate coastal zone, most DOM for bacterial utilization probably originates from primary production by phytoplankton and this is increasingly true with distance from shore. The relative importance of direct exudation of DOC and dissolved organic nitrogen (DON) from phytoplankton versus excretion from animals and leaching particles is debatable. There is a large and still growing literature on release of photosynthate from phytoplankton (Sharp, 1984; Lancelot and Billen, 1985) and we will not review the subject extensively here. However, several aspects should be emphasized. The most important point is that direct release is probably low ($\leq 10\%$ of gross photosynthesis; Sharp, 1984), except in special circumstances. For example, during the decline of *Phaeocystis* and other phytoplankton blooms, large amounts of carbohydrate can be released (Lancelot and Mathot, 1987). Observations of bacterial production greater than about 20% of the primary production (Table I) demand other DOM sources if conversion efficiencies are much lower than 50%. Most estimates of "phytoplankton exudation" are derived from some combination of size fractionation and incubation in light and dark to discriminate between total release and bacterial uptake, which occur simultaneously (e.g., Derenbach and Williams, 1974; Ward, 1984). Size fractionation, whether pre- or postincubation, has its own pitfalls, and the results of attempts to separate autotrophic and heterotrophic activity are usually ambiguous owing to the overlap in sizes among heterotrophic and cyanobacteria and small grazers (Li and Dickie, 1985, 1991). As Jumars *et al.* (1989) caution, most of these experiments fail to distinguish between DOM release directly from the phytoplankton and release from, or enhanced by, grazers. Even when samples for phytoplankton release experiments are prescreened to remove copepods and other large herbivores, most of the microzooplankton are still present. Removal of mesozooplankton may in fact stimulate microzooplankton activity, including DOC production. Thus, in most cases observations from incubation studies are overestimates of direct release, at least if tracer kinetic criteria have been satisfied (Lancelot, 1979; King and Berman, 1984; Smith, 1982; Marra *et al.*, 1981). Another major shortcoming is the great difficulty in estimating losses of DON, although a promising method has recently been introduced (Bronk and Glibert, 1991).

   Bratbak and Thingstad (1985) and Jumars *et al.* (1989) argued that because bacteria compete with phytoplankton for NH_4^+, DOC release by phytoplankton encourages competition and is evolutionarily unlikely to be large. Bjornsen (1988) stressed that release of DOM from healthy phytoplankton is almost always regarded to be an active physiological process, rather than passive exudation by molecular diffusion across cell membranes. If the passive exudation or "property tax" model of DOM release is adopted, the Bratbak and Thingstad paradox can be resolved. These various arguments suggest that direct release of DOM from phytoplankton has only limited potential for supporting high bacterial production.

4.1.1b. Release by Zooplankton. Zooplankton excrete DOM and also spill it from phytoplankton during "sloppy feeding." The later process arises during processing of large cells which cannot be ingested whole and are broken during handling (Lampert, 1978). Zooplankton excrete principally NH_4^+ and urea (which behaves more like inorganic nitrogen in that it cannot serve as a carbon or nitrogen source for bacteria; Goldman *et al.*, 1987). Amino acid excretion amounts to about 25% of the total dissolved N losses (Corner and Newell, 1967; Small *et al.*, 1983). These early results may be overestimates owing to the inadequacy of the analytical methods used, and to contamination. Copping and Lorenzen (1980) fed ^{14}C-labeled diatom cells to copepods and constructed carbon budgets for assimilation, egestion (POC), respiration (DIC), and excretion (DOC). They found that 27% of the carbon appeared as DOC, which was about twice as great as the rate of production from phytoplankton in the absence of grazers. It was not possible from their experimental design to partition the DOC losses into excretion and sloppy feeding. The low amount of label appearing in fecal pellets during long (50 hr) incubations was inconclusive as much C in the pellets may have diffused away or decomposed. Eppley *et al.* (1981) conducted similar experiments with added grazers and found similarly inconclusive results. Roy *et al.* (1989) observed that 26–35% of cellular Chl was lost to the dissolved phase passing GFF filters during feeding by copepods on large diatoms. This implied similar losses of DOC from broken cells, but no changes in dissolved free amino acids (DFAA) were observed, perhaps because of rapid bacterial uptake. These studies all indicate that DOC release from larger phytoplankton cells appears to be greater in the presence of grazers than in its absence but it still is not possible to construct budgets which differentiate among the separate mechanisms of DOC production by mesozooplankton.

Experimental observations of DOM release by microzooplankton (principally heterotrophic nanoflagellates) have been reviewed by Nagata and Kirchman (1992). Taylor *et al.* (1985) observed that individual ciliate species feeding on bacteria released 3–9% of ingested carbon as DOC, but also found that mixed assemblages released 20–88% of ingested C as DOC. The flagellate *Paraphysomonas imperforata* released 10% of ingestion as DOC when feeding on diatoms (Caron *et al.*, 1985) and 1–22% as dissolved combined amino acids (DCAA) and DFAA when feeding on bacteria (Nagata and Kirchman, in press). Andersson *et al.* (1985) found that *Ochromonas* sp. released 7% of ingestion as DFAA during bacterivory. Nagata and Kirchman (1992) established that DOC release was a function of ingestion rate, with highest release rates accompanying high ingestion rates. This is consistent with digestion theory (Jumars *et al.*, 1989) which holds that at higher ingestion rates digestion is incomplete and inefficient, leading to egestion of food particles, vacuoles, enzymes, etc., and subsequent leaching of DOM from the egesta.

The role of zooplankton supplying NH_4^+ and DOM at depth during vertical migration has been explored by Longhurst and Harrison (1988). Banse (1990) suggested that DOM supply from migratory animals might be as important a source for growing bacteria at depths below 100 m as the decay of sedimenting particles.

It would appear from these data that 25% of ingestion of mesozooplankton and protozoans is an upper limit on zooplankton DOM release, except during exceptional circumstances. Assuming then that phytoplankton release 10% of production directly and that 100% of primary production is grazed each day by zooplankton, we conclude that total DOC release from the living parts of the food web cannot routinely be much more than 35% of primary production, based on herbivory alone. Assuming further, and charitably, that oceanic bacteria are 40% efficient at converting released DOC to biomass, we estimate that bacterial production can be a maximum of 15% of primary production if it is supported by phytoplankton release during herbivory alone. DOM release during carnivory and detritivory has not been considered. Additional sources of DOM must arise from detrital particles including fecal pellets or via recycling of plant, bacterial, and animal biomass, which magnifies the utilization of phytoplankton carbon (Scavia, 1988).

4.1.2. DOC

Owing to a lack of convergence of analytical methods, there has long been controversy over the exact values of DOC concentrations even in deep ocean water where the values are stable on time scales of centuries (Mopper and Degens, 1979). Yet in spite of at least a three- to fourfold uncertainty, it has also been recognized that the oceanic DOC pool constitutes one of the largest reservoirs of freely exchangeable carbon on the planet. This argument, which excludes from consideration the carbon locked in deep sedimentary deposits (Moore and Bolin, 1986), recognizes that the processes responsible for storage of CO_2 and DOC in the deep sea also regulate the levels of CO_2 in the atmosphere, and help to determine the earth's climate. Thus, an understanding of the microbiological stability of DOC, the factors governing its conversion to CO_2, and the major site(s) of DOC oxidation are necessary for better prediction of global climate change.

Sugimura and Suzuki (1988) introduced a new high-temperature, catalytic oxidation (HTCO) method for analysis of oceanic DOC by direct injection aboard ship. They showed the DOC values in surface Pacific seawater analyzed by HTCO ranged from 200 to 400 μM, or over twice as high as values from the persulfate and other methods. The new technique also revealed unanticipated structure in depth profiles previously characterized as vertically homogeneous by earlier analyses. The new data appear to be oceanographically consistent in that HTCO-determined DOC is inversely correlated with a slope of -0.9 with the apparent oxygen utilization (AOU), an oceanographic index of the net biological utilization. This relationship, which has been observed only with HTCO instruments, suggests that DOC oxidation is the major source of respiration in the deep ocean. Since previous studies of oceanic respiration showed that the majority of oxygen utilization is by organisms passing 0.8-μm filters (i.e., bacteria and small flagellates; Pomeroy and Johannes, 1966), it follows from Sugimura and Suzuki's (1988) observations that bacterial DOC oxidation in the main thermocline and deepwater is the principal sink for oxygen, rather than, say, particle decomposition. However, Toggweiler (1989) points out a fallacy in this argument related to oceanic mixing and concludes that we cannot yet partition oxygen utilization between DOC and POC oxidation.

The new DOC techniques have also suggested that the majority of the excess DOC in surface waters not revealed by earlier methods is in molecules with molecular weights above 10,000. Thus, much of the "new" DOC concentrated in the upper ocean appears to be high-molecular-weight, possibly proteinaceous material resistant to chemical oxidation but somewhat more vulnerable to bacterial attack than DOC measured by older methods (Druffel and Williams, 1990). The sources of the oceanic DOC are unclear, though Duursma (1961) observed that plankton cycling in the North Atlantic appeared to be responsible for changing DOC concentrations nearly twofold, and Williams (1981) concluded that the major fate of primary production was the DOC pool. The classical view is that DOC from surface waters can be slowly oxidized by bacteria down to some more resistant "background" level (Barber, 1967), but that the major DOC compounds fueling bacterial metabolism are more labile compounds like amino acids maintained at nanomolar levels by rapid uptake of bacteria closely coupled to sources such as excreting phytoplankton (Billen, 1984; Fuhrman, 1987). In this model, most of the DOC cycling is accomplished via the turnover of just a small portion of the large DOC pool, while the rest of the pool remains static on the time scales of hours to weeks observed by most experimental biologists. Application of the Suzuki method has recently suggested that this view may not be entirely correct.

Kirchman *et al.* (1991) incubated 0.8-μm filtrates of North Atlantic seawater in the dark and observed the decline of DOC and concomitant increase in bacterial numbers (Fig. 6). One would predict from the "small-molecular DOC cycling model" just described that the concentrations of DOC measured over a few days would have changed

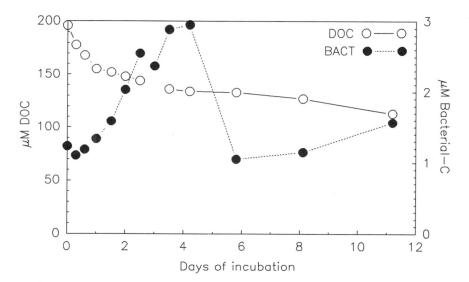

Figure 6. Bacterial growth and DOC consumption in North Atlantic surface seawater (0.8-μm filtrates incubated in the dark). These observations imply that DOC is turned over by bacterial metabolism at rates of ca. 0.05 day^{-1} and converted to biomass with an efficiency of ca. 2–9%. (Figure after Kirchman *et al.*, 1991).

by perhaps a few percent at most. The observations showed to the contrary that the DOC fell by ca. 50 μM in 2 days, while bacterial biomass tripled. The ca. 25% of the DOC which disappeared is roughly similar to the high-molecular-weight DOC fraction measured by HTCO. Kirchman *et al.* (1991) suggested that some substantial fraction of the upper ocean DOC has potential turnover times of 0.01–0.2 per day, and further speculated that bacteriovore grazing regulated the extent of DOC removal, by cropping bacteria and regenerating DOC. DOC concentrations varied by several tens of μM in surface seawater during the 1989 JGOFS North Atlantic Bloom Experiment in the northeast Atlantic Ocean, lending additional support to this claim that the "new" DOC in the surface ocean provides a relatively labile source of carbon for bacterioplankton.

These observations suggest an alternative model for DOC cycling in the upper ocean. In this model, much more of the large DOC pool appears to be available for bacterial utilization on short time scales than previously imagined. The excess DOC revealed by the HTCO technique may serve as a reservoir of carbon which bacteria can switch to and utilize at low efficiency under certain circumstances. Periodic bursts of DOC utilization may provide one explanation for occasional observations of bacterial production greater than can be explained by conventional trophic exchange models. However, a more disturbing possibility also exists: does enclosure or filtration somehow "turn on" DOC utilization? While the experimental observations are consistent with observed short-term variations in DOC levels, more work is needed to define this phenomenon.

4.1.3. Dissolved Organic and Inorganic Nitrogen

4.1.3a. Amino Acid and Ammonium Uptake.   Bacteria have $C:N$ biomass ratios of about 4 (Nagata, 1986; Goldman *et al.*, 1987; Lee and Fuhrman, 1987) and are enriched in nitrogen relative to phytoplankton and probably to the bulk DOM. Combined with observations that bacterioplankton process a large fraction of primary production (Tables I and VI; Cole *et al.*, 1988), these facts indicate that bacterioplankton must have a large impact on the nitrogen cycle in planktonic systems. It is well established that bacterial cultures can utilize ammonium and a wide array of nitrogenous organic compounds (DON) for biosynthesis and growth. However, it was generally believed that most of the production by natural bacterial assemblages was supported by DON rather than NH_4^+ uptake, and that NH_4^+ uptake was dominated by phytoplankton (Billen, 1984). Furthermore, it has been concluded that DFAA, which are a small portion of the DON pool, can support 50–100% of the bacterial production (Fuhrman, 1987, 1990; Billen and Fontigny, 1987). New research has shown conclusively that NH_4^+ also constitutes an important source of N for bacterial growth, and that bacteria are efficient competitors with phytoplankton for NH_4^+. This represents one of the most important developments contributing to a new concept of bacterial processes in plankton trophodynamics.

Eppley *et al.* (1977) observed high rates of NH_4^+ uptake relative to ^{14}C uptake in the central North Pacific and concluded from this indirect evidence that bacterioplankton took up the "extra" NH_4^+. Later, Laws *et al.* (1985) provided additional indirect evidence that bacterial NH_4^+ assimilation was important relative to the photosynthetic demand. Hagstrom et al. (1984) observed in seawater cultures with minimal contamination by phytoplankton that total amino acids (dissolved free and combined) supplied only a small percentage of the bacterial N demand and suggested that NH_4^+ supplied the major share of N for the exponentially growing cells in chemostat culture. However, it was Wheeler and Kirchman (1986) who provided the first direct evidence for bacterial NH_4^+ assimilation. They used size fractionation, specific inhibitors, and ^{15}N tracers to show that over 70% of the NH_4^+ assimilation was by bacteria, and that NH_4^+ supplied at least 20–60% of the total bacterial N demand. Fuhrman et al. (1988) corroborated these observations using radioactive ^{13}N as a tracer of ammonium uptake into the 0.2 to 0.6-μm size fraction. Suttle et al. (1990a) have used the ^{13}N approach to show that the bacteria have a greater affinity than phytoplankton for NH_4^+, allowing them to outcompete the phytoplankton at low NH_4^+ concentrations. Tupas and Koike (1990) observed that NH_4^+ satisfied 50–88% of the total N demand of bacterioplankton utilizing mussel exudate even with copious amounts of DON present. As a result of these direct observations, the view that dissolved organic N, principally free and combined amino acids satisfy the bacterial N demand can no longer be accepted without strong evidence.

Data on N utilization where sufficient independent measurements nave been made to allow estimates of the importance of bacterial NH_4^+ assimilation are presented in Table IX. These observations are complicated by several important factors, including the presence of intact autotrophs in < 1-μm filtrates, nonspecificity of metabolic inhibitors, inefficient retention of bacteria on the GFF filters required for ^{15}N analysis, uncertain conversion factors, and so forth. Billen and Fontigny (1987) and Coffin (1989) estimated total bacterial demand for N from bacterial production measurements and compared the results to direct measurements of free and combined amino acid uptake. In the

**Table IX. Ammonium Assimilation by Bacteria
and Phytoplankton[a]**

Region	%NH_4^+ uptake		%Bact N demand		Reference
	Phyto	Bact	DON	NH_4^+	
Scripps Pier, CA	—	—	5–21	79–95[b]	Hagstrom et al. (1984)
Sapelo Is., GA	22	78	73	27	Wheeler and Kirchman (1986)
Belgian coastal	—	—	100	—	Billen and Fontigny (1987)
Long Is., USA	70	30	88	12	Fuhrman et al. (1988)
Delaware Bay	—	—	100	02	Coffin (1989)
North Pacific	50	50	25	75	Kirchman et al. (1989a)
North Pacific[c]	—	—	33	62	Keil and Kirchman (1991)
Chesapeake Plume	—	—	44–131	0–565[d]	Fuhrman (1990)

[a]Bacterial uptake estimated from < 1-μm filtrates where < 10% of chlorophyll and > 90% of bacteria are in that fraction.

[b,d]Relative NH_4^+ uptake estimated from DFAA uptake and bacterial production estimates.

[c]Estimates after 36–117 hr incubation.

[d]Glutamic acid, serine, glycine, and alanine uptake only.

estuarine or coastal waters studied, there appeared to be sufficient supplies of organic N as amino acids to satisfy the bacterial N requirement. Fuhrman *et al.* (1988) compared the N requirements from production measurements to NH_4^+ uptake and estimated that in coastal Long Island Sound amino acids and other DON nearly satisfied the total N requirement. The direct measurements by Wheeler and Kirchman (1986) showed that amino acids were 73% of the total N uptake by bacteria. In contrast, Hagstrom *et al.* (1984), using an approach analogous to Coffin (1989), estimated that amino acids contributed only 5–20% of the N demand for samples from Scripps Pier, a near-oceanic water mass in the coastal zone. Finally, Kirchman *et al.* (1989a) made extensive direct measurements of both amino acid and NH_4^+ uptake in the cold (7–12°C) surface waters of the subarctic North Pacific, where NO_3^- ranges from 6 to 17 µg-at liter^{-1} year-round and where NH_4^+ values vary from 0 to 0.4 µg-at liter^{-1}. They found that the bacterial demand for N is met primarily by NH_4^+ uptake. A similar NH_4^+ requirement has also been estimated for the eastern North Atlantic during the height of the spring bloom (Kirchman and Ducklow, unpublished data).

These few observations suggest that in rich coastal waters, rapidly growing bacteria might be sustained by amino acids and other DON, whereas in more oceanic (though also nitrate-rich) regimes, NH_4^+ supplies much of the N ration. The reasons for this are unknown, but the lower fluxes and concentrations of amino acids in oceanic waters with lower plankton biomass and primary production may limit the potential for DFAA to support the bacterial demand. The importance of bacterial competition with phytoplankton for NH_4^+ may be profound. Kirchman *et al.* (1992) noted that phytoplankton might bloom if they were to outcompete bacteria for NH_4^+ in the subarctic Pacific, a region where blooms appear never to occur.

4.1.3b. Growth Limitation. The foregoing discussion of the factors governing the relative importance of DON and NH_4^+ in supporting bacterial growth raises the question of what limits bacterial activity in the sea. The identity of limiting factors for bacterioplankton growth in the classical Liebig sense, however, has not been studied very much. The dependence of bacterial production rates on phytoplankton biomass and/or production (Table VII) suggests that the supply of organic matter ultimately limits the rate of bacterial production. The low and surprisingly invariant C : N ratio of bacterial biomass (Goldman *et al.*, 1987) argues that nitrogen, not carbon, is the limiting factor.

The identity of growth-limiting nutrients has been approached by making additions of DOC, DON, and NH_4^+ to natural assemblages and observing the effect on changes in cell numbers or other measurements reflecting growth rates. In this regard, it is important to distinguish between the specific, or per capita [μ or $(1/N)(dN/dt)$] and population growth rates (dN/dt). Some treatments may change the balance between growth and removal leading to increased cell yields without actually modifying the growth rate. Sieracki and Sieburth (1985) made additions of the polysaccharide laminarin to seawater cultures and observed enhanced growth rates and accumulation only in the absence of bacteriovores. Kirchman (1990) conducted similar experiments in the subarctic North Pacific, adding glucose, glucose plus NH_4^+, amino acids, or NH_4^+ alone to seawater and assaying thymidine and leucine incorporation periodically over 1–6 days. Glucose alone stimulated thymidine incorporation rates by 5–20% above controls in three of six experiments. Amino acid addition resulted in stimulation by 31–78% in six of six experiments suggesting that organic nitrogen was limiting, whereas addition of glucose and NH_4^+ together caused just 3–20% increases of thymidine incorporation rates in six of six experiments. In other experiments, addition of NH_4^+ alone did not stimulate production rates. Kirchman concluded that bacterial *growth* was neither strictly C- nor N-limited since neither glucose nor NH_4^+ consistently stimulated thymidine incorporation. The consistent stimulatory effect of amino acids suggested that bacterial growth was energy-limited, because amino acid use in preference to NH_4^+ is energetically less expensive for the cells.

There are several problems in interpreting these experiments. If cell numbers increase over time, it is necessary to examine the specific rate of thymidine incorporation (incorporation normalized to cell numbers). Kirchman (1990) did not present these data, and it is apparent from his graphs that in some cases the increases in thymidine incorporation were reflections of the population, not the specific growth rate (see his Fig. 2). In other experiments, however, the thymidine rate clearly increased while abundance remained stable. Earlier, Ducklow and Hill (1985b) showed that thymidine incorporation increased much more rapidly than cell numbers, i.e., specific growth rates increased, in dilution cultures of Sargasso Sea water, to which no additions had been made. Kirchman (1990) noted another difficulty with such incubation experiments: often the stimulatory effect was not seen before ca. 0.5–2 days of incubation. This lag was attributed to the shift-up phenomenon whereby growth cannot increase until after some period of physiological adaptation in response to nutrient addition. But he noted that the lag period was short compared to the generation time of the cells (ca. 1 versus 10 days). Still, this leaves the question of what factors were limiting the growth rate prior to sampling somewhat uncertain.

4.2. Particulate Organic Matter

Particulate matter exists in a continuum of sizes in the ocean ranging from whales down to submicron colloids which blur the distinction between particulate and dissolved material (Wangersky, 1984). We capture and study the particle spectrum with varying success: the smallest particles escape most filters while those larger than a few tens to hundreds of microns cannot be sampled representatively in bottles because they are scarce. Particles larger than about 100 μm in diameter are transported rapidly through the water column by gravitational settling and are most conveniently captured for examination and experiments in sediment traps deployed in the ocean for periods of hours to weeks (Lee and Wakeham, 1988). Most of our knowledge about the suspended and settling particle populations come from bottle or trap samples, and the sampling artifacts arising from these methods need to be understood better to interpret the observations reviewed here.

There is potentially a large stock of detrital material available for bacterial utilization. It was once believed that most of the marine primary production was consumed by grazers, in contrast to terrestrial ecosystems in which dead plant biomass is channeled instead through detrital food chains. Today most oceanographers believe that in the coastal ocean and over large expanses of the open sea, perhaps half of the phytoplankton production escapes grazing, dies, and/or sinks to the bottom (Malone and Chervin, 1979; Walsh, 1983; Billet et al., 1983; Smetacek, 1985). There is increasing understanding of the biogeochemical significance of this material on a global scale (Lal, 1977; Watson and Whitfield, 1985). Some of this material is transported so swiftly through the water column that it arrives at the seafloor over 4 km below nearly unaltered in composition and form, and carrying intact photoautotrophs (Lampitt, 1985; Lochte and Turley, 1988). During its accumulation in the euphotic zone and its descent through the upper water column, these particles are vulnerable to leaching and microbial attack so there is a race between gravitational sedimentation and decomposition which determines the fate of each kind of particle (Pomeroy, 1984; Banse, 1990). There are three general processes which befall uningested phytoplankton: they may be ingested, or they die and decompose, or they can be scavenged onto larger particles by aggregation. If they are ingested, following some spillage of DOC they will be partly digested and repackaged in fecal matter. The significance of these processes is discussed in turn below.

4.2.1. Phytoplankton Mortality and Decomposition

Walsh (1983) reviewed the fate of phytoplankton in a monograph entitled "Death in the Sea," but left open the question as to whether phytoplankton undergo physiological death in the absence of grazer or microbial attack. Recently, viruses have been implicated as agents of phytoplankton mortality (Suttle et al., 1990b; Bratbak et al., 1990). There have been a number of studies in which phytoplankton have been incubated in nutrient-depleted medium in the dark to follow decomposition. In many cases, cells are killed by heat or freezing prior to incubation, making moot the question of the onset of mortality. Earlier work reviewed by Billen (1984) suggests first-order rate constants of $0.04-0.1$ day^{-1} for the entire cellular content of PON and DON, and 0.005 day^{-1} for the refractory fraction comprising 33% of cellular N. Fukami et al. (1985) observed rapid loss of cellular POC in the initial stages of decay of Skeletonema costatum, which slowed after 1–3 days. Pett (1989) took a more kinetic approach in following the disappearance of ^{14}C-labeled POC and DOC from unkilled S. costatum. He identified four successively more refractory fractions of the phytoplankton. A labile fraction comprising 14% of the biomass was consumed in 0.6 day. This part is the material which would support bacterial production in the euphotic zone prior to export via sinking. Other fractions making up 54, 29, and 4% of the cell mass decayed over time scales of days to weeks, months, and years, respectively. Depending on the sinking rate, the ca. 50% of the diatom biomass which decays at ca. 0.08 day^{-1} might be expected to fuel bacterial production in the midwater column below the upper 100 m, while the remaining 30–35% of the biomass is stable over longer periods, and probably contributes to the DOC pool (Williams, 1981).

4.2.2. Fecal Pellet Decomposition and Export

Fecal pellets from copepods and larger zooplankton were once thought to make up the bulk of the vertical flux of particles into the deep sea, but as more sediment trap and pump samples are examined it has become clear that the composition of the vertical flux varies in time and space, being dominated in different seasons and regions by ungrazed phytoplankton cells, organic aggregates and marine snow, or pellets (Bishop *et al.*, 1980; Urrere and Knauer, 1981; Pilskaln and Honjo, 1987; Nothig and von Bodungen, 1989). Suess (1980) and Martin *et al.* (1987) have shown that sinking particles are rapidly decomposed between 100 and 500 m, producing the characteristic exponentially decreasing vertical profile of particulate flux (Fig. 7). The processes of particle decomposition are not well understood (Banse, 1990).

Jumars *et al.* (1989) applied digestion theory and diffusion calculations to the problem of satisfying the bacterial demand for DOC, or as they termed it, "Closing the microbial loop." Their models showed that fecal pellets lose DOC and DON very rapidly following egestion. For particles with permeable outer boundaries and diameters < 1 mm, 50% of concentration gradient between the inner pellet and the surrounding water is equalized within 5 min, and most of the solute burden of 100-μm pellets will diffuse away in seconds, even in stagnant water. Thus, fecal pellet egestion provides localized, but evanescent bursts of DOM, which might be taken up by bacteria which happen to be in the right place at the right time. Bacteria colonizing the hindgut and external nether regions of zooplankton may have special adaptations to taking advantage of DOC leaching from pellets (Nagasawa and Nemoto, 1988). Jumars *et al.* (1989) concluded from their calculations that most of the bacterial production in the upper water column was supported by animal secretion rather than phytoplankton release. Williams

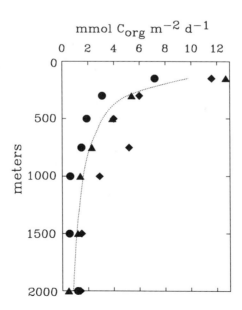

Figure 7. Vertical profiles of particulate carbon flux into sediment traps during the spring phytoplankton bloom in the north Atlantic Ocean. The decline in the flux with depth implies decomposition and dissolution of the sedimenting particles. (Data courtesy of John Martin, Moss Landing Marine Laboratory, Moss Landing, Calif.)

(1981) estimated that about half of the fecal pellet carbon was lost to the DOC pool, but nonetheless concluded that more of the DOC flux occurred prior to herbivore ingestion rather than after. The question remains unresolved, even if it is accepted that direct phytoplankton release is low (ca. 10% in contrast to Williams's 30%).

The rapid process of DOM loss from fresh pellets has not yet been addressed explicitly by experimental observation. The slower processes of bacterial colonization, growth on and decomposition of pellets have been studied (Honjo and Roman, 1978; Iturriaga, 1979; Gowing and Silver, 1983; Pomeroy et al., 1984; Jacobsen and Azam, 1984; Lampitt, Noji, and von Bodungen, 1990). All studies suggest that fecal pellets contain some bacteria within the pelletal matrix, and are colonized by others within hours of egestion. On tunicate feces, the initial colonization phase is followed by bacterial growth, then within 24–48 hr by growth of protozoans which consume the bacteria and fragment the particle (Pomeroy et al., 1984). Jacobsen and Azam (1984) observed slower solubilization of ^{14}C-labeled copepod pellets but found that attached bacteria released more dissolved ^{14}C into the water than they took up. Bacteria may compete with coprophagous animals for carbon in fecal pellets by rapidly solubilizing the particulate phase, thereby making it available to their free-living brethren (Azam and Cho, 1987).

The decay mechanisms of particulate materials which survive these relatively fast processes (seconds to days) to leave the upper 100 m are much less certain. Wiebe and Pomeroy (1972) and Ducklow et al. (1985) have established that most particles in the sea are not colonized by bacteria. The rapid succession of microbial populations observed by Pomeroy et al. (1984) and Biddanda and Pomeroy (1988) accompanied by fragmentation and decreasing lability (Pett, 1989) provides an explanation: the period during which microbial activity is associated with particles is short compared to the life span of the particles in the water column. Karl et al. (1988) compared poisoned and untreated sediment traps deployed at various depths in the water column or incubated on deck for 6–22 days and concluded from the relative amounts of microbial biomass accumulation and activity in the traps that in general, sedimenting particulate matter was a poor habitat for bacterial growth. This conclusion had been reached earlier by Ducklow et al. (1985). These observations are not consistent with the common assumption that bacteria directly decompose sedimenting particles. Since decomposition and regeneration of inorganic nutrients clearly proceed at rapid rates (Martin et al., 1987), the question is, by what means do they proceed?

Karl et al. (1988) and Cho and Azam (1988) independently suggested that bacteria make up a decreasing fraction of the sedimenting particle flux with increasing depth. Banse (1990) concluded that sampling and measurement resolution in these studies is not sufficient to establish or discount direct bacterial participation in the initial stages of decay, especially between 100 and 300 m where almost 50–75% of the reduction in flux occurs. Suess (1988), summarizing previous work, showed that 30–50% of the flux in that depth range was living biomass. Below ca. 300 m though, the observed levels of biomass and turnover rates coupled with assumptions about conversion efficiency suggest that only a small fraction of the particle decomposition could be due to the action of attached bacteria (Ducklow et al., 1985). Cho and Azam (1988) showed that free-living bacteria between 100 and 1000 m consumed DOC equivalent to ca. 50% of the vertical flux leaving the euphotic zone and hypothesized that particle decay was effected indirectly by free-living bacteria. One exception to this generalization is that phytodetritus on the seafloor is rapidly colonized by a microbiota which probably hastens its decay (Lochte and Turley, 1988; Turley and Lochte, 1990). The mechanism of this "action at a distance" is not clear, for it seems unlikely that hydrolysis could proceed via exoenzymes which were released into the water column. Thus, sedimenting particles unquestionably support an increasing fraction of microbial activity with increasing depth, but the actual means by which this occurs remains a mystery.

4.2.3. Aggregates and Attached Bacteria

Organic particles in seawater not clearly of direct phytoplankton or zooplankton origin are called organic aggregates or marine snow, although these terms lack exact definition and are also applied to macroparticles ranging from castoff larvacean houses to fresh aggregated phytodetritus. Biddanda (1988) and Biddanda and Pomeroy (1988) described the sequence of microbial populations and activity during the succession of aggregation, degradation, and disaggregation processes which characterize the life cycle of phytodetritus aggregates in the water column. He hypothesized that most organic aggregates in seawater look the same regardless of origin because all proceed through the same sequence of microbial processes. Colonization by bacteria, hydrolytic attack of the particulate matter, and bacterial biosynthesis of other polymers, followed by protozoan growth and grazing are implicated not only in the decomposition, but also in the production of organic aggregates and snow particles (Fig. 8; Biddanda, 1985). Herndl (1988) described a similar succession for the giant aggregates which form in the northern Adriatic Sea. The production and fate of marine snow appears to be regulated by bacteria and their predators, and these aggregates seem to provide—at least briefly—a fertile habitat for microbial growth (Pomeroy, 1984).

The occasional observation of the luxuriant assemblages of bacteria and associated microbes on aggregates (e.g., Wiebe and Pomeroy, 1972) has led to speculation that the total rate of bacterial production and nutrient regeneration in the water column might be dominated by the intense activity on these rare and poorly sampled micro- and macroaggregates (Caron et al., 1982; Karl, 1982). Such large particulate flocs are best sampled by divers (Alldredge, 1976). Caron et al. (1986) demonstrated that the concentration of bacteria in aggregates collected in the northwest Atlantic and Sargasso Sea was enriched by factors of 3–19 over the abundance in equal volumes of ambient water. Protozoans and microalgae were enriched by factors of 6–1300. Herndl (1988) observed bacterial enrichment factors of 2–133 for mega-aggregates (20 cm) in the Adriatic Sea. Several investigators have estimated bacterial abundance and production on aggregates and normalized the results by the aggregate density so the contribution of the attached bacteria on the aggregates to the total bacterial levels in the water can be estimated (Table X). These results all indicate that even though the abundances and production on the aggregates can be high, the attached bacteria contribute at most about 2% of the abundance and 8% of the production.

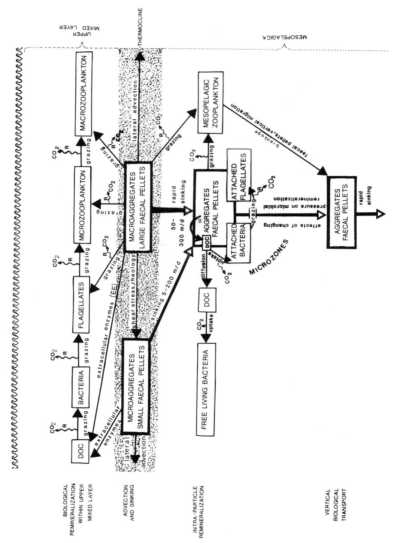

Figure 8. Transformation and transport processes responsible for formation, decomposition, and export of marine snow aggregates in the oceanic water column. (Figure courtesy of Carol Turley, Plymouth Marine Laboratory, Plymouth U.K.)

Table X. Bacterial Abundance and Production in Marine Snow[a,b]

Location/floc type	Abundance		Production		Reference
	Free	Attached	Free	Attached	
S. Cal diatom	778	0.28	1606	36	Simon et al. (1990)
S. Cal. larvacean	710	0.34	541	7	Simon et al. (1990)
S. Cal. fecal	785	0.16	573	1.3	Simon et al. (1990)
Bahamas 100–200 m	500	0.05	1294	0.04	Alldredge and Youngbluth (1985)
Calif.	218	4.3	133	10	Alldredge et al. (1986)
NW Atl. slope	602	4.3	14	0.5	Alldredge et al. (1986)
Gulf Stream ring	737	13	22	1	Alldredge et al. (1986)
Bermuda larvacean 580–760 m	30	<0.01	0.5–2.7	0.01–4	Davoll and Youngbluth (1990)
Bahamas larvacean 550–760 m	80	<0.001	0.1–14	0.01–4	Davoll and Youngbluth (1990)

[a]Abundances, 10^6 cells liter^{-1}; production ngC liter^{-1}. Attached levels expressed as % of free levels.
[b]Bacterial levels on aggregates normalized to bulk concentrations by multiplying by aggregate abundance per liter.

Observations on macroaggregates collected by divers are consistent with studies showing that bacteria attached to the more numerous suspended particles caught by Niskin bottles also contribute just a small fraction of the total activity (Azam and Hodson, 1977; Ducklow and Kirchman, 1983). These findings suggesting the preponderance of free bacteria must be tempered somewhat because the filtration methods routinely used to separate free from attached bacteria can lead to erroneous results for a variety of reasons. Bacteria may become detached from particles during filtration, may feed at surfaces while never attaching firmly in the first place (Hermansson and Marshall, 1985), or they may attach and detach during periods of fluctuating nutrient sufficiency (Power and Marshall, 1988). Even though the attached: free ratios indicated in Table X may be aliassed by these factors, errors of several orders of magnitude seem unlikely. The qualitative conclusion that water column processes are dominated by free-living bacteria seems secure.

4.2.3a. Extracellular Hydrolysis of Macromolecules and Polymers. Bacteria cannot transport compounds larger than a few oligomers in size directly into the cell without first hydrolyzing them with exoenzymes released into the surrounding water or bound to the cell wall (Azam and Cho, 1987). Billen (1984) and Billen and Fontigny (1987) state that the majority of monomeric compounds taken up by bacteria in coastal seas are the products of extracellular hydrolysis of polymers. Decho (1990) has reviewed the extraordinary diversity of exopolymers in the marine environment. Somville (1983), Hollibaugh and Azam (1983), Hoppe (1983), and Hoppe et al. (1988) have described different approaches for estimating the turnover and hydrolysis of proteins in seawater, all using analogues of naturally occurring proteins. Hollibaugh and Azam (1983), using [14]C- or ^{125}I-labeled bovine serum albumin, found that the protein pool in the Southern

California Bight had turnover times on the same order of magnitude as the leucine pool, and observed that the products of hydrolysis did not accumulate, but appeared to be taken up preferentially compared to the same compounds in bulk solution. Hoppe *et al.* (1988) followed the hydrolysis of a synthetic enzyme substrate leucine-methylcoumarinylamide which releases leucine and compared it to the uptake of ^{3}H-labeled leucine. They detected accumulation of leucine in the medium at high concentrations of the test substrate; otherwise, uptake balanced hydrolytic release. Lancelot and Billen (1984) and Billen and Fontigny (1987) also found that exoproteolytic activity closely paralleled phytoplankton protein biomass and bacterial production, indicating a close coupling between primary production, hydrolytic activities, and bacterial substrate uptake. All of these studies have established that most of the enzyme activity is associated with particles, presumably cell surfaces (Hollibaugh and Azam, 1983; Vives-Rego *et al.*, 1985). Azam and Cho (1987) speculate that this might be a general feature of bacterial nutrition in the sea: bacteria "digest" polymers at the cell surface where the products of digestion can be released in close proximity to uptake sites, thus avoiding the metabolic costs of maintaining high levels of enzymes in the bulk phase and taking up low concentrations of monomers following diffusion away from reaction sites.

4.2.3b. Microparticles. At the opposite end of the particle spectrum from aggregates and marine snow are submicron particles which pass GFF and other commonly used filters (Taguchi and Laws, 1988), and are usually classified as DOM. Recently, Koike *et al.* (1990) showed that such particles may contribute a sizeable fraction of the particle stocks in the water column. Using an electronic particle counter and epifluorescence microscopy, they established that there are about 10 million nonbacterial submicron particles per milliliter in Japanese coastal waters, i.e., about ten times the bacterial density. Further experiments suggested that the origin of these particles might be protozoan activity, e.g., egestion of undigested vacuolar contents, membrane fragments, and so forth. To some, the classification of these colloidal particles with high water content (Koike *et al.*, 1990) as POM or DOM may be mostly an operational or even semantic definition. But bacteria will encounter these particles more frequently than other "conventional" particles and plankton at the densities reported. Such particles may adsorb onto bacterial cells, like colloidal clay particles (Marshall, 1969), where they are vulnerable to hydrolysis by cell-bound enzymes. They are potentially an important source of organic matter for enzyme attack. The chemical nature and turnover of this large reservoir remains unknown.

5. Conversion Efficiency

The efficiency at which bacterioplankton convert substrate into biomass (the conversion or gross growth efficiency) is central to the concept of the "microbial loop" which is alleged to provide a mechanism for returning DOM "lost" from the food web via excretion, exudation, and leakage (Azam *et al.*, 1983). Early experiments with ^{14}C-labeled substrates suggested that in short-term incubations, some substances could be assimilated with high efficiency (Williams, 1981), leading to speculation that microbial food chains might transfer material with greater efficiency than metazoan chains (Pomeroy, 1979, 1984). This concept became incorporated into early models (Pace *et al.*, 1984; Fasham, 1985). The current status of the "link-sink" question (Ducklow *et al.*, 1986) has been reviewed by Pomeroy and Wiebe (1988) and the importance of conversion efficiencies was demonstrated in spread-sheet flow models (Ducklow, 1991). Conversion efficiency for small molecular substrates during balanced growth is governed by the C:N ratios of the bacteria and their substrates. The general model for interpreting these relationships was first presented to the marine community by Fenchel and Blackburn (1979), and has been discussed by Billen (1984), Lancelot and Billen (1985), and Goldman *et al.* (1987). This model states that the C or N balance (biosynthesis versus remineralization) is defined by the equation

$$\frac{\Delta NH_4^+}{\Delta C} = \frac{1}{C:N_s} - \frac{Y}{C:N_b} \tag{1}$$

where ΔNH_4^+ and ΔC are the NH_4^+ excretion and carbon uptake rates, and Y, $C:N_s$, and $C:N_b$ are the conversion efficiency (yield) and substrate and biomass $C:N$ ratios, respectively. As stated by Goldman *et al.* (1987), this means that after correction for respiration losses of carbon, the $C:N$ ratio of the biomass must be greater than the $C:N$ ratio of the substrate for there to be net NH_4^+ remineralization. Equation (1) suggests a rigid coupling among the $C:N$ ratios and conversion efficiency.

Billen (1984) analyzed data on NH_4^+ production from bacterial metabolism of amino acids added to seawater and found that Eq. (1) fitted the data with $Y/(C/N_b) = 0.1$ gN gC^{-1}. By assuming a bacterial $C:N$ ratio of 4, he estimated that conversion efficiency averaged 40% for the data they reviewed. Goldman *et al.* (1987) cultured bacterial assemblages on artificial media made up with mixtures of substrates designed to give $C:N_s$ ratios ranging from 1.5 to 10. They found that ΔNH_4^+ and ΔC varied in accordance with Eq. (1) also, with conversion efficiencies ranging from 40–50% at $C:N_s > 6$ to 73–94% at $C:N_s = 1.5$. They also observed that $C:N_b$ only varied from 4.2 to 6.1 (with a single observation of 9.8 excluded) when $C:N_s$ varied from 1.5 to 10. This is in general agreement with other determinations (Section 2), suggesting that for all practical purposes, $C:N_b$ can be regarded as a constant in Eq. (1).

The observation that conversion efficiency might be relatively constant at ca. 40% for $C:N_s > 6$ suggests that the widely used assumption of efficiency values around 50% (e.g., Hagstrom *et al.*, 1984; Cole *et al.*, 1988; Kirchman, 1990) might be reasonably accurate. The "HSB" model described by Billen (1984) and Billen and Fontigny (1987) provides further theoretical justification for this assumption. They showed that the flux of low-molecular-weight substrates arising from the exoenzymatic hydrolysis of proteins and other polymers was sufficient to sustain bacterial production. Their numerical simulations based on the HSB model reproduced observed variations in bacterial biomass and production in the Belgian coastal zone. These low-molecular-weight compounds are the substrates studied by Goldman *et al.* (1987). If in general bacteria use such compounds, then relatively high conversion efficiencies might be the norm.

One shortcoming of generalizing from these models is that they do not take into account the metabolic costs of particle breakdown and polymer hydrolysis. For example, Billen and Fontigny (1987) define the bacterial growth yield only for monomeric products of enzyme hydrolysis, not the overall efficiency of utilization. Another approach to determination of conversion efficiency pioneered by Newell *et al.* (1981) has been to establish substrate disappearance and biomass production during incubations with natural substrates in place of model compounds. Increasingly, a downward trend in conversion efficiency has been observed when this approach has been followed (Table XI). In the open sea, where substrates are derived from phytoplankton production, ambient DOC, and animal feces, conversion efficiencies appear to be less than 20%. Under such conditions when NH_4^+ appears to be required to meet a large fraction of N requirements and when growth may be in stationary phase (Goldman *et al.*, 1987), the costs of growth

Table XI. Bacterioplankton Conversion Efficiency

Substrate	% Eff.	Technique	Reference
Amino acids (short term)	50–95	$^{14}CO_2$ production	Williams (1981)
Amino acids (long term)	40	NH_4^+ production	Billen (1984)
Laminaria detritus	9–15	POC changes, biomass	Linley and Newell (1984)
Spartina detritus	10	POC changes, biomass	Linley and Newell (1984)
Juncus detritus	2	POC changes, biomass	Linley and Newell (1984)
Seston detritus	9	POC changes, biomass	Linley and Newell (1984)
Phytoplankton detritus	13–24	POC changes, biomass	Linley and Newell (1984)
Doliolid feces	10–20	POC change, Tdr	Pomeroy *et al.* (1984)
Ambient DOC (Roskilde estuary)	21	CO_2, biomass changes	Bjornsen (1986)
Amino acids, monosaccharides	10–30	Comparison with TdR	Billen and Fontigny (1987)
Glucose + NH_4^+	40	POC, DOC change	Goldman *et al.* (1987)
Mussel exudate	7	DOC changes, biomass	Tupas and Koike (1990)
Amino acids (short term)	53–65	^3H_2O production	Fuhrman (1990)
Amino acids (short term)	34	DFAA changes, TdR	Kirchman (1990)
Ambient DOC (Roskilde estuary)	47	O_2 change, TdR	Sand-Jensen *et al.* (1990)
Phytodetritus 450 atm, 2 C	10–60[a]	DOC, POC, biomass	Turley and Lochte (1990)
Ambient DOC (ocean)	2–8	DOC change, biomass	Kirchman *et al.* (1991)

[a]Efficiency declined as decomposition proceeded.

seem considerably higher than in the coastal ocean. In spite of this, bacterial production is a similar fraction of primary production in systems ranging from eutrophic estuaries to the oligotrophic central gyres (Table I).

If conversion efficiencies are substantially lower than the 50% commonly used to scale DOM fluxes (Cole *et al.*, 1988), then greater rates of DOC flux must be required to realize observed levels of bacterial production. These contrasts suggest much greater amounts of primary production might have to pass through bacterioplankton in oceanic systems to achieve the same ratio of bacterial to primary production as in coastal systems. The relative fluxes of readily utilizable monomers and polymeric or "aged" DOC may help explain variations in the ratio of bacterial to primary production in different systems (Table I). For example, is bacterial production a high fraction of primary production only when most of the DOM flux is fresh, easily utilized material (Hagstrom *et al.*, 1987)? Or do bacteria switch to less readily degraded substrates (Kirchman *et al.*, 1991) to maintain market share? These questions remain to be addressed in future experimental, observational, and modeling studies.

ACKNOWLEDGMENTS. This chapter was supported in part by NSF Grants OCE 8814229 and OCE 9015888 to H.W.D. and C.A.C. We are grateful to D. Bronk, M. Fletcher, J. C. Goldman, H.-G. Hoppe, D. M. Karl, R. G. Keil., D. L. Kirchman, J. Martin, T. Nagata, R. B. Rivkin, Y. Suzuki, and C. M. Turley for discussions and unpublished manuscripts and data. We also thank Peter L. Williams for continual inspiration and reality checks.

References

Admiraal, W., Beukema, J., and van Es, F. B., 1985, Seasonal fluctuations in the biomass and metabolic activity of bacterioplankton and phytoplankton in a well-mixed estuary: The Ems-Dollard Wadden Sea, *J. Plank. Res.* **76**:877–890.

Albright, L. J., and McCrae, S. K., 1987, Annual cycle of bacterial specific biovolumes in Howe Sound, a Canadian West Coast Fjord Sound, *Appl. Environ. Microbiol.* **53**:2739–2744.

Alldredge, A. L., 1976, Discarded appendicularian houses as sources of food, surface habitats, and particulate organic matter in planktonic environments, *Limnol. Oceanogr.* **21**:14–23.

Alldredge, A. L., and Youngbluth, M. J., 1985, The significance of macroscopic aggregates (marine snow) as sites for heterotrophic bacterial production in the mesopelagic zone of the subtropical Atlantic, *Deep-Sea Res.* **32**:1445–1456.

Alldredge, A. L., Cole, J. J., and Caron, D. A., 1986, Production of heterotrophic bacteria inhabiting macroscopic organic aggregates (marine snow) from surface waters, *Limnol. Oceanogr.* **31**:68–78.

Anderson, M. R., Rivkin, R. B., and Gustafson, D. E., 1991, The fate of bacterial production in McMurdo Sound in the austral spring, *Antarct. J. U.S.* (in press).

Andersson, A., Lee, C., Azam, F., and Hagstrom, A., 1985, Release of amino acids and inorganic nutrients by heterotrophic marine microflagellates, *Mar. Ecol. Prog. Ser.* **23**:99–106.

Azam, F., and Cho, B. C., 1987, Bacterial utilization of organic matter in the sea, in: *Ecology of Microbial Communities* (M. Fletcher, T. R. G. Gray, and J. G. Jones, eds.), Cambridge University Press, Cambridge, pp. 262–281.

Azam, F., and Fuhrman, J. A., 1984, Measurement of bacterioplankton growth in the sea and its regulation by environmental conditions, in: *Heterotrophic Activity in the Sea* (J. E. Hobbie and P. J. L. Williams, eds.), Plenum Press, New York, pp. 179–196.

Azam, F., and Hodson, R. E., 1977, Size distribution and activity of marine microheterotrophs, *Limnol. Oceanogr.* **22:**492–501.

Azam, F., Fenchel, T., Field, J. G., Gray, J. S., Meyer-Reil, L. A., and Thingstad, T. F., 1983, The ecological role of water-column microbes in the sea, *Mar. Ecol. Prog. Ser.* **10:**257–263.

Bailiff, M. D., and Karl, D. M., 1991, Dissolved and particulate DNA dynamics during a spring bloom in the Antarctic Peninsula region, 1986–87, *Deep Sea Res.* **38:**1077–1095.

Banse, K., 1974, On the role of bacterioplankton in the tropical ocean, *Mar. Biol.* **24:**1–5.

Banse, K., 1987, Seasonality of phytoplankton chlorophyll in the central and northern Arabian Sea, *Deep-Sea Res.* **34:**713–723.

Banse, K., 1990, New views on the degradation and disposition of organic particles as collected by sediment traps in the open sea, *Deep-Sea Res.* **37:**1177–1195.

Barber, R. T., 1967, Dissolved organic carbon from deep waters resists microbial oxidation, *Nature* **220:**274–275.

Bell, R. T., 1990, An explanation for the variability in the conversion factor deriving bacterial cell production from incorporation of [³H]-thymidine, *Limnol. Oceanogr.* **35:**910–915.

Berger, W. H., Fischer, K., Lai, C., and Wu, G., 1987, Ocean productivity and organic carbon flux, Pt. 1 Overview and maps of primary production and export production, *SIO Reference Series* 87-30, Scripps Inst. Oceanogr., La Jolla.

Biddanda, B., 1985, Microbial synthesis of macroparticulate matter, *Mar. Ecol. Prog. Ser.* **20:**241–251.

Biddanda, B. A., 1988, Microbial aggregation and degradation of phytoplankton-derived detritus in seawater. II. Microbial metabolism, *Mar. Ecol. Prog. Ser.* **42:**89–95.

Biddanda, B. A., and Pomeroy, L. R., 1988, Microbial aggregation and degradation of phytoplankton-derived detritus in seawater. I. Microbial succession, *Mar. Ecol. Prog. Ser.* **42:**79–88.

Billen, G., 1984, Heterotrophic utilization and regeneration of nitrogen, in: *Heterotrophic Activity in the Sea* (J. E. Hobbie and P. J. L. Williams, eds.), Plenum Press, New York, pp. 313–356.

Billen, G., and Fontigny, A., 1987, Dynamics of a Phaeocystis-dominated spring bloom in Belgian coastal waters. II. Bacterioplankton dynamics, *Mar. Ecol. Prog. Ser.* **37:**249–257.

Billen, G., Servais, P., and Becquevort, S., 1990, Dynamics of bacterioplankton in oligotrophic and eutrophic aquatic environments: Bottom-up or top-down control? *Hydrobiologia* **207:**37–42.

Billet, D. S. M., Lampitt, R. S., Rice, A. L., and Mantoura, R. F. C., 1983, Seasonal sedimentation of phytoplankton to the deep-sea benthos, *Nature* **302:**520–522.

Bird, D. F., and Kalff, J., 1984, Empirical relationship between bacterial abundance and chlorophyll concentration in fresh and marine waters, *Can. J. Fish. Aquat. Sci.* **41:**1015–1023.

Bishop, J. K. B., Collier, R. W., Ketten, D. R., and Edmond, J. M., 1980, The chemistry, biology and vertical flux of particulate matter from the upper 1500 m of the Panama Basin, *Deep-Sea Res.* **27:**615–640.

Bjornsen, P. K., 1986, Bacterioplankton growth yield in continuous seawater cultures, *Mar. Ecol. Prog. Ser.* **30:**191–196.

Bjornsen, P. K., 1988, Phytoplankton exudation of organic matter: Why do healthy cells do it? *Limnol. Oceanogr.* **33:**151–154.

Bjornsen, P. K., Riemann, B., Horsted, S. J., Nielsen, T. G., and Pock-Stein, J., 1988, Trophic interactions between heterotrophic nanoflagellates and bacterioplankton in manipulated seawater enclosures, *Limnol. Oceanogr.* **33:**409–420.

Borsheim, K. Y., 1990, Bacterial biomass and production rates in the Gulf Stream front regions, *Deep-Sea Res.* **37:**1297–1309.

Bratbak, G., 1985, Bacterial biovolume and biomass estimates, *Appl. Environ. Microbiol.* **49:**1488–1493.

Bratbak, G., and Dundas, I., 1984, Bacterial dry matter content and biomass estimations, *Appl. Environ. Microbiol.* **48:**755–757.

Bratbak, G., and Thingstad, T. F., 1985, Phytoplankton–bacteria interactions: An apparent paradox? Analysis of a model system with both competition and commensalism, *Mar. Ecol. Prog. Ser.* **25:**23–30.

Bratbak, G., Heldal, M., Norland, S., and Thingstad, T. F., 1990, Viruses as partners in spring bloom microbial trophodynamics, *Appl. Environ. Microbiol.* **56:**1400–1405.

Brock, T. D., 1971, Microbial growth rates in nature, *Bacteriol. Rev.* **35:**39–58.

Bronk, D., and Glibert, P. M., 1991, A ^{15}N tracer method for the measurement of dissolved organic nitrogen release by photoplankton, *Mar. Ecol. Prog. Ser.* **77:**171–182.

Burney, C. M., Davis, P. G., Johnson, K. M., and Sieburth, J. M., 1982, Diel relationship of microbial trophic groups and in situ dissolved carbohydrate dynamics in the Caribbean Sea, *Mar. Biol.* **67:**311–322.

Button, D. K., 1985, The kinetics of nutrient-limited transport and microbial growth, *Microbiol. Rev.* **49:**270–297.

Caron, D. A., Davis, P. G., Madin, L. P., and Sieburth, J. M., 1982, Heterotrophic bacteria and bacteriovorous protozoa in oceanic macroaggregates, *Science* **218:**795–797.

Caron, D. A., Goldman, J. C., Andersen, O. K., and Dennett, M. R., 1985, Nutrient cycling in a microflagellate food chain: II. Population dynamics and carbon cycling, *Mar. Ecol. Prog. Ser.* **24:**243–254.

Caron, D. A., Davis, P. G., Madin, L. P., and Sieburth, J. M., 1986, Enrichment of microbial populations in macroaggregates marine snow from surface waters of the North Atlantic, *J. Mar. Res.* **44:**543–565.

Carpenter, S. R., Kitchell, J. F., and Hodgson, J. R., 1985, Cascading trophic interactions and lake productivity, *BioScience* **35:**634–39.

Chin-Leo, G., and Kirchman, D. L., 1988, Estimating bacterial production in natural waters from the simultaneous incorporation of thymidine and leucine, *Appl. Environ. Microbiol.* **54:**1934–1939.

Cho, B. C., and Azam, F., 1988, Major role of bacteria in biogeochemical fluxes in the ocean's interior, *Nature* **332:**441–443.

Cho, B. C., and Azam, F., 1990, Biogeochemical significance of bacterial biomass in the ocean's euphotic zone, *Mar. Ecol. Prog. Ser.* **63:**253–259.

Chrzanowski, T. H., 1988, Consequences of accounting for isotopic dilution in thymidine incorporation assays, *Appl. Environ. Microbiol.* **54:**1868–1870.

Chrzanowski, T. H., and Zingmark, R. F., 1989, Bacterial abundance, biomass, and secondary production along a forest-to-ocean landscape gradient, *J. Exp. Mar. Biol. Ecol.* **125:**253–266.

Coffin, R. B., 1989, Bacterial uptake of dissolved free and combined amino acids in estuarine waters, *Limnol. Oceanogr.* **34:**531–542.

Coffin, R. B., and Sharp, J. H., 1987, Microbial trophodynamics in the Delaware Estuary, *Mar. Ecol. Prog. Ser.* **41:**253–266.

Coffin, R. B., Fry, B., Peterson, B. J., and Wright, R. T., 1989, Carbon isotopic composition of estuarine bacteria, *Limnol. Oceanogr.* **34:**1305–1310.

Coffin, R. B., Velinsky, D. J., Devereux, R., Price, W. A., and Cifuentes, L. A., 1990, Stable carbon isotope analysis of nucleic acids to trace sources of dissolved substrates used by estuarine bacteria, *Appl. Environ. Microbiol.* **56:**2012–2020.

Cole, J. J., Findlay, S., and Pace, M. L., 1988, Bacterial production in fresh and saltwater ecosystems: A cross-system overview, *Mar. Ecol. Prog. Ser.* **43:**1–10.

Copping, A. E., and Lorenzen, C. J., 1980, Carbon budget of a marine phytoplankton–herbivore system with carbon-14 as a tracer, *Limnol. Oceanogr.* **25:**873–882.

Corner, E. D. S., and Newell, B. S., 1967, On the nutrition and metabolism of zooplankton. IV. The forms of nitrogen excreted by *Calanus*, *J. Mar. Biol. Assoc. U.K.* **47:**113–120.

Cota, G. F., Kottmeier, S. T., Robinson, D. H., Smith, W. O., and Sullivan, C. W., 1990, Bacterioplankton in the marginal ice zone of the Weddell Sea: Biomass, production and metabolic activities during austral autumn, *Deep-Sea Res.* **37**:1145–1167.

Currie, D., 1990, Large-scale variability and interactions among phytoplankton, bacterioplankton and phosphorus, *Limnol. Oceanogr.* **35**:1437–1455.

Davis, P. G., Caron, D. A., Johnson, P. W., and Sieburth, J. M., 1985, Phototrophic and apochlorotic components of picoplankton and nanoplankton in the North Atlantic: Geographic, vertical, seasonal and diel distributions, *Mar. Ecol. Prog. Ser.* **21**:15–26.

Davoll, P. J., and Youngbluth, M. J., 1990. Heterotrophic activity on appendicularian Tunicata: Appendicularia houses in mesopelagic regions and their potential contribution to particle flux, *Deep-Sea Res.* **37**:285–294.

Decho, A. W., 1990, Microbial exopolymer secretions in ocean environments: Their roles in food webs and marine processes, *Oceanogr. Mar. Biol. Annu. Rev.* **28**:73–154.

Delille, D., Bouvy, M., and Cahet, G., 1988, Short-term variations of bacterioplankton in Antarctic zone: Terre Adelie area, *Microb. Ecol.* **15**:293–309.

Derenbach, J. B., and Williams, P. J. L., 1974, Autotrophic and bacterial production: Fractionation of plankton populations by differential filtration of samples from the English Channel, *Mar. Biol.* **25**:263–269.

Douglas, D. J., Novitsky, J. A., and Fournier, R. O., 1987, Microautoradiography-based enumeration of bacteria with estimates of thymidine-specific growth and production rates, *Mar. Ecol. Prog. Ser.* **36**:91–99.

Druffel, E. R. M., and Williams, P. M., 1990, Identification of a deep marine source of particulate organic carbon using bomb ^{14}C, *Nature* **347**:172–174.

Ducklow, H. W., 1982, Chesapeake Bay nutrient and plankton dynamics. 1. Bacterial biomass and production during spring tidal destratification in the York River, Virginia Estuary, *Limnol. Oceanogr.* **27**:651–659.

Ducklow, H. W., 1983, Production and fate of bacteria in the oceans, *BioScience* **33**:494–499.

Ducklow, H. W., 1984, Geographical ecology of marine bacteria: Physical and biological variability at the mesoscale, in: *Current Perspectives in Microbial Ecology* (M. J. Klug and C. A. Reddy, eds.), Amer. Soc. Microbiol., Washington, D.C., pp. 22–30.

Ducklow, H. W., 1986, Bacterial biomass in warm core Gulf Stream ring 82B: Mesoscale distributions, temporal changes, and production, *Deep-Sea Res.* **33**:1789–1812.

Ducklow, H. W., 1990, The biomass, production and fate of bacteria in coral reefs, in: *Coral Reefs* (Z. Dubinsky, ed.), Elsevier, Amsterdam, pp. 265–289.

Ducklow, H. W., 1991, The passage of carbon through microbial foodwebs: Results from flow network models, *Mar. Microb. Foodwebs* **5**:1–16.

Ducklow, H. W., 1992, Bacterioplankton distributions and production in the northwestern Indian Ocean and Gulf of Oman, September, 1986, *Deep-Sea Res.* (in press).

Ducklow, H. W., and Hill, S. M., 1985a, The growth of heterotrophic bacteria in the surface waters of warm core rings, *Limnol. Oceanogr.* **30**:239–259.

Ducklow, H. W., and Hill, S. M., 1985b, Tritiated thymidine incorporation and the growth of heterotrophic bacteria in warm core rings, *Limnol. Oceanogr.* **30**:260–272.

Ducklow, H. W., and Kirchman, D. L., 1983, Bacterial dynamics and distribution during a spring diatom bloom in the Hudson River Plume, *J. Plank. Res.* **5**:333–355.

Ducklow, H. W., and Shiah, F.-K., 1992, Estuarine bacterial production, in: *Aquatic Microbiology: An Ecological Approach* (T. Ford, ed.), Blackwell, Cambridge, Massachussets (in press).

Ducklow, H. W., Hill, S. M., and Gardner, W. D., 1985, Bacterial growth and the decomposition of particulate organic carbon collected in sediment traps, *Cont. Shelf. Res.* **44**:445–464.

Ducklow, H. W., Purdie, D. A., Williams, P. J. L., and Davies, J. M., 1986, Bacterioplankton: A sink for carbon in a coastal plankton community, *Science* **232**:865–867.

Ducklow, H. W., Peele, E. R., Hill, S. M., and Quinby, H. L., 1988, Fluxes of carbon, nitrogen and oxygen through estuarine bacterioplankton, in: *CRC Symposium Perspectives on Research in Chesapeake Bay* (M. P. Lynch and E. C. Krome, eds.), Chesapeake Research Consortium, Baltimore, pp. 511–523.

Ducklow, H. W., Fasham, M. J. R., and Vezina, A. F., 1989, Flow analysis of open sea plankton networks, in: *Network Analysis in Marine Ecology* (F. Wulff, J. G. Field, and K. H. Mann, eds.), Springer-Verlag, Berlin, pp. 159–205.

Ducklow, H. W., Kirchman, D. L., Quinby, H. L., Carlson, C. A., and Dam, H. G., 1992, Stocks and dynamics of bacterioplankton carbon during the spring phytoplankton bloom in the North Atlantic Ocean, *Deep-Sea Res.* (in press).

Duursma, E. K., 1961, Dissolved organic carbon, nitrogen and phosphorus in the sea, *Neth. J. Sea Res.* **1:**1–147.

Eppley, R. W., Sharp, J. H., Renger, E. H., Perry, M. J., and Harrison, W. G., 1977, Nitrogen assimilation by phytoplankton and other microorganisms in the surface waters of the central North Pacific ocean, *Mar. Biol.* **39:**111–120.

Eppley, R. W., Horrigan, S. G., Fuhrman, J. A., Brooks, E. R., Price, C. C., and Sellner, K., 1981, Origins of dissolved organic matter in Southern California coastal waters: Experiments on the role of zooplankton, *Mar. Ecol. Prog. Ser.* **6:**149–159.

Fasham, M. J. R., 1985, Flow analysis of materials in the marine euphotic zone, *Can. Bull. Fish. Aquat. Sci.* **213**(Suppl.):139–162.

Fasham, M. J. R., Ducklow, H. W., and McKelvie, S. M., 1990, A nitrogen-based model of plankton dynamics in the oceanic mixed layer, *J. Mar. Res.* **48:**591–639.

Fenchel, T., 1984, Suspended marine bacteria as a food source, in: *Flow of Energy and Materials in Marine Ecosystems* (M. J. Fasham, ed.), Plenum Press, New York, pp. 301–316.

Fenchel, T., and Jorgensen, B. B., 1977, Detritus food chains of aquatic ecosystems: The role of bacteria, *Adv. Microb. Ecol.* **1:**1–58.

Fenchel, T., and Blackburn, T. H., 1979, *Bacteria and Mineral Cycling,* Academic Press, New York.

Ferguson, R. L., and Palumbo, A. V., 1979, Distribution of suspended bacteria in neritic waters south of Long Island during stratified conditions, *Limnol. Oceanogr.* **24:**697–705.

Ferguson, R. L., and Rublee, P., 1976, Contribution of bacteria to standing crop of coastal plankton, *Limnol. Oceanogr.* **21:**141–145.

Ferguson, R. L., and Sunda, W. G., 1984, Utilization of amino acids by planktonic marine bacteria: Importance of clean technique and low substrate additions, *Limnol. Oceanogr.* **29:**258–274.

Fischer, B., 1894, Die bakterien des meeres nach den Untersuchungen der Plankton-Expedition unter gleikzeitiger Berucksichtigung einiger alterer und neverer Untersuchungen, *Ergeb. Plankton-Expedition Humboldt-Stiftung* **4:**1–83.

Floodgate, G. D., Fogg, G. D., Jones, D. A., Lochte, K., and Turley, C. M., 1981, Microbiological and zooplankton activity at a front in Liverpool Bay, *Nature* **290:**133–136.

Fuhrman, J. A., 1987, Close coupling between release and uptake of dissolved free amino acids in seawater studied by an isotope dilution approach, *Mar. Ecol. Prog. Ser.* **37:**45–52.

Fuhrman, J. A., 1990, Dissolved free amino acid cycling in an estuarine outflow plume, *Mar. Ecol. Prog. Ser.* **66:**197–203.

Fuhrman, J. A., and Azam, F., 1980, Bacterioplankton secondary production estimates for coastal waters of British Columbia, Antarctica, and California, *Appl. Environ. Microbiol.* **39:**1085–1095.

Fuhrman, J. A., and Azam, F., 1982, Thymidine incorporation as a measure of heterotrophic bacterioplankton production in marine surface waters: Evaluation and field results, *Mar. Biol.* **66:**109–120.

Fuhrman, J. A., Ammerman, J. W., and Azam, F., 1980, Bacterioplankton in the coastal euphotic zone: Distribution, activity, and possible relationships with phytoplankton, *Mar. Biol.* **60:**201–207.

Fuhrman, J. A., Eppley, R. W., Hagstrom, A., and Azam, F., 1985, Diel variations in bacterioplankton, phytoplankton, and related parameters in the Southern California Bight, *Mar. Ecol. Prog. Ser.* **27:**9–20.

Fuhrman, J. A., Horrigan, S. G., and Capone, D. G., 1988, Use of ^{13}N as tracer for bacterial and algal uptake of ammonium from sea water, *Mar. Ecol. Prog. Ser.* **45:**271–278.

Fuhrman, J. A., Sleeter, T. D., Carlson, C. A., and Proctor, L. M., 1989, Dominance of bacterial biomass in the Sargasso Sea and its ecological implications, *Mar. Ecol. Prog. Ser.* **57:**207–217.

Fukami, K., Simidu, U., and Taga, N., 1985, Microbial decomposition of phyto- and zooplankton in seawater. II. Changes in organic matter, *Mar. Ecol. Prog. Ser.* **21:**1–5.

Gifford, D. J., 1991, The protozoan–metazoan trophic link in pelagic ecosystems, *J. Protozool.* **38:**81–87.

Goldman, J. C., Caron, D. A., and Dennett, M. R., 1987, Regulation of gross growth efficiency and ammonium regeneration in bacteria by substrate C:N ratio, *Limnol. Oceanogr.* **32:**1239–1252.

Gowing, M. M., and Silver, M. W., 1983, Origins and microenvironments of bacteria mediating fecal pellet decomposition in the sea, *Mar. Biol.* **73:**7–16.

Griffith, P. C., Douglas, D. J., and Wainright, S. C., 1990, Metabolic activity of size-fractionated microbial plankton in estuarine, nearshore, and continental shelf waters of Georgia, *Mar. Ecol. Prog. Ser.* **59:**263–270.

Gustafson, D. E., Anderson, M. R., and Rivkin, R. B., 1991, Bacterioplankton abundance and productivity at the ice edge zone of McMurdo Sound, Antarctica, *Antarct. J. U.S.* (in press).

Hagstrom, A., Larsson, U., Horstedt, P., and Normark, S., 1979, Frequency of dividing cells, a new approach to the determination of bacterial growth rates in aquatic environments, *Appl. Environ. Microbiol.* **37:**805–812.

Hagstrom, A., Ammerman, J. W., Henrichs, S., and Azam, F., 1984, Bacterioplankton growth in seawater: II. Organic matter utilization during steady state growth in seawater culture, *Mar. Ecol. Prog. Ser.* **18:**41–48.

Hagstrom, A., Azam, F., Andersson, A., Wikner, J., and Rassoulzadegan, F., 1988, Microbial loop in an oligotrophic pelagic marine ecosystem: Possible roles of cyanobacteria and nanoflagellates in the organic fluxes, *Mar. Ecol. Prog. Ser.* **49:**171–178.

Hairston, N. G., Smith, F. E., and Slobodkin, L. B., 1960, Community structure, population control and competition, *Am. Nat.* **94:**421–425.

Hanson, R. B., and Lowery, H. K., 1983, Nucleic acid synthesis in oceanic microplankton from the Drake Passage, Antarctica: Evaluation of steady-state growth, *Mar. Biol.* **73:**79–89.

Hanson, R. B., Alvarez-Ossorio, M. T., Cal, R., Campos, M. J., Roman, M., Santiago, G., Varela, M., and Yoder, J. A., 1986a, Plankton response following a spring upwelling event in the Ria de Arosa, Spain, *Mar. Ecol. Prog. Ser.* **32:**101–113.

Hanson, R. B., Pomeroy, L. R., and Murray, R. H., 1986b, Microbial growth rates in a cold-core Gulf Stream eddy of the northwestern Sargasso Sea, *Deep-Sea Res.* **33:**427–446.

Hanson, R. B., Pomeroy, L. R., Blanton, J. O., Biddanda, B. A., Wainwright, S., Bishop, S., Yoder, J. A., and Atkinson, L. P., 1988, Climatological and hydrographic influences on nearshore food webs off the southern United States: Bacterioplankton dynamics, *Cont. Shelf Res.* **8:**1321–1344.

Hermansson, M., and Marshall, K. C., 1985, Utilization of surface localized substrate by non-adhesive marine bacteria, *Microb. Ecol.* **11:**91–105.

Herndl, G., 1988, Ecology of amorphous aggregates marine snow in the northern Adriatic Sea. II. Microbial density and activity in marine snow and its implication to overall pelagic processes, *Mar. Ecol. Prog. Ser.* **48:**265–275.

Hobbie, J. E., 1988, A comparison of the ecology of planktonic bacteria in fresh and salt water. *Limnol. Oceanogr.* **33:**750–764.

Hobbie, J. E., and Cole, J. J., 1984, Response of a detrital food web to eutrophication, *Bull. Mar. Res.* **35:**357–363.

Hobbie, J. E., Daley, R. J., and Jasper, S., 1977, Use of Nuclepore filters for counting bacteria by fluorescence microscopy, *Appl. Environ. Microbiol.* **33:**1225–1228.

Hollibaugh, J. T., 1988, Limitation of the [^{3}H]-thymidine method for estimating bacterial productivity due to thymidine metabolism, *Mar. Ecol. Prog. Ser.* **43:**19–30.

Hollibaugh, J. T., and Azam, F., 1983, Microbial degradation of dissolved proteins in seawater, *Limnol. Oceanogr.* **28**:1104–1116.

Holligan, P. M., Harris, R. P., Newell, R. C., Harbour, D. S., Head, R. N., Linley, E. A. S., Lucus, M. I., Tranter, P. R. G., and Weekly, C. M., 1984, Vertical distribution and partitioning of organic carbon in mixed, frontal, and stratified waters of the English Channel, *Mar. Ecol. Prog. Ser.* **14**:111–127.

Honjo, S., and Roman, M., 1978, Marine copepod fecal pellets: Production, preservation and sedimentation, *J. Mar. Res.* **36**:45–57.

Hoppe, H.-G., 1983, Significance of exoenzymatic activities in the ecology of brackish-water: Measurements by means of methyl-umbelliferyl substrates, *Mar. Ecol. Prog. Ser.* **11**:299–308.

Hoppe, H.-G., Kim, S. J., and Gocke, K., 1988, Microbial decomposition in aquatic environments: Combined process of extracellular enzyme activity and substrate uptake, *Appl. Environ. Microbiol.* **54**:784–790.

Iriberri, J., Unanue, M., Ayo, B., Barcina, I., and Egea, L., 1990, Bacterial production and growth rate estimation from [^{3}H]-thymidine incorporation for attached and free-living bacteria in aquatic systems, *Appl. Environ. Microbiol.* **56**:483–487.

Iturriaga, R., 1979, Bacterial activity related to sedimenting particulate matter, *Mar. Biol.* **55**:157–169.

Jacobsen, T. R., and Azam, F., 1984, Role of bacteria in copepod fecal pellet decomposition: Colonization, growth rates and mineralization, *Bull. Mar. Sci.* **35**:495–502.

Jacobsen, T. R., Pomeroy, L. R., and Blanton, J. O., 1983, Autotrophic and heterotrophic abundance and activity associated with a nearshore front off the Georgia coast, USA, *Estuarine Coastal Shelf Sci.* **17**:509–521.

Jeffrey, W. H., and Paul, J. H., 1988, Underestimation of DNA synthesis by ^{3}H-thymidine incorporation in marine bacteria, *Appl. Environ. Microbiol.* **54**:3165–3168.

Jensen, L. M., 1983, Phytoplankton release of extracellular organic carbon, molecular weight composition, and bacterial assimilation, *Mar. Ecol. Prog. Ser.* **11**:39–48.

Joint, I. R., and Morris, R. J., 1982, The role of bacteria in the turnover of organic matter in the sea, *Oceanogr. Mar. Biol. Annu. Rev.* **20**:65–118.

Joint, I. R., and Pomroy, A. J., 1983, Production of picoplankton and small nanoplankton in the Celtic Sea, *Mar. Biol.* **77**:19–27.

Joint, I. R., and Pomroy, A. J., 1987, Activity of heterotrophic bacteria in the euphotic zone of the Celtic Sea, *Mar. Ecol. Prog. Ser.* **41**:1155–1165.

Jonas, R. B., and Tuttle, J. H., 1990, Bacterioplankton and organic carbon dynamics in the lower mesohaline Chesapeake Bay, *Appl. Environ. Microbiol.* **56**:747–757.

Jumars, P. A., Penry, D. L., Baross, J. A., Perry, M. J., and Frost, B. W., 1989, Closing the microbial loop: Dissolved organic carbon pathway to heterotrophic bacteria from incomplete ingestion, digestion and absorption in animals, *Deep-Sea Res.* **36**:483–495.

Karl, D. M., 1979, Measurement of microbial activity and growth in the ocean by rates of stable ribonucleic acid synthesis, *Appl. Environ. Microbiol.* **38**:850–860.

Karl, D. M., 1980, Cellular nucleotide measurements and applications in microbial ecology, *Microbiol. Rev.* **44**:739–796.

Karl, D. M., 1982, Microbial transformations of organic matter at oceanic interfaces: A review and prospectus, *Eos* **63**:138–140.

Karl, D. M., 1986, Determination of in situ microbial biomass, viability, metabolism, and growth, in: *Bacteria in Nature* Volume 2 (J. S. Poindexter and E. R. Leadbetter, eds.), Plenum Press, New York, pp. 85–176.

Karl, D. M., and Winn, C. D., 1984, Adenine metabolism and nucleic acid synthesis: Applications to microbiological oceanography, in: *Heterotrophic Activity in the Sea* (J. E. Hobbie and P. J. L. Williams, eds.), Plenum Press, New York, pp. 197–216.

Karl, D. M., Knauer, G. A., and Martin, J. H., 1988, Downward flux of organic matter in the ocean: A particle decomposition paradox, *Nature* **332**:438–441.

Keil, R. G., and Kirchman, D. L., 1991, Contribution of dissolved free amino acids and ammonium to the nitrogen requirements of heterotrophic bacterioplankton, *Mar. Ecol. Prog. Ser.* **73**:1–10.

King, G. M., and Berman, T., 1984, Potential effects of isotopic dilution on apparent respiration in C-14 heterotrophy experiments, *Mar. Ecol. Prog. Ser.* **19**:175–180.

Kirchman, D. L., 1990, Limitation of bacterial growth by dissolved organic matter in the subarctic Pacific, *Mar. Ecol. Prog. Ser.* **62**:47–54.

Kirchman, D. L., and Hoch, M. P., 1988, Bacterial production in the Delaware Bay estuary estimated from thymidine and leucine incorporation rates, *Mar. Ecol. Prog. Ser.* **45**:169–178.

Kirchman, D. L., Ducklow, H. W., and Mitchell, R., 1982, Estimates of bacterial growth from changes in uptake rates and biomass, *Appl. Environ. Microbiol.* **44**:1296–1307.

Kirchman, D. L., Peterson, B., and Juers, D., 1984, Bacterial growth and tidal variation in bacterial abundance in the Great Sippewissett Salt Marsh, *Mar. Ecol. Prog. Ser.* **19**:247–259.

Kirchman, D. L., K'nees, E., and Hodson, R., 1985, Leucine incorporation and its potential as a measure of protein synthesis by bacteria in natural waters, *Appl. Environ. Microbiol.* **49**:599–607.

Kirchman, D. L., Keil, R. G., and Wheeler, P. A., 1989a, The effect of amino acids on ammonium utilization and regeneration by heterotrophic bacteria in the subarctic Pacific, *Deep-Sea Res.* **36**:1763–1776.

Kirchman, D. L., Soto, Y., Wambeck, F. v., and Bianchi, M., 1989b, Bacterial production in the Rhone River plume: Effect of mixing on relationships among microbial assemblages, *Mar. Ecol. Prog. Ser.* **53**:267–275.

Kirchman, D. L., Keil, R. G., Simon, M., and Welschmeyer, N. A., 1992, Biomass and production of heterotrophic bacterioplankton in the oceanic subarctic Pacific: SUPER 1987 and 1988, *Deep Sea Res.* **39** (in press).

Kirchman, D. L., Suzuki, Y., Garside, C., and Ducklow, H. W., 1991, Bacterial oxidation of dissolved organic carbon in the north Atlantic Ocean during the spring bloom, *Nature* **352**:612–614.

Koike, I., Hara, S., Terauchi, K., and Kogure, K., 1990, Role of sub-micrometre particles in the ocean, *Nature* **345**:242–244.

Koop, K., Newell, R. C., and Lucas, M. I., 1982, Biodegradation and carbon flow based on kelp Ecklonia maxima debris in a sandy beach microcosm, *Mar. Ecol. Prog. Ser.* **7**:315–326.

Kuosa, H., and Kivi, K., 1989, Bacteria and heterotrophic flagellates in the pelagic carbon cycle in the northern Baltic Sea, *Mar. Ecol. Prog. Ser.* **53**:93–100.

Kuuppo-Leinikki, P., 1990, Protozoan grazing on planktonic bacteria and its impact on bacterial population, *Mar. Ecol. Prog. Ser.* **63**:227–238.

Laanbroek, H. J., and Verplanke, J. C., 1986, Tidal variations in bacterial biomass, productivity and oxygen uptake rates in a shallow channel in the Oosterschelde basin, The Netherlands, *Mar. Ecol. Prog. Ser.* **29**:1–5.

Laanbroek, H. J., Verplanke, J. C., De Visscher, P. R. M., and De Vuyt, R., 1985, Distribution of phyto- and bacterioplankton growth and biomass parameters dissolved inorganic nutrients and free amino acids during a spring bloom in the Oosterschelde basin, The Netherlands, *Mar. Ecol. Prog. Ser.* **25**:1–11.

Lal, D., 1977, The oceanic microcosm of particles, *Science* **198**:997–1009.

Lampert, W., 1978, Release of dissolved organic carbon by grazing zooplankton, *Limnol. Oceanogr.* **25**:982–990.

Lampitt, R. S., 1985, Evidence for the seasonal deposition of detritus to the deep-sea floor and its subsequent resuspension, *Deep-Sea Res.* **32**:885–897.

Lampitt, R. S., Noji, T., and von Bodungen, B., 1990. What happens to zooplankton fecal pellets? Implications for material flux, *Mar. Biol.* **104**:15–23.

Lancelot, C., 1979, Gross excretion rates of natural marine phytoplankton and heterotrophic uptake of excreted products in the southern North Sea, as determined by short-term kinetics, *Mar. Ecol. Prog. Ser.* **1**:179–186.

Lancelot, C., and Billen, G., 1984, Activity of heterotrophic bacteria and its coupling to primary production during spring phytoplankton bloom in the southern bight of the North Sea, *Limnol. Oceanogr.* **29**:721–730.

Lancelot, C., and Billen, G., 1985, Carbon–nitrogen relationships in nutrient metabolism of coastal marine ecosystems, *Adv. Aquatic Microbiol.* **3**:263–321.

Lancelot, C., and Mathot, S., 1987, Dynamics of a *Phaeocystis*-dominated spring bloom in Belgian coastal waters. I. Phytoplanktonic activities and related parameters, *Mar. Ecol. Prog. Ser.* **37**:239–248.

Larsson, U., and Hagstrom, A., 1979, Phytoplankton exudate release as an energy source for the growth of pelagic bacteria, *Mar. Biol.* **52**:199–206.

Larsson, U., and Hagstrom, A., 1982, Fractionated phytoplankton production, exudate release and bacterial production in a Baltic eutrophication gradient, *Mar. Biol.* **67**:57–70.

Laws, E. A., Harrison, W. G., and DiTullio, G. R., 1985, A comparison of nitrogen assimilation rates based on ^{15}N uptake and autotrophic protein synthesis, *Deep-Sea Res.* **32**:85–95.

Laycock, R. A., 1974, The detrital foodchain based on seaweeds. I. Bacteria associated with the surface of Laminaria fronds, *Mar. Biol.* **25**:223–231.

Lee, C., and Wakeham, S. G., 1988, Organic matter in seawater: Biogeochemical processes. in: *Chemical Oceanography*, Vol. 9 (J. P. Riley and R. Chester, eds.), Academic Press, New York, pp. 1–44.

Lee, S., and Fuhrman, J. A., 1987, Relationships between biovolume and biomass of naturally-derived marine bacterioplankton, *Appl. Environ. Microbiol.* **52**:1298–1303.

Li, W. K. W., 1982, Estimating bacterial productivity by inorganic radiocarbon uptake: Importance of establishing time courses of uptake, *Mar. Ecol. Prog. Ser.* **8**:167–172.

Li, W. K. W., and Dickie, P. M., 1985, Metabolic inhibition of size-fractionated marine plankton radiolabelled with amino acids, glucose, bicarbonate and phosphate in the light and dark, *Microb. Ecol.* **11**:11–24.

Li, W. K. W., and Dickie, P. M., 1991, Light and dark ^{14}C uptake in dimly-lit oligotrophic waters: Relation to bacterial activity, *J. Plank. Res.* **13**(Suppl.):29–44.

Lignell, R., 1990, Excretion of organic carbon by phytoplankton: Its relation to algal biomass, primary productivity and bacterial secondary productivity in the Baltic Sea, *Mar. Ecol. Prog. Ser.* **68**:85–99.

Linley, E. A. S., and Koop, K., 1986, Significance of pelagic bacteria as a trophic resource in a coral reef lagoon, One Tree Island, Great Barrier Reef, *Mar. Biol.* **92**:457–464.

Linley, E. A. S., and Newell, R. C., 1984, Estimates of bacterial growth yields based on plant detritus, *Bull. Mar. Sci.* **35**:409–425.

Linley, E. A. S., Newell, R. C., and Lucas, M. I., 1983, Quantitative relationships between phytoplankton, bacteria and heterotrophic microflagellates in shelf waters, *Mar. Ecol. Prog. Ser.* **12**:77–89.

Lochte, K., and Pfannkuche, O., 1987, Cyclonic cold-core eddy in the northeastern Atlantic. II. Nutrients, phytoplankton and bacterioplankton, *Mar. Ecol. Prog. Ser.* **39**:153–164.

Lochte, K., and Turley, C. M., 1985, Heterotrophic activity and carbon flow via bacteria in waters associated with a tidal mixing front, Proc. 19th Eur. Mar. Biol. Symp. pp. 73–85.

Lochte, K., and Turley, C. M., 1988, Bacteria and cyanobacteria associated with phytodetritus in the deep sea, *Nature* **333**:67–69.

Longhurst, A. R., and Harrison, W. G., 1988, Vertical nitrogen flux from the oceanic euphotic zone by diel migrant zooplankton and nekton, *Deep-Sea Res.* **35**:881–890.

Longhurst, A. R., and Harrison, W. G., 1989, The biological pump: Profiles of plankton production and consumption in the upper ocean, *Prog. Oceanogr.* **22**:47–123.

Lucas, M. I., Newell, R. C., and Velimirov, B., 1981, Heterotrophic utilization of mucilage released during fragmentation of kelp Ecklonia maxima and Laminaria pallida. II. Differential utilization of dissolved organic components from kelp mucilage, *Mar. Ecol. Prog. Ser.* **4**:43–55.

Lucas, M. I., Painting, S. J., and Muir, D. G., 1986, Estimates of carbon flow through bacterioplankton

in the S. Benguela upwelling region based on ³H-thymidine incorporation and predator-free incubations, in: *Deuxième Colloque International de Bactériologie marine*, Brest, CNRS, pp. 375–383.

McManus, G. B., and Fuhrman, J. A., 1988, Clearance of bacteria-sized particles by natural populations
of nanoplankton in the Chesapeake Bay outflow plume, *Mar. Ecol. Prog. Ser.* **42:**199–206.

McManus, G. B., and Fuhrman, J. A., 1990, Mesoscale and seasonal variability of heterotrophic
nanoflagellate abundance in an estuarine outflow plume, *Mar. Ecol. Prog. Ser.* **61:**207–213.

McManus, G. B., and Peterson, W. T., 1988, Bacterioplankton production in the nearshore zone during
upwelling off central Chile, *Mar. Ecol. Prog. Ser.* **43:**11–17.

McQueen, D. J., Post, J. R., and Mills, E. L., 1986, Trophic relationships in freshwater pelagic
ecosystems, *Can. J. Fish. Aquat. Sci.* **43:**1571–1581.

Malone, T. C., and Chervin, M. B., 1979, The production and fate of phytoplankton size fractions in the
plume of the Hudson River, New York Bight, *Limnol. Oceanogr.* **24:**683–696.

Malone, T. C., and Ducklow, H. W., 1990, Microbial biomass in the coastal plume of Chesapeake Bay:
Phytoplankton–bacterioplankton relationships, *Limnol. Oceanogr.* **35:**296–312.

Malone, T. C., Kemp, W. M., Ducklow, H. W., Boynton, W. R., Tuttle, J. H., and Jonas, R. B., 1986,
Lateral variation in the production and fate of phytoplankton in a partially stratified estuary, *Mar.
Ecol. Prog. Ser.* **32:**149–160.

Marra, J., Landriau, G., and Ducklow, H. W., 1981, Tracer kinetics and plankton rate processes in
oligotrophic oceans, *Mar. Biol. Lett.* **2:**215–223.

Marshall, K. C., 1969, Orientation of clay particles sorbed on bacteria possessing different ionogenic
surfaces, *Biochim. Biophys. Acta* **193:**472–474.

Martin, J. H., Knauer, G. A., Karl, D. M., and Broenkow, W. W., 1987, VERTEX: Carbon cycling in
the northeast Pacific, *Deep-Sea Res.* **34:**267–285.

Meyer-Reil, L.-A., 1977, Bacterial growth and biomass production, in: *Microbial Ecology of a Brackish
Water Environment* (G. Rheinheimer, ed.), Springer-Verlag, Berlin, pp. 223–235.

Moore, B., III, and Bolin, B., 1986, The oceans, carbon dioxide and global change, *Oceanus* **29**(4):9–
15.

Mopper, K., and Degens, E. T., 1979, Organic carbon in the ocean: Nature and cycling, in: *The Global
Carbon Cycle* (B. Bolin, E. T. Degens, S. Kempe, and P. Ketner, eds.), Wiley, New York, pp. 293–
316.

Moriarty, D. J. W., 1984, Measurements of bacterial growth rates in some marine systems using the
incorporation of tritiated thymidine into DNA, in: *Heterotrophic Activity in the Sea* (J. E. Hobbie
and P. J. L. Williams, eds.), Plenum Press, New York, pp. 217–232.

Moriarty, D. J. W., 1985, Measurement of bacterial growth rates in aquatic systems using rates of nucleic
acid synthesis, *Adv. Microb. Ecol.* **9:**245–292.

Moriarty, D. J. W., Pollard, P. C., and Hunt, W. G., 1985, Temporal and spatial variation in bacterial
production in the water column over a coral reef, *Mar. Biol.* **85:**285–292.

Moriarty, D. J. W., Roberts, D. G., and Pollard, P. C., 1990, Primary and bacterial productivity of
tropical seagrass communities in the Gulf of Carpenteria, Australia, *Mar. Ecol. Prog. Ser.* **61:**145–
157.

Murdoch, W. W., 1966, Community structure, population control and competition—A critique, *Am.
Nat.* **100:**219–226.

Nagasawa, S., and Nemoto, T., 1988, Presence of bacteria in guts of marine crustaceans and on their
fecal pellets. *J. Plank. Res.* **10:**559–564.

Nagata, T., 1986, Carbon and nitrogen content of natural planktonic bacteria, *Appl. Environ. Microbiol.*
52:28–32.

Nagata, T., and Kirchman, D. L., 1992, Release of dissolved organic matter by heterotrophic protozoa:
Implications for microbial foodwebs, *Arch. Hydrobiol.* **35:**99–109.

Nagata, T., and Watanabe, Y., 1990, Carbon- and nitrogen-to-volume ratios of bacterioplankton grown
under different nutritional conditions, *Appl. Environ. Microbiol.* **56:**1303–1309.

Nelson, D. M., McCarthy, J. J., and Ducklow, H. W., 1989, Enhanced near-surface nutrient availability and new production resulting from the frictional decay of a Gulf Stream warm-core ring, *Deep-Sea Res.* **36**:705–714.

Newell, R. C., 1984, The biological role of detritus in the marine environment, in: *Flows of Energy and Materials in Marine Ecosystems* (M. J. Fasham, ed.), Plenum Press, New York, pp. 317–344.

Newell, R. C., and Field, J. G., 1983, Relative flux of carbon and nitrogen in a kelp-dominated system, *Mar. Biol. Lett.* **4**:249–257.

Newell, R. C., Lucas, M. I., and Linley, E. A. S., 1981, Rate of degradation and efficiency of conversion of phytoplankton debris by marine microorganisms, *Mar. Ecol. Prog. Ser.* **6**:123–136.

Newell, S. Y., and Christian, R. R., 1981, Frequency of dividing cells as an estimator of bacterial productivity, *Appl. Environ. Microbiol.* **42**:23–31.

Newell, S. Y., and Fallon, S. D., 1982, Bacterial productivity in the water column and sediments of Georgia U. S. A. coastal zone: Estimates via direct counting and parallel measurements of thymidine incorporation, *Microb. Ecol.* **8**:33–46.

Nothig, E.-M., and von Bodungen, B., 1989, Occurrence and vertical flux of faecal pellets of probably protozoan origin in the southeastern Weddell Sea Antarctica, *Mar. Ecol. Prog. Ser.* **56**:281–289.

Pace, M. L., Glasser, J. E., and Pomeroy, L. R., 1984, A simulation analysis of continental shelf food webs, *Mar. Biol.* **82**:47–63.

Painting, S. J., Lucas, M. I., and Muir, D. G., 1989, Fluctuations in heterotrophic bacterial community structure and production in response to development and decay of phytoplankton in a microcosm, *Mar. Ecol. Prog. Ser.* **53**:129–141.

Pantoja, S., González, H., and Bernal, P. A., 1989, Bacterial biomass and production in a shallow bay, *J. Plank. Res.* **11**:599–604.

Paul, J. H., Jeffrey, W. H., and deFlaun, M. F., 1985, Particulate DNA in subtropical oceanic and estuarine planktonic environments, *Mar. Biol.* **90**:95–101.

Paul, J. H., deFlaun, M. F., Jeffrey, W. H., and David, A. W., 1988, Seasonal and diel variability in dissolved DNA and in microbial biomass and activity in a subtropical estuary, *Appl. Environ. Microbiol.* **54**:718–727.

Pedros-Alio, C., and Newell, S. Y., 1989, Microautoradiographic study of thymidine uptake in brackish waters around Sapelo Island, Georgia, USA, *Mar. Ecol. Prog. Ser.* **55**:83–94.

Peele, E. R., Murray, R. E., Hanson, R. B., Pomeroy, L. R., and Hodson, R. E., 1984, Distribution of microbial biomass and secondary production in a warm core Gulf Stream ring, *Deep-Sea Res.* **32**:1393–1403.

Pett, R. J., 1989, Kinetics of microbial mineralization of organic carbon from detrital Skeletonema costatum cells, *Mar. Ecol. Prog. Ser.* **52**:123–128.

Pilskaln, C. H., and Honjo, S., 1987, The fecal pellet fraction of biogeochemical particle fluxes to the deep sea, *Global Biogeochem. Cycles* **1**:31–48.

Pomeroy, L. R., 1974, The ocean's food web: A changing paradigm, *BioScience* **24**:499–504.

Pomeroy, L. R., 1979, Secondary production mechanisms of continental shelf communities, in: *Ecological Processes in Coastal and Marine Systems* (R. J. Livingston, ed.), Plenum Press, New York, pp. 163–186.

Pomeroy, L. R., 1984, Significance of microorganisms in carbon and energy flow in marine ecosystems, in: *Current Perspectives in Microbial Ecology* (M. J. Klug and C. A. Reddy, eds.), Amer. Soc. Microbiol., Washington, D.C., pp. 405–411.

Pomeroy, L. R., 1990, Status and future needs in protozoan ecology, in: *Protozoa and Their Role in Marine Processes* (P. C. Reid, C. M. Turley, and P. H. Burkill, eds.), Springer-Verlag, Berlin, pp. 475–492.

Pomeroy, L. R., and Deibel, D., 1986, Temperature regulation of bacterial activity during the spring bloom in Newfoundland coastal waters, *Science* **233**:359–361.

Pomeroy, L. R., and Johannes, R. E., 1966, Total plankton respiration, *Deep-Sea Res.* **13**:971–973.

Pomeroy, L. R., and Wiebe, W. J., 1988, Energetics of microbial food webs, *Hydrobiologia* **159**:7–18.

Pomeroy, L. R., Atkinson, L. P., Blanton, J. O., Campbell, W. B., Jacobsen, T., Kerrick, K. H., and

Wood, A. M., 1983, Microbial distribution and abundance in response to physical and biological processes on the continental shelf of the southeastern USA, *Cont. Shelf Res.* **2**:1–20.

Pomeroy, L. R., Hanson, R. B., McGillivary, P., Sherr, B. F., Kirchman, D. L., and Deibel, D., 1984, Microbiology and chemistry of fecal products of pelagic tunicates: Rates and fates, *Bull. Mar. Sci.* **35**:426–439.

Power, K. and Marshall, K. C., 1988, Cellular growth and reproduction of marine bacteria on surface bound substrate, *Biofouling* **1**:163–174.

Rassoulzadegan, F., and Sheldon, R. W., 1986a, An experimental investigation of a flagellate–ciliate–copepod food chain with some observations relevant to the linear biomass hypothesis, *Limnol. Oceanogr.* **31**:184–188.

Rassoulzadegan, F., and Sheldon, R. W., 1986b, Predator–prey interaction of nanozooplankton and bacteria in an oligotrophic marine environment, *Limnol. Oceanogr.* **31**:1010–1021.

Riemann, B., and Bell, R. T., 1990, Advances in estimating bacterial biomass and growth in aquatic systems, *Arch. Hydrobiol.* **25**:385–402.

Riemann, B., Nielsen, P., Jeppesen, M., Marcussen, B., and Fuhrman, J. A., 1984, Diel changes in bacterial biomass and growth rates in coastal environments, determined by means of thymidine incorporation into DNA, frequency of dividing cells FDC, and microautoradiography, *Mar. Ecol. Prog. Ser.* **17**:227–235.

Riemann, B., Jorgensen, N. O., Lampert, W., and Fuhrman, J. A., 1986, Zooplankton-induced changes in dissolved free amino acids and in production rates of freshwater bacteria, *Microb. Ecol.* **12**:247–258.

Riemann, B., Bjornsen, P. K., Newell, S., and Fallon, R., 1987, Calculation of cell production of coastal marine bacteria based on measured incorporation of [^{3}H]-thymidine, *Limnol. Oceanogr.* **32**:471–476.

Riemann, B., Sorensen, H. M., Bjornsen, P. K., Horsted, S. J., Jensen, L. M., Nielsen, T. G., and Sondergaard, M., 1990, Carbon budgets of the microbial foodweb in estuarine enclosures, *Mar. Ecol. Prog. Ser.* **65**:159–170.

Rivkin, R. B., 1990, Seasonal patterns of planktonic production in McMurdo Sound, Antarctica, *Am. Zool.* **31**:5–16.

Rivkin, R. B., Putt, M., Alexander, S. P., Meritt, D., and Gaudet, L., 1989, Biomass and production in polar planktonic and sea ice microbial communities: A comparative study, *Mar. Biol.* **101**:273–283.

Robarts, R. D., Wicks, R. J., and Sephton, L. M., 1986, Spatial and temporal variations in bacterial macromolecular labeling with [methyl-^{3}H] thymidine in a hypertrophic lake, *Appl. Environ. Microbiol.* **52**:1368–1373.

Roman, M. R., Ducklow, H. W., Fuhrman, J. A., Garside, C., Glibert, P. M., Malone, T. C., and McManus, G. B., 1988, Production, consumption, and nutrient recycling in a laboratory mesocosm, *Mar. Ecol. Prog. Ser.* **42**:39–52.

Rosenberg, R., Dahl, E., Edler, L., Fyrberg, L., Granéli, E., Granéli, W., Hagstrom, A., Lindahl, O., Matos, M. O., Pettersson, K., Sahlsten, E., Tiselius, P., Turk, V., and Wikner, J., 1990, Pelagic nutrient and energy transfer during spring in the open and coastal Skagerrak, *Mar. Ecol. Prog. Ser.* **61**:215–231.

Roy, S., Harris, R. P., and Poulet, S. A., 1989, Inefficient feeding by *Calanus helgolandicus* and *Temora longicornis* on *Coscinodiscus wailesii*: Quantitative estimation using chlorophyll-type pigments and effects on dissolved free amino acids, *Mar. Ecol. Prog. Ser.* **52**:145–153.

Sand-Jensen, K., Jensen, L. M., Marcher, S., and Hansen, M., 1990, Pelagic metabolism in eutrophic coastal waters during a late summer period, *Mar. Ecol. Prog. Ser.* **65**:63–72.

Scavia, D., 1988, On the role of bacteria in secondary production, *Limnol. Oceanogr.* **33**:1220–1224.

Sellner, K. G., 1981, Primary productivity and the flux of dissolved organic matter in several marine environments, *Mar. Biol.* **65**:101–112.

Sharp, J. H., 1984, Inputs into microbial food chains, in: *Heterotrophic Activity in the Sea* (J. E. Hobbie and P. J. L. Williams, eds.), Plenum Press, New York, pp. 101–120.

Sherr, B. F., Sherr, E. B., Andrew, T. L., Fallon, R. D., and Newell, S. Y., 1986, Trophic interactions between heterotrophic protozoa and bacterioplankton in estuarine water analyzed with selective metabolic inhibitors, *Mar. Ecol. Prog. Ser.* **32:**169–179.

Sherr, B. F., Sherr, E. B., and Pedros-Alio, C., 1989, Simultaneous measurement of bacterioplankton production and protozoan bacterivory in estuarine water, *Mar. Ecol. Prog. Ser.* **54:**209–219.

Sherr, E. B., and Sherr, B. F., 1987, High rates of consumption of bacteria by pelagic ciliates, *Nature* **325:**710–711.

Sherr, E. B., Sherr, B. F., Fallon, R. D., and Newell, S. Y., 1986, Small, aloricate ciliates as a major component of the marine heterotrophic nanoplankton, *Limnol. Oceanogr.* **3:**177–183.

Sieburth, J. M., 1976, Bacterial substrates and productivity in marine ecosystems, *Annu. Rev. Ecol. Syst.* **7:**259–286.

Sieburth, J. M., 1977, International Helgoland Symposium: Convenor's report on the informal session on biomass and productivity of microorganisms in planktonic ecosystems, *Helgol. Wiss. Meeresunters.* **30:**697–704.

Sieburth, J. M., Johnson, K. M., Burney, C. M., and Lavoie, D. M., 1977, Estimation of in situ rates of heterotrophy using diurnal changes in dissolved organic matter and growth rates of picoplankton in diffusion culture, *Helgol. Wiss. Meeresunters.* **30:**565–574.

Sieracki, M. E., and Sieburth, J. M., 1985, Factors controlling the periodic fluctuation in total planktonic bacterial populations in the upper ocean: Comparison of nutrient, sunlight and predation effects, *Mar. Microb. Foodwebs* **1:**35–50.

Simon, M., and Azam, F., 1989, Protein content and protein synthesis rates of planktonic marine bacteria, *Mar. Ecol. Prog. Ser.* **51:**201–213.

Simon, M., Alldredge, A. L., and Azam, F., 1990, Bacterial carbon dynamics on marine snow, *Mar. Ecol. Prog. Ser.* **65:**205–211.

Small, L. F., Fowler, S. W., Moore, S. A., and LaRosa, J., 1983, Dissolved and fecal pellet carbon and nitrogen release by zooplankton in tropical waters, *Deep-Sea Res.* **30:**1199–1220.

Smetacek, V., 1985, Role of sinking in diatom life history cycles: Ecological, evolutionary, and geological significance, *Mar. Biol.* **84:**239–251.

Smith, R. E. H., 1982, The estimation of phytoplankton production and excretion by carbon-14, *Mar. Biol. Lett.* **3:**325–334.

Somville, M., 1983, Measurement and study of substrate specificity of exoglucosidase in natural water, *Appl. Environ. Microbiol.* **48:**1181–1185.

Sorokin, Y. I., 1971, Bacterial populations as components of oceanic ecosystems, *Mar. Biol.* **11:**101–105.

Sorokin, Y. I., 1973, Data on the biological productivity of the western tropical Pacific Ocean, *Mar. Biol.* **20:**177–196.

Sorokin, Y. I., 1981, Microheterotrophic organisms in marine ecosystems, in: *Analysis of Marine Ecosystems* (A. Longhurst, ed.), Academic Press, New York, pp. 293–342.

Sorokin, Y. I., and Mamaeva, T. I., 1991, Role of planktonic bacteria in productivity and cycling of organic matter in the eastern Pacific Ocean, *Hydrobiologia* **209:**39–50.

Steele, J. H., 1974, *The Structure of Marine Ecosystems,* Harvard University Press, Cambridge, Mass.

Suess, E., 1980, Particulate organic carbon flux in the oceans—surface productivity and oxygen utilization, *Nature* **288:**260–263.

Suess, E., 1988, Effects of microbe activity, *Nature* **333:**17–18.

Sugimura, Y., and Suzuki, Y., 1988, A high-temperature catalytic oxidation method of non-volatile dissolved organic carbon in seawater by direct injection of liquid samples, *Mar. Chem.* **14:**105–131.

Sullivan, C. W., Cota, G. F., Krempin, D. W., and Smith, J. W. O., 1990, Distribution and activity of bacterioplankton in the marginal ice zone of the Weddell–Scotia Sea during austral spring, *Mar. Ecol. Prog. Ser.* **63:**239–252.

Suttle, C. A., Fuhrman, J. A., and Capone, D. G., 1990a, Rapid ammonium cycling and concentration-dependent partitioning of ammonium and phosphate: Implications for carbon transfer in planktonic communities, *Limnol. Oceanogr.* **35**:424–433.

Suttle, C. A., Chan, A. M., and Cottrell, M. T., 1990b, Infection of phytoplankton by viruses and reduction of primary productivity, *Nature* **347**:467–469.

Taguchi, S., and Laws, E. A., 1988, On the microparticles which pass through glass fiber filter type GF/F in coastal and open waters, *J. Plank. Res.* **10**:999–1008.

Taylor, G. T., Iturriaga, R., and Sullivan, C. W., 1985, Interactions of bactivorous grazers and heterotrophic bacteria with dissolved organic matter, *Mar. Ecol. Prog. Ser.* **23**:129–141.

Toggweiler, J. R., 1989, Is the downward dissolved organic matter DOM flux important in carbon transport? in: *Productivity of the Oceans: Present and Past* (W. H. Berger, V. S. Smetacek, and G. Wefer, eds.), Wiley, New York, pp. 65–83.

Torréton, J.-P., Guiral, D., and Arfi, R., 1989, Bacterioplankton biomass and production during destratification in a monomictic eutrophic bay of a tropical lagoon, *Mar. Ecol. Prog. Ser.* **57**:53–67.

Tupas, L., and Koike, I., 1990, Amino acid and ammonium utilization by heterotrophic marine bacteria grown in enriched seawater, *Limnol. Oceanogr.* **35**:1145–1155.

Turley, C. M., and Lochte, K., 1985, Direct measurement of bacterial productivity in stratified waters close to a front in the Irish Sea, *Mar. Ecol. Prog. Ser.* **23**:209–219.

Turley, C. M., and Lochte, K., 1990, Microbial response to the input of fresh detritus to the deep-sea bed, *Paleogeogr. Paleoclimatol. Paleoecol.* **89**:3–23.

Ulanowicz, R. E., 1986, *Growth and Development: Ecosystems Phenomenology,* Springer-Verlag, Berlin.

Urrere, M. A., and Knauer, G. A., 1981, Zooplankton fecal pellet fluxes and vertical transport of particulate organic material in the pelagic environment, *J. Plank. Res.* **3**:369–387.

van Duyl, F. C., Bak, R. P. M., Kop, A. J., and Nieuwland, G., 1990, Bacteria, auto- and heterotrophic nanoflagellates, and their relations in mixed, frontal and stratified waters of the North Sea, *Neth. J. Sea Res.* **261**: 97–109.

van Es, F. B., and Meyer-Reil, L. A., 1982, Biomass and metabolic activity of heterotrophic marine bacteria, *Adv. Microb. Ecol.* **6**:111–170.

Vives-Rego, J., Billen, G., Fontigny, A., and Somville, M., 1985, Free and attached proteolytic activity in water environments, *Mar. Ecol. Prog. Ser.* **21**:245–249.

Vives-Rego, J., Martinez, J., and García-Lara, J., 1988, Assessment of bacterial production and mortality in Mediterranean coastal water, *Estuarine Coastal Shelf Sci.* **26**:331–336.

Walsh, J. J., 1983, Death in the sea: Enigmatic phytoplankton losses, *Prog. Oceanogr.* **12**:1–86.

Walsh, J. J., 1984, The role of ocean biota in accelerated ecological cycles: A temporal view, *BioScience* **34**:499–507.

Wangersky, P., 1984, Organic particles and bacteria in the ocean, in: *Heterotrophic Activity in the Sea* (J. E. Hobbie and P. J. L. Williams, eds.), Plenum Press, New York, pp. 263–287.

Ward, B. B., 1984, Photosynthesis and bacterial utilization of phytoplankton exudates: Results from pre- and post-incubation size fractions, *Oceanol. Acta* **7**:337–343.

Watson, A. J., and Whitfield, M., 1985, Composition of particles in the global ocean, *Deep-Sea Res.* **32**:1023–1039.

Watson, S. W., Novitsky, T. J., Quinby, H. L., and Valois, F. W., 1977, Determination of bacterial number and biomass in the marine environment, *Appl. Environ. Microbiol.* **33**:940–946.

Weisse, T., 1989, The microbial loop in the Red Sea: Dynamics of pelagic bacteria and heterotrophic nanoflagellates, *Mar. Ecol. Prog. Ser.* **55**:241–250.

Wheeler, P. A., and Kirchman, D. L., 1986, Utilization of inorganic and organic nitrogen by bacteria in marine systems, *Limnol. Oceanogr.* **31**:998–1009.

Wiebe, W. J., and Pomeroy, L. R., 1972, Microorganisms and their association with aggregates and detritus in the sea: A microscopic study, *Mem. Ist. Ital. Idrobiol.* **29**(Suppl.):325–352.

Wiebe, W. J., and Smith, D. F., 1977, Direct measurement of dissolved organic carbon release by phytoplankton and incorporation by microheterotrophs, *Mar. Biol.* **42**:213–233.

Wikner, J., Rassoulzadegan, F., and Hagstrom, A., 1990, Periodic bacteriovore activity balances bacterial growth in the marine environment, *Limnol. Oceanogr.* **35**:313–325.

Williams, P. J. L., 1981, Incorporation of microheterotrophic processes into the classical paradigm of the planktonic food web, *Kiel. Meeresforsch.* **5**:1–28.

Williams, P. J. L., 1984, Bacterial production in the marine food chain: The emperor's new suit of clothes? in: *Flows of Energy and Materials in Marine Ecosystems* (M. J. Fasham, ed.), Plenum Press, New York, pp. 271–299.

Williams, R., and Poulet, S. A., 1986, Relationship between the zooplankton, phytoplankton, particulate matter and dissolved free amino acids in the Celtic Sea, *Mar. Biol.* **90**:279–284.

Wolter, K., 1982, Bacterial incorporation of organic substances released by natural phytoplankton populations, *Mar. Ecol. Prog. Ser.* **7**:287–295.

Wright, R. T., 1984, Dynamics of pools of dissolved organic carbon, in: *Heterotrophic Activity in the Sea* (J. E. Hobbie and P. J. L. Williams, eds.), Plenum Press, New York, pp. 121–154.

4

Ecological Significance of Coaggregation among Oral Bacteria

PAUL E. KOLENBRANDER and JACK LONDON

1. Introduction

The human oral ecosystem is an ecologist's paradise. It is readily accessible to the investigator and contains greater than 325 species of bacteria. Within a few hours after a tooth is professionally cleaned, a succession of genera of bacteria repopulate the tooth surface. These primary colonizers are also involved in the succession of genera that accompany the progressive changes at a tooth site, when the clinical condition changes from healthy through gingivitis to the advancing stages of periodontal disease.

The bacteria are found on mucosal as well as on hard enamel surfaces. Each species appears to occupy preferentially certain surfaces. Some, like *Streptococcus salivarius* and *Veillonella atypica*, are found almost exclusively on mucosal surfaces or suspended in saliva that bathes these surfaces. Others, like *Streptococcus oralis* and *Veillonella parvula*, predominate in dental plaque. The most frequently isolated genera in plaque samples from healthy sites are *Actinomyces*, *Fusobacterium*, *Peptostreptococcus*, *Propionibacterium*, *Streptococcus*, and *Veillonella*. Gingivitis, inflammation of the gingival tissue, is accompanied by the appearance of *Capnocytophaga*, *Prevotella*, *Selenomonas*, and *Wolinella*. Gingivitis is usually a prelude to more serious periodontal disease, which is characterized by destruction of the supporting bone and ligaments. The genera that predominate in samples from periodontally diseased sites are *Actinobacillus*, *Actinomyces*, *Eubacterium*, *Fusobacterium*, *Lactobacillus*, *Peptostreptococcus*, *Porphyromonas*, *Prevotella*, *Streptococcus*, *Veillonella*, and *Wolinella*. Whereas the number of most of the genera fluctuate depending upon the conditions of health and disease, the numbers of *Fusobacterium* and *Veillonella* relative to the other genera remain high at all times. Cell-to-cell adhesion of pairs of oral bacteria and the molecules that mediate adhesion are the topics discussed in this chapter.

PAUL E. KOLENBRANDER and JACK LONDON • Laboratory of Microbial Ecology, National Institute of Dental Research, National Institutes of Health, Bethesda, Maryland 20892.

Advances in Microbial Ecology, Vol. 12, edited by K.C. Marshall. Plenum Press, New York, 1992.

183

2. Coaggregation: Definition and Description

Strains representative of each of the genera listed above (Section 1) have been tested for their ability to adhere to strains of other genera, and the results of these studies have been reviewed (Kolenbrander, 1988, 1989, 1991). Such intergeneric coaggregation, cell-to-cell recognition between genetically distinct cell types, was first reported by Gibbons and Nygaard (1970) and occurs among some strains of all of the genera (Kolenbrander, 1989). When partner cell-types are mixed, the coaggregates or clumps formed are composed of a network of interacting cells of both partners.

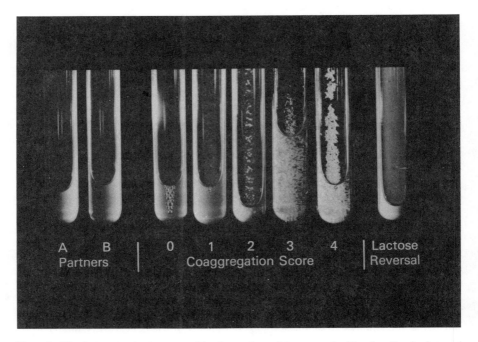

Figure 1. Visual coaggregation scores possible when partner cell types are mixed together. Equal volumes of turbid suspensions (1×10^9 cells/ml^{-1}) of two cell types (potential partners, for example tubes A and B) are mixed briefly and examined immediately for coaggregation. Suspensions are prepared in buffer consisting of the following (dissolved in 0.001 M Tris adjusted to pH 8.0): $CaCl_2$ (10^{-4} M), $MgCl_2$ (10^{-4} M), NaN_3 (0.02%), and NaCl (0.15 M). If the cell types are not coaggregation partners, the mixed cell suspension remains evenly turbid (coaggregation score of 0). If they are partners, different coaggregation scores are given for each partner pair (tubes 1 to 4) to describe the extent of formation of mixed-cell-type coaggregates; see text for details. Cells do not need to be viable: cell walls will form clumps equally well as viable or azide-killed cells. Many coaggregations are reversed to an evenly turbid suspension by addition of 0.06 M lactose, final concentration (far right tube). The tubes shown are 10×75 mm and contain 2 ml suspension. They are tilted to nearly horizontal position and are photographed from above. The exception is the tube illustrating a coaggregation score of 3, which was tilted less so that the settling flocs (coaggregates) could be shown from a slightly different perspective.

A very simple visual assay has been used to survey more than 1000 strains of oral bacteria for their ability to coaggregate with another strain (Fig. 1). Turbid suspensions with a cell density of about 1×10^9 cells ml^{-1} of each partner (Fig. 1, A and B) are mixed briefly. If they are not partners, the turbidity does not change and the pair is given a coaggregation score of 0. If they are partners, coaggregation occurs immediately and the degree of coaggregation is scored between 1 and 4. A score of 1 is given when the suspension contains finely dispersed clumps in a turbid background, and a score of 2 is given when definite clumps of bacteria are easily seen but do not settle immediately and remain in a turbid background. The strong coaggregating partners exhibit scores of 3 (clumps settle immediately with a slightly turbid supernatant) or 4 (clumps settle immediately and the supernatant is completely clear). Addition of lactose (60 mM final concentration) to a partnership exhibiting a +4 coaggregation score, often reverses coaggregation dramatically to an evenly turbid suspension (Fig. 1, tube at far right). Agitation of the partner cell mixture is important to not only cause increased partner cell collision energy but also increased collision frequency (Stratford and Wilson, 1990).

Whereas the visual assay is extremely useful for screening large numbers of strains, quantitative measurement of the coaggregation is also easily determined using radioactivity-based assays (Kolenbrander and Andersen, 1986; Lamont and Rosan, 1990). One of the cell types is labeled with a radioactive nucleic acid base or an amino acid. The radioactivity in the coaggregates is measured in the pellet after a very low-speed centrifugation ($100g$ for 1 min) (Kolenbrander and Andersen, 1986). A method published recently offers promise in the measurement of weaker coaggregations that may be disrupted by centrifugation (Lamont and Rosan, 1990). This assay is based on the immobilization of one cell type on a nitrocellulose surface and the subsequent addition of a radioactively labeled cell type. The amount of radioactivity remaining on the filter after washing the filter is a measure of the extent of the partnership.

When the interacting partners represent three or more genera, the resulting multigeneric coaggregates appear to be composed of independently acting intergeneric recognitions (Kolenbrander and Andersen, 1986). A radioactivity-based assay is useful in determining the contribution of the labeled cell type to the multigeneric coaggregate (Kolenbrander and Andersen, 1988). Competition between two genetically distinct cell types for binding to their common partner has been reported (Kolenbrander and Andersen, 1985; Kolenbrander et al., 1985). Likewise, coaggregation bridges, cooperative cell arrangements formed by the interactions of two different cell types with their common partner, have been reported (Kolenbrander and Andersen, 1984; Kolenbrander et al., 1985). In the cooperative multigeneric coaggregates, the two different cell types recognize their common partner by distinct mechanisms, whereas competition occurs when the two cell types recognize their common partner by identical mechanisms. Some bacteria, like fusobacteria, are partners to most other oral bacteria and are thus excellent candidates for coaggregation bridging and competition. Other bacteria, like selenomonads and treponemes, have very few partners and may participate in multigeneric coaggregates in only a limited way.

Although the numbers and kinds of partnerships vary, specific molecules on the respective cell surfaces appear to mediate the interactions. These molecules may be borne on fimbriae (Weiss *et al.*, 1987a), fibrils (Harty and Handley, 1989), or part of the outer membrane (Kagermeier and London, 1986; Tempro *et al.*, 1989; Kaufman and DiRienzo, 1989; Lai *et al.*, 1990). Many coaggregations involve a lectinlike protein molecule on one cell surface and its complementary carbohydrate receptor on the partner cell surface. Others may be protein–protein interactions. Most of the coaggregations discussed in this chapter are thought to involve specific molecules such as lectins and complementary carbohydrate receptors, since many of the coaggregations are prevented in the presence of lactose (Fig. 1, tube on far right). Most of the more than 500 isolates of actinomyces and streptococci examined to date (Kolenbrander, 1989, 1991; Eifuku *et al.*, 1990; Crowley *et al.*, 1987; Lamont and Rosan, 1990) coaggregate, and, of these, more than 90% exhibit some interactions that are inhibited by lactose and other related galactosides (Kolenbrander, 1989, 1991; Eifuku *et al.*, 1990; Chisari and Gismondo, 1986; Komiyama and Gibbons, 1984a,b). A surface component on one cell type may be recognized by complementary molecules on more than one partner and may be an avenue of competition between these partners. The possibility that these complementary molecules may be functionally or even structurally related is creating a rapidly developing area of research and one that will contribute greatly to our understanding of the dynamics responsible for the evolution of a complex oral microbial habitat.

3. Nascent Surfaces

3.1. Potential Role of Coaggregation in Colonization

Adhesion of oral bacteria to hard or soft tissue surfaces is of critical importance to the maintenance of bacteria in their respective econiches. Each type of surface appears to be occupied by a characteristic group of bacteria, and some species of bacteria inhabit only certain surfaces. For example, *Veillonella parvula* was not found among the 68 veillonellae isolated from the tongue dorsum (Hughes *et al.*, 1988) but constituted greater than 90% of the veillonellae of subgingival plaque (L. V. H. Moore *et al.*, 1987; W. E. C. Moore *et al.*, 1985). If adhesion is important to colonization, then *V. parvula* should coaggregate with other subgingival bacteria but not with bacteria indigenous to the tongue. Indeed, coaggregation was observed with other subgingival plaque bacteria, such as *Streptococcus sanguis* and *Actinomyces naeslundii* (Hughes *et al.*, 1988). However, strains of *V. parvula* did not recognize *S. salivarius*, a streptococcus not usually found in subgingival plaque but is the predominant streptococcus on the tongue. Conversely, most of the veillonellae (*V. atypica* and *V. dispar*) isolated from the tongue coaggregated with *S. salivarius* but not with *S. sanguis* or *A. naeslundii* (Hughes *et al.*, 1988). These data provide a firm basis for the hypothesis that coaggregation among the bacteria that occupy a given surface is an important trait that contributes to the ability of bacteria to colonize the surface.

A test of the possibility that coaggregation may affect bacterial colonization of animal teeth was performed in an elegant study using a gnotobiotic rat model system (McBride and van der Hoeven, 1981). Some *S. mutans* coaggregate with *V. parvula* (*V. alcalescens*) and this partnership was used to test this possibility. Two *S. mutans* strains were used: one coaggregated with *V. parvula* and the other did not. Both streptococci attached and colonized the teeth of monoinfected rats but *V. parvula* strains did not. However, if a coaggregation-positive *S. mutans* was allowed to adhere to the teeth before adding veillonellae, then the veillonellae were found attached and colonizing the tooth surface. In contrast, if a coaggregation-negative *S. mutans* was fed to the rats first, then there was no increase above controls in the number of veillonellae attached. van der Hoeven *et al.* (1985) extended that observation by demonstrating that coaggregation-defective mutants fail to colonize and that coaggregations that are lactose-inhibited *in vitro* are also altered *in vivo* by addition of lactose to the drinking water of the gnotobiotic animals. Taken together, these data strongly implicate coaggregation as an important mechanism in dental plaque accretion.

Another study compared the binding of coaggregating and non-coaggregating *Haemophilus parainfluenzae* to *S. sanguis* in human volunteers (Liljemark *et al.*, 1988). A monolayer of *S. sanguis* was coated onto a bovine enamel chip with a biological adhesive. The enamel chip was then mounted on a modified orthodontic appliance in the mouth of a volunteer. Tenfold higher numbers of coaggregating, as compared to non-coaggregating, *H. parainfluenzae* bound to the streptococcus-coated enamel chip. This was the first demonstration in humans where quantitative differences were measured by using a coaggregating and non-coaggregating pair of the same species.

All external surfaces on the human body are colonized by bacteria, and it is generally thought that each surface is occupied by a normal healthy population. Clinically healthy tooth surfaces are covered primarily with gram-positive bacteria like streptococci and actinomyces, which are thus likely candidates for such a normal healthy condition. Under conditions of experimental gingivitis (Theilade *et al.*, 1966; W. E. C. Moore *et al.*, 1982) or naturally occurring gingivitis (L. V. H. Moore *et al.*, 1987), gram-negative bacteria like prevotellae and capnocytophagae proliferate. These two gram-negative genera coaggregate with the two genera of gram-positive bacteria (Kolenbrander and Andersen, 1984; Kolenbrander *et al.*, 1985). Three antimicrobial compounds, cetylpyridinium chloride, chlorhexidine digluconate, and octenidine dihydrochloride, were tested and all three selectively inhibited intergeneric coaggregations composed of a gram-negative strain and a gram-positive strain, but had little effect on coaggregations between two gram-positive partners (Smith *et al.*, 1991). The observation that coaggregations among potentially healthy populations are more resistant to the actions of clinically useful antimicrobial compounds than are the interactions involving the gram-negative successors is consistent with the clinical data that such compounds are effective in preventing accretion of the later colonizers (Briner *et al.*, 1986).

3.2. Cleaned Teeth

Oral surfaces are in a constant state of flux. Epithelial surfaces are renewed through sloughing off of the outer layer of cells. The tooth surface is cleaned through oral hygiene procedures. Both nascent surfaces are immediately repopulated by bacteria. While the extent of bacterial diversity appears to be temporally limited by the "slough-off" time of epithelial surface cells, bacterial accretion on the hard surfaces continues unless interrupted by oral hygiene procedures. In the absence of such procedures, thick layers of plaque can develop.

Repopulation of a clean tooth surface occurs rapidly, as shown by a recovery of about 10^5 colony-forming units from 0.024 cm^2 of tooth surface after 4 hr (Nyvad and Kilian, 1987). After 12 hr, approximately 10^7 colony-forming units were recovered. Presented with a clean surface or a newly repopulating surface, primary colonizers must adhere either to components in the salivary glycoprotein pellicle, which coats the tooth, or to already-attached bacteria. Studies of the coaggregation properties of primary colonizers should reveal a temporal relationship between coaggregation partners and the bacterial repopulation sequence.

The most numerous colonizers of a tooth root surface during the initial 4 hr after cleaning are streptococci (67–85%) and actinomyces (8–16%) (Nyvad and Kilian, 1987). Their relative predominance on a clean enamel surface after 4 hr is 47–82 and 4–32%, respectively, for streptococci and actinomyces (Nyvad and Kilian, 1987). In a separate study of just the streptococci colonizing the enamel surface during the initial 4 hr after cleaning, 700 streptococcal isolates were identified (Nyvad and Kilian, 1990). Most were *S. oralis, S. mitis* biovar 1, and *S. sanguis; S. gordonii, S. mitis* biovar 2, and *S. mutans* were less frequently isolated. The ability of primary colonizers, such as *Actinomyces, Haemophilus, Streptococcus,* and *Veillonella,* and secondary colonizers, like *Actinobacillus, Capnocytophaga, Eubacterium, Fusobacterium, Porphyromonas, Prevotella, Selenomonas,* and *Wolinella,* to recognize each other has already been extensively investigated by using more than 700 strains; the results of these pairwise coaggregations have been compiled in two reviews (Kolenbrander, 1988, 1989).

A diagrammatic representation of the sequential nature of colonization of the tooth surface is presented in Fig. 2. The streptococci bind to salivary components (Fives-Taylor and Thompson, 1985; Lamont *et al.,* 1988; Liljemark and Bloomquist, 1981; Morris and McBride, 1984; Ogier *et al.,* 1984; Gibbons *et al.,* 1986), and as discussed later in this section, but not shown here, actinomyces also recognize salivary components in the acquired pellicle. These genera along with *Haemophilus* and *Veillonella* are the most numerous primary colonizers (Liljemark *et al.,* 1986). After initial attachment of cells to the acquired pellicle, further accretion of bacteria must occur through recognition of those bacteria already bound to the hard surface. The intergeneric coaggregations are depicted as a set of complementary symbols on the partner cells. All of the interactions shown here have been reported. Many others exist but are not included here so that the figure can be kept simple. Fusobacteria coaggregate with all 11 genera tested so far (Kolenbrander *et al.,* 1989); *Haemophilus* has not been tested as a partner of fusobacteria. Each fusobacterial strain does not coaggregate with all strains of the 11 genera. Rather, a fusobacterial strain coaggregates with a certain set of partner cell types, while another fusobacterial strain coaggregates with a different set of partners indicating that highly specific partnerships are formed. In Fig. 2, the genera are grouped and *Fusobacterium* is shown interacting with *Capnocytophaga* and other early colonizers. The arrows are included to indicate the recognition. Fusobacteria also interact with the secondary colonizers, *Porphyromonas, Wolinella,* and *Eubacterium,* and thus, illustrate how they act as a bridge between the groups of early and late colonizers.

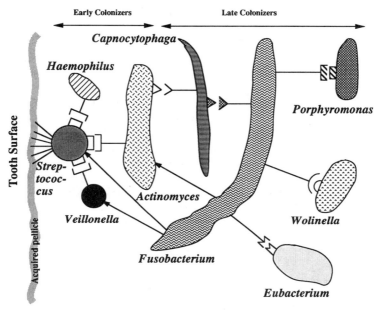

Figure 2. Diagrammatic representation of sequential attachment or accretion of bacteria on the tooth surface. Immediately after cleaning a tooth, it is coated with the acquired pellicle which is colonized primarily by streptococci. Other bacteria like actinomyces can also bind (not depicted here) to the acquired pellicle. The remainder of early colonizers include the haemophili and veillonellae. They and the actinomyces coaggregate with the streptococci by lactose-inhibitable interactions. This is shown as a complementary set of rectangular-shaped symbols. The symbol with a stem represents a component which is heat-inactivated (cell suspension is heated at 85°C for 30 min) and sensitive to protease treatment, but the cell type bearing the complementary symbol without the stem is insensitive to either treatment. The other shaped symbols depict coaggregations that are not inhibited by any known compounds. The arrows between *Fusobacterium* and the *Actinomyces*, *Streptococcus*, and *Veillonella* reflect the fact that fusobacteria coaggregate with all genera tested; *Haemophilus* has not yet been tested. Also represented here are the interactions between the fusobacteria and the late colonizing *Porphyromonas*, *Wolinella*, and *Eubacterium*. The latter three genera do not coaggregate with the early colonizing genera. Thus, the ecological succession of bacterial populations in accreting plaque is depicted.

Fusobacteria are among the most numerous bacteria found in the subgingival region of the tooth independent of whether the site exhibits symptoms of clinical health or periodontal disease. It is the only genus tested to date that coaggregates with *Eubacterium* (Kolenbrander, 1989; George *et al.*, 1991, Abstr. Am. Soc. Microbiol., p. 94) and *Wolinella* (Kolenbrander and Andersen, unpublished results), two genera found primarily in sites associated with periodontal disease (Dzink *et al.*, 1988; Moore, 1987; Tanner *et al.*, 1984). In other words, early colonizers coaggregate with each other and fusobacteria, and late colonizers coaggregate with each other or only fusobacteria. At least a portion of bacterial accretion in developing plaque is likely to occur by multigeneric coaggregations. Overall, these interactions appear to be influenced temporally by the ecological changes in the oral environment, but fusobacteria exhibit the ability to bridge the adhesion of early and later colonizing bacteria and may, thus, stabilize some of the flux in the bacterial population.

The observation of corncob formations among bacteria in dental plaque was made by Jones (1972) and Listgarten et al. (1973). These interactions occurred between a central rod-shaped cell and peripherally attached spherical cells. The completed arrangement resembles intergeneric coaggregations between cells of two morphologies (Mouton et al., 1979, 1980; DiRienzo et al., 1985). When streptococci are more than 10-fold more prevalent than fusobacteria, corncob arrangements are formed (Fig. 3A). The streptococcus also coaggregates with prevotellae (Fig. 3B), but this strain of *Prevotella* does not coaggregate with this strain of *Fusobacterium*. Thus, the strain of *Streptococcus* acts like a bridge between its two partners and forms a multigeneric coaggregate when the three strains are mixed (Fig. 3C). The arrows indicate prevotellae which are incorporated into the multigeneric coaggregate through the streptococcal coaggregation bridge. Such specificity of coaggregation partners is likely to be involved in sequential accretion of bacteria known to occur in developing plaque on the tooth surface.

Intrageneric coaggregation, interactions among bacteria within the same genus, on the other hand, has only recently been examined (Kolenbrander et al., 1990). The coaggregation properties of 122 strains of bacteria including the type strains of *S. sanguis* and *S. gordonii* as well as actinomyces and 9 other genera (*Actinobacillus, Capnocytophaga, Eubacterium, Fusobacterium, Porphyromonas, Prevotella, Rothia, Selenomonas,* and *Veillonella*) indicated that only the streptocci and the actinomyces exhibit intrageneric coaggregation (Kolenbrander et al., 1990). Even fusobacteria which coaggregate with some members of all the other 10 genera do not exhibit intrageneric coaggregation.

It is probably no coincidence that *Streptococcus* and *Actinomyces* were the only two genera that exhibited intrageneric coaggregation. Their dominance as primary colonizers may, in part, be due to their ability to recognize other primary colonizing bacteria. The fact that many of these primary colonizers did not coaggregate with secondary colonizers, and vice versa, supports the notion that a temporal relationship between colonization and coaggregation may occur. As stated earlier in this section, the primary colonizers may communicate with later colonizers through fusobacterial coaggregation bridges. Thus, while intrageneric coaggregation may be vital to initial colonization of a nascent surface, intergeneric coaggregation among fusobacteria and members of primary as well as secondary colonizers may mediate accretion and mature dental plaque development.

Both streptococci and actinomyces adhere to saliva-coated spheroidal hydroxyapatite (SHA), a model surface of the human tooth (Clark et al., 1978; Cowan et al., 1987; Kolenbrander and Celesk, 1983; Lamont et al., 1988; Morris and McBride, 1984). Secondary colonizers often do not adhere to this surface (Ciardi et al., 1987; Schwarz et al., 1987). The proline-rich proteins in human saliva which coats the tooth surface appear to mediate adhesion of human strains of *A. naeslundii* [formerly *A. viscosus* serotype II (Johnson et al., 1990)] (Cisar et al., 1988; Gibbons et al., 1988). Curiously, when the proline-rich proteins were mixed with the actinomyces, they did not

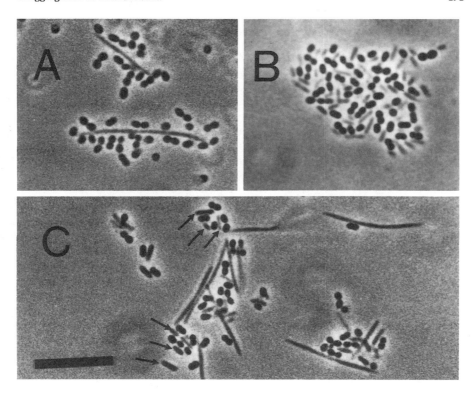

Figure 3. Phase-contrast photomicrographs of intergeneric coaggregations between *Streptococcus sanguis* C104 (spheres, panels A and B) and either *Fusobacterium nucleatum* PK1909 (long slender rods, panel A) or *Prevotella loescheii* PK1295 (short rods, panel B), and multigeneric coaggregation among the same strains from the three genera (panel C; arrows depict prevotellae). *P. loescheii* PK1295 does not coaggregate with *F. nucleatum* PK1909, but *S. sanguis* C104 coaggregates with both and acts as a coaggregation bridge between the fusobacteria and prevotellae (arrows).

inhibit binding of the bacteria to SHA. But when the proteins were mixed with the SHA, binding of the actinomyces to SHA was inhibited. The notion of cryptic receptors or cryptitopes has been suggested to characterize the hidden molecular segments that mediate adhesion of the bacteria to sites that become exposed only after binding of the proline-rich proteins to the SHA (Gibbons *et al.*, 1990).

Streptococcus gordonii also binds to proline-rich proteins, especially to the carboxy-terminal end (Ferland *et al.*, 1991). Synthetic peptides were prepared and it appears that the minimal recognition site for the *S. gordonii* adhesin is Pro-Gln. Using a different streptococcus, *S. sanguis* G9B, Bergey *et al.* (1986) showed that carbohydrate moieties of human salivary proline-rich glycoproteins can specifically interact with lectin(s) on the streptococcus.

3.3. Erupting Teeth

An untapped research area is the potential role of coaggregation in development of the bacterial successions that occur on the newly erupting teeth of infants. Considerable information is available on the kinds of bacteria found in the oral cavity of children, but no studies have been conducted on the adhesion properties of these bacteria. The remainder of this section describes what is known about the succession of the population and it is hoped that this information will spur some activity in the study of the adhesion properties of this population.

The mouth of the newborn human is usually devoid of bacteria, but, within the first day or two, the mouth is colonized almost exclusively by streptococci, including *S. salivarius* (McCarthy *et al.*, 1965). By 101 days, streptococci (both anaerobic and aerobic culture conditions) still constitute more than 95% of the culturable bacteria, veillonellae are the next most numerous anaerobic bacteria, but at this time more diversity in the population appears. Each of the 13 genera of bacteria monitored in the study was found in at least 1 of the 44 3-month-old infants examined. At 1 year, when primary teeth have erupted, fusobacteria, actinomyces, as well as veillonellae accompany the streptococci, which remain as 70% of the cultivable biota. Of these, only the streptococci and veillonellae are found in all of the children tested, whereas the other two genera are found in about 60% of the children. *A. naeslundii* is the primary actinomyces in predentate humans. Similarly, whereas *S. salivarius* is a predominant member of the salivary and mucosal biota of normal predentate infants (Carlsson *et al.*, 1970a), *S. sanguis* becomes established only after tooth eruption (Carlsson *et al.*, 1970b), and *S. mutans* is usually not found prior to the later stages of primary incisor emergence (6–8 primary incisor teeth).

The presence of the enamel surface in the oral cavity allows a new population of bacteria. As a child approaches puberty, the variety of oral bacteria becomes more similar to that found in adults. The source of each person's individual strains of bacteria is unknown but the close contact with family members or other caregivers probably influences the species of bacteria that inoculate and colonize the oral cavity. This notion is supported by the studies using *S. mutans,* which is common in adult saliva. It was shown that the unique patterns of bacteriocin production and sensitivity of isolates of *S. mutans* from mother–infant pairs were very similar suggesting that intrafamilial transmission is a likely route to establish the oral biota of children (Berkowitz and Jordan, 1975).

The nonspirochetal biotas of subgingival dental plaque from preschool children are not significantly different from those found in adults (de Araujo and Macdonald, 1964; L. V. H. Moore *et al.*, 1987). Spirochetes are found less frequently in children and when found, they are more often *Treponema socranskii* subsp. *paredis* in children as compared to adults where *T. socranskii* subsp. *buccalis* or *T. socranskii* subsp. *socranskii* are usually found (L. V. H. Moore *et al.*, 1987). The infrequent presence of spirochetes in children is consistent with the notion that spirochetes proliferate at a later time in oral cavity development when the ecological conditions are more complex.

4. Effect of Saliva on Coaggregation

Whereas saliva-coated hydroxyapatite has been used extensively as a model system (discussed below) to study bacterial adhesion, the role of saliva in coaggregation or adhesion of bacteria is uncertain. Saliva contains about 10^8 bacteria ml^{-1} (van Houte and Green, 1974; Richardson and Jones, 1958); it bathes the exposed oral surfaces so it also is likely to affect bacterial adhesion to these surfaces. It is clearly important in removal of loosely attached bacteria from solid surfaces and desquamation of soft tissue surfaces, since both bacteria and sloughed epithelial cells are in high numbers in saliva. Bacteria in saliva are viable and saliva can serve as a growth substrate (de Jong et al., 1984, 1986), suggesting that saliva may act as a carrier of cells rather than a destroyer of them. Normal salivary production is about 1 ml min^{-1}. Because of this flow rate, saliva is an effective vehicle for moving bacteria from one surface to another or for removing bacteria from the oral cavity.

Saliva is a complex mixture of a wide variety of components which include proteins, immunoglobulins, and mucins. Some oral bacteria are agglutinated by saliva (Gibbons and Spinell, 1970; Hay et al., 1971) and it appears that there are different salivary aggregation factors for different strains of bacteria (Kashket and Donaldson, 1972; Ellen et al., 1983; Gibbons et al., 1986; Ligtenberg et al., 1990). Salivary molecules such as lysozyme (Pollock et al., 1976), secretory immunoglobulin A (Bratthall and Carlen, 1978; Liljemark et al., 1979), and sialoglycoproteins (Levine et al., 1978; McBride and Gisslow, 1977) have been implicated as salivary aggregation factors. Concordant with the presence of aggregating factors in saliva is the presence of appropriate receptors on some oral bacteria as well as inhibitors of aggregation (Murakami et al., 1990; Nishikata et al., 1991). Isolation and purification of these aggregation factors and receptors has begun (Levine et al., 1987; Al-Hashimi et al., 1988; Gibbons and Hay, 1988; Babu et al., 1990) and is an active research area.

There appears to be some selectivity in the agglutination of oral bacteria by saliva (Gibbons and Spinell, 1970; Liljemark et al., 1979; Rosan et al., 1982). Some bacteria that were agglutinated by unheated saliva were not agglutinated by heated saliva (McBride and Gisslow, 1977). Heating saliva above 50°C significantly reduced its ability to aggregate S. sanguis strains G9B and M5 (Rosan et al., 1982). Aggregation of the same strains (S. sanguis M5 and ATCC10556) tested in different laboratories varied from very strong (Malamud et al., 1981) to weak or not at all (Liljemark et al., 1979; McBride and Gisslow, 1977). Results of a survey of the aggregating activity for S. sanguis M5 in saliva samples from 150 adult humans revealed no activity in some samples whereas others ranged from weak to very strong (Malamud et al., 1981). Some saliva samples that aggregated S. sanguis M5 failed to aggregate S. mutans LM7. In total, saliva that exhibited high activity for S. sanguis M5 usually possessed high activity for other strains of S. mitis, S. sanguis, and S. salivarius. Whereas the phenomenon of salivary-mediated aggregation is evident, the mechanisms involved appear to be multiple and ill-defined.

Although there are obvious difficulties in working with a complex mixture such as saliva, this is an important area of research because salivary molecules contribute significantly to the acquired pellicle, the primarily glycoprotein coating on a freshly cleaned tooth surface. Bacteria then adhere to the acquired pellicle and eventually colonize the tooth, other ecological constraints permitting.

It is important to distinguish saliva-mediated aggregation from coaggregation. Besides the fact that the former is adhesion between like cells and the latter between unlike cells, the former slowly becomes visible (minutes to hours) and the latter occurs within seconds (Ciardi et al., 1987). The former is easily dispersed by normal vortex mixing while the latter is usually unaffected or sometimes enhanced by mixing (Kolenbrander and Andersen, 1990).

The variable nature of saliva-mediated agglutination should be considered when investigating the effect if any of saliva on coaggregation. Different assay systems (Kolenbrander and Phucas, 1984; Komiyama and Gibbons, 1984b; Kolenbrander and Andersen, 1990; Lamont and Rosan, 1990) have been used to study the effect of saliva on coaggregation. In one (Kolenbrander and Phucas, 1984), the bacteria were suspended in either buffer or whole, clarified (centrifuged at 12,000g for 30 min at 4°C) unheated saliva and mixed with potential partners. Of 53 paired combinations of actinomyces, *Actinomyces naeslundii* or *Actinomyces* serovar WVa 963, and streptococci, *Streptococcus sanguis* or *S. gordonii* [formerly *S. morbillorum* (Kilian et al., 1989)], that exhibited coaggregation in buffer, all but 4 pairs gave the same coaggregation patterns when suspended in saliva (Kolenbrander and Phucas, 1984). Twenty-four pairs exhibited lactose-inhibited coaggregation in buffer; 19 of these were identical in saliva. The other five pairs either did not coaggregate or formed coaggregates that were not inhibited by lactose. Highly specific coaggregations known to occur with buffer-suspended cells (e.g., a streptococcal strain that coaggregates with a single strain of actinomyces) were unchanged when cells were suspended in saliva. Intrageneric coaggregation between streptococci also was unaffected by saliva (Kolenbrander et al., 1990). These results indicate that the coaggregation properties of both oral actinomyces and streptococci are very similar to cells suspended in either saliva or coaggregation buffer. Thus, instead of saliva-bathed surfaces acting as a barrier to coaggregation, they may in fact mediate accretion.

A quite different approach to studying effects of saliva on cell-to-cell interactions was studied by measuring the binding of radiolabeled streptococci to spermine-conjugated agarose beads coated with actinomyces (Komiyama and Gibbons, 1984b). The streptococcus–actinomyces pair exhibited lactose-inhibitable coaggregation. Lactose as well as saliva that had been depleted of streptococcal agglutinins strongly inhibited the binding of streptococci to actinomyces already bound to agarose beads. Unfortunately, the binding of the streptococci to the unoccupied spermine-coated bead was not reported so it is not possible to determine the effect of saliva or lactose on the direct binding of streptococci to beads. It was also noted by Ciardi et al. (1987) that saliva reduced adhesion of *Propionibacterium acnes* PK93 to *S. sanguis* DL1 previously bound to saliva-coated hydroxyapatite. However, the properties of the reduced adhesion in the presence of saliva were identical to those in the absence of saliva (i.e., buffer-suspended cells). In another study, Liljemark et al. (1988) used a biological adhesive to form a monolayer of *S. sanguis* on a plastic surface which was then exposed to radiolabeled *H. parainfluenzae*. No effect of saliva was noted in this coaggregation system. Coaggregation between *P. gingivalis* and *S. mitis* (Nagata *et al.*, 1990) or *S. sanguis* (Stinson *et al.*, 1991) was inhibited by saliva and serum. The results of the study by Lamont and Rosan (1990) showed that, while most coaggregations could proceed in the presence of whole saliva, some cell-to-cell interactions were inhibited by saliva and others were promoted by saliva. Taken together, the results of numerous studies of effects of saliva on coaggregation or adhesion to solid surfaces indicate inhibition by saliva of some bacterial adhesion but promotion by saliva of other bacterial adhesion. This result is not unexpected when one considers that in most ecosystems the same range of responses occurs to integral components of the systems.

It is unclear whether all of the aggregating factors are of host origin or if some are simply bacterial debris that results from degradation and lysis of bacteria by salivary lysozyme. Cell walls of bacteria as well as whole cells of bacteria coaggregate (Kolenbrander, 1988). Purified adhesin from *P. loescheii* can agglutinate partner cells of *P. loescheii* (London and Allen, 1990), and therefore, it is likely that other components of bacterial surfaces such as cell walls can also act as agglutinins of coaggregation-partner cells. The *in vivo* consequence of such agglutinations may be twofold. Agglutinated bacteria may be removed from the oral cavity by swallowing. But, on the other hand, recognition of pellicle-embedded bacterial surface parts may be a significant mechanism of bacterial accretion in developing dental plaque. Thus, highly specific kinds of recognition can result through interactions of accreting bacteria with either host-derived salivary components or pieces of lysed bacteria embedded within the acquired pellicle.

Most of the bacteria examined for their ability to coaggregate are commonly isolated from subgingival samples. The subgingival region may have little contact with saliva and is instead bathed with crevicular fluid, a secretion of serous origin (Bickel *et al.*, 1985). As with saliva, marked variability in composition of crevicular fluid was observed between people and within the same subject among different sites with the same clinical condition (Tew *et al.*, 1985). Studies with crevicular fluid have been few, because crevicular fluid is produced in microliter amounts. In a study of binding of streptococci and porphyromonads to crevicular fluid-coated hydroxyapatite, the results suggest that porphyromonads are essentially unaffected by the coating, while the adhesion of *S. sanguis* was completely inhibited (Cimasoni *et al.*, 1987). Thus, the role of either crevicular fluid or saliva in enhancing accretion, inhibiting adhesion, or causing no effect seems to be associated with the bacteria examined and not related to a universal action of host-derived molecules.

In either ecosystem, below or above the gingival margin, the bathing fluids and solid or soft tissue surfaces could be analogous to a flowing stream and rocks or other surfaces, respectively. Bacterial cells adhere and desorb continually in a changing environment. Those whose adhesion is stronger or more stable could colonize the surface even while the forces caused by the bathing fluid are favoring removal of other bacteria. On the other hand, those bacteria removed will have another chance to adhere either to a different unoccupied place on a surface or to other bacteria already attached to a different surface. The adhesion mechanisms used by oral bacteria are likely to include the highly specific recognition system observed in buffer or saliva-suspended bacteria. Similar specific recognition systems between bacteria in other ecosystems have not been explored but would seem to be present unless the oral ecosystem is unique in this property.

5. Lactose-Inhibitable Coaggregations

One of the most striking results from the survey of more than 1000 strains is the fact that the majority exhibit lactose-inhibitable coaggregation with at least one partner strain. The range of these interactions includes gram-negative partners, gram-positive partners, and mixtures of gram-negative and gram-positive partners (Fig. 4). Each interaction is represented by a complementary set of symbols that represent a lectinlike activity (heat inactivated at 85°C for 30 min; symbol with a stem) and its complementary carbohydrate-containing receptor (heat stable at 85°C for 30 min; symbol without a stem). In most cases, little is known about the structure of either the lectin or the carbohydrate.

Two foci are shown in Fig. 4: (1) interactions with *Streptococcus oralis* 34 and (2) interactions with *Fusobacterium nucleatum* PK1594. All of the lactose-inhibitable interactions of *F. nucleatum* PK1594 are with gram-negative partners that comprise members of six genera (Kolenbrander *et al.*, 1989; Kinder and Holt, 1989). The interactions are shown to be mediated by the same complementary set of symbols because a coaggregation-defective mutant of strain PK1594 fails to coaggregate with all of these partners (Ganeshkumar and Kolenbrander, unpublished results). The mutant was isolated by selecting for its failure to coaggregate with *P. gingivalis* PK1924, but it simultaneously lost the ability to coaggregate with all of the other partners. Thus, it is likely that the fusobacterial surface component is the same for all interactions, but the complementary receptors on the partners are probably structurally related and not identical. Studies using polyclonal and monoclonal antibodies against the fusobacterial adhesin (Ganeshkumar and Kolenbrander, unpublished results) should help in understanding the possibility that the adhesin may be the potential mediator of coaggregation with all six genera of partners.

The second focus of Fig. 4 presents the extensive lactose-sensitive interactions between *S. oralis* 34 and both gram-positive and gram-negative partner cells, including intrageneric coaggregations with other streptococci. As a group, the streptococci interact with five genera. Many additional interactions among the strains used in Fig. 4 cannot be shown because the partners cannot be placed near each other. For example, *Streptococcus* SM PK509 exhibits lactose-inhibitable coaggregation with *A. naeslundii* PK947, *P. loescheii* PK1295, and *V. atypica* PK1910; and *C. ochracea* ATCC33596 coaggregates with *A. naeslundii* PK947 by a lactose-sensitive mechanism. Other lactose-inhibitable coaggregations have been reported between streptococci and actinomyces (Eifuku *et al.*, 1991; Wilcox and Drucker, 1989) or *Haemophilus* (Liljemark *et al.*, 1988) and streptococci or actinomyces and *Eikenella* (Ebisu *et al.*, 1988).

At least five functionally different kinds of lactose-inhibitable interactions are

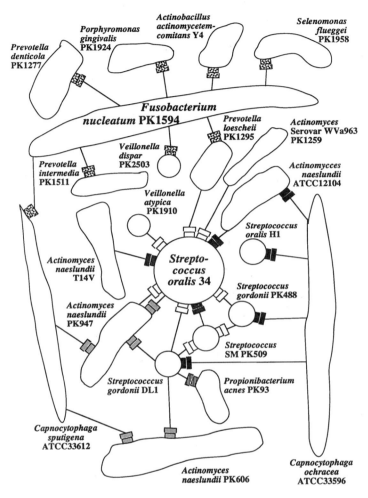

Figure 4. Diagrammatic representation of lactose-inhibitable coaggregations known to occur between pairs of oral bacteria. The complementary symbols of the same shading are thought to be functionally related and may be structurally related. Many additional interactions, both lactose-inhibitable and -noninhibitable, among these strains occur but cannot be shown (see text for explanation).

detectable among the bacteria shown surrounding the streptococci in Fig. 4. This is in sharp contrast to the single kind of lactose-inhibitable interaction between the fusobacterium and its partners. The evidence to support this model is primarily obtained from studies of coaggregation-defective mutants (Kolenbrander, 1982; Kolenbrander and Andersen, 1985, 1990; Delisle *et al.*, 1988; Weiss *et al.*, 1987a,b, 1988a; Hughes *et al.*,

1990). As with the study of the fusobacterial adhesin, the interactions between *C. ochracea* ATCC33596 and its four partners are shown to be mediated by a single symbol, the solid black rectangle. Mutants that failed to coaggregate with *S. oralis* H1 simultaneously lost the ability to coaggregate with *A. naeslundii* ATCC12104, *S. gordonii* PK488, and *Streptococcus* SM PK509 (Weiss and Kolenbrander, unpublished results). Mutants of *P. loescheii* PK1295 or *V. atypica* PK1910 (open rectangle symbols) that were isolated for failure to coaggregate with *S. oralis* 34 also were unable to coaggregate with *Streptococcus* SM PK509 (Weiss and Kolenbrander, unpublished results; Hughes *et al.*, 1990). Mutants of *S. oralis* 34 (open rectangle symbols) that were selected as ones that failed to coaggregate with *P. loescheii* PK1295, simultaneously lost the ability to coaggregate with *V. atypica* PK1910, *Actinomyces* serovar WVa963 PK1259, as well as *S. gordonii* strains PK488 and DL1. These mutants maintained coaggregation (symbol with a dense dotted pattern) with *A. naeslundii* strains T14V and ATCC12104, *Streptococcus* SM PK509, as well as their interaction, albeit by a different mechanism (symbol with a light dotted pattern), with *A. naeslundii* PK947. The interaction with *A. naeslundii* PK947 is a bimodal interaction and the mutant still coaggregated with the actinomyces through a heat-inactivated component (symbol with a light dotted pattern) on the streptococcus. The remaining interaction between *S. oralis* 34 and *A. naeslundii* T14V, *A. naeslundii* ATCC12104 and *Streptococcus* SM PK509 (symbol with a dense dotted pattern) is shown as a single kind of symbol for simplicity. The last kind of interaction (striated symbol) between *S. gordonii* DL1 and *P. acnes* PK93 is shown by a unique symbol because only strain DL1 coaggregates with PK93 (Ciardi *et al.*, 1987).

The receptors on *S. oralis* 34 (open rectangle symbols and symbols with a dense dotted pattern) are shown as two different symbols. The receptor that is recognized by *A. naeslundii* strains T14V and ATCC12104 has been purified and shown to block these coaggregations (McIntire *et al.*, 1987, 1988). It would be interesting to test this receptor for its ability to block the coaggregations between *S. oralis* 34 and its partners *V. atypica* PK1910, *P. loescheii* PK1295, *S. gordonii* PK488, and *S. gordonii* DL1. A comparison between the receptor's ability to block interactions with partners *A. naeslundii* T14V, *A. naeslundii* ATCC12104, and *Streptococcus* SM PK509 should provide evidence for different receptors that mediate a family of related lactose-sensitive lectin–carbohydrate interactions.

Some of the interactions of streptococci and their partners are quite distinct. The interaction between *C. ochracea* ATCC33596 and *S. oralis* H1 and the other three partners shown (solid black rectangle symbols) is 16-fold more efficiently inhibited by L-rhamnose or D-fucose than lactose and only poorly inhibited by *N*-acetyl-D-galactosamine (GalNAc) (Weiss *et al.*, 1987b), whereas the other interactions shown in Fig. 4 are usually inhibited by GalNAc and nearly insensitive to L-rhamnose and D-fucose.

The *F. nucleatum* PK1594–*P. gingivalis* PK1924 pair is equally sensitive to lactose, GalNAc, and D-galactose with a 50% inhibition of coaggregation at 2 mM (Kolenbrander and Andersen, 1989). Coaggregations that are equally sensitive to all three sugars have not been reported with the other lactose-sensitive coaggregations. Some coaggregating pairs like *S. oralis* 34 and *A. naeslundii* T14V are 5- to 10-fold more sensitive to lactose (about 50% inhibition with 2 mM lactose) than to the other sugars (McIntire *et al.*, 1978, 1982, 1983). Other coaggregating pairs [e.g., *S. gordonii* DL1 and *P. acnes* PK93; *S. oralis* 34 and *E. corrodens* 1073 (not shown) or *P. loescheii* PK1295] are more sensitive to GalNAc (Ciardi *et al.*, 1987; Ebisu *et al.*, 1988; Kolenbrander and Andersen, unpublished results).

A comparison of lactose-sensitive interactions among the partners of *S. oralis* 34 and the partners of *F. nucleatum* PK1594 reveals that the only common partner exhibiting lactose-sensitive interactions is *P. loescheii* PK1295. Strain PK1295 bears a receptor for the lectinlike activity of *F. nucleatum* PK1594 and expresses its own lectinlike activity that is recognized by a receptor on *S. oralis* 34. *C. sputigena* ATCC33612 is a common partner of *F. nucleatum* PK1594 and two actinomyces, strains PK947 and PK606. It is interesting that the two common partners, prevotellae and capnocytophagae, are bacteria that increase in number when the clinical health of a tooth changes to gingivitis (L. V. H. Moore *et al.*, 1987). This observation may help explain the temporal nature of the colonization of prevotellae and capnocytophagae after the streptococci and actinomyces have established themselves on the tooth surface. All other lactose-inhibitable interactions appear to be limited to either fusobacterial partners or streptococcal partners.

Extensive intrageneric coaggregations are unusual except among streptococci and to a lesser extent among actinomyces (Kolenbrander *et al.*, 1990). Although some members of the fusobacteria coaggregate with certain strains of all other genera examined thus far, they do not coaggregate among themselves. This different kind of interaction among the streptococci and actinomyces may be an integral component of the establishment of primary colonizing bacteria. The first bacteria to attach to a professionally cleaned surface have a choice of adhering to the acquired pellicle or to another bacterium already attached. Since it is known that about 80–90% of the primary colonizers are streptococci and actinomyces, the ability of these two groups of oral bacteria to adhere to close genetic relatives may be an advantage to their colonization.

Bacteria adhering later, on the other hand, have no need to coaggregate with members of the same genus. Instead, they might find greater assistance to their efforts to colonize by virtue of metabolic communication between the adherent population and the accreting population. Fusobacteria accumulate glucose in the form of intracellular glucan (Robrish and Thompson, 1989, 1990), which can be used as an energy source when glucose becomes a limiting nutrient. It is possible that small amounts of glucose are excreted which would encourage other bacteria to localize near the surface of the fusobacteria and encourage subsequent attachment. Other secondary colonizers like *Wolinella recta* produce protoheme which stimulates the growth of *P. gingivalis* and *P. melaninogenica* (Grenier and Mayrand, 1986). The latter bacterium in turn produces formate which stimulates growth of wolinellae. Almost certainly, the lactic acid produced by streptococci is utilized for a carbon and energy source by veillonellae, which in turn use succinate produced by actinomyces for synthesis of heme. The metabolic interrelationships are important determinants of successful colonization even if a successful adhesion takes place. The coordination of adhesin–receptor interactions and metabolic communication by accreting and attached bacteria is essential.

In Fig. 4, only the lactose-sensitive interactions are represented. Numerous other kinds of interactions have been observed which add to the complexity of the oral ecosystem. The characterization of some of the receptors and adhesins expressed by oral bacteria is discussed in the next several sections. This is just the beginning of a current effort in several laboratories to understand the molecular basis of bacterial adhesion to hard and soft oral tissues as well as interbacterial coaggregation.

6. Adhesins: General Comments

Interest in bacterial adhesins has burgeoned in the last five years producing major advances in our understanding of the structure–function relationships of these proteins. Investigations with certain pathogens, including the uro- and enteropathogenic Entero-bacteriaceae and oral bacteria have accounted for a significant portion of the data published about this group of proteins. Like the adhesins of the enteric bacteria, the adhesins of oral bacteria can be relegated to one of two major groups. The first consists of those adhesins that are intercalated into the outer membranes of gram-negative bacteria or the cell walls of gram-positive bacteria. Fimbria (pili)-associated adhesins constitute the second major group. In the latter group, the adhesive protein represents a "minor component" (Lindberg et al., 1987; Moch et al., 1987; Hanson et al., 1988) of the fimbrial structure itself. Functionally, many adhesins can be classified as lectins since they interact with specific carbohydrate moieties on other bacterial cells or eukaryotic cells. The remainder participate in interactions with proteins or other surface molecules. Much of the published data describing protein–protein interactions appears in preliminary reports and it is not clear whether the respective adhesin molecules are membrane- or fimbria-associated.

In contrast to the gram-negative enteric bacteria, comparatively little is known about the organization of the genomes of gram-negative oral bacteria and the mapping of their chromosomes has barely begun. A somewhat larger fund of knowledge is available for the gram-positive oral bacteria, especially certain streptococci. This lack of information has restricted the practical approaches to identifying and isolating adhesins found on oral microorganisms. Purification of adhesins by conventional chromatographic techniques has met with only limited success because adhesins appear to be present in low numbers on the cell surface and afimbriate adhesins may be difficult to dissociate from the membrane (see Section 7.2). As will become apparent from the following discussion, monospecific rabbit antisera or monoclonal antibodies have been used with a moderate degree of success to identify and purify adhesins of oral bacteria. More recently, galactosides conjugated to Sepharose beads have been used to isolate limited amounts of E. coli adhesin (Hultgren et al., 1989) and this technique may be successful in isolating limited amounts of adhesins on oral bacteria. Insertional inactivation of a possible adhesin gene in S. gordonii may also be used to identify the functional nature of the gene product and subsequent purification procedures of the adhesin (Jenkinson and Easingwood, 1990).

7. Adhesins of Gram-Negative Oral Bacteria

7.1. *Prevotella* spp. and *Porphyromonas* spp.

Among the surface proteins found on oral bacteria, those synthesized by *Prevotella* (formerly *Bacteroides,* in part) and *Porphyromonas* (formerly *Bacteroides,* in part) species have received special attention because these genera are believed to contain some of the more important periodontal pathogens (Genco and Slots, 1984). It is not surprising, therefore, that one of the first adhesins to be isolated, purified, and characterized is found on the surface of a member of this group, *P. loescheii* strain PK1295. This bacterium synthesizes at least two fimbria-associated adhesins which mediate coaggregation with *S. oralis* 34 and *A. israelii* PK14, respectively (Weiss *et al.,* 1987a). The adhesin responsible for the streptococcal interaction is a lectinlike protein which exhibits a specificity for galactosides, especially GalNAc (Weiss *et al.,* 1989). It also recognizes a variety of sialidase-treated erythrocytes. The other adhesin appears to participate in a protein–protein interaction and is not affected by mono- or oligosaccharides.

To identify and distinguish the two adhesive activities associated with the surface of the bacterium, polyclonal antisera were produced in rabbits using intact *P. loescheii* cells as the antigen. The antiserum was then absorbed with mutants that had lost the ability to coaggregate with one or the other of the two partners. Autoradiographs of immunoblots yielded presumptive evidence that the two adhesins were functionally distinct proteins (Weiss *et al.,* 1988a). Preparation of antiadhesin monoclonal antibodies confirmed that the streptococcus- and actinomyces-specific adhesins were distinct proteins with subunit molecular masses of 75 kDa and 45 kDa, respectively (Weiss *et al.,* 1988a).

The monoclonal antibodies were used to estimate the number of adhesin molecules per cell and to demonstrate that the adhesin molecules were indeed associated with the fimbriae of the bacterium. Conventional saturation experiments, using increasing levels of iodine (^{125}I)-labeled monoclonal antibodies and a constant number of bacterial cells, were subjected to a Scatchard analysis which indicated that each cell carried a maximum (theoretical) of 400 to 500 molecules of each adhesin per cell; the actual numbers are probably less than the theoretical values (Weiss *et al.,* 1988b). In immunoelectron microscopy studies, the monoclonal antibodies were used to establish that the adhesins were associated with the fimbriae of the organism. Using both direct and indirect immunogold particle techniques, it was shown that adhesin molecules were distinct from the fimbriae being located at the distal portion of the structure. They were arranged in a random fashion and were found singly, in pairs, or in small clusters (Weiss *et al.,* 1988b). Applying gold particles of different sizes coated with either the actinomyces adhesin-specific or streptococcal adhesin-specific monoclonal antibodies to cell preparations showed that both types of adhesins occasionally were observed proximal to one another. However, in general they appeared to be spatially separated and located on individual fimbriae (London *et al.,* 1989).

Using monoclonal antibodies conjugated to Sepharose A beads as an affinity matrix, sufficient purified *P. loescheii* streptococcus-specific adhesin was isolated to characterize the protein (London and Allen, 1990). The adhesin migrated in equilibrium gradient gels like a protein with a native molecular mass of 450 kDa suggesting that the adhesin may exist as a hexamer. Amino acid analysis showed that the adhesin was a hydrophilic protein with a basic pI, between 8.0 and 8.4. The purified adhesin retained its ability to bind to the galactoside-containing carbohydrate on the surface of *S. oralis* 34 and preincubation of these cells with adhesin prevented coaggregation with *P. loescheii* in conventional assays. The blocking assay was performed at a slightly acid pH, 5.6, because the adhesin undergoes autoaggregation and inactivation if the pH of the solvent phase is adjusted to the pI of the protein. At a pH near neutrality, the adhesin appeared to form soluble aggregates which were sufficiently large to form bridges between cells of *S. oralis* 34 and cause them to agglutinate. Sialidase-treated erythrocytes were also agglutinated by the adhesin at a neutral pH (Weiss *et al.*, 1989).

Other *Porphyromonas* and *Prevotella* species, specifically strains of *Porphyromonas gingivalis*, also have been assiduously screened for their ability to participate in cell-to-cell interactions. Several publications have established that *P. gingivalis* coaggregates with strains of *Fusobacterium nucleatum* in a galactoside-inhibitable interaction; however, the nature of the adhesin, which is presumed to be on the fusobacterial cells, is unknown (Kolenbrander and Andersen, 1989; Kinder and Holt, 1989). Members of *P. gingivalis* interact with an early tooth colonizer, *A. viscosus*, in a non-sugar-inhibitable and protease-resistant reaction (Ellen *et al.*, 1988). The adhesin process was inhibited by reagents that disrupt electrostatic and hydrophobic forces. In two related studies, vesicles of *P. gingivalis* were shown to mimic the intact cells by agglutinating *A. viscosus* cells. Contrary to the findings of Ellen *et al.* (1988), one study reported that the agglutination reaction was inhibited by L-arginine and to a lesser extent, lactose, whereas the second investigation found that L-arginine or protease treatment of the vesicles prevented agglutination (Singh *et al.*, 1989; Bourgeau and Mayrand, 1990). L-Arginine (and L-lysine) also inhibit coaggregation between *P. gingivalis* and strains of *S. mitis*, another early tooth-colonizing bacterium (Nagata *et al.*, 1990). Since sugars had no effect on the *P. gingivalis-S. mitis* coaggregation, the inhibition by L-arginine may be attributable to interactions between proteins on the partner cells.

In addition, protein–protein interactions appear to be responsible for the attachment of *P. gingivalis* to type IV collagen-coated hydroxyapatite particles, a model system designed to mimic oral soft tissue sites (Naito and Gibbons, 1988). Type I collagen was a less effective substrate than type IV. Using another soft tissue model, it was shown that treatment of human buccal epithelial cells with the types of destructive enzymes (proteases and sialidase) present in inflamed areas of the gingivae rendered accessible the sites suitable for attachment via adhesive molecules on the surfaces of *P. gingivalis* and *Prevotella intermedia* (Childs and Gibbons, 1990; Okuda *et al.*, 1989). Coincidently, the ability of benign oral streptococci to colonize these cell layers was diminished.

Some strains of *P. gingivalis* and *P. intermedia* possess the ability to bind to and degrade another matrix protein, fibrinogen (Lanz *et al.*, 1986, 1990). In addition to synthesizing two components (150 and 120 kDa on denaturing polyacrylamide gels) which degrade fibrinogen, a binding protein (150 kDa) specific for the substrate also is found on the cell surface (Lanz *et al.*, 1991). The fibrinogen-binding component appears to function like an adhesin which retains its activity at a temperature of 4°C. The fact that a juxtaposed protease can destroy the anchoring substratum raises the intriguing possibility that attachment may be a transient process. This circumstance would provide the bacterium with an escape mechanism from a fibrinogen (nutrient)-depleted site.

Preliminary characterizations of adhesins on *P. gingivalis* that mediate hemagglutination of human erythrocytes have been published by several laboratories (Inoshita *et al.*, 1986; Okuda *et al.*, 1986) and, in some instances, purifications were attempted (Boyd and McBride, 1984). Initial reports asserted that the adhesins were associated with the fimbriae of *P. gingivalis* (Slots and Gibbons, 1978; Okuda *et al.*, 1981). Fimbriae from a strain of *P. gingivalis* were isolated, purified, and characterized; in contrast to the fimbriae from other gram-negative bacteria, the subunits are relatively large, 40–45 kDa (Yoshimura *et al.*, 1984). However, these structures did not possess the ability to agglutinate erythrocytes. Subsequently, a protein component associated with the outer membrane was identified and used as an antigen to prepare antisera which inhibited agglutination of erythrocytes by *P. gingivalis* cells (Mouton *et al.*, 1989). The hemagglutinin appeared to exist as a single protein or complex consisting of two nonidentical polypeptides of 33 and 38 kDa, respectively. Despite the recent spate of reports, relatively little is known about the surface components that mediate the various attachment processes attributed to the porphyromonads.

7.2. Capnocytophaga spp.

All adhesins on the surface of *Capnocytophaga* species are considered to be outer membrane-associated because this group of bacteria lacks fimbriae (Holt *et al.*, 1979; Celesk and London, 1980). As shown in Figs. 2 and 4, all three species of capnocytophaga coaggregate with one or more species of gram-positive oral bacteria. *Capnocytophaga gingivalis* DR 2001 coaggregates with *A. israelii* in a neuraminic acid- or neuraminlactose-inhibitable reaction (Kagermeier *et al.*, 1984). *Capnocytophaga sputigena* ATCC33612 coaggregates with strains of *A. israelii* and *A. naeslundii* in reactions that are inhibited by neuraminic acid and rhamnose, respectively (Weiss *et al.*, 1987b). In addition to coaggregating with the same *A. israelii* and *A. naeslundii* strains as *C. sputigena*, *C. ochracea* ATCC33596 also interacts with *Streptococcus oralis* H1 in a rhamnose-inhibitable coupling (Kolenbrander and Andersen, 1984; Weiss *et al.*, 1987b).

Membrane fragments of *C. gingivalis,* prepared by ultrasonic disruption, retained the ability to mimic the intact cell and agglutinated the partner cell, *A. israelii* (Kagermeier and London, 1986). A preliminary identification of the adhesin was made by absorbing rabbit polyclonal antiserum prepared against wild-type cells with cells of a mutant defective in coaggregation. A definitive identification of the adhesin was made by preparing monoclonal antibodies against adhesin-bearing membrane fragments which completely inhibited coaggregation at nanogram levels of antibody protein (Tempro *et al.*, 1989). The adhesin was a 150-kDa protein that could be extracted from membranes with nonionic detergents.

Similarities in both the sugar inhibition patterns and the molecular masses of the putative adhesins on the surface of both *C. gingivalis* and *C. ochracea* have been reported (Weiss *et al.*, 1990) and may not be coincidental. Several lines of monoclonal antibodies prepared against vesicles of *C. ochracea* completely or partially inhibited the coaggregation between this bacterium and *S. oralis* H1 and *A. israelii*, respectively (Weiss *et al.*, 1990). Immunoblot analysis revealed that the antibodies recognized a 150-kDa membrane-associated protein. These observations suggest that the respective adhesins are functionally related. It will be of greater interest to learn whether portions of the primary structure (especially in or around the lectin-binding sites) of the two adhesin molecules were conserved during the evolutionary divergence of the three species of *Capnocytophaga*.

7.3. *Fusobacterium nucleatum*, *Haemophilus* spp., and *Treponema denticola*

The multiple lactose-inhibitable and non-lactose-inhibitable coaggregations in which *F. nucleatum* participates were described in detail in earlier sections (Sections 3.2 and 5) of this review and will not be dealt with here. The interaction of *F. nucleatum* with *Streptococcus sanguis*, that produces the typical "corn cob" configuration commonly seen in plague deposits, currently is being defined at the molecular level (Kaufman and DiRienzo, 1989). A hydrophobic 39.5-kDa polypeptide which appeared to be a major constituent of the outer membrane was isolated from the cell envelope of *F. nucleatum* and was shown to inhibit coaggregation when the purified material was preincubated with streptococcal partner cells. This preparation was also used to prepare a polyclonal antiserum that both inhibited the cell-to-cell interaction and agglutinated streptococcal cells coated with the *F. nucleatum* cell envelope protein.

F. nucleatum strain FN possesses a binding protein on its surface that recognizes galactosidic residues on certain affinity matrices and neuraminidase-treated rabbit erythrocytes (Murray *et al.*, 1987, 1988). This lectinlike protein also causes the cells to agglutinate in the presence of saliva. A preliminary identification of the hemagglutinin was achieved by solubilizing cells in detergent, resolving the proteins with denaturing PAGE, blotting onto nitrocellulose, and exposing the filter to ^{125}I-labeled asialofetuin. The radioactive glycoprotein adhered to a region on the blot equivalent to a molecular mass of 300–320 kDa. The actual receptor for the adhesin has not been identified.

Cells of *Haemophilus parainfluenzae* HP-28 coaggregate with *S. sanguis* SA-1 and bind to saliva-coated spheroidal hydroxyapatite (Liljemark *et al.*, 1985). A 34-kDa polypeptide which was one of three dominant envelope-associated proteins was extracted from the outer membranes and was purified to electrophoretic homogeneity (Lai *et al.*, 1990). Because the polypeptide inhibited coaggregation between *S. sanguis* SA-1 and *H. parainfluenzae* and inhibited attachment of *H. influenzae* to saliva-coated spheroidal hydroxyapatite, it is thought to be a major adhesin. The inhibition of both attachment processes by galactosides suggests that the putative adhesin is a lectinlike protein.

A preliminary report presented data indicating that *Treponema denticola* binds to several lines of mammalian cells via a mechanism that is mannose- or galactose-inhibitable and protease-sensitive (Weinberg and Holt, 1990). The nature of the binding protein has not yet been determined, but, as in other instances, the sugar inhibition studies suggest that the adhesin may be a lectinlike protein.

8. Adhesins of Oral Streptococci

The pivotal role played by the primary oral colonizers, which include certain species of streptococci and actinomyces, in the formation of plaque deposits has been described thoroughly earlier (see Section 3.2). The importance accorded to the attachment processes of this particular group of bacteria is reflected in the attention given to adhesive proteins on their surfaces. *Streptococcus sanguis* strain FW 213 type 1 fimbriae (not related to the mannose-sensitive fimbriae on *E. coli*) was reported to mediate attachment to saliva-coated spheroidal hydroxyapatite (SHA) (Fives-Taylor and Thompson, 1985). Antisera raised in rabbits against fimbriated *S. sanguis* cells and absorbed with nonadherent mutants blocked attachment to SHA beads (Fachon-Kalweit *et al.*, 1985). The same antiserum bound to fimbriae and the antibodies were visualized by treating the immune complex with anti-rabbit IgG-coated gold particles in immunoelectron microscopic experiments. The adhesin appears to be specific for a receptor in human saliva which is deposited on the tooth surface. A gene encoding the adhesion fimbriae was cloned into *E. coli* (Fives-Taylor *et al.*, 1987). The cloned gene expressed a 30-kDa subunit that reacted with the absorbed antiserum on immunoblots prepared from denaturing polyacrylamide gels. Subsequently, the gene was sequenced, characterized, and compared to fimbrial genes found in other oral bacteria (Fenno *et al.*, 1989). Insertional mutagenesis obliterated immunoreactivity of the polypeptide indicating that the antiserum contained antibody specific for the adhesive function.

Another group of workers cloned the gene for an adhesin from a related organism, *S. sanguis* strain 12. The protein gene product was a 36-kDa polypeptide that, like the *S. sanguis* strain FW 213 adhesin, interacted with a receptor in human saliva (Ganeshkumar *et al.*, 1988). The purified gene product expressed in *E. coli* partially inhibited attachment of *S. sanguis* strain 12 in an SHA model system. Immunoelectron microscopy indicated that antiserum raised against the gene product was not specific for the fimbriae on the surface of the cells; conversely, antiserum raised against the fimbriae did not react with the adhesive protein. It appeared unlikely, therefore, that the adhesive protein on strain 12 was a fimbrial monomer like the adhesion fimbriae of strain FW 213. However, when the nucleotide sequence of the gene for the strain 12 adhesin was determined, it showed a high degree of homology with the strain FW 213 gene (Ganeshkumar *et al.*, 1991). These anomalous reports have yet to be reconciled, but, if the viridans streptococci follow the precedent set by many enteric and oral bacteria, the adhesive protein should be a minor component associated with fimbriae rather than the fimbrial monomer itself.

9. Adhesins of Oral Actinomyces

The two antigenically distinct types of fimbriae on the surface of *A. naeslundii* (*A. viscosus*) T14V were among the first adhesive structures on oral bacteria to be studied by dental microbiologists (Cisar *et al.*, 1984). Type 1 fimbriae were implicated in the attachment of actinomyces cells to SHA beads and are considered to be one of the colonization factors of this bacterium (Cisar *et al.*, 1978). This activity was not affected by the presence of a variety of sugars. The type 2 fimbriae possessed galactoside-specific lectinlike activity that was responsible for coaggregation with certain oral streptococci and agglutination of sialidase-treated erythrocytes (Cisar, 1986). Suspensions of purified type 2 fimbriae were incapable of agglutinating either streptococcal cells or sialidase-treated erythrocytes. However, latex beads coated with these structures or fimbriae cross-linked with monoclonal antibody agglutinated both types of cells (Cisar *et al.*, 1980). This observation led to the promulgation of the hypothesis that coaggregation between *S. oralis* and *A. naeslundii* represented a reaction involving a high number (multivalent binding) of adhesin molecules that interact with receptors at a relatively low affinity.

Chromosomal DNA banks containing the genes encoding the structural subunits of the type 1 and the type 2 fimbriae of *A. naeslundii* were cloned into either plasmid or cosmid vectors (Donkersloot *et al.*, 1985; Yeung *et al.*, 1987). Both fimbrial genes were expressed in *E. coli* and positive clones were detected by immunological screening with antibodies prepared against type 1 or type 2 fimbriae. The genes were subsequently sequenced and the amino acid compositions derived from the data were compared for similarities (Yeung and Cisar, 1988, 1990). Because the respective subunits exhibited 34% amino acid homology, it was postulated that the two genes were derived from a common progenitor.

While a significant amount of information about the composition of the fimbrial subunit is available, it is not yet clear whether the adhesive properties exhibited by the type 1 and type 2 fimbriae reside within the respective fimbrial monomers or are discrete proteins associated with these structures. Recently, however, it was found that the type 1 fimbriae display a specificity for the proline-rich proteins (PRP) in saliva, specifically PRP-1 (Gibbons *et al.*, 1988). Gold particles coated with PRP-1 were used as probes to identify the areas on the fimbriae that possess the adhesin activity. Electron micrographs showed that the gold particles bound singly to various segments of the type 1 fimbriae and in relatively small numbers per cell (Leung *et al.*, 1990). The observation that large numbers of gold particles were not aligned along the length of the fimbriae but that a very small, localized number of gold particles were associated with these structures can be interpreted to mean that the PRP adhesin may be a minor component. The topological arrangement of the PRP-1-coated gold particles on *A. naeslundii* is not unlike that seen in immunoelectron micrographs of monoclonal antibody-coated gold particles on *P. loescheii* fimbria-associated adhesins (Weiss *et al.*, 1988b).

10. Receptors on Oral Bacteria

Earlier in this review (Sections 3.2 and 5), it was pointed out that many of the secondary colonizers in the oral cavity have evolved functionally similar lectinlike adhesins which take advantage of naturally occurring carbohydrates on the surface of the primary colonizing bacteria. Thus far, the best characterized receptors are polysaccharides found associated with the cell walls of the early colonizing streptococci, i.e., *S. oralis, S. sanguis,* and *S. gordonii* (see also Fig. 4).

S. oralis 34 (formerly *S. sanguis* 34) synthesizes a polysaccharide which represents one of the major surface antigens and serves as a receptor for the adhesin associated with *A. naeslundii* type 2 fimbriae (McIntire *et al.,* 1987). The purified polysaccharide inhibited coaggregation between the streptococcus and actinomyces when preincubated with the latter. Chemical analysis established that the polysaccharide consisted of repeating hexasaccharide units containing the sugars rhamnose (Rha), glucose (Glc), galactose (Gal), and GalNAc (McIntire *et al.,* 1988). The configurations, bond linkages, and anomeric forms of the respective sugars were determined by permethylation and ^{1}H or ^{31}P nuclear magnetic resonance studies. The structure was reported as:

$$[\rightarrow PO_4^- \rightarrow 6)\text{-}\alpha\text{-}D\text{-}Galp\text{NAc}(1 \rightarrow 3)\text{-}\beta\text{-}L\text{-}Rhap(1 \rightarrow 4)\text{-}\beta\text{-}D\text{-}Glcp(1 \rightarrow 6)\text{-}\beta\text{-}D\text{-}Galf$$
$$(1 \rightarrow 6)\text{-}\beta\text{-}D\text{-}Galp\text{NAc}(1 \rightarrow 3)\text{-}\alpha\text{-}D\text{-}Galp(1 \rightarrow]_n$$

and contains a phosphodiester group at the nonreducing end of the oligomer. The hexasaccharide unit appears to have only a single antigenic epitope which corresponds to the disaccharide, GalNAc–Rha. Inhibition studies with various sugars and oligosaccharides indicated that the GalNAc–Gal disaccharide at the reducing end of the molecule serves as the binding site for the *A. naeslundii* lectin (McIntire *et al.,* 1988).

The carbohydrate receptor on *S. oralis* H1 that contains the recognition site for the *C. ochracea* adhesin was isolated and characterized (Cassels and London, 1989). Like the *S. oralis* 34 receptor, the polysaccharide consisted of hexasaccharide units and both the purified hexasaccharide and polysaccharide inhibited coaggregation between *S. oralis* H1 and *C. ochracea;* the former was four times more effective on a weight basis than the latter. The hexasaccharide is composed of Rha, Gal, and Glc. Plasma desorption mass spectrometry, ^{1}H and ^{13}C nuclear magnetic resonance spectroscopy, and gas chromatography were used to determine the anomeric forms of the sugars, their glycoside linkages, and absolute configurations within the hexasaccharide unit (Cassels *et al.,* 1990). The deduced structure was:

$$\alpha\text{-}L\text{-}Rhap(1 \rightarrow 2)\text{-}\alpha\text{-}L\text{-}Rhap(1 \rightarrow 3)\text{-}\alpha\text{-}D\text{-}Galp(1 \rightarrow 3)\text{-}\beta\text{-}D\text{-}Galp(1 \rightarrow 4)\text{-}\beta\text{-}D\text{-}Glcp$$
$$(1 \rightarrow 3)\text{-}\alpha/\beta\text{-}D\text{-}Gal$$

Like the *S. oralis* 34 hexasaccharide unit, the *S. oralis* H1 oligomer also contains a phosphodiester moiety but it does not appear to be linked to the sugar on the reducing end of the unit. Since the most effective inhibitor of coaggregation was Rha, it seems likely that the Rha–Rha disaccharide is the receptor binding site recognized by the *C. ochracea* adhesin (Weiss *et al.,* 1987b; Cassels and London, 1989).

S. oralis J22 participates in coaggregation reactions with partner strains similar to those reported for *S. oralis* 34; however, the receptor polysaccharide on the former appears to be immunologically distinct from the receptor on the latter (Cisar *et al.,* 1989). Despite the immunological differences, when the polysaccharide from *S. oralis*

J22 was purified and its structure resolved by circular dichroism and nuclear magnetic resonance spectroscopy (Abeygunawardana *et al.*, 1990), the structures of the two receptors were similar. The *S. oralis* J22 polysaccharide consists of heptasaccharide units containing the same sugars as the *S. oralis* 34 hexasaccharide plus an additional branched Rha residue:

$$[\rightarrow PO_4^- \rightarrow 6)\text{-}\alpha\text{-}\text{D-Gal}p\text{NAc}(1\rightarrow 3)\text{-}\beta\text{-}\text{L-Rha}p(1\rightarrow 4)\text{-}\beta\text{-}\text{D-Glc}p(1\rightarrow 6)\text{-}\beta\text{-}$$
$$\downarrow$$
$$\alpha\text{-}\text{L-Rha}p(1\rightarrow 2)\text{-}$$

$$\text{D-Gal}f(1\rightarrow 6)\text{-}\beta\text{-}\text{D-Gal}p(1\rightarrow 3)\text{-}\alpha\text{-}\text{D-Gal}p\text{NAc-}(1\rightarrow]_n$$

If the GalNAc–Rha disaccharide also serves as the major antigenic determinant for the *S. oralis* J22 polysaccharide, the covalently bound branched rhamnose residue may be responsible for altering the conformation of the epitope and hence the immunological response to the heptasaccharide. Thus, a relatively minor addition can have far-reaching ramifications by dictating the manner in which the host's immune system will perceive the altered molecule.

11. Concluding Remarks

The relative constancy of the gas phase, temperature, and nutrient supply within the oral cavity appears to have provided a stable and hospitable environment that has encouraged the development of a complex microbiota (Moore, 1987; Moore *et al.*, 1988). It is easy to envisage how so suitable a habitat supplied the driving force for the evolution of the variety of complex attachment mechanisms touched on in this review. The frequency with which multiple adhesins of differing specificities occur among individual species of oral bacteria is testimony to the survival value of these surface molecules. Pressure to utilize both carbohydrate and noncarbohydrate receptors located on the early tooth- and tissue-colonizing streptococci appears to have encouraged a degree of specialization in the evolution of adhesin molecules that might not be tolerated in other less hospitable natural habitats. One notable example of the consequences of this directed evolutionary pressure can be seen in the ubiquitous fashion with which a galactoside-containing polysaccharide of *S. oralis* 34 has been used as a receptor (Kolenbrander, 1991). This polysaccharide is recognized by adhesins found on species of four diverse genera of oral bacteria: *Actinomyces, Prevotella, Veillonella,* and *Streptococcus* (see Fig. 4). From preliminary immunological studies (London *et al.*, unpublished results), it does not appear that this genetically diverse group of bacteria have evolved structurally similar adhesins. And, it is equally improbable that these bacteria acquired a common adhesive protein via horizontal evolution of some ancestral adhesin gene. However, these theories can be tested soon using DNA probes representing one or more of the adhesin genes. It is likely that only the region of the genes coding for the binding sites will exhibit some homology reflecting the similarities in modes of attachment. In this instance, environmental pressures may have been sufficiently strong to result in the convergent evolution of isofunctional adhesins.

Unlike some like intestinal bacteria (Nowicki *et al.*, 1984), a significant number of the oral microbiota have acquired the ability to synthesize different adhesive proteins simultaneously. Fabricating a complete complement of adhesins in a constitutive fashion enhances both the options for colonization and the chances of survival of these microorganisms. The value of a lectinlike adhesin increases dramatically when the protein recognizes a sugar or a group of sugars found both in a bacterial polysaccharide and in a eukaryotic glycoconjugate (Weiss *et al.*, 1989). In these instances, however, it is difficult, if not impossible, to ascertain which of the two receptors provided the impetus for the evolution of the adhesin. A few years ago, discovering multiple adhesins on a single bacterium might have been considered a remarkable finding. Today, a more pertinent question seems to be how many bacterial adhesins remain undetected and unknown. Surprisingly few functionally distinct adhesins have been found (Fig. 4). An inductive process triggered by some environmental parameter or a tactile signal generated by another prokaryotic or eukaryotic cell is essential for their expression. Just as the pressures of the oral habitat influenced and directed the evolution of adhesins, these proteins now define the ecosystem.

References

Abeygunawardana, C., Bush, C. A., and Cisar, J. O., 1990, Complete structure of the polysaccharide from *Streptococcus sanguis* J22, *Biochemistry* **29:**234–248.

Al-Hashimi, I., Dickinson, D. P., and Levine, M. J., 1988, Purification, molecular cloning, and sequencing of salivary cystatin SA-I, *J. Biol. Chem.* **263:**9381–9387.

Babu, J. P., Dabbous, M. K., and Abraham, S. N., 1991, Isolation and characterization of a 180-kilodalton salivary glycoprotein which mediates the attachment of *Actinomyces naeslundii* to human buccal epithelial cells, *J. Periodont. Res.* **26:**97–106.

Bergey, E. J., Levine, M. J., Reddy, M. S., Bradway, S. D., and Al-Hashimi, I., 1986, Use of the photoaffinity cross-linking agent N-hydroxysuccinimidyl-4-azidosalicylic acid to characterize salivary-glycoprotein–bacterial interactions, *Biochem. J.* **234:**43–48.

Berkowitz, R. J., and Jordan, H. V., 1975, Similarity of bacteriocins of *Streptococcus mutans* from mother and infant, *Arch. Oral Biol.* **20:**725–730.

Bickel, M., Cimasoni, G., and Andersen, E., 1985, Flow and albumin content of early (pre-inflammatory) gingival crevicular fluid from human subjects, *Arch. Oral Biol.* **30:**599–602.

Bourgeau, G., and Mayrand, D., 1990, Aggregation of *Actinomyces* strains by extracellular vesicles produced by *Bacteroides gingivalis, Can. J. Microbiol.* **36:**362–365.

Boyd, J., and McBride, B. C., 1984, Fractionation of hemagglutinating and bacterial binding adhesins of *Bacteroides gingivalis, Infect. Immun.* **45:**403–409.

Bratthall, D., and Carlen, A., 1978, Salivary agglutinins and secretory IgA reactions with oral streptococci, *Scand. J. Dent. Res.* **86:**430–443.

Briner, W. W., Grossman, E., Buckner, R. Y., Rebitski, G. F., Sox, T. E., Setser, R. E., and Ebert, M. L., 1986, Effect of chlorhexidine gluconate mouthrinse on plaque bacteria, *J. Periodont. Res. (Suppl.)* **16:**44–52.

Carlsson, J., Grahnén, H., Jonsson, G., and Wikner, S., 1970a, Early establishment of *Streptococcus salivarius* in the mouth of infants, *J. Dent. Res.* **49:**415–419.

Carlsson, J., Grahnén, H., Jonsson, G., and Wikner, S., 1970b, Establishment of *Streptococcus sanguis* in the mouths of infants, *Arch. Oral Biol.* **15**:1143–1148.

Cassels, F. J., and London, J., 1989, Isolation of a coaggregation-inhibiting cell wall polysaccharide from *Streptococcus sanguis* H1, *J. Bacteriol.* **171**:4019–4025.

Cassels, F. J., Fales, H. M., London, J., Carlson, R. W., and van Halbeek, H., 1990, Structure of a streptococcal adhesin carbohydrate receptor, *J. Biol. Chem.* **265**:14127–14135.

Celesk, R., and London, J., 1980, Attachment of oral *Cytophaga* species to hydroxyapatite-containing surfaces, *Infect. Immun.* **29**:768–777.

Childs, W. C., and Gibbons, R. J., 1990, Selective modulation of bacterial attachment to oral epithelial cells by enzyme activities associated with poor oral hygiene, *J. Periodont. Res.* **25**:172–178.

Chisari, G., and Gismondo, M. R., 1986, Coaggregation between *Actinomyces viscosus* with *Streptococcus pyogenes* and *Streptococcus agalactiae, Microbiologica* **9**:393–398.

Ciardi, J. E., McCray, G. F. A., Kolenbrander, P. E., and Lau, A., 1987, Cell-to-cell interaction of *Streptococcus sanguis* and *Propionibacterium acnes* on saliva-coated hydroxyapatite, *Infect. Immun.* **55**:1441–1446.

Cimasoni, G., Song, M., and McBride, B. C., 1987, Effect of crevicular fluid and lysosomal enzymes on the adhesion of streptococci and bacteroides to hydroxyapatite, *Infect. Immun.* **55**:1484–1489.

Cisar, J. O., 1986, Fimbrial lectins of the oral actinomyces, in: *Microbial Lectins and Agglutinins* (D. Mirelman, ed.), Wiley, New York, pp. 183–196.

Cisar, J. O., Vatter, A., and McIntire, F. C., 1978, Identification of the virulence-associated antigen on the surface fibrils of *Actinomyces viscosus* T14, *Infect. Immun.* **19**:313–319.

Cisar, J. O., Barsumian, E. L., Curl, S. H., Vatter, A. E., Sandberg, A. L., and Siraganian, R. P., 1980, The use of monoclonal antibodies on the study of lactose-sensitive adhesion of *Actinomyces viscosus* T14V, *J. Reticuloendothel. Soc.* **28**:73s–79s.

Cisar, J. O., Sandberg, A. L., and Mergenhagen, S. E., 1984, The function and distribution of different fimbriae on strains of *Actinomyces viscosus* and *Actinomyces naeslundii, J. Dent. Res.* **63**:393–396.

Cisar, J. O., Vatter, A. E., Clark, W. B., Curl, S. H., Hurst-Calderone, S., and Sandberg, A. L., 1988, Mutants of *Actinomyces viscosus* T14V lacking type 1, type 2 or both types of fimbriae, *Infect. Immun.* **56**:2984–2989.

Cisar, J. O., Brennan, M. J., and Sandberg, A. L., 1989, Bacterial and host receptors for the *Actinomyces* spp. fimbrial lectin, in: *Molecular Mechanisms of Microbial Adhesion* (L. Switalski, M. Hook, and E. Beachey, eds.), Springer-Verlag, Berlin, pp. 164–170.

Clark, W. B., Bammann, L. L., and Gibbons, R. J., 1978, Comparative estimates of bacterial affinities and adsorption sites on hydroxyapatite surfaces, *Infect. Immun.* **19**:846–853.

Cowan, M. M., Taylor, K. G., and Doyle, R. J., 1987, Energetics of the initial phase of adhesion of *Streptococcus sanguis* to hydroxylapatite, *J. Bacteriol.* **169**:2995–3000.

Crowley, P. J., Fischlschweiger, W., Coleman, S. E., and Bleiweis, A. S., 1987, Intergeneric bacterial coaggregations involving mutans streptococci and oral actinomyces, *Infect. Immun.* **55**:2695–2700.

de Araujo, W. C., and Macdonald, J. B., 1964, The gingival crevice microbiota in five preschool children, *Arch. Oral Biol.* **9**:227–228.

de Jong, M. H., van der Hoeven, J. S., van Os, J. H., and Olijve, J. H., 1984, Growth of oral *Streptococcus* species and *Actinomyces viscosus* in human saliva, *Appl. Environ. Microbiol.* **47**:901–904.

de Jong, M. H., van der Hoeven, J. S., and van Os, J. H., 1986, Growth of micro-organisms from supragingival dental plaque on saliva agar, *J. Dent. Res.* **65**:85–88.

Delisle, A. L., Donkersloot, J. A., Kolenbrander, P. E., and Tylenda, C. A., 1988, Use of lytic bacteriophage for *Actinomyces viscosus* T14V as a probe for cell surface components mediating intergeneric coaggregation, *Infect. Immun.* **56**:54–59.

DiRienzo, J. M., Porter-Kaufman, J., Haller, J., and Rosan, B., 1985, Corncob formation: A morphological model for molecular studies of bacterial interactions, in: *Molecular Basis of Oral*

Microbial Adhesion (S. E. Mergenhagen and B. Rosan, eds.), American Society for Microbiology, Washington, D.C., pp. 172–176.

Donkersloot, J. A., Cisar, J. O., Wax, E. M., Harr, R. J., and Chassy, B. M., 1985, Expression of *Actinomyces viscosus* antigens in *Escherichia coli:* Cloning of a structural gene (fimA) for type 2 fimbriae, *J. Bacteriol.* **162:**1075–1078.

Dzink, J. L., Socransky, S. S., and Haffajee, A. D., 1988, The predominant cultivable microbiota of active and inactive lesions of destructive periodontal diseases, *J. Clin. Periodontol.* **15:**316–323.

Ebisu, S., Nakae, H., and Okada, H., 1988, Coaggregation of *Eikenella corrodens* with oral bacteria mediated by bacterial lectin-like substance, *Ádv. Dent. Res.* **2:**323–327.

Eifuku, H., Yakushiji, T., Mizuno, J., Kudo, N., and Inoue, M., 1990, Cellular coaggregation of oral *Streptococcus milleri* with actinomyces, *Infect. Immun.* **58:**163–168.

Eifuku, H., Kitada, K., Yakushiji, T., and Inoue, M., 1991, Lactose-sensitive and -insensitive cell surface interactions of oral *Streptococcus milleri* strains and actinomyces, *Infect. Immun.* **59:**460–463.

Ellen, R. P., Bratthall, D., Borgström, M., and Howley, T. P., 1983, *Actinomyces viscosus* and *Actinomyces naeslundii* agglutinins in human saliva, *Scand. J. Dent. Res.* **91:**263–273.

Ellen, R. P., Schwarz-Faulkner, S., and Grove, D. A., 1988, Coaggregation among periodontal pathogens, emphasizing *Bacteroides gingivalis–Actinomyces viscosus* cohesion on a saliva-coated mineral surface, *Can. J. Microbiol.* **34:**299–306.

Fachon-Kalweit, S., Elder, B. L., and Fives-Taylor, P., 1985, Antibodies that bind to fimbriae block adhesion of *Streptococcus sanguis* to saliva-coated hydroxyapatite, *Infect. Immun.* **48:**617–624.

Fenno, J. C., LeBlanc, D. J., and Fives-Taylor, P., 1989, Nucleotide sequence analysis of a type 1 fimbrial gene of *Streptococcus sanguis* FW213, *Infect. Immun.* **57:**3527–3533.

Ferland, M. S., Gibbons, R. J., Hay, D. I., Schluckebier, S. K., and Schlesinger, D. H., 1991, A segment of salivary acidic proline-rich proteins which promotes adhesion of *Streptococcus gordonii* to hydroxyapatite, *J. Dent. Res. Abstr.* **70:**581.

Fives-Taylor, P. M., and Thompson, D. W., 1985, Surface properties of *Streptococcus sanguis* FW213 mutants nonadherent to saliva-coated hydroxyapatite, *Infect. Immun.* **47:**752–759.

Fives-Taylor, P. M., Macrina, F. L., Pritchard, T. J., and Peene, S. S., 1987, Expression of *Streptococcus sanguis* antigens in *Escherichia coli:* Cloning of a structural gene for adhesion fimbriae, *Infect. Immun.* **55:**123–128.

Ganeshkumar, N., Song, M., and McBride, B. C., 1988, Cloning of a *Streptococcus sanguis* adhesin which mediates binding to saliva-coated hydroxyapatite, *Infect. Immun.* **56:**1150–1157.

Ganeshkumar, N., Hannam, P. M., Kolenbrander, P. E., and McBride, B. C., 1991, Nucleotide sequence of a gene coding for a saliva-binding protein (SsaB) from *Streptococcus sanguis* 12 and possible role of the protein in coaggregation with actinomyces, *Infect. Immun.* **59:**1093–1099.

Genco, R. J., and Slots, J., 1984, Host responses in periodontal diseases, *J. Dent. Res.* **63:**441–451.

George, K. S., Falkler, W. A., Baumgartner, J. C., and Hall, E. R., 1991, Coaggregation studies of *Eubacterium* species, *Abstr. Am. Soc. Microbiol.* p. 94.

Gibbons, R. J., and Hay, D. I., 1988, Human salivary acidic proline-rich proteins and statherin promote the attachment of *Actinomyces viscosus* LY7 to apatitic surfaces, *Infect. Immun.* **56:**439–445.

Gibbons, R. J., and Nygaard, M., 1970, Interbacterial aggregation of plaque bacteria, *Arch. Oral Biol.* **15:**1397–1400.

Gibbons, R. J., and Spinell, D. M., 1970, Salivary-induced aggregation of plaque bacteria, in: *Dental Plaque* (W. D. McHugh, ed.), Livingstone, Edinburgh, pp. 207–215.

Gibbons, R. J., Cohen, L., and Hay, D. I., 1986, Strains of *Streptococcus mutans* and *Streptococcus sobrinus* attach to different pellicle receptors, *Infect. Immun.* **52:**555–561.

Gibbons, R. J., Hay, D. I., Cisar, J. O., and Clark, W. B., 1988, Adsorbed salivary proline-rich protein-1 and statherin: Receptors for type 1 fimbriae of *Actinomyces viscosus* T14V-J1 on apatitic surfaces, *Infect. Immun.* **56:**2990–2993.

Gibbons, R. J., Hay, D. I., Childs, W. C., III, and Davis, G., 1990, Role of cryptic receptors (cryptitopes) in bacterial adhesion to oral surfaces, *Arch. Oral Biol.* **35**:107s–114s.

Grenier, D., and Mayrand, D., 1986, Nutritional relationships between oral bacteria, *Infect. Immun.* **53**:616–620.

Hanson, M. S., Hempe, S. J., and Brinton, C. C., Jr., 1988, Purification of the *Escherichia coli* type 1 pilin and minor pilus proteins and partial characterization of the adhesin protein, *J. Bacteriol.* **170**:3350–3358.

Harty, D. W. S., and Handley, P. S., 1989, Expression of the surface properties of the fibrillar *Streptococcus salivarius* HB and its adhesion deficient mutants grown in continuous culture under glucose limitation, *J. Gen. Microbiol.* **135**:2611–2621.

Hay, D. I., Gibbons, R. J., and Spinell, D. M., 1971, Characteristics of some high molecular weight constituents with bacterial aggregating activity from whole saliva and dental plaque, *Caries Res.* **5**:111–123.

Holt, S. C., Leadbetter, E. R., and Socransky, S. S., 1979, Capnocytophaga: New genus of gram-negative gliding bacteria. II. Morphology and ultrastructure, *Arch. Microbiol.* **122**:17–27.

Hughes, C. V., Kolenbrander, P. E., Andersen, R. N., and Moore, L. V. H., 1988, Coaggregation properties of human oral *Veillonella* spp.: Relationship to colonization site and oral ecology, *Appl. Environ. Microbiol.* **54**:1957–1963.

Hughes, C. V., Roseberry, C. A., and Kolenbrander, P. E., 1990, Isolation and characterization of coaggregation-defective mutants of *Veillonella atypica*, *Arch. Oral Biol.* **35**:123S–125S.

Hultgren, S. J., Lindberg, F., Magnusson, G., Kihlberg, J., Tennent, J., and Normark, S., 1989, The PapG adhesin of uropathogenic *Escherichia coli* contains separate regions for receptor binding and for the incorporation into the pilus, *Proc. Natl. Acad. Sci. USA* **86**:4357–4361.

Inoshita, E., Amano, A., Hanioka, T., Tamagawa, H., Shizukuishi, S., and Tsunemitsu, A., 1986, Isolation and some properties of exohemagglutinin from the culture medium of *Bacteroides gingivalis* 381, *Infect. Immun.* **52**:421–427.

Jenkinson, H. F., and Easingwood, R. A., 1990, Insertional inactivation of the gene encoding a 76-kilodalton cell surface polypeptide in *Streptococcus gordonii* Challis has a pleiotopic effect on cell surface composition and properties, *Infect. Immun.* **58**:3689–3697.

Johnson, J. L., Moore, L. V. H., Kaneko, B., and Moore, W. E. C., 1990, *Actinomyces georgiae* sp. nov., *Actinomyces gerencseriae* sp. nov., designation of two genospecies of *Actinomyces naeslundii*, and inclusion of *A. naeslundii* serotypes II and III and *Actinomyces viscosus* serotype II in *A. naeslundii* genospecies 2, *Int. J. Syst. Bacteriol.* **40**:273–286.

Jones, S. J., 1972, A special relationship between spherical and filamentous microorganisms in mature human dental plaque, *Arch. Oral Biol.* **17**:613–616.

Kagermeier, A. S., and London, J., 1986, Identification and preliminary characterization of a lectinlike protein from *Capnocytophaga gingivalis* (emended), *Infect. Immun.* **51**:490–494.

Kagermeier, A. S., London, J., and Kolenbrander, P. E., 1984, Evidence for the participation of N-acetylated amino sugars in the coaggregation between *Cytophaga* species strain DR2001 and *Actinomyces israelii* PK16, *Infect. Immun.* **44**:299–305.

Kashket, S., and Donaldson, C. G., 1972, Saliva-induced aggregation of oral streptococci, *J. Bacteriol.* **112**:1127–1133.

Kaufman, J., and DiRienzo, J. M., 1989, Isolation of a corncob (coaggregation) receptor polypeptide from *Fusobacterium nucleatum*, *Infect. Immun.* **57**:331–337.

Kilian, M., Mikkelsen, L., and Henrichsen, J., 1989, Taxonomic study of viridans streptococci: Description of *Streptococcus gordonii* sp. nov. and emended descriptions of *Streptococcus sanguis* (White and Niven 1946), *Streptococcus oralis* (Bridge and Sneath 1982), and *Streptococcus mitis* (Andrewes and Horder 1906), *Int. J. Syst. Bacteriol.* **39**:417–484.

Kinder, S. A., and Holt, S. C., 1989, Characterization of coaggregation between *Bacteroides gingivalis* T22 and *Fusobacterium nucleatum* T18, *Infect. Immun.* **57**:3425–3433.

Kolenbrander, P. E., 1982, Isolation and characterization of coaggregation-defective mutants of *Actinomyces viscosus, Actinomyces naeslundii,* and *Streptococcus sanguis, Infect. Immun.* **37:**1200–1208.

Kolenbrander, P. E., 1988, Intergeneric coaggregation among human oral bacteria and ecology of dental plaque, *Annu. Rev. Microbiol.* **42:**627–656.

Kolenbrander, P. E., 1989, Surface recognition among oral bacteria: Multigeneric coaggregations and their mediators, *Crit. Rev. Microbiol.* **17:**137–159.

Kolenbrander, P. E., 1991, Coaggregation: Adherence in the human oral microbial ecosystem, in: *Microbiol Cell-Cell Interactions* (M. Dworkin, ed.), American Society for Microbiology, Washington, D.C., pp. 303–329.

Kolenbrander, P. E., and Andersen, R. N., 1984, Cell-to-cell interactions of *Capnocytophaga* and *Bacteroides* species with other oral bacteria and their potential role in development of plaque, *J. Periodont. Res.* **19:**564–569.

Kolenbrander, P. E., and Andersen, R. N., 1985, Use of coaggregation-defective mutants to study the relationships of cell-to-cell interactions and oral microbial ecology, in: *Molecular Basis of Oral Microbial Adhesion* (S. E. Mergenhagen and B. Rosan, eds.), American Society for Microbiology, Washington, D.C., pp. 164–171.

Kolenbrander, P. E., and Andersen, R. N., 1986, Multigeneric aggregations among oral bacteria: A network of independent cell-to-cell interactions, *J. Bacteriol.* **168:**851–859.

Kolenbrander, P. E., and Andersen, R. N., 1988, Intergeneric rosettes: Sequestered surface recognition among human periodontal bacteria, *Appl. Environ. Microbiol.* **54:**1046–1050.

Kolenbrander, P. E., and Andersen, R. N., 1989, Inhibition of coaggregation between *Fusobacterium nucleatum* and *Porphyromonas (Bacteroides) gingivalis* by lactose and related sugars, *Infect. Immun.* **57:**3204–3209.

Kolenbrander, P. E., and Andersen, R. N., 1990, Characterization of *Streptococcus gordonii (S. sanguis)* PK488 adhesin-mediated coaggregation with *Actinomyces naeslundii* PK606, *Infect. Immun.* **58:**3064–3072.

Kolenbrander, P. E., and Celesk, R. A., 1983, Coaggregation of human oral *Cytophaga* species and *Actinomyces israelii, Infect. Immun.* **40:**1178–1185.

Kolenbrander, P. E., and Phucas, C. S., 1984, Effect of saliva on coaggregation of oral *Actinomyces* and *Streptococcus* species, *Infect. Immun.* **44:**228–233.

Kolenbrander, P. E., Andersen, R. N., and Holdeman, L. V., 1985, Coaggregation of oral *Bacteroides* species with other bacteria: Central role in coaggregation bridges and competitions, *Infect. Immun.* **48:**741–746.

Kolenbrander, P. E., Andersen, R. N., and Moore, L. V. H., 1989, Coaggregation of *Fusobacterium nucleatum, Selenomonas flueggei, Selenomonas infelix, Selenomonas noxia,* and *Selenomonas sputigena* with strains from 11 genera of oral bacteria, *Infect. Immun.* **57:**3194–3203.

Kolenbrander, P. E., Andersen, R. N., and Moore, L. V. H., 1990, Intrageneric coaggregation among strains of human oral bacteria: Potential role in primary colonization of the tooth surface, *Appl. Environ. Microbiol.* **56:**3890–3894.

Komiyama, K., and Gibbons, R. J., 1984a, Interbacterial adhesion between *Actinomyces viscosus* and strains of *Streptococcus pyogenes, Streptococcus agalactiae,* and *Pseudomonas aeruginosa, Infect. Immun.* **44:**86–90.

Komiyama, K., and Gibbons, R. J., 1984b, Inhibition of lactose-reversible adhesion between *Actinomyces viscosus* and oral streptococci by salivary components, *Caries Res.* **18:**193–200.

Lai, C.-H., Bloomquist, C., and Liljemark, W. F., 1990, Purification and characterization of an outer membrane protein adhesin from *Haemophilus parainfluenzae* HP-28, *Infect. Immun.* **58:**3833–3839.

Lamont, R. J., and Rosan, B., 1990, Adhesion of mutans streptococci to other oral bacteria, *Infect. Immun.* **58:**1738–1743.

Lamont, R. J., Rosan, B., Murphy, G. M., and Baker, C. T., 1988, *Streptococcus sanguis* surface antigens and their interactions with saliva, *Infect. Immun.* **56**:64–70.

Lanz, M. S., Rowland, R. W., Switalski, L. M., and Hook, M., 1986, Interactions of *Bacteroides gingivalis* with fibrinogen, *Infect. Immun.* **54**:654–658.

Lanz, M. S., Allen, R. D., Bounelis, P., Switalski, L. M., and Hook, M., 1990, *Bacteroides gingivalis* and *Bacteroides intermedius* recognize different sites on human fibrinogen, *J. Bacteriol.* **172**:716–726.

Lanz, M. S., Allen, R. D., Vail, T. A., Switalski, L. M., and Hook, M., 1991, Specific cell components of *Bacteroides gingivalis* mediate binding and degradation of human fibrinogen, *J. Bacteriol.* **173**:495–504.

Leung, K.-P., Nesbitt, W. E., Fischlschweiger, W., Hay, D. I., and Clark, W. B., 1990, Binding of colloidal gold-labeled salivary proline-rich proteins to *Actinomyces viscosus* type 1 fimbriae, *Infect. Immun.* **58**:1986–1991.

Levine, M. J., Herzberg, M. C., Levine, M. S., Ellison, S. A., Stinson, M. W., Li, H. C., and Van Dyke, T., 1978, Specificity of salivary–bacterial interactions: Role of terminal sialic acid residues in the interaction of salivary glycoproteins with *Streptococcus sanguis* and *Streptococcus mutans*, *Infect. Immun.* **19**:107–115.

Levine, M. J., Reddy, M. S., Tabak, L. A., Loomis, R. E., Bergey, E. J., Jones, P. C., Cohen, R. E., Stinson, M. W., and Al-Hashimi, I., 1987, Structural aspects of salivary glycoproteins, *J. Dent. Res.* **66**:436–441.

Ligtenberg, A. J. M., Veerman, E. C. I., DeGraff, J., and Nieuw Amerongen, A. V., 1990, Saliva-induced aggregation of oral streptococci and the influence of blood group reactive substances, *Arch. Oral Biol.* **35**:141S–143S.

Liljemark, W. F., and Bloomquist, C. G., 1981, Isolation of a protein-containing cell surface component from *Streptococcus sanguis* which affects its adhesion to saliva-coated hydroxyapatite, *Infect. Immun.* **34**:428–434.

Liljemark, W. F., Bloomquist, C. G., and Ofstehage, J. C., 1979, Aggregation and adhesion of *Streptococcus sanguis*: Role of human salivary immunoglobulin A, *Infect. Immun.* **26**:1104–1110.

Liljemark, W. F., Bloomquist, C. G., and Fenner, L. J., 1985, Characteristics of the adhesion of oral *Haemophilus* species to an experimental salivary pellicle and to other oral bacteria, in: *Molecular Basis of Oral Microbial Adhesion* (S. E. Mergenhagen and B. Rosan, eds.), American Society for Microbiology, Washington, D.C., pp. 94–102.

Liljemark, W. F., Fenner, L. J., and Bloomquist, C. G., 1986, In vivo colonization of salivary pellicle by *Haemophilus*, *Actinomyces* and *Streptococcus* species, *Caries Res.* **20**:481–497.

Liljemark, W. F., Bloomquist, C. G., Coulter, M. C., Fenner, L. J., Skopek, R. J., and Schachtele, C. F., 1988, Utilization of a continuous streptococcal surface to measure interbacterial adhesion *in vitro* and *in vivo*, *J. Dent. Res.* **67**:1455–1460.

Lindberg, F., Lund, B., Johansson, L., and Normark, S., 1987, Localization of the receptor-binding protein adhesin at the tip of the bacterial pilus, *Nature* **328**:84–87.

Listgarten, M. A., Mayo, H., and Amsterdam, M., 1973, Ultrastructure of the attachment device between coccal and filamentous microorganisms in "corn cob" formation of dental plaque, *Arch. Oral Biol.* **18**:651–656.

London, J., and Allen, J., 1990, Purification and characterization of a *Bacteroides loeschei* adhesin that interacts with procaryotic and eucaryotic cells, *J. Bacteriol.* **172**:2527–2534.

London, J., Hand, A. R., Weiss, E. I., and Allen, J., 1989, *Bacteroides loeschei* PK1295 cells express two distinct adhesins simultaneously, *Infect. Immun.* **57**:3940–3944.

McBride, B. C., and Gisslow, M. T., 1977, Role of sialic acid in saliva-induced aggregation of *Streptococcus sanguis*, *Infect. Immun.* **18**:35–40.

McBride, B. C., and van der Hoeven, J. S., 1981, Role of interbacterial adhesion in colonization of the oral cavities of gnotobiotic rats infected with *Streptococcus mutans* and *Veillonella alcalescens*, *Infect. Immun.* **33**:467–472.

McCarthy, C., Snyder, M. L., and Parker, R. B., 1965, The indigenous oral biota of man. I. The newborn to the 1-year-old infant, *Arch. Oral Biol.* **10**:61–70.

McIntire, F. C., Vatter, A. E., Baros, J., and Arnold, J., 1978, Mechanism of coaggregation between *Actinomyces viscosus* T14V and *Streptococcus sanguis* 34, *Infect. Immun.* **21**:978–988.

McIntire, F. C., Crosby, L. K., and Vatter, A. E., 1982, Inhibitors of coaggregation between *Actinomyces viscosus* T14V and *Streptococcus sanguis* 34: β-Galactosides, related sugars, and anionic amphipathic compounds, *Infect. Immun.* **36**:371–378.

McIntire, F. C., Crosby, L. K., Barlow, J. J., and Matta, K. L., 1983, Structural preferences of β-galactoside-reactive lectins on *Actinomyces viscosus* T14V and *Actinomyces naeslundii* WVU45, *Infect. Immun.* **41**:848–850.

McIntire, F. C., Bush, C. A., Wu, S.-S., Li, S.-C., Li, Y.-T., McNeil, M., Tjoa, S. S., and Fennessey, P. V., 1987, Structure of a new hexasaccharide from the coaggregation polysaccharide of *Streptococcus sanguis* 34, *Carbohydr. Res.* **166**:133–143.

McIntire, F. C., Crosby, L. K., Vatter, A. E., Cisar, J. O., McNeil, M. R., Bush, C. A., Tjoa, S. S., and Fennessey, P. V., 1988, A polysaccharide from *Streptococcus sanguis* 34 that inhibits coaggregation of *S. sanguis* 34 with *Actinomyces viscosus* T14V, *J. Bacteriol.* **170**:2229–2235.

Malamud, D., Appelbaum, B., Kline, R., and Golub, E. E., 1981, Bacterial aggregating activity in human saliva: Comparisons of bacterial species and strains, *Infect. Immun.* **31**:1003–1006.

Moch, T., Hoschutsky, H., Hacker, J., Kroncke, K.-D., and Jann, K., 1987, Isolation and characterization of the a-sialyl-β-2,3-galactosyl-specific adhesin from fimbriated *Escherichia coli*, *Proc. Natl. Acad. Sci. USA* **84**:3462–3466.

Moore, L. V. H., Moore, W. E. C., Cato, E. P., Smibert, R. M., Burmeister, J. A., Best, A. M., and Ranney, R. R., 1987, Bacteriology of human gingivitis, *J. Dent. Res.* **66**:989–995.

Moore, W. E. C., 1987, Microbiology of periodontal disease, *J. Periodont. Res.* **22**:335–341.

Moore, W. E. C., Holdeman, L. V., Cato, E. P., Smibert, R. M., Good, I. J., Burmeister, J. A., Palcanis, K. G., and Ranney, R. R., 1982. Bacteriology of experimental gingivitis in young adult humans, *Infect. Immun.* **38**:651–667.

Moore, W. E. C., Holdeman, L. V., Cato, E. P., Smibert, R. M., Burmeister, J. A., Palcanis, K. G., and Ranney, R. R., 1985, Comparative bacteriology of juvenile periodontitis, *Infect. Immun.* **48**:507–519.

Moore, W. E. C., Moore, L. V. H., and Cato, E. P., 1988, You and your biota, *U.S. Federation of Culture Collections Newsletter* **18**:7–22.

Morris, E. J., and McBride, B. C., 1984, Adhesion of *Streptococcus sanguis* to saliva-coated hydroxyapatite: Evidence for two binding sites, *Infect. Immun.* **43**:656–663.

Mouton, C., Reynolds, H. S., Gasiecki, E. A., and Genco, R. J., 1979, *In vitro* adhesion of tufted oral streptococci to *Bacterionema matruchotii*, *Curr. Microbiol.* **3**:181–186.

Mouton, C., Reynolds, H. S., and Genco, R. J., 1980, Characterization of tufted streptocci isolated from the "corn cob" configuration of human dental plaque, *Infect. Immun.* **27**:235–245.

Mouton, C., Bouchard, D., Deslauriers, M., and Lamonde, L., 1989, Immunochemical identification and preliminary characterization of a nonfimbrial hemagglutinating adhesin of *Bacteroides gingivalis*, *Infect. Immun.* **57**:566–573.

Murakami, Y., Amano, A., Takagaki, M., Shizukuishi, S., Tsunemitsu, A., and Aimoto, S., 1990, Purification and characterization from human parotid secretion of a peptide which inhibits hemagglutination of *Bacteroides gingivalis* 381, *FEMS Microbiol. Lett.* **72**:275–280.

Murray, P. A., Matarese, V., Hoover, C. I., and Winkler, J. R., 1987, The identification of oral microbial lectins by cell affinity chromatography, *FEMS Lett.* **40**:123–127.

Murray, P. A., Kern, D. G., and Winkler, J. R., 1988, Identification of a galactose-binding lectin on *Fusobacterium nucleatum* FN-2, *Infect. Immun.* **56**:1314–1319.

Nagata, H., Murakami, Y., Inoshita, E., Shizukuishi, S., and Tsunemitsu, A., 1990, Inhibitory effect of human plasma and saliva on co-aggregation between *Bacteroides gingivalis* and *Streptococcus mitis*, *J. Dent. Res.* **69**:1476–1479.

Naito, Y., and Gibbons, R. J., 1988, Attachment of *Bacteroides gingivalis* to collagenous substrata, *J. Dent. Res.* **67**:1075–1080.

Nishikata, M., Kanehira, T., Oh, H., Tani, H., Tazaki, M., and Kuboki, Y., 1991, Salivary histatin as an inhibitor of a protease produced by the oral bacterium *Bacteroides gingivalis, Biochem. Biophys. Res. Commun.* **174**:625–630.

Nowicki, B., Rhen, M., Vaisanen-Rhen, V., Pere, A., and Korhonen, T. K., 1984, Immunofluorescence study of fimbrial phase variation in *Escherichia coli* KS71, *J. Bacteriol.* **160**:691–695.

Nyvad, B., and Kilian, M., 1987, Microbiology of the early colonization of human enamel and root surfaces in vivo, *Scand. J. Dent. Res.* **95**:369–380.

Nyvad, B., and Kilian, M., 1990, Comparison of the initial streptococcal microflora on dental enamel in caries-active and in caries-inactive individuals, *Caries Res.* **24**:267–272.

Ogier, J. A., Klein, J. P., Sommer, P., and Frank, R. M., 1984, Identification and preliminary characterization of saliva-interacting surface antigens of *Streptococcus mutans* by immunoblotting, ligand blotting, and immunoprecipitation, *Infect. Immun.* **45**:107–112.

Okuda, K., Slots, J., and Genco, R. J., 1981, *Bacteroides gingivalis, Bacteroides asaccharolyticus* and *Bacteroides melaninogenicus* sub species: Cell surface morphology and adhesion to erythrocytes and human buccal epithelial cells, *Curr. Microbiol.* **6**:7–12.

Okuda, K., Yamamoto, A., Naito, Y., Takazoe, I., Slots, J., and Genco, R. J., 1986, Purification and properties of hemagglutinin from culture supernatant of *Bacteroides gingivalis, Infect. Immun.* **54**:659–665.

Okuda, K., Ono, M., and Kato, T., 1989, Neuraminidase enhances attachment of *Bacteroides intermedius* to human erythrocytes and buccal epithelial cells, *Infect. Immun.* **57**:1635–1637.

Pollock, J. J., Iacono, V. J., Bicker, H. G., MacKay, B. J., Katona, L. I., Taichman, L. B., and Thomas, E., 1976, The binding, aggregation and lytic properties of lysozyme, in: *Microbial Aspects of Dental Caries*, Sp. Suppl. Microbiol. Abstr., Vol. 2 (H. M. Stiles, W. J. Loesche, and T. C. O'Brien, eds.), Information Retrieval Inc., Washington, D.C., pp. 325–352.

Richardson, R. L., and Jones, M., 1958, A bacteriologic census of human saliva, *J. Dent. Res.* **37**:697–709.

Robrish, S. A., and Thompson, J., 1989, Na$^+$ requirement for glutamate-dependent sugar transport by *Fusobacterium nucleatum* ATCC 10953, *Curr. Microbiol.* **19**:329–334.

Robrish, S. A., and Thompson, J., 1990, Regulation of fructose metabolism and polymer synthesis by *Fusobacterium nucleatum* ATCC 10953, *J. Bacteriol.* **172**:5714–5723.

Rosan, B., Malamud, D., Appelbaum, B., and Golub, E., 1982, Characteristic differences between saliva-dependent aggregation and adhesion of streptococci, *Infect. Immun.* **35**:86–90.

Schwarz, S., Ellen, R. P., and Grove, D. A., 1987, *Bacteroides gingivalis–Actinomyces viscosus* cohesive interactions as measured by a quantitative binding assay, *Infect. Immun.* **55**:2391–2397.

Singh, U., Grenier, D., and McBride, B. C., 1989, *Bacteroides gingivalis* vesicles mediate attachment of streptococci to serum-coated hydroxyapatite, *Oral Microbiol. Immunol.* **4**:199–203.

Slots, J., and Gibbons, R. J., 1978, Attachment of *Bacteroides melaninogenicus* subsp. *asaccharolyticus* to oral surfaces and its possible role in colonization of the mouth and of periodontal pockets, *Infect. Immun.* **19**:254–264.

Smith, R. N., Andersen, R. N., and Kolenbrander, P. E., 1991, Inhibition of intergeneric coaggregation among oral bacteria by cetylpyridinium chloride, chlorhexidine digluconate, and octenidine dihydrochloride, *J. Periodont. Res.* **26**:422–428.

Stinson, M. W., Safulko, K., and Levine, M. J., 1991, Adhesion of *Porphyromonas (Bacteroides) gingivalis* to *Streptococcus sanguis* in vitro, *Infect. Immun.* **59**:102–108.

Stratford, M., and Wilson, P. D. G., 1990, Agitation effects on microbial cell–cell interactions, *Lett. Appl. Microbiol.* **11**:1–6.

Tanner, A. C. R., Socransky, S. S., and Goodson, J. M., 1984, Microbiota of periodontal pockets losing crestal alveolar bone, *J. Periodont. Res.* **19**:279–291.

Tempro, P., Cassels, F., Siraganian, R., Hand, A. R., and London, J., 1989, Use of adhesin-specific monoclonal antibodies to identify and localize an adhesin on the surface of *Capnocytophaga gingivalis* DR2001, *Infect. Immun.* **57**:3418–3424.

Tew, J. G., Marshall, D. R., Burmeister, J. A., and Ranney, R. R., 1985, Relationship between gingival crevicular fluid and serum antibody titers in young adults with generalized and localized periodontitis, *Infect. Immun.* **49**:487–493.

Theilade, E., Wright, W. H., Jensen, S. B., and Löe, H., 1966, Experimental gingivitis in man. II. A longitudinal clinical and bacteriological investigation, *J. Periodont. Res.* **1**:1–13.

van der Hoeven, J. S., de Jong, M. H., and Kolenbrander, P. E., 1985, In vivo studies of microbial adhesion in dental plaque, in: *Molecular Basis of Oral Microbial Adhesion* (S. E. Mergenhagen, and B. Rosan, eds.), American Society for Microbiology, Washington, D.C., pp. 220–227.

van Houte, J., and Green, D. B., 1974, Relationship between the concentration of bacteria in saliva and the colonization of teeth in humans, *Infect. Immun.* **9**:624–630.

Weinberg, A., and Holt, S. C., 1990, Interaction of *Treponema denticola* TD-4, GM-1, and MS25 with human gingival fibroblasts, *Infect. Immun.* **58**:1720–1729.

Weiss, E. I., Kolenbrander, P. E., London, J., Hand, A. R., and Andersen, R. N., 1987a, Frimbria-associated proteins of *Bacteroides loescheii* PK1295 mediate intergeneric coaggregations, *J. Bacteriol.* **169**:4215–4222.

Weiss, E. I., London, J., Kolenbrander, P. E., Kagermeier, A. S., and Andersen, R. N., 1987b, Characterization of lectinlike surface components on *Capnocytophaga ochracea* ATCC33596 that mediate coaggregation with gram-positive oral bacteria, *Infect. Immun.* **55**:1198–1202.

Weiss, E. I., London, J., Kolenbrander, P. E., Andersen, R. N., Fischler, C., and Siraganian, R. P., 1988a, Characterization of monoclonal antibodies to fimbria-associated adhesins of *Bacteroides loescheii* PK1295, *Infect. Immun.* **56**:219–224.

Weiss, E. I., London, J., Kolenbrander, P. E., Hand, A. R., and Siraganian, R., 1988b, Localization and enumeration of fimbria-associated adhesins of *Bacteroides loescheii*, *J. Bacteriol.* **170**:1123–1128.

Weiss, E. I., London, J., Kolenbrander, P. E., and Andersen, R. N., 1989, Fimbria-associated adhesin of *Bacteroides loeschei* that recognizes receptors on procaryotic and eucaryotic cells, *Infect. Immun.* **57**:2912–2913.

Weiss, E. I., Eli, I., Shenitzki, B., and Smorodinsky, M., 1990, Identification of the rhamnose-sensitive adhesin of *Capnocytophaga ochracea* ATCC 33596, *Arch. Oral Biol.* **35**:127S–130S.

Willcox, M. D. P., and Drucker, D. B., 1989, Surface structures, co-aggregation and adhesion phenomena of *Streptococcus oralis* and related species, *Microbios* **59**:19–29.

Yeung, M. K., and Cisar, J. O., 1988, Cloning and nucleotide sequence of a gene for *Actinomyces naeslundii* WVU45 type 2 fimbriae, *J. Bacteriol.* **170**:3803–3809.

Yeung, M. K., and Cisar, J. O., 1990, Sequence homology between the subunits of two immunologically and functionally distinct types of fimbriae of *Actinomyces* spp., *J. Bacteriol.* **172**:2462–2468.

Yeung, M. K., Chassy, B. M., and Cisar, J. O., 1987, Cloning and expression of a type 1 fimbrial subunit of *Actinomyces viscosus* T14V, *J. Bacteriol.* **169**:1678–1683.

Yoshimura, F., Takahashi, K., Yoshinobu, N., and Suzuki, T., 1984, Purification and characterization of a novel type of fimbriae from the oral anaerobe *Bacteroides gingivalis*, *J. Bacteriol.* **160**:949–957.

5

Ribosomal RNA Analysis of Microorganisms as They Occur in Nature

DAVID M. WARD, MARY M. BATESON, ROLAND WELLER, and ALYSON L. RUFF-ROBERTS

1. Introduction

Advances in molecular biology are now providing the means for solving long-standing problems in microbiology. One of the best examples is the development of a rational approach to the phylogenetic classification of microorganisms, based on comparative analysis of slowly evolving molecular components, most notably ribosomal RNAs (Woese, 1987). Molecular biologists and microbiologists have been quick to recognize how rRNA sequence variation could be used to answer major questions limiting progress in microbial ecology. Only a few years after the initial rRNA-based phylogenetic observations were published (Woese and Fox, 1977), the 16S rRNA molecule was used to characterize *Prochloron*, an uncultivated symbiont of marine invertebrates (Seewaldt and Stackebrandt, 1982), and the smallest ribosomal RNA molecule, 5S rRNA, was used to analyze the composition of a few simple microbial communities (Stahl *et al.*, 1984, 1985; Lane *et al.*, 1985b). Some further ecologic work with 5S rRNA has appeared (Colwell *et al.*, 1989), but extensive community analysis with this molecule is complicated by the difficulty of physically separating 5S rRNAs, and by the relatively small size and thus limited information content of this molecule. In the last few years, considerable emphasis has been given in both microbial phylogeny and microbial ecology to the development of methods for studying the larger and more informative rRNAs. Most of the work has been with small ribosomal subunit rRNA (SSU rRNA, 16S in prokaryotes and 18S in eukaryotes), though a limited amount of work has been done with the larger rRNAs of large ribosomal subunits (here termed LSU rRNA, 23S in prokaryotes and 28S in eukaryotes) and with internal transcribed spacer (ITS) regions separating rRNA genes.

DAVID M. WARD, MARY M. BATESON, ROLAND WELLER, and ALYSON L. RUFF-ROBERTS • Department of Microbiology, Montana State University, Bozeman, Montana 59717.
Advances in Microbial Ecology, Vol. 12, edited by K.C. Marshall. Plenum Press, New York, 1992.

This review will focus almost exclusively on the use of SSU rRNA in microbial ecology. The original methods were proposed in two articles published in 1986 (Pace *et al.*, 1986; Olsen *et al.*, 1986). Since then, many new approaches have been developed, only some of which have been considered in review (Stahl, 1986; Ward, 1989; DeLong, 1991). We hope to orient the reader by providing an overview of the various methods and guidance to appropriate primary literature. More importantly, the recent application of rRNA-based methods has given us a first look at how these methods can be used to address fundamental questions in microbial ecology. The results have profound implications for our understanding of microbes in nature and disease (Olsen, 1990; Eisenstein, 1990). Thus, our primary objective is to review these results and to draw from them insights as to important directions for future molecular microbial ecology research.

The need for molecular approaches in microbial ecology arises from the limitations of the methods with which we have become familiar. A little over a century has passed since the invention of elective enrichment culture as a rational approach to the cultivation of naturally occurring microorganisms. Microbiologists have used this method to gain a rich knowledge of diverse types of microorganisms. At a recent conference on molecular microbial ecology (Braunschweig, Germany, May 1990), we were reminded by Dr. Norbert Pfennig that the microbial ecologists who developed and formalized the elective enrichment approach were also those who expressed the original concerns about the limitations of the method. Beijerinck, as translated by van Niel (1949), inferred that the elective culture method could exhibit biases, as his approach might lead to

> . . . the discovery of living organisms that appear under predetermined conditions, either because they alone can develop, *or because they are the more fit and win out over their competitors.*[a]

Winogradsky (1949) was more explicit in expressing his concern over the use of culture methods to investigate naturally occurring microorganisms, stating that

> it is only a minority which develop in the conventional media that are offered. . . . The microflora is not understood either qualitatively or quantitatively.[b]

As microbial ecology has developed, microbial ecologists have continued to express the opinion that the inadequacies of culture methods limit progress in this field (Table I).

Cell component analysis provides a culture-independent means of investigating microbes as they occur in nature. While several types of cell components have been analyzed, the larger rRNA molecules offer an amount and type of information which makes them one of the best culture-independent descriptors of microorganisms. Hundreds to thousands of nucleotides of rRNA sequence information can be obtained. The sequence information has phylogenetic meaning and can be analyzed in the context of a large and growing data base of rRNA sequences of cultivated and uncultivated microorganisms. The sequence information also provides a systematic approach to developing

---

[a]Italics are ours.
[b]Translated from Winogradsky (1949) (p. 461) by Dr. Chris Pinet, Montana State University Modern Languages Dept.

Table I. Citations Indicating the Inadequacy of Microscopic and Culture Methods for Describing Microbial Communities

Citation	Reference
"There are still many microbes whose natural functions are as yet unknown since they have not been encountered in elective culture."	van Niel (1955)
"It is thus impossible to isolate a truly representative fraction of the bacteria and fungi living in natural environments . . . a conventional description of the number and species composition of microorganisms from natural environments [is] difficult, if not impossible."	Rosswall and Kvillner (1978)
" . . . it is currently impossible to determine accurately the species diversity of the heterotrophic bacteria in typical aquatic habitats . . . ."	Staley (1980)
" . . . most certainly those microbes domesticated and kept in captivity in culture collections represent only a minor portion of the species that have evolved."	Wolfe (1981)
"It is clearly difficult to devise objective procedures for the isolation of unknown microbes."	Williams et al. (1984)
" . . . bacteriologists who rely on cultural methods to identify species, face the problem of selectivity and thus the inevitable underestimation of community diversity."	Atlas (1984)
" . . . one isolates pure cultures from nature and then categorizes them . . . then . . . one determines a diversity index. Diversity of what? Not of the natural population, since we have already shown above that culture procedures do not provide representative samples of the natural populations."	Brock (1987)
"If we cannot define the natural community, if we are unable to isolate the majority of bacteria present, how can we assess the transfer and survival of recombinant DNA in the environment?"	Jones (1987)
"Less than 20% of the bacteria are known."	Wayne et al. (1987)

oligodeoxynucleotide probes which can be hybridized to nucleic acids of microorganisms contributing specific rRNA sequences to natural communities. Hence, the autecology of microorganisms can be studied whether or not they have ever been cultivated.

2. rRNAs as Descriptive Cell Components

As essential components of the protein synthesis machinery, rRNAs are universally distributed among cellular life forms, and are therefore useful for studies of all microorganisms except viruses. As slowly evolving genetic elements, they are useful in

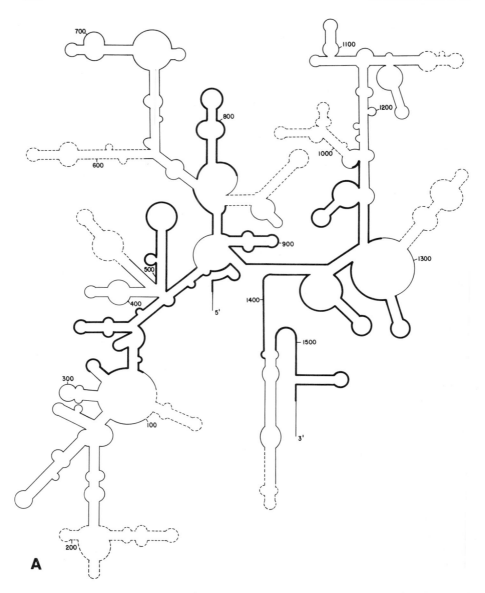

Figure 1. (A) Schematic of the *Escherichia coli* SSU rRNA secondary structure proposed by Gutell *et al.* (1985), highlighting primary sequence domains of nearly universal conservation (thick lines), intermediate conservation (normal lines), or hypervariability (dashed lines) according to Gray *et al.* (1984). Numbers indicate the positions of nucleotides from the 5' end, according to the *E. coli* 16S rRNA sequence (Brosius *et al.*, 1978). (B) 16S rRNA sequence type I retrieved from the Octopus Spring cyanobacterial mat, superimposed over the same secondary structure. Nucleotides that differ from the *E. coli* sequence are marked with arrowheads. Domains that characterize this sequence as that of a cyanobacterium are illustrated by lines (features of primary structure) or asterisks (features of secondary structure) adjacent to the sequence data.

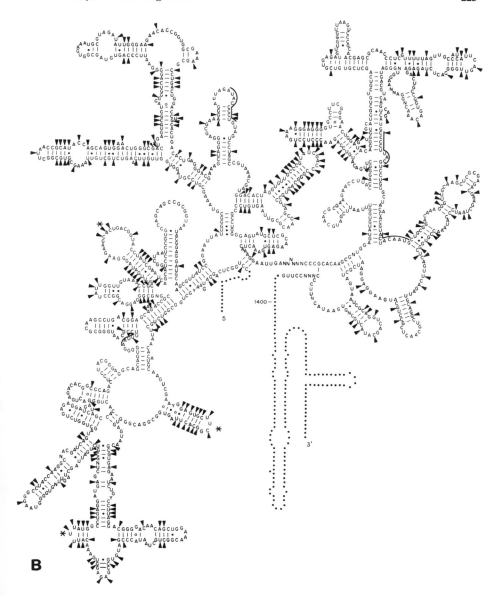

B

Figure 1. (*Continued*)

comparing distantly related species (Woese, 1987). This makes rRNA particularly useful for studies of microbial community ecology, where a broad and unknown diversity of microorganisms is likely to exist.

Comparative analyses have shown that rRNA molecules have a highly conserved secondary structure, as exhibited for SSU rRNA in Fig. 1A. The primary structure is a mosaic of domains that vary in terms of the degree of conservation of primary nucleotide sequence. Some domains show nearly universal conservation, probably related to the conserved functions attributed to these sequence stretches. These regions can be used to advantage in manipulating all SSU rRNA molecules in cloning and sequencing reactions, or as targets for hybridization probing of SSU rRNAs of all organisms. Much of the molecule exhibits an intermediate level of conservation in which primary sequence differences occur, but in which secondary structure is preserved. Such regions may contain domains which are conserved in specific phylogenetic groups, and which may be useful in cloning, sequencing, or probing sets of related species. Other regions are more highly variable in primary nucleotide sequence. These regions facilitate the design of oligonucleotide probes that can hybridize with the SSU rRNA of specific microorganisms.

The utility of rRNA sequences (or probes designed to complement them) for distinguishing between microorganisms of different genera, species, or strains depends on the phylogenetic relationships within the microbial group in question. In some cases, strains of a single species, defined by their phenotypic similarity (e.g., *Bacteroides succinogenes*), have been found to have dissimilar 16S rRNA sequences. Here, it can be said that species- and even strain-specificity can be achieved (Amann *et al.*, 1990b) (see Section 3.2.1). In other cases, bacteria classified into different genera and species on the basis of phenotypic variation have been found to exhibit a high degree of conservation in their rRNA sequences. The enteric bacteria provide an example (Fig. 2). Whereas the genomes of distantly related enteric bacteria (e.g., *Escherichia coli* and *Proteus vulgaris*) are less than 10% similar, the conservative 16S rRNA sequences have more than 90% of their nucleotides in common. Closer relatives show less 16S rRNA sequence difference. For instance, less than 1% difference in 16S rRNA sequence exists between *E. coli* and some *Shigella* species. To resolve such close relatives, one must use genetic or epigenetic elements with a lower degree of evolutionary conservation. Sufficient sequence variation might be found among the larger and more variable LSU rRNAs (Stackebrandt *et al.*, 1991). Yet more variation may exist in the ITS regions between rRNA genes (Barry *et al.*, 1991; Gardes *et al.*, 1991). The total genome exhibits on average much greater variation than rRNA gene sequences (Fig. 2; see Devereux *et al.*, 1989; Amann *et al.*, 1992a). Thus, it should be possible to identify genes or gene products with sufficient sequence variation to resolve groups of highly related microorganisms.

The information provided by rRNA sequences is phylogenetic. If the reader is not familiar with evolutionary relationships as determined by rRNA sequence variation, recent reviews of the subject (Woese, 1987; Woese *et al.*, 1990) may be useful for understanding the rRNA-based ecological results we discuss below. For simplicity we

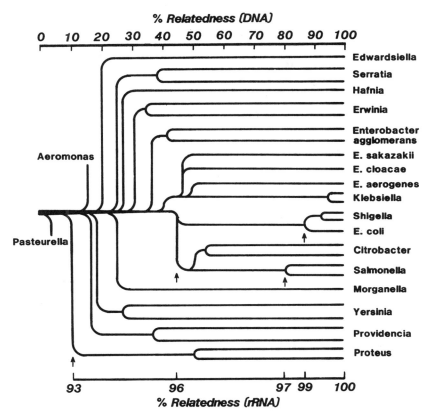

Figure 2. Correlation between percentage relatedness of enteric bacteria based on DNA–DNA hybridization of the total genome and 16S rRNA sequence variation. (Reproduced with permission from Lane and Collins, 1991).

will refer to the primary lines of descent defined by molecular phylogeny as kingdoms, and to their primary subdivisions as phyla, realizing that there is debate as to how to reconcile traditional taxonomic terminology with patterns of relatedness defined by molecular systematics. We are still at a very early stage of understanding how phenotypic characteristics correlate with the phylogenetic history of microorganisms. As microbial ecologists we are particularly interested in the physiology of microorganisms, but unfortunately it is at present only possible to infer physiologic information from phylogenetic information for a few microbial groups. The cyanobacteria and methanogenic bacteria, for example, constitute phylogenetic groups not known to contain microorganisms of other physiologies. Methane-oxidizing bacteria apparently constitute clusters, which so far include mainly organisms of this metabolic type, within the beta

and gamma subdivisions of the proteobacterial phylum (Tsuji *et al.*, 1990). In many
cases, however, a knowledge of phylogeny does not permit direct inference of physiology.

3. rRNA Methods Useful in Microbial Ecology

An overview of the two major approaches for using rRNA sequence information to
evaluate naturally occurring microorganisms is presented in Fig. 3. One approach involves the retrieval of naturally occurring rRNA sequences from a microbial community
by cloning and sequencing. Here, the question is one of community composition. Once

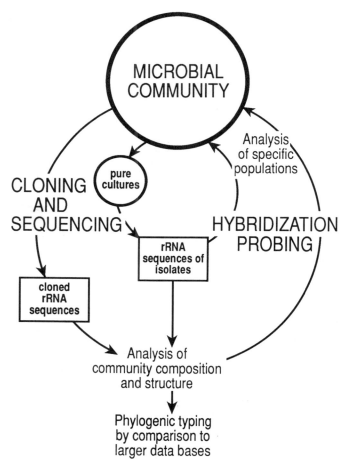

Figure 3. General approaches to the use of rRNA methods in microbial ecology.

unique sequence types have been found, they can be compared to a data base of sequences obtained from pure-cultured microorganisms. As shown in Fig. 3, such a data base might contain sequences of species cultivated from the community being analyzed, so that comparison would indicate whether a naturally occurring rRNA sequence type represents a community member which had been detected before in culture. Comparison to larger data bases that include sequences from representatives of major lines of evolutionary descent leads to phylogenetic typing of the retrieved sequences whether contributed by a cultivated or an uncultivated community member.

A second approach involves the development of hybridization probes which complement rRNA sequence domains. Such probes could be designed to react with all rRNAs, with rRNAs of specific phylogenetic groups, or with unique rRNAs, in concert with the variable degrees of conservation of different regions of the rRNA molecule. rRNA-based hybridization probes have typically been used in autecologic studies of the occurrence of specific microorganisms or phylogenetically related groups of microorganisms constituting populations within a community. They can be designed for either cultivated or uncultivated species.

3.1. Cloning and Sequencing Naturally Occurring rRNAs

The several different approaches to obtaining rRNA sequences which have been reported are summarized in Fig. 4. Either the rRNA molecules or the genes which encode their sequences, can be the starting point for sequence retrieval. However, the information retrieved is different when the gene, as opposed to the rRNA itself, is the target for analysis.

The rRNA gene pool should reflect the contributions of all inhabitants of the community sampled, and should thus provide a qualitative measure of community composition. Active and inactive species present in a sample at the time of collection should be represented, as both would possess rRNA genes. However, the meaning of rRNA gene abundance with respect to the relative contributions of each member of the community is not clear. Gene abundance for a particular species should be determined by the number of individuals of that species times the number of rRNA gene copies per cell. Since the rRNA gene copy number varies widely among microorganism (Pace *et al.*, 1986), the relationship between gene abundance and organism abundance is not constant.

The abundance of the gene product, rRNA in ribosomes, theoretically provides both qualitative and quantitative information about the most actively growing members of a community. Studies of a few well-characterized microorganisms have shown that ribosome content (and thus rRNA content) is regulated in proportion to growth rate (Srivastava and Schlessinger, 1990). If this pattern of ribosome expression occurs generally among diverse types of microorganisms, the abundance of rRNAs of each community member should be a function of both the number of individual microorganisms of a species and their growth rates. The relative abundance of different rRNA sequence types should therefore provide a measure of the relative contribution of each actively growing community member to the protein synthesis capacity of the entire community.

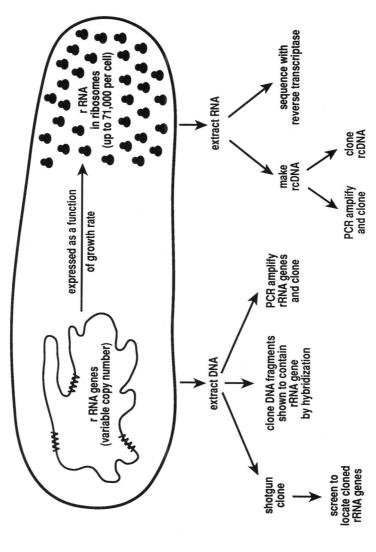

Figure 4. Approaches to the retrieval of rRNA sequence information from naturally occurring microorganisms. Although a single cell is shown, in nature one would expect numerous individuals within many populations of the community.

3.1.1. Retrieval of rRNA Sequences from Natural Communities

The method originally proposed by Pace *et al.* (1986) and Olsen *et al.* (1986) for retrieving SSU rRNA genes involves shotgun cloning of DNA extracted from a natural microbial community (Fig. 5A). A relatively large amount of high-molecular-weight DNA is partially digested with a restriction enzyme to produce 10- to 20-kb fragments that are cloned into a suitable vector. The resultant library is equivalent to a "genomic" library for all of the DNA extracted from a community. It must therefore be screened by

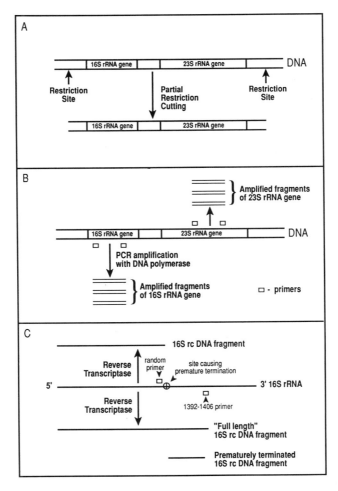

Figure 5. Three common approaches to retrieval of rRNA sequences from natural microbial communities. **(A)** Shotgun cloning, **(B)** polymerase chain reaction, and **(C)** 16S rcDNA synthesis.

hybridization with rRNA probes to identify the clones which bear rRNA genes; these occur in only about 0.125 to 0.3% of the clones (Olsen *et al.*, 1986; Schmidt *et al.*, 1991a). An advantage of this method is that individual clones may possess sequence information for more than one rRNA molecule and for closely linked genes, which can be retrieved by chromosome walking methods.

Unterman *et al.* (1989) used hybridization screening prior to cloning to produce a more selective library containing SSU rRNA genes. High-molecular-weight DNA was completely digested with restriction enzymes, and size-fractionated on agarose gels. A Southern blot analysis was performed in which an *E. coli* 16 S rRNA gene was used as a hybridization probe to identify restriction fragments containing 16 S rRNA genes of bacteria native to the sample. These fragments were recovered from the gel and cloned to produce a library enriched in 16 S rRNA sequences. As other restriction fragments of similar size were also recovered, individual clones bearing 16 S rRNA genes were subsequently identified by hybridization probe screening of the library. The method was applied to the study of a relatively simple symbiosis between bacteria and aphids (Section 4.5). It could not be used to analyze a complex microbial community because 16 S rRNA genes would occur in restriction fragments of virtually all size classes.

The polymerase chain reaction (PCR) has been applied by many investigators to selectively recover portions of SSU or LSU rRNA genes and ITS regions from pure-cultured microorganisms, lyophilized cultures, herbarium and museum specimens, and from inhabitants of natural samples (Medlin *et al.*, 1988; Bottger, 1989; Edwards *et al.*, 1989; Chen *et al.*, 1989; Stahl *et al.*, 1989; Witt *et al.*, 1989; Kemmerling *et al.*, 1990; Giovannoni *et al.*, 1990a; Bruns *et al.*, 1990; Persing *et al.*, 1990; Relman *et al.*, 1990; Wilson *et al.*, 1990; Anderson *et al.*, 1991; Britschgi and Giovannoni, 1991; Deng and Hiruki, 1991; Gardes *et al.*, 1991; Weisburg *et al.*, 1991; Spring *et al.*, 1992; Fuhrman *et al.*, 1992). Oligonucleotide primers complementing sequence regions which either are universally conserved or are conserved within specific phylogenetic groups are used in conjunction with the PCR reaction to exponentially amplify the region between the primers (Fig. 5B). PCR products are then cloned to produce a library that contains almost exclusively recombinants bearing the desired genes, thus reducing the labor intensiveness of library screening. The PCR approach is particularly advantageous when limited amounts of DNA are available for analysis. SSU rRNA genes have been re-covered from as few as three cells (Tsai and Olson, 1992). Possible cloning biases result from the dependence of this approach on primers which must be annealed to the DNA. This and other possible complications which can arise during the use of PCR reactions to retrieve rRNA or ITS sequences will be considered in Section 3.3.2.

We have developed a selective approach to retrieval of SSU rRNA sequences as cDNA (hence, termed rcDNA) (Weller and Ward, 1989). The method takes advantage of the natural amplification of rRNA sequence information when the gene product is expressed in actively growing microorganisms, theoretically permitting quantitative analysis of a microbial community. The method is based on selective priming of cDNA synthesis at the universally conserved SSU rRNA domain at positions 1392–1406 (Fig. 5C, downward reactions). Alternatively, priming at sites conserved within specific phylogenetic groups could be used to recover the rRNA sequences from discrete populations within a community. Cloning of SSU rcDNA results in libraries which almost exclusively contain SSU rRNA-bearing clones. For some SSU rRNA molecules, premature termination of cDNA synthesis occurs, apparently due to the presence of modified nucleotides at or near positions 966 and 967 (Kemmerling *et al.*, 1990; Weller *et al.*, 1991). This limits the amount of sequence retrieved to the ca. 400 nucleotides which occur between the priming site and the modification site. Weller *et al.* (1991) have more recently developed an alternative approach to SSU rcDNA synthesis which involves priming with a mixture of hexanucleotides of random sequence. The selectivity for SSU rRNA sequences is preserved by purification of small ribosomal subunits before extraction of RNA and subsequent cDNA synthesis. This approach permits priming "downstream" from modification sites, and recovery of over 900 nucleotides of the SSU rRNA sequence from molecules exhibiting premature terminations (Fig. 5C, upward reaction). Like the PCR approach, when specific primers are used the cDNA approach is subject to possible cloning biases resulting from imperfect annealing of the primer to SSU rRNA (see Section 3.3.2).

A combination of the cDNA and PCR approaches has also been used to accomplish amplification of SSU rRNA sequences, rather than the genes that encode them (Stahl *et al.*, 1989; Wilson *et al.*, 1989; Kemmerling *et al.*, 1990; Amann *et al.*, 1992b). cDNA produced from SSU rRNA templates is used as a template for PCR amplification.

Perhaps the most straightforward approach to recovering rRNA sequence information from natural samples has been the direct sequencing of rRNA. This method was originally applied to sequencing 5S rRNAs obtained from simple microbial communities of limited composition. Each unique 5S rRNA sequence type was first purified on high-resolution polyacrylamide gels before sequencing (Stahl *et al.*, 1984, 1985; Lane *et al.*, 1985b). Lane *et al.* (1985a, 1988) later proposed the use of reverse transcriptase for rapidly determining SSU rRNA sequences. Oligonucleotides complementing highly conserved domains of the SSU rRNA (see also Embley *et al.*, 1988) serve as primers for sequencing reactions. Because of the difficulty of gel purification of SSU rRNAs, the method is generally restricted to use on pure cultures. However, Distel *et al.* (1988) were able to use this approach to successfully determine the sequences of bacterial symbionts of marine invertebrates, which apparently so dominated the microbial community within the host that unambiguous sequences could be determined (see Section 4.2.3).

3.1.2. Analysis of Cloned rRNA Sequences

Once rRNA sequences have been cloned, many steps are required to obtain and analyze the unique sequences contributed by individual community members. Many of these steps have been considered in previous reviews (Olsen, 1987, 1988; Pace *et al.*, 1986; Olsen *et al.*, 1986) and will only be briefly reemphasized here.

3.1.2a. Screening to Find Unique Sequence Types. All methods of retrieving rRNA sequences lead to the production of libraries containing many clones with identical rRNA sequences. Though identity between sequences is best established by comparing complete sequences, the labor intensiveness of such an effort severely limits the total number of sequences in a library that can be analyzed. As a compromise, several alternatives have been employed to group clones into those likely to contain identical rRNA sequences. Strategies include

1. Sequence analysis of small but informative domains (Giovannoni *et al.*, 1990a; Ward *et al.*, 1990a; Weller *et al.*, 1991, submitted)
2. Single-nucleotide pattern matching (i.e., the distribution of a specific nucleotide within an rRNA domain as revealed by gel analysis of a single dideoxy-nucleotide sequencing reaction) (Ward *et al.*, 1990b; Schmidt *et al.*, 1991a)
3. Hybridization probe screening (Britschgi and Giovannoni, 1991; Liesack and Stackebrandt, submitted)
4. Size analysis of nucleic acid fragments generated by restriction enzyme digests of rRNA genes and flanking sequence regions (restriction fragment length polymorphism) (Gardes *et al.*, 1991; Britschgi and Giovannoni, 1991)

It is important to recognize that all of these methods could miss differences that are located in domains (or nucleotides) not analyzed, or that do not occur at restriction sites investigated. The chances of observing differences are obviously increased if variable regions are included in the analysis. Despite their shortcomings, these compromises have permitted sequencing efforts to be focused initially on clones known to possess different sequence types.

3.1.2b. Sequence Alignment and Restricted Sequence Analysis. Observed differences between sequences can be due to mutational change or could be artifacts of misalignment (i.e., due to comparison of nucleotides which occupy different positions in the two molecules being compared). The alignment of rRNA molecules is facilitated by the relatively high degree of primary sequence conservation among rRNA molecules, and by the conservation of secondary structure which enables one to match corresponding stretches of double-stranded regions with their complements. Note, for instance, that while the primary nucleotide sequence of the naturally occurring 16S rRNA molecule shown in Fig. 1B differs significantly from that of *E. coli,* it is possible to align the two sequences based on consideration of complementarity between the two single-stranded portions of double-stranded regions. The ease of alignment is greatly reduced in variable regions. For this reason, such regions are often eliminated from comparative analysis. This conservative approach has been referred to as *restricted* or *masked* analysis. If the sequences being compared are so closely related as to permit accurate alignment in variable regions, they can be compared in a complete (i.e., *unrestricted* or *unmasked*) analysis of all sequence data.

3.1.2c. Comparative Sequence Analysis. Sequence Similarity. The similarity between any pair of aligned sequences can be used to establish identity, or to suggest a possible phylogenetic affiliation. The actual percent similarity value varies as a function of the number and position of the nucleotides being compared. For instance, the sequence similarity between the same two rRNA molecules will be higher in a restricted than in a complete analysis, since the complete sequence analysis includes regions which are more highly variable. There are no absolute percent similarity values that can always be used to define various taxonomic levels, but analysis of representative sequences in a particular region under investigation can provide a general framework for interpreting sequence similarity results (see Section 4.1.1). If percent similarity data point to a possible intraphylum relationship, a sequence can be aligned to its closest relative and reanalyzed. When an identical relationship between two sequences is suggested by a restricted analysis, unrestricted analysis can be performed to provide a more rigorous test of identity, because it should be possible to make an accurate alignment even in variable regions for identical or nearly identical molecules.

Tree Analysis. Phylogenetic trees provide a means of comparing sets of sequences and inferring phylogenetic relatedness among them. Several treeing approaches have been employed and compared (Olsen, 1987; Lake, 1987; Gouy and Li, 1989). All methods are sensitive to alignment, assumptions made about mutational rates at each position (Olsen, 1987), the types of sequences used in an analysis, and the amount of sequence data (Gouy and Li, 1989). There is, in fact, a considerable amount of uncertainty in phylogenetic trees that span taxa as diverse as phyla within a kingdom (Sneath, 1989). In general, more sequence data will increase the validity of the analysis. Methods for evaluating the confidence in tree analysis are available (Felsenstein, 1985).

Signature Analysis. A third approach to analysis of the phylogenetic type of a sequence is the molecular detail it contains. Comparative analysis of large numbers of sequences has revealed diagnostic features of primary and secondary structure (Woese, 1987; Woese et al., 1985; Winker and Woese, 1991) which can be used to verify a phylogenetic affiliation suggested by sequence similarity or tree analysis. For example, the natural sequence in Fig. 1B contains short stretches of nucleotides and truncated loops which are characteristic features of nearly all cyanobacterial sequences.

3.2. rRNA-Based Hybridization Probes

One of the major advantages of using rRNAs for ecological investigations is that they can be used as targets for hybridization probes designed to detect microorganisms, even those which have not been cultivated. Excellent reviews of rRNA-based hybridization probing methods have recently appeared (Stahl and Amann, 1990; Lane and Collins, 1991), to which the reader is referred for methodologic details.

There are two basic approaches to hybridization probing of rRNA or rRNA gene sequences (Fig. 6). If the sequence is known, it is possible to design and chemically synthesize short oligonucleotide DNA probes (usually on the order of 15 to 30 nucleotides) that should have predictable reactivities. Alternatively, rRNA, or portions of its sequence copied by cloning or various methods of *in vivo* or *in vitro* enzymatic transcription, can be used as a probe. An advantage of this approach is that the sequence need not be known in order to design the probe.

3.2.1. Chemically Synthesized Oligonucleotide Probes

This approach capitalizes on the knowledge of sequence variation in different regions of rRNA molecules and on the ability to chemically synthesize short DNA oligomers. Oligonucleotide hybridization probes complementing either SSU rRNA, LSU rRNA, or ITS regions have now been developed for a wide variety of micro-

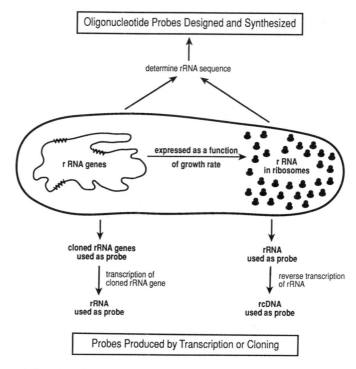

Figure 6. Overview of approaches to the development of rRNA-based hybridization probes.

organisms, including some uncultivated species (Table II). Oligonucleotides that complement hypervariable domains may react with the rRNA of specific microorganisms. Oligonucleotides that complement domains of intermediate variability react more broadly with members of specific phylogenetic groups. Oligonucleotides that complement universally conserved regions have general reactivity and can be used to assay the total amount of rRNA in a sample.

The design of oligonucleotide hybridization probes depends on background knowledge of the phylogeny of the group to be probed. The two essential requirements are that the group contain members which are phylogenetically related yet distinct from other microorganisms, and that the members of the group exhibit sufficient rRNA sequence variation to permit their resolution. A pertinent example is provided in the work of Stahl and his colleagues (Montgomery *et al.*, 1988; Stahl *et al.*, 1988; Amann *et al.*, 1990b) who extensively studied the phylogenetic relationships among *Fibrobacter* strains based on 16 S rRNA sequence variation. Since the group was phylogenetically coherent (Fig. 7A), it was possible to design oligonucleotide probes that react with all or specific sets of *Fibrobacter* species and subspecies (Table II, Section IV). For example, probes complementing positions in semiconserved domains could be designed to react with all *Fibro-*

bacter strains, or with all strains belonging to the species *F. succinogenes*. Probes complementing positions within a variable domain should be designed to react with *F. succinogenes* subspecies *succinogenes* or with strains of the other genus, *F. intestinalis*. The differential probe reactivities were based on an increasing number of mismatches between probe and target sequence as the phylogenetic distance between them increased (i.e., percent similarity decreased). This is illustrated in Fig. 7A for the *F. succinogenes* ssp. *succinogenes*-specific probe, which exhibits one to three mismatches with strains of *F. succinogenes* ssp. *elongata* and six mismatches with a strain of the other species, *F. intestinalis*.

Short oligonucleotides can be made to penetrate a range of microbial cell types after cells are fixed with formaldehyde and treated with methanol or ethanol (Table II). Since the number of rRNA molecules within cells can be large (up to 71,000 copies in actively growing cells; Bremer and Dennis, 1987), it is possible to achieve an intracellular response with rRNA probes. The type of cell reacting with an rRNA probe can be visualized by microautoradiography if the probe is radioactively labeled (Giovannoni *et al.*, 1988a); or by enzyme-linked analysis of biotinylated probes (Edman *et al.*, 1988; Zarda *et al.*, 1991). Recently, methods for fluorescent labeling of rRNA-based oligonucleotide probes have been developed (DeLong *et al.*, 1989b; DeLong and Shah, 1990; Amann *et al.*, 1990b; Tsien *et al.*, 1990), which enable detection by fluorescence microscopy (Fig. 7B and C) and by flow cytometry (Amann *et al.*, 1990a; Bertin *et al.*, 1990; DeLong and Shah, 1990). This permits the power of flow cytometry to be applied to the analysis of populations comprised of specific microorganisms (cultivated or uncultivated) as well as specific phylogenetic groups of microorganisms in natural samples.

The specificity of the *F. succinogenes* ssp. *succinogenes*-specific probe is demonstrated in the intracellular probe responses shown in Fig. 7B and C. Under the hybridization conditions employed, the probe was able to distinguish between ssp. *succinogenes* and ssp. *elongata* strain REH9-1 (three mismatches). The probe could also distinguish *F. succinogenes* spp. *succinogenes* from *F. intestinalis* (six mismatches; see Amann *et al.*, 1990b, for data). The probe specificity deteriorated when there was only a single base mismatch between probe and target (e.g., between ssp. *succinogenes* and ssp. *elongata* strain HM2). The specificity can be improved by making hybridization conditions more stringent (e.g., higher hybridization temperature), but the reactivity of the probe with its homologous target is also reduced under these conditions.

3.2.2. Cloned or Transcribed Probes

Because all rRNA sequences share a high degree of sequence similarity, rRNA fragments from one microorganism may be used to probe rRNA genes of another. As an example, SSU rRNAs from representative eubacteria, archaebacteria, and eukaryotes have been used in combination as "mixed kingdom" probes (e.g., Schmidt *et al.*, 1991a) or under conditions in which each rRNA reacts specifically with rRNA genes of members of the homologous kingdom (e.g., Giovannoni *et al.*, 1990b). Alternatively, rcDNA (Edelstein, 1986; Wilkinson *et al.*, 1986), cloned rRNA genes (Schleifer *et al.*,

Table II. Microorganisms and Microbial Groups for Which rRNA-Based Oligonucleotide Probes Have Been Developed[a]

Organism	Target	Approximate domain	SSU domain type[b]	Direct evidence of intracellular response	Reference
I. Cultivated bacterial species					
Actinomyces israelii	16S	209–241	V	—	Stackebrandt and Charfreitag (1990)
Actinobacillus actino-mycetumcomitans	16S	820–860	V	—	Chuba *et al.* (1988)
"	"	NP	V	—	Dix *et al.* (1990)
Aeromonas salmonida	16S	446–488	V	—	Barry *et al.* (1990)
Bacteroides asaccharolyticus	16S	645–674	V	—	Chuba *et al.* (1988)
forsythus	16S	NP	V	—	Dix *et al.* (1990)
gingivalis	16S	827–859	V	—	Chuba *et al.* (1988)
"	"	NP	V	—	Dix *et al.* (1990), Moncla *et al.* (1990)
intermedius	16S	651–681	V	—	Chuba *et al.* (1988)
"	"	NP	—	—	Dix *et al.* (1990)
Borrelia burgdorferi	16S	1448–1465	V	—	Persing *et al.* (1990)
Campylobacter spp.	16S	NP	—	—	Romaniuk and Trust (1987)
pylori	16S	NP	V	—	Morotomi *et al.* (1989)
fetus	16S	1017–1044	V	—	Wesley *et al.* (1991)
hyointestinalis	16S	1017–1044	V	—	"
Chloroflexus aurantiacus	16S	1272–1294	V	—	Ruff and Ward (1991)
Clostridium difficile	16S	583–604	S	—	Wilson *et al.* (1988)
"	"	752–767	V	—	"
"	"	1285–1300	V	—	"
perfringens	ITS	—	—	—	Barry *et al.* (1991)
Ehrlichia chaffeensis	16S	NP	—	—	Anderson *et al.* (1992)
Eikenella corrodens	16S	NP	V	—	Dix *et al.* (1990)
Enterococcus spp.	23S	—	—	—	Betzl *et al.* (1990)
Francisella sp.	16S	1274–1290	V	—	Forsman *et al.* (1990)
Frankia spp.	16S	180–240	V	—	Hahn *et al.* (1990a,b)
"	"	1020–1042	V	—	"
Fusobacterium nucleatum[c]	16S	NP	V	—	Dix *et al.* (1990)

Haemophilus aphrophilus	16S	825–890	V	—	Chuba et al. (1988)
"	"	NP	V	—	Dix et al. (1990)
ducreyi	16S	NP	V	—	Rossan et al. (1991)
	23S	NP	V	—	"
Helicobacter pylori	16S	76–97	V	—	Hoshina et al. (1990)
Lachnospira spp.	16S	207–226	V	—	Stahl et al. (1988)
Lactobacillus spp.	16S	60–110	V	—	Hensiek et al. (1992)
	23S	NP	V	—	Hertel et al. (1991)
Lactococcus spp.	16S	212–233	V	Yes	Salama et al. (1991), Klijn et al. (1991)
lactis spp. cremoris	"	68–87	V	Yes	Betzl et al. (1990)
lactis	23S	—	—	—	Klijn et al. (1991)
Leuconostoc spp.	16S	NP	V	—	Wang et al. (1991)
Listeria monocytogenes	16S	NP	—	—	Gobel et al. (1987)
Mycoplasma pneumonia	16S	458–477	V	—	
	"	1018–1050	V	—	
Neisseria spp.	16S	70–100	V	—	Rossau et al. (1989)
	"	180–200	V	—	"
	"	433–488	V	—	"
	"	633–663	V	—	"
	"	827–860	V	—	"
	"	1000–1024	V	—	"
	"	1420–1475	V	—	"
	23S	80–105	—	—	"
	"	270–290	—	—	"

[a]Other pathogenic bacteria for which probes have been developed are listed by Lane and Colling (1991). References in Section 3.1.1 that deal with PCR methodology include primers which could also be used as probes. The rapid expansion of rRNA-based oligonucleotide or PCR probe technology is indicated by numerous American Society for Microbiology abstracts describing additional probes for specific detection of Acanthamoeba (Asgari et al., 1991), Blastomyces dermatitidis (Sandin et al., 1991), Borrelia burgdorferi (Schwartz et al., 1991), Chlamydia trachomatis (Hosein et al., 1991), Giardia lamblia (Weiss et al., 1991), Histoplasma capsulatum (Pratt-Rippin et al., 1991), Neisseria gonorrhoeae (Lu et al., 1991), and Ureaplasma urealyticum (Gonzales et al., 1991; Hammond et al., 1991), and for the general detection of septicemia (Leong and Greisen, 1991).

[b]According to domains suggested by Gray et al. (1984) for SSU rRNA: V = hypervariable; S = semiconserved; U = nearly universally conserved (see Fig. 1A). In cases labeled "NP" it was not possible to determine the 16S rRNA domain type.

[c]Not specific.

(continued)

Table II. (*Continued*)

Organism	Target	Approximate domain	SSU domain type[b]	Direct evidence of intracellular response	Reference
"	"	345–370	—	—	"
"	"	1437–1463	—	—	"
"	"	1529–1555	—	—	"
"	"	1704–1746	—	—	"
"	"	2290–2320	—	—	"
Proteus spp.	16S	181–204	V	—	Haun and Gobel (1987)
"	"	829–857	V	—	"
Rickettsia spp.	16S	677–701	S	—	Wilson *et al.* (1989; personal communication)
"	"	833–856	V	—	"
Rickettsia rickettsia	16S	738–754	S	—	Dix *et al.* (1990)
Streptococcus intermedius	16S	NP	V	—	Ruff and Ward (1991)
Synechococcus lividus	16S	1272–1294	V	—	Jensen *et al.* (1990)
Treponema hyodysenteriae	16S	623–655	V	—	Rehnstam *et al.* (1989)
Vibrio anguillarum	16S	430–545	V	—	Dix *et al.* (1990)
Wolinella recta	16S	NP	V	—	Putz *et al.* (1990)
Xenorhabdus spp.	16S	455–485	V	—	Distel *et al.* (1991)
Shipworm bacterial symbiont	16S	637–662	V	Yes	DeLong *et al.* (1989b)
Proteobacterial wasp symbiont	16S	59–79	V	Yes	
II. Cultivated eukaryotic species					
Laccaria bicolor strains	ITS	—	—	—	Gardes *et al.* (1991)
Plasmodium berghei	18S	271–308	V	—	Gunderson *et al.* (1987)
falciparum	18S	178–198	V	—	Waters and McCutchan (1989)
"	"	663–687	V	—	McCutchan *et al.* (1988)
malariae	"	"	V	—	Waters and McCutchan (1989)
ovale	"	"	V	—	"
vivax	"	"	V	—	"

Pneumocystis carinii	18S	593–623	V	Yes	Edman et al. (1988)
"	"	1243–1265	V	Yes	"
"	"	1451–1461	V	Yes	"
Trichomonas vaginalis	18S	NP	V	—	Speer and White (1991); M. White
Tritichomonas foetus	18S	NP	V	—	(personal communication)
III. Uncultivated bacterial species					
Holospora spp.	16S	NP	—	Yes	Amann et al. (1991)
"	23S	NP	—	Yes	"
Magnetotactic bacteria	16S	NP	—	Yes	Spring et al. (1992)
Marine Proteobacteria	16S	178–220	V	—	Giovannoni et al. (1990a)
Thermophilic cyanobacterium	16S	1272–1294	V	—	Ruff and Ward (1991)
Thermophilic *Chloroflexus* relative	16S	1272–1294	V	—	"
Sulfate-reducing bacteria	16S	647–665	V/S	Yes	Amann et al. (1992b)
IV. Groups of phylogenetically related microorganisms					
Borrelia burgdorferi	16S	631–652	V	—	Marconi et al. (1992)
subspecies	16S	84–98	V	—	Marconi et al. (1992)
"	16S	181–199	V	—	Marconi et al. (1992)
other spp.	16S	631–652	V	—	Marconi et al. (1992)
Fibrobacter spp.	16S	225–245	S	—	Stahl et al. (1988); Amann et al. (1990b)
"	"	650–669	S	—	"
F. succinogenes spp.	"	207–226	V	Yes	"
succinogenes	"	207–226	V	Yes	"
F. intestinalis	"	1242–1265	V	Yes	"
Sulfate-reducing bacteria	16S	385–402	U	Yes	Amann et al. (1990a)
Desulfovibrio spp.	"	687–702	S	Yes	Devereux et al. (1990)
Desulfobulbus spp.	"	660–679	S	—	"
Desulfobacterium spp.	"	221–240	S	—	"
Desulfobacter spp.	"	129–146	S	—	"
"	"	220–239	S	—	"

(continued)

Table II. (*Continued*)

Organism	Target	Approximate domain	SSU domain type [b]	Direct evidence of intracellular response	Reference
Desulfococcus multivorans and relatives	"	813–840	U/V	—	"
Other species	"	804–821	U/V	—	"
Methylotrophic bacteria					
Type I	16S	197–216	V	Yes	Tsien *et al.* (1990)
Type II	"	142–159	V	Yes	"
Streptomyces spp.					
Genus-specific	16S	929–937	U	—	Stackebrandt *et al.* (1991);
Group-specific	"	956–973	U	—	Witt *et al.* (1989);
	"	982–998	U/S	—	Kemmerling *et al.* (1990)
	"	1007–1024	V	—	"
	"	1102–1122	S	—	"
	"	1130–1152	V	—	"
Species-specific[d]	"	156–205	V	—	"
	23S	1518–1645	—	—	"
All fungi	18S	NP	—	—	Chan *et al.* (1991)
All eubacteria	16S	338–355	U/S	Yes	Amann *et al.* (1990a)
	"	927–944	U	Yes	Giovannoni *et al.* (1988a, 1990a)
All eukaryotes	18S	502–516	U	Yes	Amann *et al.* (1990a)
	"	1195–1209	S	Yes	Giovannoni *et al.* (1988a, 1990a)
All archaebacteria	16S	338–361	U/S	—	Giovannoni *et al.* (1990a)
	"	915	U	—	Amann *et al.* (1990b)
	"	1206–1239	U	Yes	DeLong *et al.* (1989b)
All organisms	SSU	519–536	U	Yes	Giovannoni *et al.* (1988a, 1990a)
	"	907	U	—	Stahl *et al.* (1989)
	"	1392–1406	U	Yes	Amann *et al.* (1990a)

[d]Not all species can be discriminated.

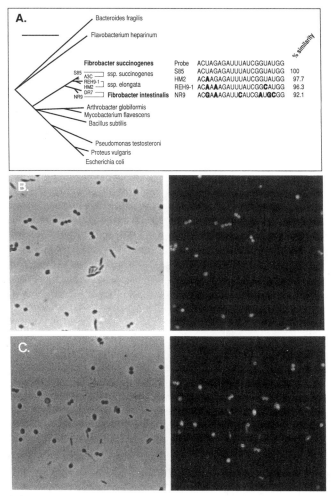

Figure 7. The design and reactivity of a 16S rRNA-based oligonucleotide hybridization probe for detection of *Fibrobacter succinogenes* ssp. *succinogenes* (modified from Amann *et al.*, 1990b, 1992a, with permission). **(A)** Distance matrix phylogenetic tree showing uniqueness of all *Fibrobacter* strains relative to other eubacteria, and major phylogenetic subdivisions within this genus. Bar indicates an evolutionary distance of 0.1 fixed point mutation per nucleotide. Nucleotide sequences of the target domain (position 207–226) for the probe and *Fibrobacter* strains are shown, highlighting the mismatches with the probe (bold) and percent similarity between 16S rRNA sequences of each strain and *F. succinogenes* ssp. *succinogenes* strain S85. **(B, C)** Intracellular reactivity of tetramethyl rhodamine-labeled probe with mixtures of fixed cells of the homologous strain (*F. succinogenes* ssp. *succinogenes* strain S85, cocci) and a nonhomologous subspecies with **(B)** three mismatches (ssp. *elongata* strain REH9-1, rods), and **(C)** one mismatch (ssp. *elongata* strain HM2, rods). Phase-contrast view on left; fluorescence view on right. See Amann *et al.* (1990b) for reaction conditions.

1985; Regensburger *et al.*, 1988; Razin *et al.*, 1984; Festl *et al.*, 1986; Gobel and Stanbridge, 1984; Cheema *et al.*, 1991), or RNA probes produced by transcription from cloned rRNA genes (Bertin *et al.*, 1990; Schmidt *et al.*, 1991b) have been used as probes (see Fig. 6). The specificity of all types of cloned or transcribed probes may suffer from the inclusion of conserved as well as variable regions of the rRNA molecule. Approaches to increasing the specificity have been proposed (Schmidt *et al.*, 1991b). Cloned or transcribed probes are usually much longer than chemically synthesized oligonucleotide probes. This limits their penetrability into cells, though it has been established that probes up to 150 nucleotide in length can penetrate fixed cells (DeLong and Shah, 1990), permitting intracellular analysis by fluorescence (Bauman and Bentvelzen, 1988) and microautoradiography (Gall and Pardue, 1969; John *et al.*, 1969). Permeability of fixed cells can be increased by enzymatic treatment (e.g., lysozyme, proteases), but overtreatment can destroy cellular integrity (E. DeLong, Woods Hole Oceanographic Institute, personal communication).

3.3. Potential Problems with Ecological Uses of rRNA Methods

It is important to appreciate that these molecular approaches are not without limitations. They should be applied with caution until we better understand how serious these problems may be. The following sections emphasize some points of concern.

3.3.1. Bias in Retrieving Nucleic Acids from Natural Environments

Accurate analysis of naturally occurring microorganisms, by either cloning and sequencing or hybridization probing approaches, depends on the unbiased recovery of nucleic acids from natural samples. Although several methods have been proposed for obtaining nucleic acids from natural environments (e.g., Fuhrman *et al.*, 1988; Holben *et al.*, 1988; Steffan *et al.*, 1988; Somerville *et al.*, 1989), there is no guarantee that any method recovers *all* of the naturally occurring DNA or RNA. There is clearly a need to investigate various methods for their efficiency of DNA or RNA recovery. There is already evidence that sampling bias can result from cell recovery procedures that select against certain types of microorganisms (Hahn *et al.*, 1990a), from enzymatic degradation of nucleic acids before analysis (Gobel *et al.*, 1987; Bauman and Bentvelzen, 1988), or from failure to lyse some members of a mixed natural community (see Section 4.1.1). Mechanical lysis protocols such as French Press cell lysis, glass beadbeating, and sonication may be more rigorous than enzymatic lysis methods, but cannot be applied when the cloning method requires high-molecular-weight DNA. rRNAs, protected by their high degree of secondary structure and association with ribosomal proteins, may be less prone to shearing than DNA. It may be possible to reduce the shearing of DNA during French Press cell lysis by performing lysis under conditions of high Na^+ and Mg^{2+} concentration (our unpublished observations).

Humic substances coextracted with nucleic acids may prevent subsequent enzymatic treatments. Strategies for removing humic substances include absorption to polyvinylpolypyrrolidone (see Weller and Ward, 1989), gel purification (Devereux and Mundfrom, 1992; Tsai *et al.*, 1992), and dilution (Tsai and Olson, 1992).

3.3.2. Cloning Biases

The PCR and cDNA cloning methods depend on the specific hybridization of oligonucleotide primers to DNA or RNA templates. The discovery of an intron within a universally conserved region of an archaebacterial 16S rRNA gene (Wickham *et al.*, 1992) illustrates how this might be qualitatively prevented in some microorganisms. Such a 16S rRNA sequence would not have been retrieved in a PCR reaction dependent on annealing of a primer complementary to the region in question but could have been retrieved by shotgun cloning or cDNA approaches. Imperfect primer annealing could result from inappropriate hybridization stringency. Nonspecific priming has resulted in the recovery of LSU rRNA sequences in SSU rcDNA libraries (our unpublished results), and of SSU rRNA gene sequences not targeted by primers designed to select for specific phylogenetic groups (Stahl *et al.*, 1989; Giovannoni *et al.*, 1990a; Amann *et al.*, 1992b; see Section 4.2.1a). Small sequence differences in the universally conserved regions of some SSU rRNAs (see Weller *et al.*, 1991) could be the basis of differential annealing of universal primers. There is also concern that the PCR reaction may not amplify all naturally occurring SSU rRNA sequences to the same extent, creating a difference in the relative abundances of naturally occurring and cloned SSU rRNA sequences. This has led to the suggestion that a combination of the most-probable-number (MPN) and PCR methods may permit quantitation (Toranzos and Alvarez, 1992; Endo *et al.*, 1992). Here, the MPN technique (i.e., dilution) controls quantitation, while PCR merely amplifies the signal.

A number of other concerns have been expressed about the PCR approach, including retrieval of rRNA sequences from microorganisms or nucleic acids which contaminate laboratory and commercial reagents (Schmidt *et al.*, 1991c; Relman *et al.*, 1990; Rand and Houck, 1991), and the production of chimeric rRNA sequences which arise as hybrids of two different rRNA sequence types (Liesack *et al.*, 1991). These problems could obviously result in detection of rRNA sequences not native to natural samples, complicating community analysis.

3.3.3. Fidelity of rRNA Sequence Retrieval

Shotgun, PCR, and rcDNA cloning methods have each been used to produce libraries, which, as expected, contain clones with identical rRNA sequences (Ward *et al.*, 1990a; Giovannoni *et al.*, 1990a; Relman *et al.*, 1990; Schmidt *et al.*, 1991a; Anderson *et al.*, 1991). This provides a very high level of confidence in the ability of all of these methods to accurately copy rRNA sequence information. However, in each of the above studies, nearly identical sequences which sometimes differ at the level of 1 to 2% in unrestricted analysis have also been observed. Small differences have also been observed in rRNA sequences retrieved from pure-cultured or co-cultured microorganisms with either the PCR (Liesack *et al.*, 1991; Weisburg *et al.*, 1991) or the cDNA method (Ward *et al.*, 1990b; Weller *et al.*, submitted). It is difficult to prove that differences of this magnitude are not introduced during polymerase reactions (Mizutani and Temin, 1976; Saiki *et al.*, 1988; Ennis *et al.*, 1990; Eckert and Kunkel, 1990). rRNAs exhibiting larger differences can almost certainly be taken as unique sequence types. The presumption that unique sequence types represent the contributions of unique species is complicated by the known occurrence of more than one rRNA sequence type in the same organism. For instance, *Plasmodium* spp. express alternate rRNA sequence types in different developmental stages (Gunderson *et al.*, 1987; McCutchan *et al.*, 1988). In other microorganisms, such as the archaebacterium *Haloarcula marismortui*, different rRNA sequences are simultaneously expressed (Mylvaganam and Dennis, 1991).

3.3.4. Hybridization Probe Reactivity

3.3.4a. Specificity. The reactivity of a probe cannot be predicted exactly. It is thus essential to empirically establish the specificity of any probe. This should include cross-reaction studies with the closest relatives (in terms of rRNA sequence similarity or other phylogenetically based information). It must always be assumed that undiscovered sequence types may cross-react with a probe thought to be specific, or that undiscovered close relatives will fail to react with a probe designed to hybridize with rRNA from all members of a group (see example in Section 4.3). Thus, it is wise to accept the advice given by Amann *et al.* (1992a) that "probes should be regarded as tools subject to refinement."

The conserved nature of rRNA sequences limits the resolving power of rRNA-based hybridization probes. Perhaps this has been most clearly seen in the clinical probe industry where the examination of large numbers of closely related pathogenic species has led to the generalization that "highly specific rRNA probes are not necessarily always possible" (Lane and Collins, 1991). A similar conclusion has been reached from studies of 77 streptomycete species which are close phylogenetic relatives (Stackebrandt *et al.*, 1991). Approaches to improving probe specificity for species with nearly identical rRNA sequences are reviewed by Lane and Collins (1991) and Stahl and Amann (1990).

3.3.4b. Sensitivity. Effective probe design depends on achieving an appropriate balance between specificity and signal strength. A variety of probe labeling techniques (e.g., radiolabeling, fluorescence, enzymatic, chemiluminescence) have been suggested; each method has advantages and disadvantages as to sensitivity and stability of the probe. Probes labeled with ^{32}P are probably the most sensitive, but are also the most short-lived. They have been used successfully to probe components of natural communities at a level of approximately 0.1% of the total community rRNA (see Section 4.3). In clinical situations it is often necessary to detect pathogenic microorganisms with great sensitivity. This has prompted the development of methods for enhancement of signal-to-noise ratio (Lane and Collins, 1991). One approach involves purification of specific target rRNA molecules before probing. Hybridization probes attached to magnetic beads are used to control the selection of the desired rRNA sequence. The magnetic bead approach may have many interesting applications in microbial ecology as it should enable the recovery of specific sequence types from a mixture. The PCR reaction can also be used to amplify target rRNA sequences for direct detection of fragments of characteristic length (Boddinghaus *et al.*, 1990; Hoshina *et al.*, 1990; Gaydos *et al.*, 1992), which can also be probed by oligonucleotides complementary to sections of the

PCR-amplified domain (Wilson *et al.*, 1989; Barry *et al.*, 1990, 1991; Ho *et al.*, 1991; Klijn *et al.*, 1991; Anderson *et al.*, 1992). Approaches to enhancing the signal itself include the use of multiple hybridization probes that react specifically with different parts of the same rRNA molecule (Amann *et al.*, 1990a), the addition of homopolymer tails to oligonucleotide probes to provide multiple secondary binding sites for labeled "reporter" probes (DeLong and Shah, 1990), enzymatic amplification of the signal after the probe has reacted with its target (see Lane and Collins, 1991) and indirect labelling with fluorescent antibody directed at antigens linked to oligonucleotide probes (Zarda *et al.*, 1991). Such approaches may be necessary in investigations of minor or slow-growing members of natural communities whose rRNA contributions or rRNA content per cell would likely be low. Many of the approaches which have been developed so far may not enhance signals quantitatively, or would not be appropriate for intracellular signal enhancement. Ecological investigations may, however, require quantitative or intracellular use.

3.3.4c. Accessibility of Target. Intracellular probing requires the penetration of probe through outer cell barriers. Although it cannot be assumed that penetration will always occur, so far a wide variety of cell types, including microorganisms of various phylogenies and physiologies, have been successfully probed intracellularly (Table II). Universal probes have been found to react to variable degree with the mixture of cell types present in natural samples (see Sections 4.2.3 and 4.3). Probe detection methods that depend on the entry of even larger molecules (e.g., proteins) have limited application (Bertin *et al.*, 1990; Zarda *et al.*, 1991), unless suitable methods for disruption of exterior wall layers are found.

Once in a cell, a probe must react with target sequences in the rRNA molecule. rRNAs are complicated targets for hybridization because of their natural tendency to form double-stranded regions. Thus, hybridization probes may have to compete with complementary rRNA domains in order to react with their targets. Successful probing of a number of different regions of SSU and LSU rRNA molecules (Table II) suggests that this may not be generally prohibitive, although differential responses for probes directed at different sites of the same rRNA molecule have been reported (Zarda *et al.*, 1991).

3.3.4d. Quantitative Use of Probes. In the case of cultivated species, the rRNA of an organism may be used to empirically standardize the response of a probe. However, in the case of uncultivated species the rRNA is not available. Attempts have been made to quantify the significance of uncultivated species by two approaches (Giovannoni *et al.*, 1990a). The average responses of group-specific or universal probes have been determined by measuring their reactivities with rRNA of representative pure cultures; the assumption was made that the probes should exhibit similar reactivities with rRNA of uncultivated species of similar phylogeny. The response of a more specific probe was estimated by determining the absolute number of target molecules probed. This required saturation of targets with probe and knowledge of the specific activity of the probe. It should be possible to produce rRNA fragments for an uncultivated species by *in vitro* transcription of cloned rRNA genes or rcDNA. However, the suitability of such RNA as a standard for the native full-length and possibly modified rRNA needs to be explored.

3.3.5. Accessibility of Sequence Data

The rate of determination of rRNA sequence data has increased to the point that many more sequences are in personal computer files than in the literature. There is concern that the lack of accessibility of these sequences has limited progress in both phylogenetic and ecologic applications of rRNA methods (Walch *et al.*, 1989). While general data bases (e.g., GenBank, EMBL) serve as a repository for some sequences, the data are not aligned relative to other rRNA sequences. A central collection of aligned rRNA sequence data is now under development at the University of Illinois (Olsen *et al.*, 1991). It is now possible to interact with this facility to obtain sequences or phylogenetic analysis of new sequences. The contribution of new sequences to this data base will ensure that this rapidly growing collection remains complete.

4. Ecological Applications of rRNA Methods

The methods described above have only recently been applied to investigations of microorganisms in different natural habitats. We are thus at the leading edge of a new molecular view of microorganisms in their natural settings. In most of the remainder of this review we will update progress on a habitat-by-habitat basis. In the final section we will draw what generalizations seem justified on the basis of results at hand.

4.1. Hot Spring Environments

4.1.1. The Octopus Spring Cyanobacterial Mat as a Model Community

We have extensively investigated one microbial community as a natural model for studies of microbial community ecology (Ward *et al.*, 1987, 1989b). The cyanobacterial mat growing in a 50 to 55°C region of Octopus Spring in Yellowstone National Park is stable with respect to many of the environmental features that vary in other habitats, and the composition of the mat community is arguably simpler than in less extreme environments (Brock, 1978). The mat has been studied by numerous microbiologists who have used a variety of approaches (see Brock, 1978; Ward *et al.*, 1987, 1989b). In particular, microorganisms of a variety of physiologic and phylogenetic types have been cultivated from this or other similar geothermal habitats. We have thus been able to construct an SSU rRNA sequence data base for microorganisms relevant to the mat (Bateson *et al.*, 1989, 1990; Ward *et al.*, 1990b), which we have used to test the hypothesis that the culture collection does not adequately describe the microbiota of the community.

We have used the cDNA cloning approach to investigate the naturally occurring inhabitants of this mat. We have prepared several independent SSU rcDNA libraries from RNA extracted from the mat, all but one of which were prepared using the selective primer complementary to positions 1392–1406 to initiate cDNA synthesis from SSU rRNA templates. We have analyzed more than 50 clones from these libraries by determining complete or partial SSU rcDNA sequences. Most of the sequences can

Table III. Similarity among SSU rcDNA Sequence Types Obtained from the 55°C Octopus Spring Cyanobacterial Mat

% similarity (restricted[b]/unrestricted) with sequence type[c]

Sequence type[a]	A	B	I	J	C	H	K	L	D	M	F	N	G	E	O
A	—	97.1	89.4	88.7											
B	98.4	—	90.9	88.9											
I	94.7	95.9	—	93.7											
J	93.7	95.6	87.8	—											
C	85.6	86.7	83.5	83.6	—										
H	86.8	88.5	87.1	84.2	82.8	—									
K	88.6	88.5	87.8	84.7	81.7	93.2	—								
L	84.8	83.6	84.4	82.7	80.5	83.2	87.8	—							
D	87.7	87.5	85.1	82.4	74.3	84.9	90.0	79.6	—						
M	82.4	82.9	81.9	78.9	83.0	87.8	88.5	82.0	88.9	—					
F	84.5	85.3	82.9	79.2	76.4	90.9	91.5	79.4	90.4	93.5	—				
N	81.5	81.2	82.9	80.4	74.7	83.2	89.5	78.5	76.4	82.9	83.7	—			
G	85.5	85.3	85.1	83.7	80.8	86.1	89.9	83.7	82.9	84.9	85.3	95.1	—		
E	86.1	87.1	84.7	83.7	86.0	87.8	87.3	84.7	84.9	91.8	89.1	81.9	86.3	—	
O	90.0	89.0	86.1	84.9	82.4	87.1	87.8	79.5	85.8	88.6	85.5	85.7	86.1	87.8	—

[a] We define a sequence type on the basis of its uniqueness relative to other sequences with which it can be compared, and thus the probability that it is contributed by a unique community member. Each sequence type is designated by an alphabetic letter. The clone number is used. The clone number designates the source (e.g., OS means Octopus Spring), the Library number (roman numeral, modified by S or L if selection for short or long rcDNAs preceded cloning), and the number of the individual clone in that library (Arabic numeral).

[b] Data were restricted as described in Ward et al. (1990a). All sequence data have been submitted to the Genebank sequence data base. Values may differ from those previously reported due to the greater number of nucleotides now available for analysis (see Section 3.1.2c).

[c] For reference, sequence similarity values corresponding to various taxonomic levels were calculated from sequences of a set of pure-cultured microorganisms, with analysis restricted to the same domains: interkingdom similarities range from 67.1 to 82.1%, interphylum similarities range from 76.4 to 88.4%, and intraphylum similarities range from 85.9 to 100%.

be readily aligned with other SSU rRNA sequences, demonstrating the selectivity of the method. The SSU rcDNAs we have cloned appear to be accurate replicas of the natural SSU rRNA sequences, as revealed by the redundancy of sequences within and between libraries (see Ward *et al.*, 1990a; Section 4.1.1c) and by molecular details of cloned SSU rcDNA molecules (Fig. 1B). Many of the sequences we have examined from libraries prepared via specific priming of cDNA synthesis are relatively short (a few hundred nucleotides between the 1392–1406 priming site and positions 966–967). The random-priming approach to cDNA synthesis (Weller *et al.*, 1991) has provided a means of obtaining longer sequence information for some molecules, though the lack of overlap has not permitted comparison of the sequences in the randomly primed library to the shorter sequences from specifically primed libraries.

   4.1.1a. Predominance of Uncultivated Community Members. Based on those sequences which overlap in the region adjacent to the 1392–1406 priming site, we have so far been able to establish with certainty the presence of at least 15 unique 16 S rRNA sequence types in the mat (Ward *et al.*, 1990a; Weller *et al.*, submitted; and subsequent unpublished results). These are compared in the pairwise sequence similarity matrix presented in Table III. Sequence types were established on the basis of differences in percent similarity (in unrestricted analysis including at least one variable region) in excess of 1–2 % which might be attributed to cloning or sequencing artifacts. In all but a single case (sequence types A and B), differences in similarity values exceeded this level even in restricted analysis. Perhaps the most important result is that none of the 15 sequence types matches with the sequence of any microorganism which has been culti-vated from the mat or other similar geothermal habitat (shown for eight sequence types in Table IV). The closest relationship we have observed between sequences obtained directly from the mat and those of geothermal isolates is 94.2% in a restricted analysis (90.2% unrestricted). This suggests that the mat contains a large number of uncultivated inhabitants.

   4.1.1b. Phylogenetic Types and Diversity of Community Members. The phy-logenetic affiliations of the microorganisms contributing many of the sequence types have been revealed by sequence similarity data, and in the case of long sequences by tree and signature analysis. Four related sequence types (A, B, I, and J; percent similarity > 93.7% in restricted analysis, see box in Table III) show high similarity with cyanobac-terial sequences (Table IV). Those sequence types which were long enough for distance matrix tree analysis also cluster with cyanobacterial sequences (Fig. 8). All of these sequence types exhibit molecular details characteristic of cyanobacteria (see example in Fig. 1B). As the cyanobacteria are known to form a distinct phylogenetic cluster (Giovannoni *et al.*, 1988b), it seems safe to infer that these four Octopus Spring sequence types are contributed by microorganisms with cyanobacterial physiology. The complexity of the cyanobacterial population of the mat community must therefore be greater than previously thought. Pure culture and microscopic observations have led to the interpretation that *Synechococcus lividus* was the sole cyanobacterium producing the mat (Ward *et al.*, 1987, 1989b). The phylogenetic diversity among these uncultivated cyanobacteria is considerable (Table III), representing on the order of one half of the evolutionary distance observed among the cyanobacteria so far investigated (Giovannoni *et al.*, 1988b).

Sequence type C shows highest similarity with the sequence of *Chloroflexus aurantiacus*, a member of the eubacterial phylum containing green nonsulfur bacteria and relatives (Table IV). Another clone, OS-V-L-20 (Weller *et al.*, submitted), whose rRNA insert is 86.6% similar in restricted analysis to sequence type C, also shows a relationship with the *C. aurantiacus* sequence. These relationships are verified by tree (Fig. 8) and signature analysis. In contrast to the situation with cyanobacteria, it is difficult to infer a photosynthetic bacterial physiology for the organisms which contribute these sequences, as the phylum containing green nonsulfur bacteria also contains nonphotosynthetic members. For instance, *Herpetosiphon aurantiacus* and *Thermomicrobium roseum* are aerobic chemoorganotrophic bacteria which have been isolated from geothermal habitats. Diol lipids distinctive of *T. roseum* have been detected in the Octopus Spring mat (Ward *et al.*, 1989a).

Sequence type H shows high similarity to representatives of the spirochete subdivision within the spirochete eubacterial phylum (Table IV) (Weller *et al.*, submitted). Clone OS-V-L-7 exhibits a relationship with members of the leptospira subdivision of the spirochete phylum in both similarity (Table IV) and tree analysis (Fig. 8).

We have so far been unable to demonstrate a relationship between several other long sequences (types K and L and clone OS-VI-L-4) with known eubacterial phyla. This is most intriguing as it might suggest that the mat contains inhabitants of as yet undiscovered phylogenetic types.

The mat community exhibits considerable phylogenetic diversity between populations, with most similarity values between sequence types typical of the interphylum range (Table III). So far, only eubacterial sequences have been detected, consistent with the very low concentrations of lipid cell components characteristic of archaebacteria (i.e., isoprenoid ethers, Ward *et al.*, 1985) and eukaryotes (i.e., sterols, Ward *et al.*, 1989a).

4.1.1c. Community Structure. We have used the cDNA approach because of its theoretical potential to provide quantitative information about community structure (see Section 3.1). In this regard, it is interesting that three different libraries constructed from RNA extracted after French Press lysis show similar abundances of sequence types, despite differences in cDNA synthesis and cloning protocols (Fig. 9). For example, 7 of 10 sequences examined in library III were of type A (cyanobacterial phylogeny). Similarly, 3 of 5 sequences in the randomly primed library VI were from a single cyanobacterium (Weller *et al.*, 1991), which we suspect is of type B (Weller *et al.*, submitted). Library V-S, which contains clones whose 16 S rcDNA inserts were less than about 400 nucleotides in length, was also predominated by type-B cyanobacterial sequences (Weller *et al.*, submitted). Thus, there appears to be a general predominance of cyanobacterial sequences in these three libraries, even though the specific predominating cyanobacterium may vary with as yet unknown spatial or temporal variables. In contrast, two libraries appear to be biased against a predominating cyanobacterial sequence type. Library V-L, constructed after size selection for long SSU rcDNAs, contains only a

Table IV. Restricted Similarities between Some Octopus Spring Cyanobacterial Mat SSU rcDNA Sequence Types and SSU rRNA Sequences of Bacteria Cultivated from This or Other Geothermal Habitats, or Characteristic of Known Bacterial Phyla

Isolates[c]	% restricted[a] similarly with sequence type[b]							
	A	B	I	J	C	OSVL20	H	OSVL7
I. Octopus Spring isolates[c]								
Synechococcus lividus	90.6	91.7	94.2	92.8	78.1	78.0	83.5	80.3
Chloroflexus aurantiacus	85.9	86.7	81.9	81.1	89.9	89.3	83.2	82.8
Thermomicrobium roseum	87.3	86.9	83.1	81.5	83.9	86.2	83.0	83.3
Herpetosiphon aurantiacus	85.0	85.5	83.1	81.8	88.7	85.5	80.8	82.5
Thermus aquaticus	81.1	80.4	81.0	78.7	81.3	82.3	86.7	84.8
Isosphaera pallida	85.4	84.7	80.5	80.8	81.3	76.4	83.2	81.4
Thermobacteroides acetoethylicus	88.5	88.1	84.0	82.3	80.5	80.2	88.1	87.5
Thermoanaerobacter ethanolicus	86.7	86.1	83.8	81.5	80.5	81.5	86.7	87.9
Thermoanaerobium brockii	85.8	85.2	83.8	81.5	80.3	81.3	85.8	87.2
Clostridium thermohydrosulfuricum	88.6	88.3	84.6	82.7	81.3	81.0	88.7	88.6
Clostridium thermoautotrophicum	91.8	92.2	88.4	87.4	82.3	80.6	91.4	90.5
Clostridium thermosulfurogenes	86.8	87.4	82.5	82.6	79.9	78.4	84.8	84.1
Thermodesulfobacterium commune	83.4	83.2	79.8	78.5	80.7	79.6	86.1	84.4
Methanobacterium thermoautotrophicum	76.2	77.8	73.0	71.9	69.3	70.7	74.4	70.0

II. Representatives of known bacterial phyla

Anacystis nidulans	93.8	94.8	95.0	92.7	81.6	81.0	87.9	83.6
Escherichia coli	88.3	88.5	86.1	84.8	82.3	82.3	86.2	87.3
Agrobacterium tumefaciens	90.2	90.9	87.6	85.3	82.0	82.1	87.2	84.7
Pseudomonas testosteroni	86.6	87.7	85.1	83.7	81.6	82.9	85.8	86.6
Desulfovibrio desulfuricans	88.3	88.9	86.2	83.6	80.1	81.9	84.1	84.6
Chlorobium vibrioforme	85.2	85.5	84.2	82.6	83.5	80.8	83.2	87.0
Spirochaeta halophila	90.0	90.1	85.0	84.4	80.8	79.8	94.8	87.4
Leptonema illini	88.3	88.5	84.8	82.9	81.6	80.4	91.3	94.3
Flavobacterium heparinum	85.4	85.9	82.6	80.1	78.3	76.0	88.1	83.1
Chlamydia psittaci	85.7	85.9	82.6	81.8	78.4	77.4	87.0	82.0
Thermotoga maritima	88.6	88.1	83.3	81.3	81.2	78.5	87.5	83.8
Halobacterium cutirubrum	74.2	74.6	69.8	67.7	65.8	66.8	74.7	64.5
Thermoproteus tenax	79.0	79.0	71.6	71.9	71.4	69.2	76.8	70.9

[a] See Table III footnotes.

[b] References to original sequence data may be found in Ward et al. (1990a,b), Weller et al. (1991 submitted), Oyaizu and Woese (1985), Yang et al. (1985). All naturally occuring sequences have been submitted to the Genebank sequence data base. The percent similarity values may not be exactly as previously reported (e.g., in Ward et al., 1990a) due to the increased number of nucleotides now available for analysis (see Section 3.1.2c).

[c] Includes some isolates from other geothermal sources.

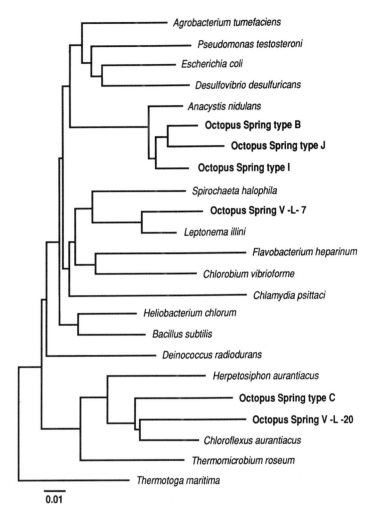

Figure 8. Distance matrix phylogenetic tree illustrating the phylogenetic affiliations of 16S rcDNA sequence types retrieved from the 50 to 55°C Octopus Spring cyanobacterial mat community relative to representatives of the major eubacterial phyla. The tree was rooted with the sequence of *Methanobacterium formicicum*. The bar indicates an evolutionary distance of 0.01 fixed point mutation per nucleotide along the horizontal component only. Sequence data were restricted as described in Table III. Approximate correspondence with percent similarity data can be determined by reference to specific pairs of sequence types in Table III. Sources of sequences are given in Table IV.

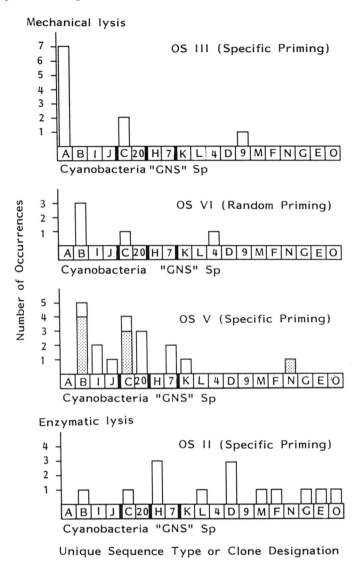

Figure 9. Frequencies of unique 16S rcDNA sequence types and clones in different libraries produced from the 50 to 55°C Octopus Spring cyanobacterial mat RNA. Methods of lysis and cloning are indicated. Library V is actually two libraries produced from a single rcDNA synthesis in which short rcDNAs (library V–S, dotted bars) were cloned separately from long rcDNAs (library V–L, open bars) (see Weller *et al.*, submitted).

single type-B sequence. Library II, produced from RNA extracted after enzymatic lysis, has also been found to contain a single type-B sequence. This raises suspicion that size selection and lysis protocols can introduce biases. Type-C sequences, contributed by a relative of *Chloroflexus aurantiacus,* were found in lower abundance in all libraries.

A greater variety of sequence types exists in the two libraries that select against the predominating cyanobacterial sequence type. Included are the three other cyanobacterial sequence types, the other relative of green nonsulfur bacteria, and both spirochete sequence types described in the preceding section, and numerous additional sequence types whose phylogenetic affiliations remain unknown. The inability to relate these sequence types to known phylogenetic or physiologic groups limits our ability to understand the ecological significance of the results. However, the variety of sequences recovered in lower relative abundances has fueled our suspicion that apart from the other cyanobacterial types, these may be contributed by community members that occupy a secondary trophic level. We speculate that diversity may increase due to an increase in the variety of substrates made available by primary producers to microorganisms occupying higher trophic levels. This diversity should, of course, exist in libraries dominated by cyanobacterial sequences as well, but more effort would be required to observe it.

We have not yet discovered the sequence of either an archaebacterium or the phylogenetically distinctive sulfate reducer isolated from this mat, *Thermodesulfobacterium commune.* This may be a consequence of their roles as terminal members of the anaerobic food chain involved in mat decomposition (Ward *et al.,* 1987). As such they would occupy the highest trophic level of the mat community and thus be least abundant. This might also explain why we have not yet discovered sequences corresponding to the several fermentative bacteria which have been isolated from the mat, and whose population densities may be relatively low.

The emerging view of community structure (dominance of phototrophs over chemoorganotrophic decomposers, and of the latter over methanogenic and sulfate-reducing bacteria) is sensible for this type of mat community. It is further supported by the relative abundances and vertical profiles of distinctive lipid cell components in the mat (Zeng *et al.,* 1992a,b; Ward *et al.,* 1989a).

4.1.1d. Oligonucleotide Probe Studies of Phototrophic Community Members. We are in the process of applying rRNA-based oligonucleotide hybridization probe techniques to study the autecology of the organisms whose sequences we have discovered. For example, the four cyanobacterial 16S rcDNA sequences (types A, B, I, and J), as well as the 16S rRNA sequence of the pure-cultured hot spring cyanobacterium *S. lividus,* were used to design oligonucleotide probes which complement unique sequences at positions 1272–1294 (Ruff and Ward, 1991). Because of the phylogenetic similarity of sequence types A and B (97.1% in unrestricted analysis) there is only a single nucleotide difference in the target region, complicating the discrimination of these two sequence types. However, a minimum of four mismatches exists between all other cyanobacterial sequence types and *S. lividus,* providing a basis for discriminating between all other cultivated or uncultivated cyanobacterial sequence types using specifically designed oligonucleotide probes (Fig. 10). A probe which reacts with the type-A and -B sequences reacts with RNA extracted after French Press lysis of 50 to 55°C Octopus Spring mat samples, consistent with the predominance of these sequence types in

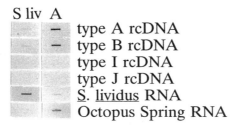

type A rcDNA
type B rcDNA
type I rcDNA
type J rcDNA
S. lividus RNA
Octopus Spring RNA

Figure 10. Hybridization of 16S rRNA-based oligonucleotide probes targeting cultivated (*Synechococcus lividus,*) or uncultivated (Type A) cyanobacteria of the Octopus Spring cyanobacterial mat with RNA of the mat or *S. lividus*, or 16S rcDNA of uncultivated cyanobacterial sequence types (A, B, I, and J) retrieved from the mat. Target nucleic acids (0.25 pmole) were denatured and bound to Nytran membranes, then hybridized with ^{35}S-labeled (Sambrook *et al.*, 1989) probes complementary to 16S rRNA positions 1272–1294. Hybridization reactions were carried out in $6 \times$ SSC//10/$\times$ Denhardt's solution/1% SDS/500 μg/ml^{-1} poly-D-adenosine/100 μg/ml^{-1} tRNA at 54°C, and membranes were washed in $3 \times$ SSC/0.1% SDS at 54°C (see Sambrook *et al.*, 1989), before exposing autoradiograms. Probes: *S. lividus*, 5'-CGTGGTTTAAGAGATTAGCTCG; type A, 5'CCACGTTTAGGCGATTAGTTCC.

rcDNA libraries. In contrast, the lack of reaction with a probe specific for *S. lividus* (Fig. 10) suggests the relative insignificance of this species in the Octopus Spring mat. The *S. lividus* strain we study (Y-7c-7b-S) was originally isolated from a cyanobacterial mat of a pH 6 pool at Clearwater Springs. We have recently observed a strong reaction between the *S. lividus* probe and RNA extracted from this mat. This suggests that morphologically similar but phylogenetically distinct unicellular cyanobacteria may inhabit hot springs of different pH. The mistaken impression of the importance of *S. lividus* in the Octopus Spring mat may have resulted from an oversimplification of the diversity that exists among thermophilic unicellular cyanobacteria.

Similarly, a probe specific for the type-C sequence is more reactive with 50 to 55°C Octopus Spring mat RNA than is a probe specific for the sequence of a *C. aurantiacus* strain originally isolated from the 59°C Octopus Spring cyanobacterial mat (Y-400) (Ruff and Ward, 1991). The *C. aurantiacus* probe did react with RNA from a 70°C Octopus Spring mat sample, suggesting that the isolate may be a high-temperature strain.

4.1.2. The Octopus Spring Source Pool

A limited amount of information is available from 5S rRNA analysis of the 91–93°C Octopus Spring source pool (Stahl *et al.*, 1985). It had been previously demonstrated that bacteria would attach to and grow on glass surfaces incubated in the source pool, but attempts to cultivate these bacteria failed (see Brock, 1978). Stahl *et al.* (1985) sampled the community by an *in situ* enrichment on Pyrex wool suspended for several days in the source pool. Three different 5S rRNA sequence types purified on high-resolution gels were found to comprise about 90% of the retrieved 5 S rRNA. Comparison to a sequence data base revealed that two sequence types were contributed by eubacteria, most closely related to *Thermus* species. One sequence type was from an archaebacterium, most closely related to members of the sulfur-dependent group. Precise phylogenetic affiliations could not be determined due to the limited amount of sequence data provided in the 5S rRNA molecule and the limited number of 5S rRNA sequences available for comparison. A parallel analysis of SSU rRNA sequences (Wickham *et al.*, 1992) has recently led to the very interesting discovery that some SSU rRNA genes from this habitat contain intervening sequences within universally conserved regions (see Section 3.3.2.).

4.2. Marine and Freshwater Environments

4.2.1. Near-Surface Marine Picoplankton

Bacteria concentrated from oligotrophic waters by tangential flow filtration in the 0.1 to 10 μm size class (Giovannoni *et al.*, 1990b) have been analyzed by two research groups. Water was sampled from a depth of 1 to 3 m, but was suspected to represent the upper 90 m of the water column. In both cases, DNA was extracted after enzymatic lysis, which by microscopic examination appeared to be efficient. Many of the results from these independent analyses can be compared, as shown in Fig. 11.

4.2.1a. Sargasso Sea. Giovannoni *et al.* (1990a) used the PCR approach to amplify portions of the SSU rRNA genes present in DNA extracted from a sample collected at Hydrostation S in the Sargasso Sea. The amplification primers were designed to favor the recovery of cyanobacterial sequences, so that this was essentially intended as a study of cyanobacterial population biology. Partial sequences of 12 randomly selected cloned SSU rRNA genes were determined and compared between positions 101 and 344, a domain which contains a variable region. Redundancy within the library was found, indicating high fidelity of the PCR reaction in copying SSU rRNA gene sequences. Six unique sequence types could be established. All sequences were aligned with respect to secondary structure and no evidence of chimeric artifacts was observed. Distance matrix tree analysis suggested that the six sequence types cluster into two groups of three. These groups were shown by analysis of representative longer sequences to belong to the cyanobacterial phylum (clones SAR6 and SAR7 in Fig. 11A) and to the alpha subdivision of the proteobacterial phylum (clones SAR1 and SAR11 in Fig. 11B). The cyanobacterial sequences resembled those of cyanobacteria cultivated from marine picoplankton samples (*Synechococcus* strains in Fig. 11A), one exhibiting 96.5% similarity (unrestricted analysis). However, none of the cloned sequences were identical to those of cultivated cyanobacteria. Either the sequences of appropriate cultivated cyanobacteria were not available for analysis, or the seawater picoplankton like the hot spring mat contains as yet uncultivated cyanobacteria. As judged from tree data, the uncultivated cyanobacterial sequences were relatively closely related (about 95 to 98% in unrestricted analysis). Similarly, the proteobacterial sequences were closely related (about 95 to 99% in unrestricted analysis). They were not, however, identical to the sequences of cultivated proteobacteria which were available for analysis. More recently, work on another Sargasso Sea library, produced by the PCR approach using general primers complementing most eubacterial SSU rRNA sequences, is leading to the discovery of new sequence types, including additional proteobacterial inhabitants of the community (Britschgi and Giovannoni, 1991).

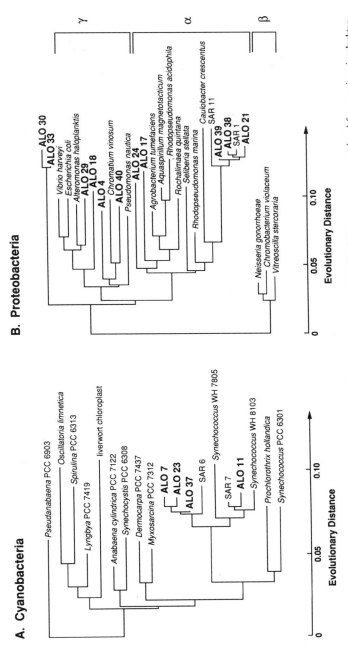

Figure 11. Distance matrix phylogenetic trees of cyanobacterial (A) or proteobacterial (B) 16S rRNA sequence types retrieved from marine picoplankton communities of the Sargasso Sea (SAR) or the north-central Pacific Ocean Aloha site (ALO). Units of evolutionary distance are the number of fixed point mutations per nucleotide. (Reproduced with permission from Schmidt *et al.*, 1991a).

An oligonucleotide probe designed to hybridize with rRNAs of all three members of the proteobacterial cluster was used to probe RNA extracted from picoplankton samples. Collectively, these sequence types represented 12.5% of the SSU rRNA of the Sargasso Sea sample. The percentage importance of these proteobacteria was lower in several coastal picoplankton samples, suggesting that the organisms contributing these sequences may be more abundant in relatively oligotrophic offshore waters. Kingdom-specific oligonucleotide hybridization probes were used to demonstrate that eubacteria and eukaryotes contributed 81% and 19%, respectively, of the SSU rRNA in the sample (Giovannoni *et al.*, 1990a,b).

4.2.1b. North-Central Pacific Ocean. Work on a Pacific Ocean Aloha site picoplankton sample (DeLong *et al.*, 1989a; DeLong, 1991; Schmidt *et al.*, 1991a) has provided a most interesting verification of the Sargasso Sea study. DNA extracted from the sample was used to prepare a shotgun cloned library which was then screened by hybridization with a "mixed-kingdom" SSU rRNA probe to identify cloned SSU rRNA genes. Thirty-eight clones bearing SSU rRNA genes were recovered. Hybridization with kingdom-specific probes revealed the presence of a single eukaryotic sequence type, with the remainder all eubacterial types. Sixteen unique sequence types were identified after screening by the single nucleotide pattern matching method (see Section 3.1.2a), and to a limited extent by partial sequencing of clones. Sequence data were obtained for a region between positions 250 and 500, which includes a variable domain. Four sequence types (ALO sequences in Fig. 11A) show high affinity with cyanobacterial sequences, especially with marine cyanobacterial picoplankton isolates. The sequences of uncultivated cyanobacteria in the Aloha sample were strikingly similar to those recovered from the Sargasso Sea with which they can be compared (95.5 to 98.5% in unrestricted analysis; DeLong, 1991). Eleven diverse proteobacterial sequence types were found (ALO sequences in Fig. 11B), including members of the alpha and gamma subdivisions of the proteobacterial phylum. As with cyanobacterial sequences, none were identical to the available sequences of cultivated proteobacteria. Some of the alpha subdivision sequences were very highly related if not identical to the proteobacterial sequences discovered in the Sargasso Sea sample (96.5 to 99.8% similar in unrestricted analysis; DeLong, 1991). The single eukaryotic sequence type was most closely related to the dinoflagellate *Prorocentrum* (90% in an unrestricted analysis).

The striking similarity among inhabitants of the Sargasso Sea and Pacific Ocean samples is paralleled by the similarity of the DNAs extracted from three different oceanic samples and compared by DNA–DNA hybridization (Lee and Fuhrman, 1990). Perhaps these observations reflect the similarity among open ocean habitats. Both DNA–DNA hybridization and SSU rRNA-based probe hybridization results suggest that the microbiota of coastal waters may be quite different from that of open ocean water. Recently, rRNA sequences of novel archaebacteria have been discovered in coastal surface waters (DeLong, 1992).

Unless there were sampling or cloning biases, the shotgun cloned library produced from the Aloha sample should in theory record the gene frequencies of the inhabitants of the picoplankton community. In this respect it is interesting that nearly half of the 38 sequences investigated were contributed by a few different cyanobacteria, with a single cyanobacterial type predominant (T. Schmidt, Miami University, personal communication). Except for the single eukaryotic sequence, the remaining sequences were from a variety of proteobacteria, each of which apparently contributes fewer genes to the SSU rRNA gene pool. Although gene frequencies do not necessarily equate to population densities (see Section 3.1), the results hint at a pattern that is sensible for the structure of a microbial community driven by photosynthetic processes.

4.2.2. Subsurface Marine Picoplankton

Fuhrman *et al.* (1992) investigated bacterioplankton collected by filtration from oligotrophic water samples from 100 m and 500 m depths in the California Current (Pacific Ocean). DNA was extracted by hot SDS treatment, and portions of 16S rRNA genes were retrieved by PCR amplification using primers that span the region between positions 537 and 1390. Five of seven sequences from the 500 m sample, and two of ten from the 100 m sample were shown to be archaebacterial, but these were only distantly related to other known archaebacteria. The difference between these results and those for near-surface picoplankton may relate to the greater depth at which samples were collected.

4.2.3. Sediments

Oligonucleotide probes for sulfate-reducing bacteria were used to investigate RNA extracted from a coastal sediment in Santa Rosa Sound near Gulf Breeze, Florida (Devereux *et al.*, 1990). An extensive 16S rRNA sequence data base (Devereux *et al.*, 1989) suggested that most of the cultivated sulfate-reducing bacteria comprise a coherent phylogenetic cluster within the delta subdivision of the proteobacterial phylum. Since physiologically distinct sulfate reducers seem to form coherent groups within this cluster, probes for various physiologic types of sulfate reducers could be developed (Table II, Section IV).

Probes which hybridize to universally conserved domains were used to measure total SSU rRNA. The response was greatest with RNA extracted from surface sediment and decreased with depth over the upper 10 cm, indicating a general decrease in the magnitude (and/or activity) of the sediment microbial community with depth. This is consistent with previous observations that suggested such a pattern for systems receiving their energy from the overlying water column (Ward and Winfrey, 1985). Probes specific for SSU rRNAs of various physiologic groups of sulfate-reducing bacteria reacted at much lower levels (<0.1–3.4% of total SSU rRNA). Collectively, the probe responses for various sulfate reducer groups summed to 4.7% of the SSU rRNA extracted from the sediment sampled 4 cm below the surface where the maximum sulfate reducer probe response was observed. A relatively small sulfate reducer population within a sediment microbial community seems consistent with the high trophic position of these organisms as terminal members of anaerobic food chains (Ward and Winfrey, 1985). However, the depth at which sulfate reducer probes responded maximally did not coincide with the depth of maximum sulfate reduction. Furthermore, the strongest response (3.4%) was with a probe designed to react with *Desulfovibrio* spp. Since the substrate flow in sulfate reduction in marine sediments would be expected to favor the acetate-metabolizing sulfate-reducing bacteria, it was surprising that a probe designed to react with *Desulfobacter* species was about fourfold less reactive. These observations raise the concern that the sulfate-reducing bacteria probed may not be the predominating sulfate-reducing bacteria in this marine sediment. The ability to carry out sulfate reduction is found in members of at least three other phylogenetic groups which are sufficiently distinct from proteobacteria that probes should not cross-react (e.g., *Desulfotomaculum* spp. in the gram-positive phylum, *Thermodesulfobacterium commune*, and *Archaeoglobus fulvidus;* Woese, 1987; Achenbach-Richter *et al.*, 1987).

These probes are being used to further characterize the microbiota of marine (Devereux *et al.*, 1991) and freshwater (Winfrey *et al.*, 1991) sediments. In the former study the probes are being used as intracellular stains, so that sulfate reducers can be compared to "total" bacterial counts based either on the universal rRNA probe response or on DAPI staining. Both rRNA probes reacted with a relatively low percentage of the DAPI-stained cells (up to 16%). This might indicate poor probe penetration into cells and/or low ribosome content. Short-term enrichment (up to 48 hr) in a culture medium designed to favor sulfate reducers did not increase the relative response with the sulfate reducer-specific probe, although addition of molybdate, an inhibitor of sulfate reduction, did decrease the probe response.

Studies of magnetotactic bacteria inhabiting lake sediment have also been reported (Amann *et al.*, 1992). Cells selected by magnetic attraction have been used to obtain DNA for PCR amplification of SSU rRNA genes. Twenty-one different rRNA sequence types have been retrieved, most showing phylogenetic relatedness to the alpha group of proteobacteria. It was interesting that a sequence identical to that of *Mycobacterium chitae* was retrieved. The significance of this was not discussed but might be interesting as *M. chitae* was apparently cultivated from soil. Oligonucleotide probes complementing unique regions of the more frequently occurring alpha group proteobacterial sequences were used to verify the relevance of these sequences to the sediment system. This was important as PCR amplification did not always result in libraries dominated by sequences characteristic of this proteobacterial group. Since whole cells were probed directly, it was possible to observe that three different alpha group proteobacterial sequences were contributed by organisms with coccoid morphology. This is a population which is obviously more complex than it looks.

4.2.4. Symbionts of Marine Animals

Various symbioses between bacteria and marine invertebrate hosts have been, or are currently being, explored with rRNA-based methodology. Assuming that such relationships were likely to involve a single, or at least a predominating, symbiotic bacterial species Seewaldt and Stackebrandt (1982) retrieved 16S rRNA from *Prochloron*, a photosynthetic prokaryote symbiont of colonial ascidians, and demonstrated its relationship to cyanobacteria through comparative analysis of fragments of the 16S rRNA sequence. Using the same reasoning, Distel *et al.* (1988) purified bacterial symbionts from a variety of invertebrate hosts by differential centrifugation methods and determined 16S rRNA sequences directly by reverse transcriptase sequencing of extracted

RNA. Sequence data supported the assumed simplicity of the symbiont community, since unambiguous sequences were obtained, and symbiont sequences from different individuals of the same host species were identical. Similarity among tube worm symbionts has recently been verified by DNA–DNA hybridization results (Edwards and Nelson, 1991).

Studies of several clam, tube worm, and mollusk species thought to harbor sulfur-oxidizing symbionts revealed that the predominating bacteria belong to a phylogenetically coherent and unique line of descent in the gamma subdivision of the proteobacterial phylum (Distel *et al.*, 1988), extending earlier results based on 5S rRNA sequences of deep-sea vent clams and tube worms (Stahl *et al.*, 1984). The symbionts are unique in each animal species. The phylogenetic relationships among symbionts of three lucinid clams studied parallel the suspected evolutionary relationships among the host animals. This is consistent with the possibility that the bacteria coevolved with their hosts, following an ancestral initiation of the partnership. However, the similarities between symbionts of the tube worm, *Riftia pachyptila,* and of the lucinid clams, or between symbionts of two deep-sea vent bivalves which are classified in different orders, suggests the possibility of lateral transfer of symbionts between unrelated hosts. Knowledge of the relationships between sulfur-oxidizing and methane-oxidizing bacterial symbionts and their invertebrate hosts is expanding through current work (Distel, 1991).

The symbiosis between bacteria and wood-boring clams (also known by the common name "shipworms") has also been investigated (Distel *et al.*, 1991). In this case, cellulolytic, N_2-fixing bacteria were cultivated from the gill tissues of four different clam genera collected from geographically disparate sites. The isolates were found to have identical 16S rRNA sequences. This was taken as evidence that this symbiotic relationship is either relatively recent or that exchange of symbionts among animals is relatively efficient. An oligonucleotide probe designed to complement a unique domain within this 16S rRNA sequence was used to confirm the relevance of the isolates to the host animal. This was shown by hybridization of the probe with RNA extracted from gill tissues, and by direct intracellular staining of the bacterial symbionts within the gill tissue.

SSU rRNA sequences of algal symbionts of a variety of invertebrate species have been investigated by the PCR approach (Rowan and Powers, 1991). Many of the algal symbionts have not previously been cultivated. rRNA sequences of algal symbionts from 22 animal host species were grouped into ten phylogenetic clusters, although it was suspected that each cluster may underestimate the true diversity among the algal symbionts due to the inability of SSU rRNA sequence variation to resolve these highly related species. The general lack of correlation between patterns of phylogenetic relatedness of hosts and symbionts suggested that lateral transfer of symbionts among hosts has occurred.

The PCR approach has also recently been used to investigate symbionts living within gill tissue of the American oyster (Pelletier *et al.*, 1991). A spirochete, *Cristispira,* has been described as a symbiont but has never been cultivated from this animal. In addition to a spirochete-like 16S rRNA sequence, a mycoplasma-like 16S rRNA sequence was obtained. Because of its morphology, the latter symbiont might have evaded microscopic detection within host cells. The contributions of these two species are currently being explored by 16S rRNA-based oligonucleotide probe methods (B. Paster, Forsyth Dental Center, personal communication).

SSU rRNA sequences of uncultivated luminescent bacteria inhabiting the light organs of anamalopid flashlight fishes have also been investigated (Haygood *et al,.* 1991; Wolfe and Haygood, 1992). These were found to be related to, but not identical to, the SSU rRNA sequences of luminous bacteria cultivated from seawater or from the light organs of other fish species. In other work, the eubacterial nature of extremely large symbionts of surgeonfish has been demonstrated through retrieval of the symbiont's SSU rRNA sequence and intracellular staining with a hybridization probe complementary to a unique sequence region (Angert *et al.*, 1992). The bacterium is apparently a member of the low G + C subdivision of the gram positive phylum.

4.3. Gastrointestinal Tract Environments

Stahl (1988) and co-workers have initiated a study of the role played by cultivated rumen bacteria in fiber digestion in this habitat. *Bacteroides succinogenes,* considered to be a dominant fiber-digesting inhabitant of the rumen and cecum, has been the focus of their attention. Comparative analysis of 16S rRNA sequences of different strains led to the discovery of the phylogenetic novelty of *B. succinogenes* (Montgomery *et al.*, 1988), and to the transfer of these strains to a new genus, *Fibrobacter,* to distinguish them from *Bacteroides* species which belong to another eubacterial phylum (Fig. 7A). Oligonucleotide probes designed to hybridize with the 16S rRNA of all *Fibrobacter* species or with members of individual *Fibrobacter* species (see Section 3.2.1 and Table II, Section IV) were used to study the dynamics of these populations within the bovine rumen in response to addition of monensin, an antibiotic used to stimulate feeding efficiency in ruminants (Stahl *et al.*, 1988). A probe designed to react with the 16S rRNA of *Lachnospira multiparus,* a gram-positive bacterium known to be sensitive to monensin, was also used.

Perhaps the most striking result was the very low reactivity of all probes compared to the reactivity of a universal probe (as shown in Fig. 12A, less than 1% of total rumen SSU rRNA). In an independent study (Briesacher *et al.*, 1992), levels in the range of 5.4 to 6.6% were reported. This seems surprising for organisms that degrade cellulose, the major energy source entering the rumen. Unless *Fibrobacter* 16S rRNA is selected against during the extraction of nucleic acids, two hypotheses present themselves. It is possible that these isolates are not the predominant cellulolytic rumen bacteria. Alternatively, a diverse collection of cellulolytic bacteria each with relatively low population density, as opposed to one or a few predominating species, may share this energy source.

An intriguing finding was the periodic fluctuation in *Fibrobacter* and *Lachnospira* 16S rRNA assayed by these probes (Fig. 12A). This could have been due to changes in population density, changes in growth rate, or both. Cycling occurred at approximately 10-day intervals and thus does not appear to be related to daily feeding schedule. Although the periodicity may have been caused by addition of monensin, fluctuations

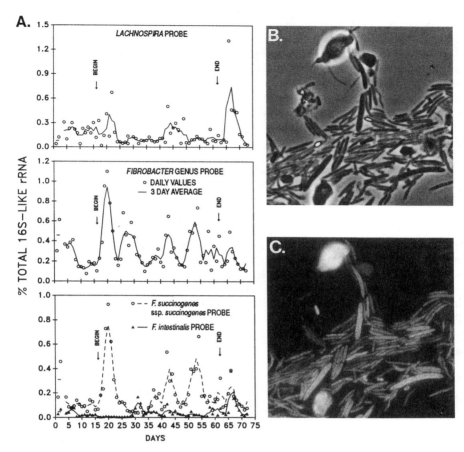

Figure 12. 16S rRNA-based oligonucleotide hybridization probe studies of rumen and cecal habitats (modified with permission from Stahl *et al.*, 1988, and Amann *et al.*, 1990b). (A) Hybridization with extracted bovine rumen RNA of probes targeting (top) *Lachnospira multivora,* (middle) all *Fibrobacter* species, and (bottom) *F. succinogenes* ssp. *succinogenes* (dashed line) or *F. intestinalis* (solid line). The antibiotic monensin was added or removed from the daily diet as shown by arrows. (B, C) Photomicrographs of mouse cecum contents by phase-contrast microscopy (B) and fluorescence microscopy (C) after reaction with a tetramethyl rhodamine-labeled universal SSU rRNA probe.

seem to have possibly occurred during the period prior to its addition. Since neither population was systematically eliminated following monensin treatment, the results were taken to suggest that the effects of monensin on the rumen microbiota are more likely due to metabolic shifts within existing populations of fermentative bacteria than to population changes. An alternative interpretation is that variations in a more important cellulolytic population could have been missed by probing species that contribute relatively little to rumen cellulolytic activity.

Probes designed to react with members of the two *Fibrobacter* species sometimes did not account for all of the SSU rRNA detected by the *Fibrobacter* genus probe (e.g., compare middle and lower panels of Fig. 12A between days 25 and 30). This might be explained by the presence of variants of *Fibrobacter* species that contain different 16S rRNA sequences and thus do not react with either species-specific probe. In fact, at the time of the study, the *F. succinogenes* ssp. *succinogenes*-specific probe was thought to probe all members of this species, but additional strains were subsequently discovered (e.g., strains of *F. succinogenes* ssp. *elongata*) that did not react with this probe (Amann *et al.*, 1990b, 1992a; see Fig. 7).

It was not possible to use fluorescence-labeled *Fibrobacter* probes in intracellular hybridization reactions because of the intense background autofluorescence of rumen contents. However, fluorescent intracellular probing of cecal contents has recently been reported (Amann *et al.*, 1990b). Universal probes reacted with most cells of a mouse cecal sample (Fig. 12B and C), providing evidence of the general penetrability of oligonucleotides in what is presumably a diverse collection of cecal inhabitants. Probes designed to react with *Fibrobacter intestinalis* successfully probed cells of these species when they were artificially seeded into cecal samples. Bacteria indigenous to cecal samples also reacted with the probe, though in low frequency (about one in 10^4 cells), indicating that this species is likely to have low abundance in the cecum, or that most indigenous *F. intestinalis* cells have a ribosome content too low to react strongly with the probe.

4.4. Terrestrial Environments

4.4.1. Soil

An extensive study of streptomycete 16S rRNA sequences (Stackebrandt *et al.*, 1991; Witt *et al.*, 1989; Kemmerling *et al.*, 1990) has led to the realization that streptomycetes comprise a phylogenetically coherent group within the high-G+C subdivision of the gram-positive eubacterial phylum. This makes possible the application of rRNA methods to study their ecology. Unfortunately, the relationships among streptomycetes are so close that there is insufficient 16S rRNA sequence variation to enable resolution of all species. The more variable regions of 23S rRNA may offer promise in achieving higher resolution (Stackebrandt *et al.*, 1991). Oligonucleotides designed to target the 16S rRNAs of all streptomycetes, or groups of related streptomycete species (Table II, Section IV), were used to investigate DNA extracted from soil humus (Witt *et al.*, 1989). The oligonucleotides were used as primers with the PCR approach to amplify portions of the DNA, providing qualitative evidence for the presence of streptomycetes in the sample.

A general investigation of Australian soil has been undertaken (Liesack and Stackebrandt, in press and submitted). 16S rRNA genes were retrieved after PCR amplification and cloning. Partial sequences of 30 clones were compared, leading to the design of oligonucleotide hybridization probes specific to related sets of sequences. These probes were used to screen another 83 clones. About half the clones formed three clusters within the alpha subdivision of the proteobacteria. Seven sequences related to planctomycete bacteria were recovered, which was interesting since cultivated members of this group are known only from aquatic habitats. About a quarter of the clones formed a cluster which is unrelated to known eubacteria and which may constitute a new eubacterial phylum. No sequences identical to those of cultivated species were found. Other soil or groundwater bacterial communities are currently under investigation using similar methods (Herrick *et al.*, 1992; Gevertz, 1992; Young *et al.*, 1992).

4.4.2. Root Nodules

Frankia spp. also comprise a phylogenetically coherent cluster within the gram-positive high-G+C subdivision, enabling the design of rRNA-based oligonucleotide probes (Hahn *et al.*, 1989, 1990a,b). As with the streptomycetes, the relatively high similarity among *Frankia* 16S rRNA sequences, and between 16S rRNA sequences of *Frankia* and those of other actinomycetes, limits the resolving power of these probes. The probes have been used to demonstrate the recovery of *Frankia* added to sterile soils, after a 10-week period of host plant growth. The nodulation of plants acts as a natural enrichment for the added *Frankia,* which can then be detected by probing RNA extracted from the nodules. The successful probing of 16S rRNA from the inoculated strain within nodular tissue constitutes a verification of the ability of the inoculated strain to initiate infection. The competitiveness of two *Frankia* strains was shown to be proportional to their fractional importance in the inoculum, using an oligonucleotide probe that could distinguish between the strains under very stringent hybridization conditions. Extensive study of the competitiveness of different strains would not be possible with these 16S rRNA probes, due to the very high relatedness among the strains.

4.4.3. Mycorrhizae

An effort is under way to characterize fungi that form mycorrhizal associations with plants (Bruns *et al.*, 1990; Gardes *et al.*, 1991). Because these microorganisms lack morphologic variation and are difficult to cultivate, their true representation in soil or in mycorrhizal associations is not known. LSU rRNA gene sequences, or the sequences of ITS regions were targeted for these analyses because the high relatedness among fungi necessitated greater resolving power. The general strategy was to amplify portions fungal mitochondrial LSU rRNA genes or fungal ITS regions with the PCR approach. The PCR amplification was advantageous in permitting analysis of DNA extracted from very small mycorrhizal samples (1–5 mm long, 1–5 μg). The primers used were specific to fungi and did not amplify rRNA or ITS regions of the plant host. Either the LSU rRNA gene or ITS amplification products were then characterized by analysis of restriction fragment length polymorphism (RFLP; see Section 3.1.2a), sequence comparison, or oligonucleotide probe hybridization.

In one study (Gardes *et al.*, 1991), ITS regions of different fungal genera were found to exhibit different RFLP patterns. However, four *Laccaria* species exhibited only two RFLP patterns suggesting that RFLP patterns would not offer species-specificity.

There was, however, sufficient variation among the ITS sequences to permit the distinction of not only these four species, but also some different strains of single species. On this basis an oligonucleotide probe was constructed that could distinguish between two *L. bicolor* strains. This provides evidence that ITS regions may provide sufficient sequence variability to resolve among very highly related microorganisms. The RFLP approach was used to demonstrate that pine and spruce seedlings inoculated with *L. bicolor* and planted in reforestation sites became contaminated with another mycorrhizal fungus, *Thelephora terrestris,* whose RFLP pattern was different. In various trials, *T. terrestris* either outcompeted *L. bicolor* or the two fungi coexisted on the plant root. The results were verified by the use of RFLP patterns for PCR-amplified portions of LSU rRNA genes of fungal mitochondria, which were also characteristic for these two fungal genera.

Recently, Bruns *et al.* (1991) have begun a study of the mycorrhizal symbionts of an achlorophylous plant, *Pterospora andromedia,* which parasitizes conifers. Again, the PCR approach was used to obtain portions of the fungal mitochondrial LSU rRNA gene. Amplification products were probed with oligonucleotides specific for different genera of mycorrhizal fungi. All *Pterospora* symbionts belonged to the fungal genus *Rhizopogon,* unusual because this fungus was thought to be restricted to coniferous hosts.

Studies of vesicular-arbuscular endomycorrhizal fungi colonizing plant roots are also in progress (Simon *et al.,* 1992; Klein *et al.,* 1992).

4.4.4 Endolithic Microorganisms

An investigation of 5S rRNA extracted from an Antarctic endolithic community has been performed (Colwell *et al.,* 1989). A single predominant 5S rRNA band was found upon gel purification of rRNA extracted directly from the few millimeter surface layer of rock samples. Comparison to other 5S rRNA sequences suggested that this molecule was contributed by a member of the gamma subdivision of the proteobacterial phylum, possibly a new member of the Vibrionaceae.

4.5. Insect Symbionts

Unterman *et al.* (1989) used a selective cloning approach (Section 3.1.1) to recover 16S rRNA genes of two bacterial symbionts of the pea aphid, which have so far evaded cultivation. The two 16S rRNA gene sequences were 88.1% similar in unrestricted analysis. On the basis of distance matrix tree and signature analysis, both appear to be contributed by members of the gamma subdivision of the proteobacterial phylum. The fact that only two SSU rRNA genes were observed was taken as evidence that the diversity within the aphid microbiota is low. This paralleled microscopic observations of two morphologically distinct symbiotic bacteria, though the relationship between the recovered sequences and the microscopically observed symbionts should be verified (e.g., through hybridization with sequence-specific probes). Subsequent analysis has shown that symbionts of ten additional aphid species are closely related to what is the more predominant of the two symbionts, leading to speculation that the relationship between aphids and their major symbiont resulted from a single ancestral infection (M. Munson and P. Baumann, University of California—Davis, personal communication).

Ongoing studies of other symbionts are directed at resolving the microbial etiology of insect reproduction complications. The PCR strategy has been used to retrieve rickettsia-like SSU sequences from the eggs of wasps (R. Stouthamer and J. Werren, University of Rochester, personal communication) and other insects (S. O'Neill and H. Robertson, University of Illinois, personal communication). Oligonucleotide probes specific for a bacterium thought to be involved in controlling sex ratios in wasps have been used to demonstrate that the "son killer" bacterium can be transmitted across a broad range of wasp host species via flies which are commonly parasitized by different wasps (S. W. Skinner, A. Grimes, J. Dutton, and E. F. DeLong, personal communication). Similarly, 16S rRNA gene sequences have been retrieved from the testes of moths (Krueger *et al.*, 1992), but these have not yet been characterized.

A novel application of rRNA methodology is being applied to characterize patterns of community composition within the cricket hindgut (Santo Domingo *et al.*, 1991). The PCR approach is being used to retrieve about 300 nucleotides of SSU rRNA sequence. These amplification products are then digested with restriction enzymes so that the fragments generate a community rRNA RFLP pattern on gels. While the conserved nature of rRNA sequences is likely to limit the degree to which this method can resolve among community members, the method has been useful in monitoring changes in the predominant populations following perturbations. Different RFLP profiles were observed for each of five different diets fed to the crickets (Santo Domingo *et al.*, 1992).

4.6. Experimental Bioreactors

rRNA methods have been used to study sulfate-reducing and methane-producing bacterial populations which may be in competition within fixed-bed bioreactors. The experimental microbial communities were developed under anaerobic conditions from groundwater enriched with glucose in the presence or absence of sulfate (Stahl *et al.*, 1989; Kane *et al.*, 1991; Amann *et al.*, 1992b; D. Stahl, University of Illinois, personal communication). Because these microbial groups are phylogenetically coherent (or nearly so, see Section 4.2.3), it was possible to design oligonucleotides for use as probes and as primers for cDNA synthesis from SSU rRNA and subsequent PCR amplification and cloning of naturally occurring 16S rRNA sequences. A primer unique to all sulfate-reducing bacteria of the delta subdivision of the proteobacterial phylum was used together with a universal primer to amplify about 500 nucleotides between positions 385 and 907 of 16S rRNA sequences of sulfate-reducing bacteria inhabiting one of the bioreactors. Cloned 16S rRNA sequences resembled, but were not identical to, 16S rRNA sequences of cultivated proteobacterial sulfate-reducing bacteria. Oligonucleotide probes complementing the two sulfate-reducing bacterial sequences were used as intracellular stains to demonstrate that thin rod-shaped and vibrio-shaped cells contain these sequences within the biofilm. Most recently, these probes were used to monitor enrichment cultures that led to the cultivation of a sulfate-reducing bacterium that has an SSU rRNA sequence identical to one of those recovered directly from the biofilm (Poulsen *et al.* 1992).

Oligonucleotide probes were used to study the populations of proteobacterial sulfate reducers and methanogenic bacteria relative to total SSU rRNA in these bioreactors (D. Stahl, personal communication). In both systems, rRNA of the two groups accounted for a low percentage of the total SSU rRNA, perhaps because of their high trophic status as terminal members of anaerobic food chains. In the high-sulfate bioreactor, sulfate reducer rRNA was more abundant than methanogen rRNA. In the low-sulfate bioreactor, both groups accounted for similar amounts of rRNA, surprising since ongoing methane production suggested that methanogens outcompeted sulfate reducers for major fermentation intermediates. Addition of sulfate to the low-sulfate bioreactor resulted in a decline of methanogens relative to sulfate reducers, but did not result in a rapid increase of sulfate reducer rRNA. This suggested that following addition of sulfate, an existing sulfate reducer population may be able to compete more effectively for major fermentation products. It is possible that prior to sulfate addition, sulfate reducers might serve as acetogenic bacteria, metabolizing fermentation intermediates to H_2 and acetate to supply methanogens.

4.7. Industrial Microbiology Applications

A study of the natural inhabitants of copper leaching pond mud from the Chino mine dump, Kennecott Copper Corp., based on analysis of 5S rRNA, has been performed (Lane *et al.*, 1985b). Two unique 5S rRNA sequence types were recovered. One was identical to the 5S rRNA sequence of *Thiobacillus ferrooxidans*, while the other did not match a sequence in the data base. Its phylogenetic affiliation is with the proteobacteria.

rRNA-based oligonucleotide probes have been developed for distinguishing the desirable from the undesirable members of industrial milk fermentation (Betzl *et al.*, 1990). Probes targeting 23S rRNA can be used to discern colonies of *Lactococcus lactis* from those of a common contaminant, *Enterococcus* spp. Probes targeting 16S rRNA can be used to detect *L. lactis* ssp. *cremoris* (Salama *et al.*, 1991). Other hybridization probes useful for detection of lactic acid bacteria (Klijn *et al.*, 1991; Hertel *et al.*, 1992) and *Listeria monocytogenes* will probably be of use in the food microbiology industry.

4.8. Pathogens in the Host Environment

4.8.1. Detection of Cultivated Pathogens

The strategy of using hybridization probes that complement rRNA sequences for rapid detection of pathogenic microorganisms has been rigorously investigated by clinical microbiologists and the clinical industry. This has not only led to useful tools for clinical analysis, but also to very large rRNA sequence data bases for phylogenetic groups containing pathogenic microorganisms, and to the development of methods which should have general utility in microbial ecology. Some pathogens for which rRNA-based hybridization probes have been developed are listed in Table II (Sections I and II); more are listed in Lane and Collins (1991). Such probes have been shown to function in clinical specimens (e.g., Haun and Gobel, 1987; Edman *et al.*, 1988; Morotomi *et al.*, 1989; Dix *et al.*, 1990; Hoshina *et al.*, 1990) and experimental animals (e.g., Forsman *et al.*, 1990). Oligonucleotide probes that target rRNA have also been used to study animal diseases. For example, probes specific for fish pathogens, *Vibrio anguillarum* and *Aeromonas salmonida*, were used to demonstrate the presence of the pathogens after experimental infection (Rehnstam *et al.*, 1989; Barry *et al.*, 1990). Similarly, an oligonucleotide specific for *Treponema hyodysenteriae* was used to detect this pathogen in the feces of experimentally induced cases of swine dysentery (Jensen *et al.*, 1990).

Probe strategies have also been used in epidemiologic surveys. For instance, Persing *et al.* (1990) recently used oligonucleotide probes to evaluate portions of *Borrelia* SSU rRNA gene sequences retrieved as PCR products from museum tick specimens. Their results suggested that *B. burgdorferi*, the etiologic agent of Lyme disease, was present in the animal reservoir 25–35 years before the clinical illness was recognized. Studies of *B. burgdorferi* infection rates in ticks are ongoing (Schwartz *et al.*, 1991). Another major approach, referred to as ribotyping, involves the evaluation of RFLP patterns defined by rRNA gene and surrounding sequences. This has been used in epidemiologic studies of cultivated pathogens (e.g., Goering and Duensing, 1990; Patton *et al.*, 1991; Reagan *et al.*, 1990; Tram *et al.*, 1990).

4.8.2. The Nature of Uncultivated Pathogens

4.8.2a. Human Bacillary Angiomatosis. rRNA cloning and sequencing methods have recently been used to characterize the possible etiologic agent of bacillary angiomatosis (Relman *et al.*, 1990). This disease involves a proliferation of small blood vessels in the skin and visceral organs in immunocompromised patients, including patients infected with human immunodeficiency virus. It is presumed to be an infectious disease on the basis of microscopic observation of bacteria in diseased tissue, but the etiologic agent has so far evaded cultivation.

DNA extracted from diseased or control tissues was used as a template for PCR amplification reactions. When primers complementing universally conserved regions of SSU rRNA were used, amplification products were obtained from DNA extracted from uninfected tissue, attributed to the presence of normal microbiota. A fragment of about 480 nucleotides between priming sites near positions 930 and 1390 recovered from diseased tissue of a patient with bacillary angiomatosis, but not from healthy individuals, was taken as a likely candidate for the SSU rRNA contributed by the pathogen. Specific primers were designed from this sequence and used to more selectively amplify a 241-nucleotide fragment between positions 1017 and 1298 from DNA extracted from different diseased tissues of four patients. Although identical sequences were found in three of the four patients, small sequence variations (up to 1.7% in unrestricted analysis) were found between individually cloned SSU rRNA genes recovered from the same or different patients. This heterogeneity was considered to have most likely resulted from errors introduced by DNA polymerase during PCR amplification, though mixed infection by highly related species or small-scale intraspecies variation in SSU rRNA sequence could not be ruled out as possible alternative explanations. Phylogenetic analysis of these sequence fragments suggested their affiliation with members of the alpha subdivision of the proteobacterial phylum, and specifically with the intracellular parasite *Rochalimaea quintana* (98.3% in restricted analysis).

The discovery of this sequence type in the tissues of four diseased patients provides compelling evidence that this sequence correspond to the etiologic agent. However, in the absence of a cultivated pathogen, Koch's postulates cannot be tested. Hybridization probes targeting the sequence, especially when used intracellularly, could be used to prove that the microorganism contributing the cloned 16S rRNA sequence is also the microorganism predominating in the infected tissue. This would be especially useful in cases where the PCR reaction is employed, since the technique is so sensitive and the possibility of recovering artifactual sequences has been clearly demonstrated.

4.8.2b. Human Ehrlichiosis. The PCR approach was used to retrieve 16S rRNA gene fragments from two patients with ehrlichiosis, an intracellular bacterial infection similar to Rocky Mountain Spotted Fever (Anderson *et al.*, 1991). The sequence recovered was related to but distinct from those of other *Ehrlichia* spp., a group related to rickettsia, leading to the proposal that the bacterium possessing this sequence should belong to a new species, *E. chaffeensis.* PCR primers and an oligonucleotide hybridization probe specific to the *E. chaffeensis* 16S rRNA sequence were used to demonstrate the presence of this organism in the blood of infected patients as well as ticks (Anderson *et al.*, 1992). This provided evidence consistent with the hypothesis that *E. chaffeensis* is the etiologic agent, and challenges the notion that *E. canis* causes the disease. The results also give insight as to the vector tick species and the possible animal reservoir.

4.8.2c. Whipple's Disease in Humans. The PCR approach has been used to retrieve a 16S rRNA gene sequence from patients with Whipple's disease, usually a diarrheal disease of the small bowel (K. Wilson, Duke Univ., personal communication). The sequence bears phylogenetic resemblance to members of the high G + C subdivision of the gram positive eubacterial phylum.

4.8.2d. Ruminant Intracellular Pathogen. A similar study of an obligate intracellular pathogen of ruminant erythrocytes has recently been performed (Weisburg *et al.*, 1991). DNA extracted from cells of *Anaplasma marginale*, purified from infected host cells by density gradient centrifugation, was amplified with the PCR reaction using primers designed to complement many eubacterial 16S rRNA sequences. A cloned amplification product contained a 16S rRNA gene, which was shown to be most closely related to rickettsial 16S rRNA sequences within the alpha subdivision of the proteobacterial phylum. Again, this constitutes only circumstantial evidence that the organism contributing the 16S rRNA sequence is the etiologic agent.

4.8.2e. Mycoplasma-like Organisms in Plant Infections. PCR primers designed to selectively amplify 16S rRNA sequences of mycoplasma were applied to the investigation of uncultivated mycoplasma-like organisms experimentally maintained in plant culture (Deng and Hiruki, 1991). The nature of the sequences retrieved has not yet been determined.

4.9. Microbial Interactions

Uncultivated bacterial symbionts of *Paramecium caudatum* were investigated using the PCR approach for retrieval of SSU and LSU rRNA genes (Amann *et al.*, 1991). The SSU rRNA sequence suggests that this bacterium, *Holospora obtusa*, is a member of the alpha group of proteobacteria and is somewhat related to rickettsia. An oligonucleotide probe complementing a unique portion of the LSU rRNA sequence was used as an intracellular stain to differentiate between *H. obtosa* and other endosymbiotic bacteria of *P. caudatum*.

Defined mixed cultures of the morphologically similar *Ruminococcus albus, R. flavifaciens*, and *Fibrobacter succinogenes* have been investigated in competition experiments using 16S rRNA-based hybridization probes to monitor population changes (Odenyo *et al.*, 1992). Given the results mentioned above (see Section 4.3) which may challenge the relevance of *F. succinogenes* as a major rumen cellulolytic species, it is interesting that *F. succinogenes* was less competitive than these other species when grown on cellulose. One wonders whether other naturally occurring—and possibly more relevant—cellulolytic species are present in the rumen awaiting cultivation.

5. The State of the Art

Microbial ecology studies employing rRNA technologies are expanding at a rapid pace. The popularity of these methods provides evidence of their value for addressing long-standing problems in the field. The coming years will be exciting as the molecular results provide new insights into the ecology of microorganisms. However, we caution the reader that uncertainties about the methods remain.

5.1. rRNA Methodology

Various rRNA-based methods have now been developed and used to address ecologic questions. Different cloning and hybridization approaches can be used to advantage in obtaining different kinds of information of ecologic relevance. The initial applications have provided great confidence in the utility of all approaches to provide substantial amounts of accurate information about many of the naturally occurring microorganisms. The fidelity of all approaches in copying rRNA sequence information has been very high, and except in cases of minor sequence variation or in cases where intercistronic variation is significant, we can be reasonably certain that sequence differences reflect the inputs of different microorganisms. Replication within and between environments has also already been observed, further supporting the high fidelity of rRNA cloning and sequencing methods.

In the initial applications, we have encountered evidence that SSU rRNA sequences are not always able to resolve highly related microbial species. However, the earliest investigations of LSU rRNA and ITS regions have shown that they provide higher resolution. Of course, the question asked dictates the need for resolving power, and thus the choice of molecule to be analyzed.

Evidence of sampling and cloning biases have been observed in early applications of rRNA methodology. These limitations will be important to understand, and hopefully solve, as they would restrict the ability of rRNA methods to provide a reasonably comprehensive view of the inhabitants of natural microbial communities.

The sensitivity of rRNA-based oligonucleotide probes needs to be improved. In clinical applications, probe insensitivity increases the threshold number of pathogen cells required for detection. Amplification strategies like PCR should help solve such problems. In environmental applications, low ribosome density per cell may limit probe sensitivity. The development of stronger signals could significantly increase the utility of intracellular staining with rRNA-based oligonucleotide probes for ecologic investigations of microbial communities (Zarda *et al.*, 1991).

One of the greatest challenges for future method refinement will be to link the phylogenetic information provided by rRNA sequences with the physiological functions of the microorganisms that contribute them. One approach which has been attempted is the use of phylogenetically based hybridization probes in conjunction with environmental perturbation to discover how specific microorganisms respond to changing environmental conditions (see Sections 4.2.3, 4.3 and 4.6). Probes could also be used in conjunction with other methods for analyzing physiologic function. For example, it might be possible to simultaneously use intracellular rRNA probes with autofluorescence, microautoradiography (after radiolabeling with appropriate substrates), immunologic probes directed at specific enzymes, or other DNA probes that target genes of physiologic relevance (e.g., Holben and Tiedje, 1988; Holben *et al.*, 1988; Ka and Holben, 1991; Kirshtein *et al.*, 1991; Lovell and Hui, 1989, 1991; Tsien *et al.*, 1991; Herrick *et al.*, 1992).

5.2. Ecological Applications of rRNA Methods

rRNA methods are providing a new and in some cases provocative view of naturally occurring microorganisms. In several cases (e.g., geothermal source pools, symbionts, diseased tissue), rRNA methods have enabled a first look at microbial inhabitants known to have resisted cultivation. In habitats from which microorganisms have readily been cultivated, the view revealed by rRNA methods is very different from that provided by culture methods. This can be directly seen in cloning and sequencing results. Numerous rRNA sequence types have already been retrieved from several environments. With few exceptions, natural rRNA sequences differ from the rRNA sequences of cultivated species, even when the species have been cultivated from the same habitat (see Section 4.1.1).

So far the presence of cultivated microorganisms in a natural system has only been verified in a few hybridization probe studies. More typically, low probe reactivities have been observed. We must be careful to consider the ecology of systems when interpreting low probe responses. For example, a cultivated species may play a minor role in a community, possibly as a consequence of its high trophic status (see Sections 4.2.3 and 4.6). However, in cases where the role of a microorganism is suspected to be important (e.g., cyanobacteria in cyanobacterial mats and rumen cellulolytic bacteria) the insignificance of the cultivated species seems surprising. In contrast, it has been relatively easy to demonstrate with rRNA-targeted probes the importance of species whose rRNA sequences are readily recovered by cloning approaches.

These initial findings seem to confirm the speculation that few of the extant microorganisms have been cultivated. rRNA methods even suggest that the predominating species in some natural environments may not be those we have cultivated. Why might this be so? Preferring the optimistic view that uncultivated microorganisms are not necessarily "uncultivatable", we question how well microbiologists understand the relationship between the physiological needs of microorganisms and the features of natural and culture environments that control their competitiveness. Is there a greater probability of enriching a predominating species from certain environments, perhaps those with restricted microbial diversity (e.g., extreme environments, symbioses, diseased tissue, experimental mixed cultures)? Are the chances of choosing the most appropriate environmental conditions for our enrichment cultures lower than we have suspected? Have we overlooked some (perhaps only a few) key differences between natural and culture environments? Although the problem of reproducing the appropriate natural conditions may be especially severe in enrichment culture where selection for the most fit microorganism occurs, it may exist as well for direct cultivation methods—the conditions of the medium may simply not satisfy the requirements of the microorganism sought. Pfennig (Braunschweig, 1990) has asked us to recall that the original concept of elective culture involved careful observation of how a specific microorganism responds to moderate changes of environment. rRNA-based hybridization probes may provide the means by which we can monitor enrichments to observe the conditions under which they succeed or fail in enriching particular uncultivated species (see Section 4.6). They are also beginning to provide a means of detailed study of the distributions and behavior of uncultivated microorganisms, and this in turn may give insight into how to develop more appropriate culture methods.

If it is true that we know few of the naturally occurring microorganisms, the direct exploration of the inhabitants of natural microbial communities can be expected to have a significant influence on our understanding of microbial phylogeny. How representative are cultivated species of the phylogenetic (and physiologic?) diversity within the microbial world? Although rRNA sequences of natural occurring microorganisms appear to be mainly those of uncultivated species, they have so far mainly fit into phylogenetic groups already discovered among cultivated species (e.g., cyanobacteria, green nonsulfur bacteria, proteobacteria, spirochetes, gram-positive eubacteria, planctomycete bacteria, dinoflagellates, fungi). It is interesting that proteobacteria of various types have been found in several different habitats (e.g., marine picoplankton, sediments, symbionts of marine invertebrates and insects, an endolithic community, mine pond mud, soil, and diseased tissues). This is evidently a reflection of the diversity of proteobacterial phenotypes. Some of the rRNA sequences retrieved from natural habitats (e.g., hot spring cyanobacterial mat, soil, seawater) may, however, represent novel lines of phylogenetic descent. Further investigation will undoubtedly lead to a better appreciation of natural microbial biodiversity.

As these new molecular methods are refined and as the amount of sequence data increases, we will undoubtedly learn much about the population and community ecology of microorganisms. It is already clear, for instance, that morphology underestimates diversity within populations and that culture collections underestimate community composition. Using the model hot spring mat community as an example, we have discovered that several diverse cyanobacteria are disguised by a common morphology. We have not recovered the rRNA sequence of a single cultivated species in the course of discovering at least 15 sequences of uncultivated species (see Section 4.1.1). The *extent* to which natural microbial community complexity has been underestimated should be learned as the census of inhabitants of natural microbial communities progresses.

Even though only a few communities have been analyzed, and analyses are at a very early stage (with only a few tens of sequences per community analyzed), comparison of different communities is beginning to raise questions about similarities in the way microbial communities may be structured. For example, near-surface marine picoplankton and a hot spring cyanobacterial mat, both light-dependent communities, seem to be predominated by a single cyanobacterium. Other community members are less abundant but more diverse. Does diversity change between trophic levels and is this related to the greater range of substrates made available as autotrophs convert simple nutrients to diverse cellular components? Phylogenetic diversity seems greater in the hot spring mat than in the marine picoplankton community. This is true for both the cyanobacterial population (unrestricted similarity values of 86.7–90.9% in mat versus 95–98% in picoplankton) and the remaining eubacteria (numerous phyla in mat versus single phylum in picoplankton). Is the diversity within natural microbial communities different in different habitats? What controls the microbial diversity at the population and community level? Undoubtedly, microbial ecologists can benefit from principles already discovered by macroecologists.

rRNA methods circumvent some of the limitations of traditional microbiological methods, and have thus opened a new age of discovery in microbiology. Their application is rapidly becoming pervasive in clinical and ecological laboratories. It would be interesting to know how Beijerinck and Winogradsky would view the initial results with these new approaches. We imagine that they would not be surprised, since they had forewarned us about the potential of culture methods to select for microorganisms whose importance in culture exceeds their importance in nature. Winogradsky, for example, commented on how we should interpret the importance of the readily cultivated spore-forming bacilli to soil microbial communities:

> They draw attention to themselves, whereas the other forms, being less docile, or even resistant, escape observation.*

More than ever we should realize the importance of verifying, rather than assuming, the significance of a cultivated microorganism (or its behavior under laboratory conditions)

---

*Translated from Winogradsky (1949) (p. 461) by Gijs Kuenen, Tech. University, Delft.

in the natural environment. We should, of course, keep in mind that these molecular methods have limitations of their own. As the earliest results begin to challenge our traditional views in microbial ecology, we should be careful not to overinterpret them. However, we should also keep an open mind to the possibility that continued application of these methods may require us to adopt a new way of thinking about microorganisms as they occur in nature.

ACKNOWLEDGMENTS. Many of the results we have reviewed were just emerging as we prepared our manuscript. We thank Rudy Amann, Paul Baumann, Tom Bruns, Ed DeLong, Rich Devereux, Dan Distel, Steve Giovannoni, Dave Lane, Scott O'Neill, Gary Olsen, Norman Pace, Hans Paerl, Bruce Paster, Tom Schmidt, Erko Stackenbrandt, Dave Stahl, Will Weisburg, Jack Werren, Ken Wilson, and Carl Woese for providing information and discussion in advance of publication so that our review would be up-to-date. We especially thank Ed DeLong, Ken Wilson, and Gijs Kuenen, for their critical reviews of the manuscript. We also thank Dr. Chris Pinet and Dr. Gijs Kuenen for assistance in translation. Our research has been sponsored by grants (BSR-8506602, -8818358, and -8907611) from the National Science Foundation.

References

Achenbach-Richter, L., Stetter, K. O., and Woese, C. R., 1987, A possible biochemical missing link among archaebacteria, *Nature* **327**:348–349.

Amann, R. I., Binder, B. J., Olson, R. J., Chisholm, S. W., Devereux, R., and Stahl, D. A., 1990a, Combination of 16S rRNA-targeted oligonucleotide probes with flow cytometry for analyzing mixed microbial populations, *Appl. Environ. Microbiol.* **56**:1919–1925.

Amann, R. I., Krumholz, L., and Stahl, D. A. 1990b, Fluorescent-oligonucleotide probing of whole cells for determinative, phylogenetic, and environmental studies in microbiology, *J. Bacteriol.* **172**:762–770.

Amann, R., Springer, N., Ludwig, W., Gortz, H., and Schleifer, K., 1991, Identification *in situ* and phylogeny of uncultured bacterial endosymbionts, *Nature* **351**:161–164.

Amann, R. I., Lin, C., Key, R., Montgomery, L., and Stahl, D. A., 1992a, Diversity among *Fibrobacter* isolates: Towards a phylogenetic and habitat-based classification, *Syst. Appl. Microbiol.* **15**, 23–31.

Amann, R. I., Stromley, J., Devereux, R., Key, R., and Stahl, D. A., 1992b, Molecular and microscopic identification of sulfate-reducing bacteria in multispecies biofilms, *Appl. Environ. Microbiol.* **58**:614–623.

Anderson, B. E., Dawson, J. E., Jones, D. C., and Wilson, K. H., 1991, *Ehrlichia chaffeensis,* a new species associated with human ehrlichiosis, *J. Clin. Microbiol.* **29**:2838–2842.

Anderson, B. E., Sumner, J. W., Dawson, J. E., Tzianabos, T., Greene, C. R., Olson, J. G., Fishbein, D. B., Olsen-Rasmussen, M., Holloway, B. P. George, E. H., and Azad, A. F., 1992, Detection of the etiologic agent of human ehrlichiosis by polymerase chain reaction, *J. Clin. Microbiol.* **30**:775–780.

Angert, E. R., Cements, K. D., and Pace, N. R., 1992, The largest prokaryote, *Abstr. Annu. Meet. Am. Soc. Microbiol.* p. 248.

Asgari, M., Lai, S., and Henney, H. R., 1991, *Acanthamoeba* DNA probe, *Abstr. Annu. Meet., Am. Soc. Microbiol.,* p. 83.

Atlas, R. M., 1984, Use of microbial diversity measurements to assess environmental stress, in *Current*

Perspectives in Microbial Ecology (M. J. Klug and C. A. Reddy, eds.), Am. Soc. Microbiol., Washington, D.C., pp. 540–545.

Barry, T., Powell, R., and Gannon, F., 1990, A general method to generate DNA probes for microorganisms, *Biotechnology* **8:**233–236.

Barry, T., Colleran, G., Glennon, M., Dunican, L. K., and Gannon, F., 1991, The 16s/23s ribosomal spacer region as a target for DNA probes to identify eubacteria, *PCR Meth. Appl.* **1:**51–56.

Bateson, M. M., Wiegel, J., and Ward, D. M., 1989, Comparative analysis of 16S ribosomal RNA sequences of thermophilic fermentative bacteria isolated from hot spring cyanobacterial mats, *Syst. Appl. Microbiol.* **12:**1–7.

Bateson, M. M., Thibault, K. J., and Ward, D. M., 1990, Comparative analysis of 16S ribosomal RNA sequences of *Thermus* species, *Syst. Appl. Microbiol.* **13:**8–13.

Bauman, J. G. J., and Bentvelzen, P., 1988, Flow cytometric detection of ribosomal RNA in suspended cells by fluorescent in situ hybridization, *Cytometry* **9:**517–524.

Bertin, B., Broux, O., and van Hoegarden, M., 1990, Flow cytometric detection of yeast by *in situ* hybridization with a fluorescent ribosomal RNA probe, *J. Microbiol. Meth.* **12:**1–12.

Betzl, D., Ludwig, W., and Schleifer, K. H., 1990, Identification of lactococci and enterococci by colony hybridization with 23S rRNA-targeted oligonucleotide probes, *Appl. Environ. Microbiol.* **56:**2927–2929.

Boddinghaus, B., Rogall, T., Flohr, T., Blocker, H., and Bottger, E. C., 1990, Detection and identification of mycobacteria by amplification of rRNA, *J. Clin. Microbiol.* **28:**1751–1759.

Bottger, E. C., 1989, Rapid determination of bacterial ribosomal RNA sequences by direct sequencing of enzymatically amplified DNA, *FEMS Microbiol. Lett.* **65:**171–176.

Bremer, H., and Dennis, P. P., 1987, Modulation of chemical composition and other parameters of the cell by growth rate, in: *Escherichia coli and Salmonella typhimurium Cellular and Molecular Biology*, Vol. 2 (F. C. Neidhart, J. L. Ingraham, K. Brooks Low, B. Magasanik, M. Shaechter, and H. E. Umbarger, eds.), Am. Soc. Microbiol., Washington, D.C., pp. 1527–1542.

Briesacher, S. L., May, T. Grigsby, K. N., Kerley, M. S., Anthony, R. V., and Paterson, J. A., 1992, Use of DNA probes to monitor nutritional effects on ruminal prokaryotes and *Fibrobacter succinogenes* S85, *J. Anim. Sci.* **70:**289–295.

Britschgi, T. B., and Giovannoni, S. J., 1991, Phylogenetic analysis of a natural marine bacterioplankton population by rRNA gene cloning and sequencing, *Appl. Environ. Microbiol.* **57:**1707–1713.

Brock, T. D., 1978, *Thermophilic Microorganisms and Life at High Temperatures*, Springer-Verlag, Berlin.

Brock, T. D., 1987, The study of microorganisms in situ: Progress and problems, *Symp. Soc. Gen. Microbiol.* **41:**1–17.

Brosius, J., Palmer, M. L., Kennedy, P. J., and Noller, H. F., 1978, Complete nucleotide sequence of a 16S ribosomal RNA gene from *Escherichia coli, Proc. Natl. Acad. Sci. USA* **75:**4801–4805.

Bruns, T. D., Fogel, R., and Taylor, J. W., 1990, Amplification and sequencing of DNA from fungal herbarium specimens, *Mycologia* **82:**175–184.

Bruns, T. D., Cullings, K. W., and Szaro, T. M., 1991, Pine drops, *Pterospora andromedia,* is specifically associated with *Rhizopogon* or a closely related taxon over a broad geographic range, *Mycol. Soc. Am. Newsl.* **42:**8.

Chan, S. W., Vera-Garcia, M., Chen, P., Weisburg, W. G., Barns, S. M., and Klinger, J. D., 1991, Rapid detection of fungemia using a prototype Q-beta amplified nucleic acid hybridization assay, *Abstr. Annu. Meet. Am. Soc. Microbiol.* p. 360.

Cheema, M. A., Schumacher, H. R., and Hudson, A. P., 1991, RNA-directed molecular hybridization screening: evidence for inapparent chlamydial infection, *Am. J. Med. Sci.* **302:**261–268.

Chen, K., Neimark, H., Rumore, P., and Steinman, C. R., 1989, Broad range DNA probes for detecting and amplifying eubacterial nucleic acids, *FEMS Microbiol. Lett.* **57:**19–24.

Chuba, P. J., Pelz, K., Krekeler, G., De Isele, T. S., and Gobel, U., 1988, Synthetic oligodeoxynucleotide probes for the rapid detection of bacteria associated with human periodontitis, *J. Gen. Microbiol.* **134:**1931–1938.

Colwell, R. R., MacDonell, M. T., and Swartz, D., 1989, Identification of an antarctic endolithic microorganism by 5S rRNA sequence analysis, *Syst. Appl. Microbiol.* **11:**182–186.

DeLong, E. F., 1991, Molecular systematics, microbial ecology and single cell analysis, in: *Oceanography*, NATO ASI Series, Vol. 27 (S. Demers, ed.), Springer-Verlag, Berlin, pp. 237–257.

DeLong, E. F., 1992, Archaea in coastal marine environments, *Proc. Natl. Acad. Sci. USA* **89:**5685–5689.

DeLong, E. F., and Shah, J., 1990, Fluorescent, ribosomal RNA probes for clinical application: A research review, *Diagn. Clin. Test.* **28:**41–44.

DeLong, E. F., Schmidt, T. M., and Pace, N. R., 1989a, Analysis of single cells and oligotrophic picoplankton populations using 16S rRNA sequences, in: *Recent Advances in Microbial Ecology* (T. Hattori, Y. Ishida, Y. Maruyama, R. Y. Morita, and A. Uchida, eds.), Japan Sci. Soc. Press, Tokyo, pp. 697–701.

DeLong, E. F., Wickham, G. S., and Pace, N. R., 1989b, Phylogenetic stains: Ribosomal RNA-based probes for the identification of single cells, *Science* **243:**1360–1363.

Deng, S., and Hiruki, C., 1991, Amplification of 16S rRNA genes from culturable and nonculturable mollicutes, *J. Microbiol. Meth.* **14:**53–61.

Devereux, R., Delaney, M., Widdel, F., and Stahl, D. A., 1989, Natural relationships among sulfate-reducing eubacteria, *J. Bacteriol.* **171:**6689–6695.

Devereux, R., Winfrey, J., Winfrey, M. R., and Stahl, D. A., 1990, Application of 16S rRNA probes to correlate communities of sulfate-reducing bacteria with sulfate reduction and mercury methylation in a marine sediment, *Abstr. Annu. Meet. Am. Soc. Microbiol.* p. 328.

Devereux, R., Liebert, C., Barkay, T., and Stahl, D. A., 1991, Hybridization of fluorescent dye-labeled rRNA probes to bacteria extracted from sandy marine sediment, *Abstr. Annu. Meet. Am. Soc. Microbiol.* p. 297.

Devereux, R., and Mundfrom, G., 1992, Amplification of 16S rRNA genes from microbial communities within marine sediments by the polymerase chain reaction, *Abstr. Ann. Meet. Am. Soc. Microbiol.* p. 389.

Distel, D., 1991, Analysis of the phylogenetic origins of autotrophic bacteria symbioses in marine bivalves by 16S rRNA sequence analysis, *Abstr. Annu. Meet. Am. Soc. Microbiol.* p. 177.

Distel, D. L., Lane, D. J., Olsen, G. J., Giovannoni, S. J., Pace, B., Pace, N. R., Stahl, D. A., and Felbeck, H., 1988, Sulfur-oxidizing bacterial endosymbionts: Analysis of phylogeny and specificity by 16S rRNA sequences, *J. Bacteriol.* **170:**2506–2510.

Distel, D. L., DeLong, E. F., and Waterbury, J. B., 1991, Phylogenetic characterization and in situ localization of the bacterial symbiont of shipworms (Teredinidae: Bivalva) by using 16S rRNA sequence analysis and oligodeoxynucleotide probe hybridization, *Appl. Environ. Microbiol.* **57:**2376–2382.

Dix, K., Watanabe, S. M., McArdle, S., Lee, D. I., Randolph, C., Moncla, B., and Schwartz, D. E., 1990, Species-specific oligodeoxynucleotide probes for the identification of periodontal bacteria, *J. Clin. Microbiol.* **28:**319–323.

Eckert, K. A., and Kunkel, T. A., 1990, High fidelity DNA synthesis by the *Thermus aquaticus* DNA polymerase, *Nucleic Acids Res.* **18:**3739–3744.

Edelstein, P. H., 1986, Evaluation of the Gen-Probe DNA probe for the detection of legionellae in culture, *J. Clin. Microbiol.* **23:**481–484.

Edman, J. C., Kovacs, J. A., Masur, H., Santi, D. V., Elwood, H. J., and Sogin, M. L., 1988, Ribosomal RNA sequence shows *Pneumocystis carinii* to be a member of the fungi, *Nature* **334:**519–522.

Edwards, D. B., and Nelson, D. C., 1991, DNA–DNA solution hybridization studies of the bacterial symbionts of hydrothermal vent tube worms (*Riftia pachyptila* and *Tevnia jerichonana*), *Appl. Environ. Microbiol.* **57:**1082–1088.

Edwards, U., Rogall, T., Blocker, H., Emde, M., and Bottger, E. C., 1989, Isolation and direct complete nucleotide determination of entire genes. Characterization of a gene coding for 16S ribosomal RNA, *Nucleic Acids Res.* **17**:7843–7853.

Eisenstein, B. I., 1990, New opportunistic infections—More opportunities, *New Engl. J. Med.* **323**:1625–1627.

Embley, T. M., Smida, J., and Stackebrandt, E., 1988, Reverse transcriptase sequencing of 16S ribosomal RNA from *Faenia rectivirgula, Pseudonocardia thermophila* and *Saccharopolyspora hirsuta,* three wall type IV actinomycetes which lack mycolic acids, *J. Gen. Microbiol.* **134**:961–966.

Endo, G., Koseki, T., and Oikawa, E., 1992, Quantitative detection of microorganism by PCR-MPN method, *Abstr. Ann. Meet. Am. Soc. Microbiol.* p. 390.

Ennis, P. D., Zemmour, J., Salter, R. D., and Parham, P., 1990, Rapid cloning of HLA-A, B cDNA by using the polymerase chain reaction: Frequency and nature of errors produced in amplification, *Proc. Natl. Acad. Sci. USA* **87**:2833–2837.

Felsenstein, J., 1985, Confidence limits on phylogenies: An approach using the bootstrap, *Evolution* **39**:783–791.

Festl, H., Ludwig, W., and Schleifer, K. H., 1986, DNA hybridization probe for the *Pseudomonas fluorescens* group, *Appl. Environ. Microbiol.* **52**:1190–1194.

Forsman, M., Sandstrom, G., and Jaurin, B., 1990, Identification of *Francisella* species and discrimination of type A and type B strains of *F. tularensis* by 16S rRNA analysis, *Appl. Environ. Microbiol.* **56**:949–955.

Fuhrman, J. A., Comeau, D. E., Hagstrom, A., and Chan, A. M., 1988, Extraction from natural planktonic microorganisms of DNA suitable for molecular biological studies, *Appl. Environ. Microbiol.* **54**:1426–1429.

Fuhrman, J. A., McCallum, K., and Davis, A. A., 1992, Novel major archaebacterial group from marine plankton, *Nature* **356**:148–149.

Gall, J. G., and Pardue, M. L., 1969, Formation and detection of RNA–DNA hybrid molecules in cytological preparations, *Proc. Natl. Acad. Sci. USA* **63**:378–383.

Gardes, M., White, T. J., Fortin, J. A., Bruns, T. D., and Taylor, J. W., 1991, Identification of indigenous and introduced symbiotic fungi in ectomycorrhizae by amplification of nuclear and mitochondrial ribosomal DNA, *Can. J. Bot.* **69**:180–190.

Gaydos, C. A., Quinn, T. C., and Eiden, J. J., 1992, Identification of *Chlamydia pneumoniae* by DNA amplification of the 16S rRNA gene, *J. Clin. Microbiol.* **30**:796–800.

Gevertz, D., 1992, Use of a chemiluminescent-labeled DNA probe to measure bacterial populations in oil field brines, *Abstr. Annu. Meet. Am. Soc. Microbiol.* p. 389.

Giovannoni, S. J., DeLong, E. F., Olsen, G. J., and Pace, N. R., 1988a, Phylogenetic group-specific oligodeoxynucleotide probes for identification of single microbial cells, *J. Bacteriol.* **170**:720–726.

Giovannoni, S. J., Turner, S., Olsen, G. J., Barns, S., Lane, D. J., and Pace, N. R., 1988b, Evolutionary relationships among cyanobacteria and green chloroplasts, *J. Bacteriol.* **170**:3584–3592.

Giovannoni, S. J., Britschgi, T. B., Moyer, C. L., and Field, K. G., 1990a, Genetic diversity in Sargasso Sea bacterioplankton, *Nature* **345**:60–63.

Giovannoni, S. J., DeLong, E. F., Schmidt, T. M., and Pace, N. R., 1990b, Tangential flow filtration and preliminary phylogenetic analysis of marine picoplankton, *Appl. Environ. Microbiol.* **56**:2572–2575.

Gobel, U. B., and Stanbridge, E. J., 1984, Cloned mycoplasma ribosomal RNA genes for the detection of mycoplasma contamination in tissue cultures, *Science* **226**:1211–1213.

Gobel, U. B., Geiser, A., and Stanbridge, E. J. 1987, Oligonucleotide probes complementary to variable regions of ribosomal RNA discriminate between *Mycoplasma* species, *J. Gen. Microbiol.* **133**:1969–1974.

Goering, R. V., and Duensing, T. D., 1990, Rapid field inversion gel electrophoresis in combination with an rRNA gene probe in the epidemiological evaluation of staphylococci, *J. Clin. Microbiol.* **28**:426–429.

Gonzales, F. R., Deveze-Doyle, S., Kranig-Brown, D., Sherrill, S., Bee, G., Hammond, P., Shaw, S. B., and Johnson, R., 1991, A non-isotopic DNA probe for the specific detection of *Ureaplasma, Abstr. Annu. Meet. Am. Soc. Microbiol.* p. 81.

Gouy, M., and Li, W.-H., 1989, Phylogenetic analysis based on rRNA sequences supports the archaebacterial rather than the eocyte tree, *Nature* **339**:145–147.

Gray, M. W., Sankoff, D., and Cedergren, R. J., 1984, On the evolutionary descent of organisms and organelles: A global phylogeny based on a highly conserved structural core in small subunit ribosomal RNA, *Nucleic Acids Res.* **12**:5837–5852.

Gunderson, J. H., Sogin, M. L., Wollett, G., Hollingdale, M., de la Cruz, V. F., Waters, A. P., and McCutchan, T. F., 1987, Structurally distinct, stage-specific ribosomes occur in *Plasmodium, Science* **238**:933–937.

Gutell, R. R., Weiser, B., Woese, C. R., and Noller, H. F., 1985, Comparative anatomy of 16-S-like ribosomal RNA, *Prog. Nucleic Acid Res. Mol. Biol.* **32**:155–216.

Hahn, D., Dorsch, M., Stackebrandt, E., and Akkermans, A. D. L., 1989, Synthetic oligonucleotide probes for identification of *Frankia* strains, *Plant Soil* **118**:211–219.

Hahn, D., Kester, R., Starrenburg, M. J. C., and Akkermans, A. D. L., 1990a, Extraction of ribosomal RNA from soil for detection of *Frankia* with oligonucleotide probes, *Arch. Microbiol.* **154**:329–335.

Hahn, D., Starrenburg, M. J. C., and Akkermans, A. D. L., 1990b, Oligonucleotide probes that hybridize with rRNA as a tool to study *Frankia* strains in root nodules, *Appl. Environ. Microbiol.* **56**:1342–1346.

Hammond, P. W., Gonzales, F. R., Deveze-Doyle, S., and Carter, N. M., 1991, Biotype specific probes for *Ureaplasma urealyticum, Abstr. Annu. Meet. Am. Soc. Microbiol.* p. 81.

Haun, G., and Gobel, U., 1987, Oligonucleotide probes for genus-, species- and subspecies-specific identification of representatives of the genus *Proteus, FEMS Microbiol. Lett.* **43**:187–193.

Haygood, M., Rosson, R., and Distel, D., 1991, Relationship of the unculturable luminous bacterial symbionts of anomalopid fishes to the culturable marine luminous bacteria determined by 16S rRNA phylogenetic analysis, *Abstr. Annu. Meet. Am. Soc. Microbiol.* p. 177.

Hensiek, R., Krupp, G., and Stackebrandt, E., 1992, Development of diagnostic oligonucleotide probes for four *Lactobacillus* species occurring in the intestinal tract, *System. Appl. Microbiol.* **15**:123–128.

Herrick, J. B., Madsen, E. L., and Ghiorse, W. C., 1992, PCR detection of biodegradation genes from environmental samples: an approach to the study of bacterial populations in their native habitats, *Abstr. Annu. Meet. Am. Soc. Microbiol.* p. 350.

Hertel, C., Ludwig, W., Obst, M., Vogel, R. F., Hammes, W. P., and Schleifer, K. H., 1991, 23S rRNA-targeted oligonucleotide probes for the rapid identification of meat lactobacilli, *System. Appl. Microbiol.* **14**:173–177.

Ho, S., Hoyle, J. A., Lewis, F. A., Secker, A. D., Cross, D., Mapstone, N. P., Dixon, M. F., Wyatt, J. I., Tompkins, D. S., Taylor, G. R., and Quirke, P., 1991, Direct polymerase chain reaction test for detection of *Helicobacter pylori* in humans and animals. *J. Clin. Microbiol.* **29**:2543–2549.

Holben, W. E., and Tiedje, J. M., 1988, Application of nucleic acid hybridization in microbial ecology, *Ecology* **69**:561–568.

Holben, W. E., Jansson, J. K., Chelm, B. K., and Tiedje, J. M., 1988, DNA probe method for the detection of specific microorganisms in the soil bacterial community, *Appl. Environ. Microbiol.* **54**:703–711.

Hosein, I., Kaunitz, A., Craft, S., and Holland, R., 1991, Evaluation of the Gen Prob PACE 2 DNA probe for direct detection of *C. trachomatis* in female genital infections, *Abstr. Annu. Meet. Am. Soc. Microbiol.* p. 80.

Hoshina, S., Kahn, S. M., Jiang, W., Green, P. H. R., Neu, H. C., Chin, N., Morotomi, M., LoGerfo, P., and Weinstein, I. B., 1990, Direct detection and amplification of *Helicobacter pylori* ribosomal 16S gene segments from gastric endoscopic biopsies, *Diagn. Microbiol. Infect. Dis.* **13**:473–479.

Jensen, N. S., Casey, T. A., and Stanton, T. B., 1990, Detection and identification of *Treponema hyodysenteriae* by using oligodeoxynucleotide probes complementary to 16S rRNA, *J. Clin. Microbiol.* **28**:2717–2721.

John, H. A., Birnstiel, M. L., and Jones, K. W., 1969, RNA–DNA hybrids at the cytological level, *Nature* **223**:582–587.

Jones, J. G., 1987, Diversity in freshwater microbiology, *Symp. Soc. Gen. Microbiol.* **41**:235–259.

Ka, J. O., and Holben, W. E., 1991, Use of gene probes to detect 2,4-D degrading populations in soil microcosms maintained under selective pressure, *Abstr. Annu. Meet. Am. Soc. Microbiol.* p. 296.

Kane, M. D., Stromley, J. M., Raskin, L., and Stahl, D. A., 1991, Molecular analysis of the phylogenetic diversity and ecology of sulfidogenic and methanogenic biofilm communities, *Abstr. Annu. Meet. Am. Soc. Microbiol.* p. 309.

Kemmerling, C., Witt, D., Liesack, W., Weyland, H., and Stackebrandt, E., 1990, Approaches for the molecular identification of streptomycetes in marine environment, in: *Current Topics in Marine Biotechnology* (S. Miyachi, I. Karube, and Y. Eshida, eds.), Japan Soc. Mar. Biotechnol., Tokyo, pp. 423–426.

Kirshtein, J. D., Paerl, H. W., and Zehr, J., 1991, Amplification, cloning and sequencing of a *nif*H segment from aquatic microorganisms and natural communities, *Appl. Environ. Microbiol.* **57**:2645–2650.

Klein, D. A., McGurk, S., Tiffney, W. N., and Eveleigh, D. E., 1992, Vesicular-arbuscular mycorrhizae of natural and restored sand dunes, *Abstr. Annu. Meet. Am. Soc. Microbiol.* p. 398.

Klijn, N., Weerkamp, A. H., and de Vos, W. M., 1991, Identification of mesophilic lactic acid bacteria by using polymerase chain reaction-amplified variable regions of 16S rRNA and specific DNA probes, *Appl. Environ. Microbiol.* **57**:3390–3393.

Krueger, C., DeGrugillier, M., and Narang, S., 1992, PCR amplification of prokaryotic 16S rRNA genes from moth-testes (*Heliothis* spp.) extracts, *Abstr. Annu. Meet. Am. Soc. Microbiol.* p. 291.

Lake, J. A., 1987, A rate-independent technique for analysis of nucleic acid sequences: Evolutionary parsimony, *Mol. Biol. Evol.* **4**:167–191.

Lane, D. J., and Collins, M. L., Current methods for detection of DNA/ribosomal RNA hybrids, in: *Proc. 6th Int. Congress on Rapid Methods and Automation in Microbiology and Immunology* (A. Vahen, R. C. Tilton, and A. Balows, eds.), Springer-Verlag, Berlin, pp. 54–75.

Lane, D. J., Pace, B., Olsen, G. J., Stahl, D. A., Sogin, M. L., and Pace, N. R., 1985a, Rapid determination of 16S ribosomal RNA sequences for phylogenetic analyses, *Proc. Natl. Acad. Sci. USA* **82**:6955–6959.

Lane, D. J., Stahl, D. A., Olsen, G. J., Heller, D. J., and Pace, N. R., 1985b, Phylogenetic analysis of the genera *Thiobacillus* and *Thiomicrospira* by 5S rRNA sequences, *J. Bacteriol.* **163**:75–81.

Lane, D. J., Field, K. G., Olsen, G. J., and Pace, N. R., 1988, Reverse transcriptase sequencing of ribosomal RNA for phylogenetic analysis, *Methods Enzymol.* **167**:138–144.

Lee, S., and Fuhrman, J. A., 1990, DNA hybridization to compare species compositions of natural bacterioplankton assemblages, *Appl. Environ. Microbiol.* **56**:739–746.

Leong, D. U., and Greisen, K. S., 1991, An assay for the detection of septicemia based on the polymerase chain reaction, *Abstr. Annu. Meet. Am. Soc. Microbiol.* p. 361.

Liesack, W., Weyland, H., and Stackebrandt, E., 1991, Potential risks of gene amplification by PCR as determined by 16S rDNA analysis of a mixed-culture of strict barophilic bacteria, *Microb. Ecol.* **21**:191–198.

Liesack, W., and Stackebrandt, E., 1992, Unculturable microbes detected by molecular sequences and probes, *Biodiversity and Conservation* (in press).

Liesack, W., and Stackebrandt, E., 1992, Occurrence of novel types of bacteria as revealed by analysis of the genetic material isolated from an Australian terrestrial environment, *J. Bacteriol.* (submitted).

Lovell, C. R., and Hui, Y., 1989, Homology among formyltetrahydrofolate synthetase structural genes from acetogenic bacteria, *Abstr. Annu. Meet. Am. Soc. Microbiol.* p. 234.

Lovell, C. R., and Hui, Y., 1991, Development and testing of a functional group specific DNA probe for the acetogenic bacteria, *Abstr. Annu. Meet. Am. Soc. Microbiol.* p. 300.

Lu, S. Y., Kao, S.-Y., Silver, S., Purohit, A., Longiaru, M., and White, T. J., 1991, Detection of *Neisseria gonorrhoeae* and *Chlamydia trachomatis* in a combined system by PCR, *Abstr. Annu. Meet. Am. Soc. Microbiol.* p. 361.

Marconi, R. T., Lubke, L., Hauglum, W., and Garon, C. F., 1992, Species-specific identification of and distinction between *Borrelia burgdorferi* genomic groups by using 16S rRNA-directed oligonucleotide probes, *J. Clin. Microbiol.* 30:628–632.

McCutchan, T. F., de la Cruz, V. F., Lal, A. A., Gunderson, J. H., Elwood, H. J., and Sogin, M. L., 1988, Primary sequences of two small subunit ribosomal RNA genes from *Plasmodium falciparum*, *Mol. Biochem. Parasitol.* 28:63–68.

Medlin, L., Elwood, H. J., Stickel, S., and Sogin, M. L., 1988, The characterization of enzymatically amplified eukaryotic 16 S-like rRNA-coding regions, *Gene* 71:491–499.

Mizutani, S., and Temin, H. M., 1976, Incorporation of noncomplementary nucleotides at high frequencies by ribodeoxyvirus DNA polymerases and *Escherichia coli* DNA polymerase I, *Biochemistry* 15:1510–1516.

Moncla, B. J., Braham, P., Dix, K., Watanabe, S., and Schwartz, D., 1990, Use of synthetic oligonucleotide DNA probes for the identification of *Bacteroides gingivalis*, *J. Clin. Microbiol.* 28:324–327.

Moncla, B. J., Motley, S. T., Braham, P., Ewing, L., Adams, T. H., and Vermeulen, N. M. J., 1991, Use of synthetic oligonucleotide DNA probes for identification and direct detection of *Bacteroides forsythus* in plaque samples, *J. Clin. Microbiol.* 29:2158–2162.

Montgomery, L., Flesher, B., and Stahl, D., 1988, Transfer of *Bacteroides succinogenes* (Hungate) to *Fibrobacter* gen. nov. as *Fibrobacter succinogenes* comb. nov. Description of *Fibrobacter intestinalis* sp. nov., *Int. J. Syst. Bacteriol.* 38:430–435.

Morotomi, M., Hoshina, S., Green, P., Neu, H. C., LoGerfo, P., Watanabe, I., Mutai, M., and Weinstein, I. B., 1989, Oligonucleotide probe for detection and identification of *Campylobacter pylori*, *J. Clin. Microbiol.* 27:2652–2655.

Mylvaganam, S., and Dennis, P. P., 1992, Sequence heterogeneity between the two genes encoding 16S rRNA from the halophilic archaebacterium *Haloarcula marismortui*, *Genetics* 130:399–410.

Odenyo, A. A., Mackie, R. I., and White, B. A., 1992, The use of 16S ribosomal RNA targeted oligonucleotide probes to study competition between ruminal fibrolytic bacteria, *Abstr. Ann. Meet. Am. Soc. Microbiol.* p. 396.

Olsen, G. J., 1987, Earliest phylogenetic branchings: Comparing rRNA-based evolutionary trees inferred with various techniques, *Cold Spring Harbor Symp. Quant. Biol.* 52:825–837.

Olsen, G. J., 1988, Phylogenetic analysis using ribosomal RNA, *Methods Enzymol.* 164:793–812.

Olsen, G. J., 1990, Variation among the masses, *Nature* 345:20.

Olsen, G. J., Lane, D. J., Giovannoni, S. J., and Pace, N. R., 1986, Microbial ecology and evolution: A ribosomal RNA approach, *Annu. Rev. Microbiol.* 40:337–365.

Olsen, G. J., Larsen, N., and Woese, C. R., 1991, The ribosomal RNA database project, *Nucleic Acids Res.* 19:2017–2021.

Oyaizu, H., and Woese, C. R., 1985, Phylogenetic relationship among the sulfate respiring bacteria, myxobacteria, and purple bacteria, *Syst. Appl. Microbiol.* 6:257–263.

Pace, N. R., Stahl, D. A., Lane, D. J., and Olsen, G. J., 1986, The analysis of natural microbial populations by ribosomal RNA sequences, *Adv. Microbiol. Ecol.* 9:1–55.

Patton, C. M., Wachsmuth, I. K., Evins, G. M., Kiehlbauch, J. A., Plikaytis, B. D., Troup, N., Tompkins, L., and Lior, H., 1991, Evaluation of 10 methods to distinguish epidemic-associated *Campylobacter* strains, *J. Clin. Microbiol.* 29:680–688.

Pelletier, D. A., Paster, B. J., Weisburg, W. G., Dewhirst, F. E., Dannenberg, S., and Schroeder, I., 1991, *Cristispira* phylogeny by 16S rRNA sequence comparison of amplified bacterial DNA from crystalline styles, *Abstr. Annu. Meet. Am. Soc. Microbiol.* p. 243.

Persing, D. H., Telford, S. R., Rys, P. N., Dodge, D. E., White, T. J., Malawista, S. E., and Spielman, A., 1990, Detection of *Borrelia burgdorferi* DNA in museum specimens of *Ixodes dammini* ticks, *Science* 249:1420–1423.

Poulsen, L. K., Kane, M. D., and Stahl, D. A., 1992, Use of an oligonucleotide hybridization probe designed from environmentally derived 16S rRNA sequences to monitor enrichment and isolation of sulfate-reducing bacteria, *Abstr. Ann. Meet. Am. Soc. Microbiol.* p. 345.

Pratt-Rippin, K., Hall, G., and Rutherford, I., 1991, Evaluation of a chemiluminescent DNA probe assay for the identification of *Histoplasma capsulatum* isolates, *Abstr. Annu. Meet. Am. Soc. Microbiol.* p. 83.

Putz, J., Meinert, F., Wyss, U., Ehlers, R., and Stackebrandt, E., 1990, Development and application of oligonucleotide probes for molecular identification of *Xenorhabdus* species, *Appl. Environ. Microbiol.* **56:**181–186.

Rand, K., and Houck, H., 1991, Identification of bacterial DNA contaminating Taq enzyme, *Abstr. Annu. Meet. Am. Soc. Microbiol.* p. 83.

Razin, S., Gross, M., Wormser, M., Pollack, Y., and Glaser, G., 1984, Detection of mycoplasmas infecting cell cultures by DNA hybridization, *In Vitro* **20:**404–408.

Reagan, D. R., Pfaller, M. A., Hollis, R. J., and Wenzel, R. P., 1990, Characterization of the sequence of colonization and nosocomial candidemia using DNA fingerprinting and a DNA probe, *J. Clin. Microbiol.* **28:**2733–2738.

Regensburger, A., Ludwig, W., and Schleifer, K. H., 1988, DNA probes with different specificities from a cloned 23S rRNA gene of *Micrococcus luteus, J. Gen. Microbiol.* **134:**1197–1204.

Rehnstam, A., Norqvist, A., Wolf-watz, H., and Hagstrom, A., 1989, Identification of *Vibrio anguillarum* in fish by using partial 16S rRNA-sequences and a specific 16S rRNA oligonucleotide probe, *Appl. Environ. Microbiol.* **55:**1907–1910.

Relman, D. A., Loutit, J. S., Schmidt, T. M., Falkow, S., and Tompkins, L. S., 1990, The agent of bacillary angiomatosis: An approach to the identification of uncultured pathogens, *N. Engl. J. Med.* **323:**1573–1580.

Romaniuk, P. J., and Trust, T. J., 1987, Identification of *Campylobacter* species by Southern hybridization of genomic DNA using an oligonucleotide probe for 16S rRNA genes, *FEMS Microbiol. Lett.* **43:**331–335.

Rossau, R., Vanmechelen, E., De Ley, J., and Van Heuverswijn, H., 1989, Specific *Neisseria gonorrhoeae* DNA-probes derived from ribosomal RNA, *J. Gen. Microbiol.* **135:**1735–1745.

Rossau, R., Duhamel, M., Jannes, G., Decourt, J. L., and van Heuverswyn, H., 1991, The development of specific rRNA-derived oligonucleotide probes for *Haemophilus ducreyi,* the causative agent of chancroid, *J. Gen. Microbiol.* **137:**277–285.

Rosswall, T., and Kvillner, E., 1978, Principal-components and factor analysis for the description of microbial populations, *Adv. Microb. Ecol.* **2:**1–48.

Rowan, R., and Powers, D. A., 1991, A molecular genetic classification of zooxanthellae and the evolution of animal–algal symbioses, *Science* **251:**1348–1351.

Ruff, A. L., and Ward, D. M., 1991, 16S rRNA-based oligonucleotide probe analysis of hot spring photosynthetic procaryotes, *Abstr. Annu. Meet. Am. Soc. Microbiol.* p. 194.

Saiki, R. K., Gelfand, D. H., Stoffel, S., Scharf, S. J., Higuchi, R., Horn, G. T., Mullis, K. B., and Erlich, H. A., 1988, Primer-directed enzymatic amplification of DNA with a thermostable DNA polymerase, *Science* **239:**487–491.

Salama, M., Sandine, W., and Giovannoni, S., 1991, Development and application of oligonucleotide probes for identification of *Lactococcus lactis* subsp. *cremoris, Appl. Environ. Microbiol.* **57:**1313–1318.

Sambrook, J., Fritsch, E. F., and Maniatis, T., 1989, *Molecular Cloning: A Laboratory Manual,* Cold Spring Harbor Laboratory Press, Cold Spring Harbor, N.Y.

Sandin, R. L., Hall, G., and Longworth, D. L., 1991, Confirmation of infection by an exo-antigen negative *Blastomyces dermatitidis* by way of a chemiluminescent-labelled DNA probe, *Abstr. Annu. Meet. Am. Soc. Microbiol.* p. 83.

Santo Domingo, J. W., Kaufman, M. G., and Klug, M. J., 1991, Use of 16S rRNA gene probes to study structural changes in bacterial communities in the hindgut of the house cricket, *Acheta domesticus,* *Abstr. Annu. Meet. Am. Soc. Microbiol.* p. 313.

Santo Domingo, J. W., Kaufman, M. G., and Klug, M. J., 1992, Effects of dietary perturbation on the hindgut bacterial community in crickets (*Acheta domesticus*), *Abstr. Ann. Meet. Am. Soc. Microbiol.* p. 396.

Schleifer, K. H., Ludwig, W., Kraus, J., and Festl, H., 1985, Cloned ribosomal ribonucleic acid genes from *Pseudomonas aeruginosa* as probes for conserved deoxyribonucleic acid sequences, *Int. J. Syst. Bacteriol.* **35:**231–236.

Schmidt, T. M., DeLong, E. F., and Pace, N. R., 1991a, Analysis of a marine picoplankton community by 16S rRNA gene cloning and sequencing, *J. Bacteriol.* **173:**4371–4378.

Schmidt, T. M., DeLong, E. F., and Pace, N. R., 1991b, Phylogenetic identification of uncultivated microorganisms in natural habitats, in: *Rapid Methods and Automation in Microbiology and Immunology* (A. Vaheri, R. C. Tilton, and A. Balows, eds.), Springer-Verlag, Berlin, pp. 37–46.

Schmidt, T. M., Pace, B., and Pace, N. R., 1991c, Detection of DNA contamination in *Taq* polymerase, *Biotechniques* **11:**176–177.

Schwartz, J., Daniels, T., Gazumyan, A., Weissensee, P., Fish, D., and Schwartz, I., 1991, Determination of *B. burgdorferi* infection rates in *Ixodes dammini* ticks by three methods, *Abstr. Annu. Meet. Am. Soc. Microbiol.* p. 80.

Seewaldt, E., and Stackebrandt, E., 198?, ? artial sequence of 16S ribosomal RNA and the phylogeny of *Prochloron, Nature* **295:**618–620.

Simon, L., Lalonde, M., and Bruns, T. D., 1992, Specific amplification of 18S fungal ribosomal genes from vesicular-arbuscular endomycorrhizal fungi colonizing roots, *Appl. Environ. Microbiol.* **58:**291–295.

Sneath, P. H. A., 1989, Analysis and interpretation of sequence data for bacterial systematics: The view of a numerical taxonomist, *Syst Appl. Microbiol.* **12:**15–31.

Somerville, C. C., Knight, I. T., Straube, W. L., and Colwell, R. R., 1989, Simple, rapid method for direct isolation of nucleic acids from aquatic environments, *Appl. Environ. Microbiol.* **55:**548–554.

Speer, C. A., and White, M. W., 1991, Bovine trichomoniasis, *Large Anim. Vet.* **46:**18–20.

Spring, S., Amann, R., Ludwig, W., Schleifer, K., and Petersen, N., 1992, Phylogenetic diversity and identification of nonculturable magnetotactic bacteria, *System. Appl. Microbiol.* **15:**116–122.

Srivastava, A. K., and Schlessinger, D., 1990, Mechanism and regulation of bacterial ribosomal RNA processing, *Annu. Rev. Microbiol.* **44:**105–129.

Stackebrandt, E., and Charfreitag, O., 1990, Partial 16S rRNA primary structure of five *Actinomyces* species: Phylogenetic implications and development of an *Actinomyces israelii*-specific oligonucleotide probe, *J. Gen. Microbiol.* **136:**37–43.

Stackebrandt, E., Witt, D., Kemmerling, C., Kroppenstedt, R., and Liesack, W., 1991, Designation of streptomycete 16S and 23S rRNA-based target regions for oligonucleotide probes, *Appl. Environ. Microbiol.* **57:**1468–1477.

Stahl, D. A., 1986, Evolution, ecology, and diagnosis: Unity in variety, *Bio/Technology* **4:**623–628.

Stahl, D. A., 1988, Phylogenetically based studies of microbial ecosystem perturbation, in: *Biotechnology for Crop Protection* (P. A. Hedin, J. J. Menn, and R. M. Hollingworth, eds.), Am. Chem. Soc., Washington, D.C., pp. 373–390.

Stahl, D. A., and Amann, R., 1990, Development and application of nucleic acid probes, in: *Molecular Biology Methods for Bacillus* (C. R. Harwood and S. M. Cutting, eds.), Wiley, New York, pp. 203–245.

Stahl, D. A., Lane, D. J., Olsen, G. J., and Pace, N. R., 1984, Analysis of hydrothermal vent-associated symbionts by ribosomal RNA sequences, *Science* **224:**409–411.

Stahl, D. A., Lane, D. J., Olsen, G. J., and Pace, N. R., 1985, Characterization of a Yellowstone hot spring microbial community by 5S rRNA sequences, *Appl. Environ. Microbiol.* **49:**1379–1384.

Stahl, D. A., Flesher, B., Mansfield, H. R., and Montgomery, L., 1988, Use of phylogenetically based hybridization probes for studies of ruminal microbial ecology, *Appl. Environ. Microbiol.* **54**:1079–1084.

Stahl, D. A., Devereux, R., Amann, R. I., Flesher, B., Lin, C., and Stromley, J., 1989, Ribosomal RNA based studies of natural microbial diversity and ecology, in: *Recent Advances in Microbial Ecology* (T. Hattori, Y. Ishida, Y. Maruyama, R. Y. Morita, and A. Uchida, eds.), Japan Sci. Soc. Press, Tokyo, pp. 669–673.

Staley, J. T., 1980, Diversity of aquatic heterotrophic bacterial communities, in: *Microbiology—1980* (D. Schlessinger, ed.), Am. Soc. Microbiol., Washington, D.C., pp. 321–322.

Steffan, R. J., Goksoyr, J., Bej, A. K., and Atlas, R. M., 1988, Recovery of DNA from soils and sediments, *Appl. Environ. Microbiol.* **54**:2908–2915.

Toranzos, G. A., and Alvarez, A. J., 1992, Quantifying PCR templates using the most probable number polymerase chain reaction (MPN-PCR), *Abstr. Ann. Meet. Am. Soc. Microbiol.* 390.

Tram, C., Simonet, M., Nicolas, M.-H., Offredo, C., Grimont, F., LeFevre, M., Ageron, E., DeBure, A., and Grimont, P. A. D., 1990, Molecular typing of nosocomial isolates of *Legionella pneumophila* serogroup 3, *J. Clin. Microbiol.* **28**:242–245.

Tsai, Y., and Olson, B. H., 1992, Detection of low numbers of bacterial cells in soils and sediments by polymerase chain reaction, *Appl. Environ. Microbiol.* **58**:754–757.

Tsai, Y., Palmer, C. J., Sangermano, L., and Olsen, B., 1992, A rapid method to purify bacterial DNA from humic substances for polymerase chain reaction, *Abstr. Ann. Meet. Am. Soc. Microbiol.* p. 389.

Tsien, H. C., Bratina, B. J., Tsuji, K., and Hanson, R. S., 1990, Use of oligodeoxynucleotide signature probes for identification of physiological groups of methylotrophic bacteria, *Appl. Environ. Microbiol.* **56**:2858–2865.

Tsien, H. C., Alvarez-Cohen, L., McCarty, P. L., and Hanson, R. S., 1991, Use of soluble methane monooxygenase component B gene probe for the detection of trichloroethylene degrading methanotrophs, *Abstr. Annu. Meet. Am. Soc. Microbiol.* p. 285.

Tsuji, K., Tsien, H. C., Hanson, R. S., DePalma, S. R., Scholtz, R., and LaRoche, S., 1990, 16S ribosomal RNA sequence analysis for determination of phylogenetic relationship among methylotrophs, *J. Gen. Microbiol.* **136**:1–10.

Unterman, B. M., Baumann, P., and McLean, D. L., 1989, Pea aphid symbiont relationships established by analysis of 16S rRNAs, *J. Bacteriol.* **171**:2970–2974.

van Niel, C. B., 1949, The "Delft School" and the rise of general microbiology, *Bacteriol. Rev.* **13**:161–174.

van Niel, C. B., 1955, Natural selection in the microbial world, *J. Gen. Microbiol.* **13**:201–217.

Walch, M., Hamilton, W. A., Handley, P. S., Holm, N. C., Kuenen, J. G., Revsbech, N. P., Rubio, M. A., Stahl, D. A., Wanner, O., Ward, D. M., Wilderer, P. A., and Wimpenny, J. W. T., 1989, Spatial distribution of biotic and abiotic components in the biofilm, in: *Structure and Function of Biofilms* (W. G. Characklis and P. A. Wilderer, eds.), Wiley, New York, pp. 165–190.

Wang, R.-F., Cao, W.-W., and Johnson, M. G., 1991, Development of a 16S RNA-based oligomer probe specific for *Listeria monocytogenes, Appl. Environ. Microbiol.* **57**:3666–3670.

Ward, D. M., 1989, Molecular probes for analysis of microbial communities, in: *Structure and Function of Biofilms* (W. G. Characklis and P. A. Wilderer, eds.), Wiley, New York, pp. 145–163.

Ward, D. M., and Winfrey, M. R., 1985, Interactions between methanogenic and sulfate-reducing bacteria in sediments, *Adv. Agric. Microbiol.* **3**:141–179.

Ward, D. M., Brassell, S. C., and Eglinton, G., 1985, Archaebacterial lipids in hot spring microbial mats, *Nature* **318**:656–659.

Ward, D. M., Tayne, T. A., Anderson, K. L., and Bateson, M. M., 1987, Community structure and interactions among community members in hot spring cyanobacterial mats, *Symp. Soc. Gen. Microbiol.* **41**:179–210.

Ward, D. M., Shiea, J., Zeng, Y. B., Dobson, G., Brassell, S., and Eglinton, G., 1989a, Lipid biochemical markers and the composition of microbial mats, in: *Microbial Mats: Physiological Ecology of Benthic Microbial Communities* (Y. Cohen and E. Rosenberg, eds.), Am. Soc. Microbiol., Washington, D.C., pp. 439–454.

Ward, D. M., Weller, R., Shiea, J., Castenholz, R. W., and Cohen, Y., 1989b, Hot spring microbial mats: Anoxygenic and oxygenic mats of possible evolutionary significance, in: *Microbial Mats: Physiological Ecology of Benthic Microbial Communities* (Y. Cohen and E. Rosenberg, eds.), Am. Soc. Microbiol., Washington, D.C., pp. 3–15.

Ward, D. M., Weller, R., and Bateson, M. M., 1990a, 16S rRNA sequences reveal numerous uncultured microorganisms in a natural community, *Nature* 345:63–65.

Ward, D. M., Weller, R., and Bateson, M. M., 1990b, 16S rRNA sequences reveal uncultured inhabitants of a well-studied thermal community, *FEMS Microbiol. Rev.* 75:105–116.

Waters, A. P., and McCutchan, T. F., 1989, Rapid, sensitive diagnosis of malaria based on ribosomal RNA, *Lancet* (Vol. 1) 1343–1346.

Wayne, L. G., Brenner, D. J., Colwell, R. R., Grimont, P. A. D., Kandler, O., Krichevsky, M. I., Moore, L. H., Moore, W. E. C., Murray, R. G. E., Stackebrandt, E., Starr, M. P., and Truper, H. G., 1987, Report of the ad hoc committee on reconciliation of approaches to bacterial systematics, *Int. J. Syst. Bacteriol.* 37:463–464.

Weisburg, W. G., Barns, S. M., Pelletier, D. A., and Lane, D. J., 1991, 16S ribosomal DNA amplification for phylogenetic study, *J. Bacteriol.* 173:697–703.

Weiss, J. B., Nash, T. E., Jarroll, E., van Keulen, H., and White, T. J., 1991, Specific detection of *Giardia lamblia (G. duodenalis)* by the polymerase chain reaction, *Abstr. Annu. Meet. Am. Soc. Microbiol.* p. 48.

Weller, R., and Ward, D. M., 1989, Selective recovery of 16S rRNA sequences from natural microbial communities in the form of cDNA, *Appl. Environ. Microbiol.* 55:1818–1822.

Weller, R., Weller, J. W., and Ward, D. M., 1991, 16S rRNA sequences of uncultivated hot spring cyanobacterial mat inhabitants retrieved as randomly primed cDNA, *Appl. Environ. Microbiol.* 57:1146–1151.

Weller, R., Bateson, M. M., Heimbuch, B. K., Kopczynski, E. D., and Ward, D. M., 1992, Uncultivated cyanobacteria, *Chloroflexus*-like and spirochete-like inhabitants of a hot spring microbial mat. *Appl. Environ. Microbiol.* (submitted).

Wesley, I. V., Wesley, R. D., Cardella, M., Dewhirst, F. E., and Paster, B. J., 1991, Oligodeoxynucleotide probes for *Campylobacter fetus* and *Campylobacter hyointestinalis* based on 16S rRNA sequences, *J. Clin. Microbiol.* 29:1812–1817.

Wickham, G. S., Lane, D. J., Kim, S., and Pace, N. R., 1992, Intervening sequences in the 16S ribosomal RNA genes of naturally occurring hyperthermophilic archaebacteria, *Abstr. Ann. Meet. Am. Soc. Microbiol.* p. 239.

Wilkinson, H. W., Sampson, J. S., and Plikaytis, B. B., 1986, Evaluation of a commercial gene probe for identification of *Legionella* cultures, *J. Clin. Microbiol.* 23:217–220.

Williams, S. T., Goodfellow, M., and Vickers, J. C., 1984, New Microbes from old habitats? *Symp. Soc. Gen. Microbiol* 36(2):219-256.

Wilson, K. H., Blitchington, R., Hindenach, B., and Greene, R. C., 1988, Species-specific oligonucleotide probes for rRNA of *Clostridium difficile* and related species, *J. Clin. Microbiol.* 26:2484–2488.

Wilson, K. H., Blitchington, R., Shah, P., McDonald, G., Gilmore, R. D., and Mallavia, L. P., 1989, Probe directed at a segment of *Rickettsia rickettsii* rRNA amplified with polymerase chain reaction, *J. Clin. Microbiol.* 27:2692–2696.

Wilson, K. H., Blitchington, R. B., and Greene, R. C., 1990, Amplification of bacterial 16S ribosomal DNA with polymerase chain reaction, *J. Clin. Microbiol.* 28:1942–1946.

Winfrey, J., Devereux, R., and Winfrey, M. R., 1991, Use of 16S rRNA-targeted probes to correlate community structure of sulfate-reducing bacteria with mercury methylation in freshwater sediments, *Abstr. Annu. Meet. Am. Soc. Microbiol.* p. 319.

Winker, S., and Woese, C. R., 1991, A definition of the domains *Archaea, Bacteria,* and *Eucarya* in terms of small subunit ribosomal RNA characteristics, *System. Appl. Microbiol.* **14:**305–310.

Winogradsky, S., 1949, *Microbiologie du sol, problemes et methodes,* Barneoud Freres, France.

Witt, D., Liesack, W., and Stackebrandt, E., 1989, Identification of streptomycetes by 16S rRNA sequences and oligonucleotide probes, in: *Recent Advances in Microbial Ecology* (T. Hattori, Y. Ishida, Y. Maruyama, R. Y. Morita, and A. Uchida, eds.), Japan Sci. Soc. Press, Tokyo, pp. 679–684.

Woese, C. R., 1987, Bacterial evolution, *Microbiol. Rev.* **51:**221–271.

Woese, C. R., and Fox, G. E., 1977, Phylogenetic structure of the prokaryotic domain: The primary kingdoms, *Proc. Natl. Acad. Sci. USA* **74:**5088–5090.

Woese, C. R., Stackebrandt, E., Macke, T. J., and Fox, G. E., 1985, A phylogenetic definition of the major eubacterial taxa, *Syst. Appl. Microbiol.* **6:**143–151.

Woese, C. R., Kandler, O., and Wheelis, M. L., 1990, Towards a natural system of organisms: Proposal for the domains Archaea, Bacteria, and Eucarya, *Proc. Natl. Acad. Sci. USA* **87:**4576–4579.

Wolfe, R. S., 1981, Foreword, in: *The Procaryotes,* Vol. I (M. P. Starr, H. Stolp, H. G. Truper, A. Balows, and H. G. Schlegel, eds.), Springer-Verlag, Berlin, pp. v–vi.

Wolfe, C., and Haygood, M., 1992, Reduced copy number of ribosomal RNA genes in the luminous bacterial symbiont of *Kryptophanaron alfredi* relative to culturable luminous bacteria, *Abstr. Ann. Meet. Am. Soc. Microbiol.* p. 196.

Yang, D., Oyaizu, Y., Oyaizu, H., Olsen, G. J., and Woese, C. R., 1985, Mitochondrial origins, *Proc. Natl. Acad. Sci. USA* **82:**4443–4447.

Young, C., Burghoff, R., Keim, L., Lute, J., and Hinton, S., 1992, Molecular characterization of soil bacterial populations using 16S ribosomal DNA sequence analysis, *Abstr. Ann. Meet. Am. Soc. Microbiol.* p. 293.

Zarda, B., Amann, R., Wallner, G., and Schleifer, K., 1991, Identification of single bacterial cells using digoxigenin-labelled, rRNA-targeted oligonucleotides, *J. Gen. Microbiol.* **137:**2823–2830.

Zeng, Y. B., Ward, D. M., Brassell, S., and Eglinton, G., 1992a, Biogeochemistry of hot spring environments. 2. Lipid compositions of Yellowstone (Wyoming, U.S.A.) cyanobacterial and *Chloroflexus* mats, *Chem. Geol.* **95:**327–345.

Zeng, Y. B., Ward, D. M., Brassell, S., and Eglinton, G., 1992b, Biogeochemistry of hot spring environments. 3. Apolar and polar lipids in the biologically active layers of a cyanobacterial mat, *Chem. Geol.* **95:**347–360.

6

Hydrocarbon Biodegradation and Oil Spill Bioremediation

RONALD M. ATLAS and RICHARD BARTHA

1. Microbial Metabolism of Hydrocarbons

Much of the early work on the microbial utilization of petroleum hydrocarbons, conducted in the 1950s and 1960s, was done with the goal of using hydrocarbons as substrates for producing microbial biomass (Shennan, 1984; Champagnat, 1964; Champagnat and Llewelyn, 1962; Cooney *et al.*, 1980; Ballerini, 1978). Petroleum was viewed as an inexpensive carbon source and single cell protein (microbial biomass) was considered as a possible solution to the perceived impending world food shortage for the predicted global population explosion. Applied studies focused on optimizing microbial growth on low- to middle-molecular-weight hydrocarbons. These studies developed fermentor designs for large-scale single cell protein production with agitation and aeration systems that permitted high rates of microbial growth on soluble and highly emulsified hydrocarbon substrates. High-speed impellers (>800 rpm) were used to mix the hydrocarbon substrates and high rates of forced aeration with baffles within the fermentors were used to supply the molecular oxygen necessary for the microbial utilization of hydrocarbons (Hatch, 1975; Prokop and Sobotka, 1975). Optimized microbial growth in these fermentors consumes as much as 100,000 g hydrocarbon/m^3 per day (Kanazawa, 1975).

With the focus on hydrocarbon utilization, basic research studies elucidated the metabolic pathways of alkane, cycloalkane, and aromatic hydrocarbon utilization. There have been a number of reviews on the metabolism of hydrocarbons based upon these studies (Gudin and Syratt, 1975; Foster, 1962a,b; Gibson, 1968, 1972; Higgins and Gilbert, 1978; Hopper, 1978; Markovetz, 1971; McKenna and Kallio, 1964; National Academy of Sciences, 1975; Perry, 1977, 1979; Pirnik *et al.*, 1974; Rogoff, 1961; Stirling *et al.*, 1977; Trudgill, 1978; Van der Linden and Thijsse, 1965).

RONALD M. ATLAS • Department of Biology, University of Louisville, Louisville, Kentucky 40292.   RICHARD BARTHA • Department of Biochemistry and Microbiology, Cook College, Rutgers University, New Brunswick, New Jersey 08903.
Advances in Microbial Ecology, Vol. 12, edited by K.C. Marshall. Plenum Press, New York, 1992.

Studies on alkane biodegradation have shown that the microbial degradation of *n*-alkanes normally proceeds by a monoterminal attack; usually a primary alcohol is formed followed by an aldehyde and a monocarboxylic acid (Foster, 1962a,b; McKenna and Kallio, 1965; Miller and Johnson, 1966; Ratledge, 1978; Van der Linden and Thijsse, 1964; Van Eyk and Bartels, 1968; ZoBell, 1950). Further degradation of the carboxylic acid proceeds by β-oxidation with the subsequent formation of two-carbon-unit-shorter fatty acids and acetyl coenzyme A, with eventual liberation of CO_2. Fatty acids formed during the biodegradation of alkanes accumulate sometimes (Atlas and Bartha, 1973a; King and Perry, 1975), but generally the initial addition of oxygen to the hydrocarbon is the rate-limiting step and once the carboxylic acid is formed it is metabolized rapidly. Subterminal oxidation occurs sometimes, with formation of a secondary alcohol and subsequent ketone, but this does not appear to be the primary metabolic pathway utilized by most *n*-alkane-utilizing microorganisms (Markovetz, 1971). Highly branched isoprenoid alkanes, such as pristane, have been found to undergo omega oxidation, with formation of dicarboxylic acids as the major degradative pathway (McKenna and Kallio, 1971; Pirnik, 1977; Pirnik *et al.*, 1974). Methyl branching generally increases the resistance of hydrocarbons to microbial attack (Fall *et al.*, 1979; McKenna and Kallio, 1964; Pirnik, 1977; Schaeffer *et al.*, 1979).

The microbial metabolism of cyclic hydrocarbons and related compounds has been reviewed by Perry (1979). Cycloalkanes, including condensed cycloalkanes, have been reported to be substrates for co-oxidation by monooxygenases with formation of a cyclic alcohol subsequently dehydrogenated to a ketone. A second monooxygenase, usually from a different microorganism, is required to introduce an oxygen into the cyclic ketone, lactonizing the ring and preparing it for cleavage (Austin *et al.*, 1977a,b; Beam and Perry, 1973, 1974a,b; Perry, 1979). Degradation of substituted cycloalkanes appears to occur more readily than degradation of the unsubstituted forms, particularly if there is an *n*-alkane substituent of adequate chain length (Perry, 1979; Soli, 1973).

The degradation of aromatic hydrocarbons has been reviewed by Gibson and others (Cripps and Watkinson, 1978; Gibson, 1968, 1971, 1977a,b; Gibson and Yeh, 1973; Hopper, 1978; Rogoff, 1961; Cain, 1980; Cerniglia, 1984). Extensive methyl substitution can inhibit initial oxidation (Atlas *et al.*, 1981; Cripps and Watkinson, 1978). Initial enzymatic attack may be on the alkyl substituent or, alternatively, directly on the ring (Gibson, 1971).

The bacterial degradation of aromatic compounds normally involves dioxygenase action resulting in the formation of a diol that spontaneously decays to catechol. This is followed by oxidative cleavage and formation of a diacid such as *cis,cis*-muconic acid (*ortho* cleavage), or 2-hydroxy-*cis,cis*-muconic semialdehyde (*meta* cleavage). In contrast, oxidation of aromatic hydrocarbons in eukaryotic organisms has been found to form over an arene oxide, a *trans*-dihydrodiol. For example, fungi have been shown to oxidize naphthalene to form *trans*-1,2-dihydroxy-1,2-dihydronaphthalene (Cerniglia and Gibson, 1977, 1978; Cerniglia *et al.*, 1978; Ferris *et al.*, 1976). The results indicate that only one atom of molecular oxygen is incorporated into the aromatic nucleus by fungi during metabolism of aromatic hydrocarbons, as has been found for mammalian aryl hydrocarbon hydroxylase systems.

Condensed ring aromatic structures are subject to microbial degradation by a metabolic pathway similar to that of monocyclic structures (Cripps and Watkinson, 1978; Dean-Raymond and Bartha, 1975; Gibson, 1975; ZoBell, 1971). Interestingly, the induction of enzymes for polycyclic aromatic hydrocarbon degradation depends upon lower-molecular-weight aromatics such as naphthalene (Heitkamp et al., 1988); the finding that the enzymes for degrading at least some polycyclic aromatic hydrocarbons are not induced by the substrate itself is important and may explain the apparent resistance of these compounds to microbial attack.

The genetics of toluene and naphthalene metabolism have been studied and reviewed (Yen and Serdar, 1988; Sayler, 1991). The TOL and NAH catabolic plasmids are well characterized. These two closely related plasmids contain entire genetic operons for catabolism of xylenes and toluene (in the case of TOL) and naphthalene (in the case of NAH7). Both plasmids, TOL and NAH7, have a dual operon for an upper and a lower pathway. The upper pathway for naphthalene degradation results in conversion of naphthalene to salicylate and the lower pathway in the oxidation of salicylate. Both the upper and lower pathway coded for in NAH7 are induced by benzoate. For TOL, the upper pathway is induced by toluene and results in formation of benzoate from toluene and toluate from xylenes. The lower pathway is benzoate inducible and responsible for the meta-cleavage pathway of toluate and benzoate degradation.

In an interesting recent study, Burlage et al. (1990) fused a fragment from plasmid NAH7, which contains a promoter for the upper pathway of naphthalene degradation by pseudomonads, to the lux genes of Vibrio fisheri, which controls light generation. They were able then to use bioluminescence to monitor naphthalene catabolism by the microorganism when it was growing on a complex substrate mixture. Induction of bioluminescence was demonstrated to coincide with naphthalene degradation. A delay in bioluminescence was observed when naphthalene was added to exponentially growing cells, suggesting that the Pseudomonas strain optimally used naphthalene during periods of slow rather than rapid growth.

2. Factors Influencing Rates of Hydrocarbon Biodegradation

By the late 1960s it was apparent that because of the world's limited petroleum resources, there would be inevitable shortages and an eventual energy crisis. Hence, petroleum could not serve as the inexpensive substrate for microbial biomass production to feed the world. There was also a shift in public concern in that era to the environment. The wreck of the tanker Torrey Canyon in 1969 focused that environmental concern on the fate of hydrocarbon pollutants in the oceans. There was an almost immediate shift in research interest to the biodegradation of oil under real environmental conditions. The aim was to see how fast microorganisms could convert hydrocarbons to carbon dioxide and water with little concern for the amount of protein produced. Rather than trying to optimize conditions for maximal biomass production, experiments were conducted to determine the factors limiting the rates of petroleum biodegradation in the environment.

These studies showed that the fate of petroleum hydrocarbons in the environment is largely determined by the populations of hydrocarbon-degrading microorganisms and the abiotic factors that control the growth of those populations (Atlas and Bartha, 1973e). Factors which influence rates of microbial growth and enzymatic activities affect the rates of petroleum hydrocarbon biodegradation. The persistence of petroleum pollutants depends on the quantity and quality of the hydrocarbon mixture and on the properties of the affected ecosystem. In one encironment petroleum hydrocarbons can persist almost indefinitely, whereas under another set of conditions the same hydrocarbons can be completely biodegraded within a relatively few hours or days.

Studies on the microbial degradation of hydrocarbons, including determination of the effects of environmental parameters on biodegradation rates, elucidation of metabolic pathways and genetic bases for hydrocarbon assimilation by microorganisms, and examination of the effects of hydrocarbon contamination on microorganisms and microbial communities have been areas of intense interest and the subjects of several reviews (Atlas, 1977, 1981, 1984; Atlas and Bartha, 1973e; Bartha, 1986; Colwell and Walker, 1977; National Academy of Sciences, 1985; Leahy and Colwell, 1990). Rates of biodegradation under optimal laboratory conditions have been reported to be as high as 2500–100,000 g/m^3 per day (Bartha and Atlas, 1987). Under *in situ* conditions, petroleum biodegradation rates are orders of magnitude lower. *In situ* natural rates have been reported in the range 0.001–60 g/m^3 per day (Bartha and Atlas, 1977; Bartha, 1986). The microbial degradation of petroleum in the environment is limited primarily by abiotic factors, including temperature, nutrients such as nitrogen and/or phosphorus, and oxygen (Atlas, 1981, 1984; Bartha, 1986; Leahy and Colwell, 1990).

The biodegradation of petroleum and other hydrocarbons in the environment is a complex process, whose quantitative and qualitative aspects depend on the nature and amount of the oil or hydrocarbons present, the ambient and seasonal environmental conditions, and the composition of the indigenous microbial community (Atlas, 1981; Leahy and Colwell, 1990; Cooney, 1990). Microbial degradation of oil has been shown to occur by attack on the aliphatic or light aromatic fractions of the oil. Although some studies have reported their removal at high rates under optimal conditions (Rontani *et al.*, 1985; Shiaris, 1989), high-molecular-weight aromatics, resins, and asphaltenes are generally considered to be recalcitrant or exhibit only very low rates of biodegradation. In aquatic ecosystems, dispersion and emulsification of oil in slicks appear to be prerequisites for rapid biodegradation; large masses of mousse, tarballs, or high concentrations of oil in quiescent environments tend to persist because of the limited surface areas available for microbial activity. Petroleum spilled on or applied to soil is largely adsorbed to particulate matter, decreasing its toxicity, but possibly also contributing to its persistence.

2.1. Chemical Composition of Oil

Microbial degradation of oil released into the environment has been shown to occur by attack on the saturate and low-molecular-weight aromatic fractions of the oil. Veryhigh-molecular-weight aromatics, resins, and asphaltenes are considered to be recalcitrant or exhibiting only very low rates of biodegradation, but some studies have reported the biodegradation of some of the higher-molecular-weight aromatic and as-phaltene compounds in petroleum (Leahy and Colwell, 1990). The n-alkanes are readily degraded and usually considered the most readily degraded compounds in petroleum (Davies and Hughes, 1968; Kator et al., 1971; Kator and Herwig, 1977; Treccani, 1964; ZoBell, 1946). Biodegradation of n-alkanes with molecular weights up to n-C_{44} have been demonstrated (Haines and Alexander, 1974).

There have been some reports, however, of low-molecular-weight aromatics being attacked more rapidly than the alkanes (Fedorak and Westlake, 1981a,b). Foght et al. (1990) reported that the microorganisms that degrade aromatic hydrocarbons may be distinct from those that attack aliphatic hydrocarbons. Microbial isolates that utilize hexadecane cannot grow on phenanthrene and vice versa. Thus, the degradation of different classes of hydrocarbons may be carried out by totally different populations of microorganisms.

Polynuclear aromatic hydrocarbons are more difficult to biodegrade than one- and two-ring aromatics (Atlas, 1981; Leahy and Colwell, 1990). As biodegradation pro-ceeds, branched hydrocarbons, such as pristane and phytane, and substituted poly-nuclear aromatics, such as C_3 phenanthrenes, usually constitute an increasing proportion of the residual hydrocarbon mixture (Atlas et al., 1981; Fedorak and Westlake, 1981a; Herbes and Schwall, 1978; Wade et al., 1989). Condensed ring aromatic hydrocarbons are even more resistant to enzymatic attack; for example, Lee and Ryan (1976) found that biodegradation rates were over 1000 times higher for naphthalene than for ben-zopyrenes. Structures with four or more condensed rings are attacked, in some cases, by co-oxidation and degraded further as a result of commensalism (Barnsley, 1975; Cripps and Watkinson, 1978; Gibson, 1975; Walker and Colwell, 1974a; Walker et al., 1975, 1976). Although they rarely serve as growth substrates, these compounds are converted at slow rates to carbon dioxide and water microorganisms. Recently, mycobacteria have been isolated that utilize pyrene, a four-ring polynuclear aromatic hydrocarbon (PAH), as their principal carbon source (Heitkamp and Cerniglia, 1989).

There have been several reports of the direct oxidative and co-oxidative degradation of both substituted and unsubstituted cycloalkanes. Some cycloalkanes in spilled pe-troleum are relatively resistant to microbial attack (Donoghue et al., 1976; Ooyama and Foster, 1965; Perry, 1979; Stirling et al., 1977; Trudgill, 1978). Complex alicyclic compounds, such as hopanes (tripentacyclic compounds), are among the most persistent components of petroleum spillages in the environment (Atlas et al., 1981).

Many branched and cyclic hydrocarbons undoubtedly are removed as environmen-tal contaminants after oil spills as a result of co-oxidation (Perry, 1979; Raymond and Jamison, 1971; Raymond et al., 1967). Keck et al., (1989) found evidence of co-oxidation of aromatic hydrocarbons in soil; they found that four- and five-ring PAHs disappeared rapidly from soils amended with complex wastes. In soils, PAH disap-pearance does not necessarily involve complete conversion to carbon dioxide and water. Partially oxidized PAH compounds may be incorporated into soil humus (Bossert et al., 1984). Bertrand et al. (1983) found that the microbial degradation of asphaltenes and resins, which had previously been considered relatively recalcitrant to biodegradation, may be due to co-oxidation. Rontani et al. (1985) also found evidence for co-oxidation of asphaltenes; they reported degradation of asphaltenic compounds in mixed bacterial cultures to be dependent upon the presence of n-alkanes 12 to 18 carbon atoms in length.

2.2. Physical State of Oil Pollutants

The physical state of petroleum hydrocarbons has a marked effect on their biodegradation. At very low concentrations, hydrocarbons are soluble in water, but most oil spill incidents release petroleum hydrocarbons in concentrations far in excess of the solubility limits (Boylan and Tripp, 1971; Frankenfeld, 1973; Harrison *et al.*, 1975; McAuliffe, 1966). The degree of spreading determines in part the surface area of oil available for microbial colonization by hydrocarbon-degrading microorganisms; in aquatic systems, the oil normally spreads, forming a thin slick (Berridge *et al.*, 1968). The degree of spreading is reduced at low temperatures because of the viscosity of the oil. In soils, petroleum hydrocarbons are absorbed by plant matter and soil particles, limiting its spreading.

When oil does not spread, there is limited surface area for microbial attack. Colwell *et al.* (1978) postulated that oil from the Metula spill persisted in part because of limited surface area for microbial attack in the tar balls and oil aggregates that formed. Biodegradation of hydrocarbons occurs at the oil–water interface. When oil mixes with water, it typically forms an emulsion. If an oil-in-water emulsion with small droplet size is formed, there is ample surface area at the oil–water interface for rapid microbial metabolism of hydrocarbons. However, if a water-in-oil emulsion forms a thick "mousse," rates of oil biodegradation are slowed. Following the IXTOC well blowout in 1979 for example, studies showed that the thick mousse was extremely resistant to microbial attack (Atlas *et al.*, 1980a), whereas oil dispersed as small droplets in the water column was biodegraded very rapidly (Pfaender *et al.*, 1980; Buckley *et al.*, 1980). It has also been shown that dispersants that do not contain toxic solvents can greatly enhance rates of petroleum biodegradation (Atlas and Bartha, 1973c). Mulkins-Philips and Steward (1974), Gatellier (1971), Gatellier *et al.* (1971), and Robichaux and Myrick (1972) all demonstrated that some dispersants enhance rates of oil biodegradation. Many hydrocarbon-degrading microorganisms produce emulsifying agents (bioemulsifiers) that facilitate their abilities to degrade hydrocarbons (Abbott and Gledhill, 1971; Guire *et al.*, 1973; Reisfeld *et al.*, 1972; Zajic *et al.*, 1974; Zajic and Steffens, 1984; Bertrand *et al.*, 1983; Mattei *et al.*, 1986).

Emulsification aids the true dissolution of hydrocarbons in water and also provides an enlarged surface area for direct contact of microorganisms with liquid hydrocarbon droplets. It appears that microorganisms can efficiently transport into their cells dissolved liquid hydrocarbons. In contrast, hydrocarbons that are solid at the growth temperature, appear to be taken up only in the dissolved state (Wodzinski and Coyle, 1974). As the water solubility of many solid hydrocarbons is extremely low, transport limitation can cause an apparent recalcitrance of otherwise degradable hydrocarbons. This was demonstrated by packaging highly recalcitrant n-hexatriacontane (C_{36}) into liposomes (Miller and Bartha, 1989). Hexatriacontane transported in this manner into the cells of a *Pseudomonas* strain originally isolated on n-octadecane (C_{18}) utilized the C_{36} hydrocarbon at the same rate as the water-soluble substrate succinate.

2.3. Hydrocarbon-Degrading Microbial Populations

Hydrocarbon-degrading bacteria and fungi are widely distributed in marine, fresh-water, and soil habitats. Bacteria and yeasts appear to be the prevalent hydrocarbon degraders in aquatic ecosystems (Cooney and Summers, 1976). Filamentous fungi and bacteria are the main hydrocarbon utilizers in soil ecosystems. The most prevalent genera of hydrocarbon-utilizing microorganisms in aquatic environments appear to be *Pseudomonas, Achromobacter, Arthrobacter, Micrococcus, Nocardia, Vibrio, Acineto-bacter, Brevibacterium, Corynebacterium, Flavobacterium, Candida, Rhodotorula,* and *Sporobolomyces* (Bartha and Atlas, 1977). In most marine environments, the listed bacteria and yeasts appear to be the dominant hydrocarbon degraders, but from the Persian Gulf, the isolation of hydrocarbon-degrading *Rhodococcus* and filamentous fungi such as *Aspergillus, Mucor, Fusarium,* and *Penicilium* was also reported (Sorkhoh *et al.,* 1990). The possibility that the latter were allochthonous terrestrial microorganisms blown in by the wind from adjacent desert regions cannot be excluded. Essentially the same bacterial genera with the addition of *Alcaligenes* and *Mycobacterium* and numerous filamentous fungi were isolated from the soil environment as hydrocarbon degraders (Bossert and Bartha, 1984).

The overall ability to degrade oil depends upon the generic composition of the microbial community and in particular the enzymes produced by the hydrocarbon-degrading species (Applied Biotreatment Association, 1990). An ability to isolate high numbers of certain oil-degrading microorganisms from an environment is commonly taken as evidence that they are the most active oil degraders of that environment. This projection is questionable, but *in situ* measurements of hydrocarbon biodegradation activity are few. Using selective inhibitors, Song *et al.* (1986) determined that in a field soil with no hydrocarbon spill history, 80% of added hexadecane was degraded by bacteria and only 20% by fungi. In the same soil, glucose degradation was shared evenly by the bacterial and fungal population segments.

Prior exposure of a microbial community to hydrocarbons is important in determining how rapidly subsequent hydrocarbon inputs can be biodegraded (Leahy and Colwell, 1990). A large number of studies have demonstrated sizable increases in populations of hydrocarbon-utilizing microorganisms when environmental samples are exposed to petroleum hydrocarbons (Amund and Igiri, 1990; Atlas *et al.,* 1980b; Atlas and Bartha, 1972a, 1973d; Calomiris *et al.,* 1976; Davis, 1956; Kator, 1973; Lode, 1986; Perry and Cerniglia, 1973; Pritchard and Starr, 1973; Soli, 1973; Taxler, 1973; Song and Bartha, 1990; Sexstone and Atlas, 1977; ZoBell, 1973b). In unpolluted environments, hydrocarbon degraders generally constitute less than 1% of the microbial community, whereas in oil-polluted ecosystems, hydrocarbon degraders often represent 1–10% of microorganisms (Atlas, 1981). In some extreme cases (Mulkins-Philips and Stewart, 1974; Song and Bartha, 1990), over 90% of the total microbial community of polluted environments proved to be hydrocarbon utilizers. The degree of elevation above comparable unpolluted sites appears to quantitatively reflect the degree or extent of exposure of that ecosystem to hydrocarbon contaminants.

Communities exposed to hydrocarbons become adapted, exhibiting selective enrichment and genetic changes resulting in increased proportions of hydrocarbon-degrading bacteria and bacterial plasmids encoding hydrocarbon catabolic genes (Leahy and Colwell, 1990). Because adapted microbial communities have higher proportions of hydrocarbon degraders, they can respond to the presence of hydrocarbon pollutants within hours. In the case of the *Amoco Cadiz* and *Tanio* spills along the coast of Brittany, France, for example, the adapted hydrocarbon-degrading populations increased by several orders of magnitude within a day of the spills and biodegradation occurred as fast or faster than evaporation in the days following these spills (Atlas *et al.*, 1981).

As may be expected, easily utilizable hydrocarbons have the most dramatic effects on numbers. In one study, jet fuel contamination increased direct microbial counts and mycelial length by two to four orders of magnitude and cultural counts of hydrocarbon degraders by as much as five orders of magnitude (Song and Bartha, 1990).

In an aqueous medium, it may be critical to maintain high biomass in contact with the hydrocarbons to be degraded. Bertrand *et al.* (1983) and Mattei *et al.* (1985) found that they could greatly increase crude oil biodegradation in a continuous culture seawater reactor if they passed the effluent through an ultrafilter that retained the biomass within the reactor.

2.4. Temperature

Hydrocarbon biodegradation can occur over a wide range of temperatures, and psychrotrophic, mesophilic, and thermophilic hydrocarbon-utilizing microorganisms have been isolated. Temperature affects the rates of microbial hydrocarbon-degrading activities by its effect on the physical nature and chemical composition of the oil (particularly the surface area available for microbial colonization and the hydrocarbons remaining after evaporation for microbial metabolic attack) and the rates of hydrocarbon metabolism by microorganisms (Atlas, 1981; Leahy and Colwell, 1990). At low temperatures the viscosity of oil increases and the volatilization of toxic short-chain alkanes is reduced, thus delaying the onset of biodegradation (Atlas and Bartha, 1972c; Atlas, 1975; Walker and Colwell, 1974b). Low winter temperatures can limit rates of hydrocarbon biodegradation, increasing residence time of oil pollutants (Bodennec *et al.*, 1987; Pritchard, 1990).

In a recent diesel oil spill from the *Bahia Paraiso* in the Antarctic, Kennicutt (1990) reported turnover rates, measured as [^{14}C]hexadecane mineralization, in excess of 2 years. This was considerably slower than the rates previously measured in Arctic zones.

Rates of degradation are generally observed to decrease with decreasing temperature; this is believed to be a result primarily of decreased rates of enzymatic activity, or the Q_{10} effect. In addition, solidification of some hydrocarbons decreases their availability. Nevertheless, ZoBell (1973a) and Traxler (1973) reported hydrocarbon degradation at temperatures below 0°C. Higher temperatures increase the rates of hydrocarbon metabolism to a maximum, typically in the range of 20 to 30°C, above which the toxicity of hydrocarbons is increased and biodegradation slows down (Dibble and Bartha, 1979b; Bossert and Bartha, 1984; Hogan *et al.*, 1989). However, Klug and Markovetz (1967a,b) and Mateles *et al.* (1967) reported hydrocarbon degradation at temperatures as high as 70°C. Thermophilic alkane-utilizing bacteria, including obligate hydrocarbon utilizers, have been isolated from deep-sea thermal vent regions and other hot environments (Perry, 1985; Bazylinski *et al.*, 1989).

2.5. Oxygen

The initial steps in the biodegradation of hydrocarbons by bacteria and fungi involve the oxidation of the substrate by oxygenases for which molecular oxygen is required (Atlas, 1984). Aerobic conditions are, therefore, necessary for this route of microbial oxidation of hydrocarbons in the environment. The availability of oxygen in soils, sediments, and aquifers is often limiting and dependent on the type of soil and whether the soil is waterlogged (Jobson *et al.*, 1979). Anaerobic degradation of aromatic petroleum hydrocarbons by microorganisms was reported (Ward and Brock, 1978; Grbic-Gallic and Vogel, 1987; Vogel and Grbic-Gallic, 1986; Zeyer *et al.*, 1986, 1990). Hambrick *et al.* (1980) followed the $^{14}CO_2$ release from radiolabeled *n*-hexadecane and naphthalene in estuarine sediment slurries incubated for 1 month at preset and controlled redox potentials ranging from -250 to $+510$mV. At the lowest redox potentials, naphthalene biodegradation was undetectable during the 1-month experiment, and hexadecane biodegradation was at least four times lower than at the high redox potential. This laboratory study, along with field measurements (Ward and Brock, 1978; Ward *et al.*, 1980; Delaune *et al.*, 1980), led to the general conclusion that the ecological and environmental significance of anaerobic hydrocarbon biodegradation is very low as compared to anaerobic biodegradation.

More recently, numerous reports appeared on the anaerobic biodegradation of some low-molecular-weight aromatic hydrocarbons (Grbic-Gallic and Vogel, 1987; Vogel and Grbic-Gallic, 1986; Zeyer *et al.*, 1986). Although definitely slower than the aerobic process, the degradation rates of toluene and *m*-xylene in anaerobic soil columns were considered to be promising for aquifer bioremediation (Zeyer *et al.*, 1990).

2.6. Nutrients

Since microorganisms require nitrogen, phosphorus, and other mineral nutrients for incorporation into biomass, the availability of these within the area of hydrocarbon degradation is critical. A few investigators have concluded that nitrogen and phosphorus are not limiting in seawater (Kinney *et al.*, 1969), but this conclusion was reached when oil was present only at very low concentrations in true solution and when degradation was severely limited by low water temperatures. The great majority of investigators reported that concentrations of available nitrogen and phosphorus in seawater are severely limiting to microbial hydrocarbon degradation (Atlas and Bartha, 1972b; Bartha and Atlas, 1973; Floodgate, 1973, 1979; Gunkel, 1967; LePetit and Barthelemy, 1968; LePetit and N'Guyen, 1976). When considering an oil slick, there is a mass of carbon available for microbial growth within a limited area and the hydrocarbon-degrading microorganisms must rely on the nutrients available in that limited volume of water in direct contact with the oil. When considering soluble hydrocarbons, nitrogen and phosphorus are probably not limiting since the solubility of the hydrocarbons is so low as to preclude establishment of an unfavorable C/N or C/P ratio.

Floodgate (1979), in considering the limitations of nutrients to biodegradation of hydrocarbons in the sea, proposed the concept of determining "nitrogen demand," analogous to the concept of biochemical oxygen demand. Based on Kuwait crude oil at 14°C, the nitrogen demand was found to be 4 nmole of nitrogen per μg oil. Colwell *et al.* (1978) concluded that oil from the *Metulla* spill was degraded slowly in the marine environment, most probably because of limitations imposed by the relatively low concentrations of nitrogen and phosphorus available in seawater.

In addition to N and P, in clean offshore seawater the low availability of iron was also found to limit hydrocarbon biodegradation, but the same limitation was not evident in sediment-rich nearshore seawater (Dibble and Bartha, 1976). No other mineral nutrients were found or are suspected to be limiting for oil biodegradation in seawater, but in some freshwater environments the sulfate concentration may be insufficient to support optimal oil biodegradation (Bartha, 1986; Jobson *et al*, 1974).

Much like in aquatic environments, nitrogen and phosphorus availability may also limit hydrocarbon biodegradation in terrestrial situations (Dibble and Bartha, 1979b; Bossert and Bartha, 1984; Bartha, 1986).

2.7. Reaction (pH)

Seawater is well buffered by the carbonate–bicarbonate–carbon dioxide system and a pH around 8.5 is remarkably uniform throughout the oceans. For these reasons, the effects of pH on oil biodegradation in the marine environment has received only limited attention (Hambrick *et al.*, 1980). The optimum pH was found to be 8.0 and experience shows that the natural pH of seawater is permissive of high rates of oil biodegradation when other limitations are remedied. Bodies of fresh water are generally less well buffered and exhibit wide ranges of pH, but as to the effect of these on oil biodegradation, systematic investigations have not been reported. In agricultural soils pH is often controlled by amendments, and the effect of pH on hydrocarbon biodegradation in soil has received some attention (Vanlooke *et al.*, 1975; Verstraete *et al.*, 1976; Dibble and Bartha, 1979b; Bossert and Bartha, 1984; Bartha, 1986). With the exception of calcareous and desert soils, most soils have a more or less acidic pH. Excess acidity of agricultural soils is neutralized by "liming," i.e., the application of ground limestone (calcium/magnesium carbonate).

Raising of the original pH of soil from 6.0 to 7.8 increased the rate of hydrocarbon biodegradation (Dibble and Bartha, 1979b). The buffering capacity of each soil sets a practical limit to pH adjustment and no absolute pH optimum was established, but pH 7.0–7.8 appeared to be very close to the optimum. As bacteria have a pH optimum at or above neutrality, whereas most fungi are tolerant to lower pH, the favorable effect of liming on hydrocarbon biodegradation is consistent with a bacterial dominance in terrestrial hydrocarbon biodegradation (Song *et al.*, 1986).

3. Assessing Bioremediation

Recognizing that rates of hydrocarbon biodegradation often are limited by environmental constraints or possibly by the lack of suitable microbial populations, it is possible to carry out bioremediation programs to overcome these limitation (Bluestone, 1986; Zitrides, 1990). Bioremediation involves the use of microorganisms to remove pollutants (Atlas and Pramer, 1990). The two general approaches to bioremediation are environmental modification, such as through fertilizer application and aeration, and addition of adapted microbial hydrocarbon degraders by seeding. The spill of more than 200,000 barrels of crude oil from the oil tanker *Exxon Valdez* in Prince William Sound, Alaska on March 24, 1989 (Hagar, 1989), as well as smaller spills in Texas, Rhode Island, and the Delaware Bay (Anonymous, 1989), focused attention on the problem of hydrocarbon contamination in marine and estuarine environments and the potential use of bioremediation to remove petroleum pollutants.

Bioremediation most often uses microorganisms and their biodegradative capacity to remove pollutants. The end-products of effective bioremediation, such as water and carbon dioxide, are nontoxic and can be accommodated without harm to the environment and living organisms. Using bioremediation to remove pollutants is inexpensive as compared to physical methods for decontaminating the environment, which are extraordinarily expensive. Over $1 million a day was spent in an attempt that was only partially successful to clean up the oiled rocks of Prince William Sound, Alaska using water washing and other physical means after the *Exxon* tanker ran aground there. Neither the government nor private industry can afford the cost of cleaning up the nation's petroleum-contaminated sites by physical means. Therefore, a renewed interest in bioremediation has developed (Beardsley, 1989). While current technologies call for moving large quantities of toxic waste-contaminated soil to incinerators, bioremediation can be performed on-site and requires simple equipment that is readily available. Bioremediation, though, is not the solution for all environmental pollution problems. Like other technologies, bioremediation has limitations as to the materials that can be treated, conditions at the treatment site, and the time that is available for the treatment.

No national coordinated response plan for oil spill bioremediation currently exists (Gregorio, 1991). A subcommittee of the EPA's Biotreatment Action Committee Task Force, therefore, was formed in June 1990 to discuss the development of a National Bioremediation Spill Response Plan. Such a plan would attempt to maximize the potential for the biotreatment of oil spills by focusing and channeling the sundry research and development efforts into a single coordinated plan. The plan would also create and test a scheme for using bioremediation in dealing with oil spilled anywhere in the United States, including open ocean areas, harbors, shorelines, estuaries, rivers, or on land. Petroleum hydrocarbon-degrading bacterial supplies and nutrients would be pretested; the indigenous bacterial populations in representative areas would be evaluated to develop an appropriate matrix of materials for optimizing bacterial cell/oil/nutrient/water interface; supplies and equipment would be identified, tested, and procured. Detailed written procedures for sampling, evaluating, and preparing the spill site, as well as for performing and monitoring the biotreatment program would be developed.

A bioremediation panel of the American Academy of Microbiology at the request of the U.S. EPA considered the potential applications of bioremediation to the Persian Gulf oil spill—the world's largest spill estimated at 460 million gallons of Kuwait crude oil (R. R. Colwell, personal communication). The panel concluded that for the long-term recovery of the Persian Gulf, bioremediation should be of value. Addition of fertilizers, as well as microorganisms, is an approach to be considered, particularly for nearshore and coastal regions. Data from laboratory studies suggest that additions of microorganisms to the open ocean should not cause significant adverse effects, either directly to sensitive marine species or indirectly to the environment by causing an increase in bacterial biomass or eutrophication. The panel pointed out, however, that the potential for bioremediation of oil at sea is limited. Of the options available, the application of large quantities of oil-degrading bacteria and nutrients to support their growth can be considered. At the present time, there are no definitive scientific data that unequivocally demonstrate that addition of large quantities of oil-degrading bacteria to oil in the open ocean leads to removal of the oil by biodegradation. Addition of microorganisms to oil in controlled laboratory studies has been shown to enhance biodegradation, but conclusive data from field experiments are not available and will be difficult to obtain. Generally, microbial degradation of oil, even under the most favorable of laboratory conditions, takes weeks to months. The purpose and documented result of the use of bioremediation is to enhance degradation over extended time periods, rather than to achieve short-term or immediate results.

3.1. Laboratory Efficacy Testing

To demonstrate that a bioremediation technology is potentially useful, it is important that the ability to enhance the rates of hydrocarbon biodegradation be demonstrated under controlled conditions. This generally cannot be accomplished *in situ* and thus must be accomplished in laboratory experiments. Laboratory experiments demonstrate the potential a particular treatment may have to stimulate the removal of petroleum pollutants from a contaminated site (Bailey *et al.*, 1973). Laboratory experiments that closely model real environmental conditions are most likely to produce relevant results (Buckley *et al.*, 1980; Bertrand *et al.*, 1983). In many cases this involves using samples collected in the field that contain the indigenous microbial populations. In such experiments it is important to include appropriate controls, such as sterile treatments, to separate the effects of the abiotic weathering of oil from actual biodegradation. Such experiments do not replace the need for field demonstrations but are critical for establishing the scientific credibility of specific bioremediation strategies. They are also useful for screening potential bioremediation treatments.

The parameters typically measured in laboratory tests of bioremediation efficacy include enumeration of microbial populations, measurement of rates of microbial respiration (oxygen consumption and/or carbon dioxide production), and determination of rates of hydrocarbon degradation (disappearance of individual hydrocarbons and/or total hydrocarbons). The methodologies employed in these measurements are critical. It is assumed, for example, that bioremediation of oil pollutants will result in elevated populations of hydrocarbon degraders. Many of the organisms that form colonies on agar-based hydrocarbon media grow on agar contaminants rather than on hydrocarbons (Atlas, 1979). Therefore, confirmatory tests are needed. In some studies, isolates have been tested in liquid culture with more rigorous criteria, such as measuring actual hydrocarbon disappearance, to establish that particular organisms are, in fact, hydrocarbon degraders. These tests often have shown that less than 30% of the organisms that form colonies on oil agar actually are capable of metabolizing hydrocarbons. Most-probable-number type of enumeration of hydrocarbon degraders in liquid medium are reliable but often laborious (Song and Bartha, 1990). Brown and Braddock (1990) developed a rapid most probable number procedure based on emulsification of oil seen as disruption of a surface oil slick in microtiter plates.

To overcome the limitations inherent in methods that examine only growth of microorganisms in the presence of oil, methods have been developed that utilize indicators of hydrocarbon metabolism. For example, dyes can be used to demonstrate the actual metabolism of aromatic hydrocarbons by specific organisms on agar plates or in liquid culture in microtiter plates (Shiaris and Cooney, 1983). Colony hybridization procedures have also been employed to positively identify the colony-forming units with the genetic capacity for degrading specific aromatic hydrocarbons, for example, by using gene probes for the naphthalene catabolic genes (Sayler et al., 1985). Using genetic markers it has been possible to demonstrate the persistence of specific hydrocarbon-degrading populations in the environment for months in hydrocarbon-contaminated sites (Jain and Sayler, 1987; Jain et al., 1987). The production of radiolabeled carbon dioxide from radiolabeled hydrocarbon substrates also can be used to demonstrate hydrocarbon utilization (Caparello and LaRock, 1975). Such production of $^{14}CO_2$ from radiolabeled hexadecane has been used with a most probable number format to enumerate hydrocarbon degraders with certainty that the number of organisms determined reflects the real number of hydrocarbon degraders in the sample (Atlas, 1979). A general shortcoming of counting procedures as measures of bioremediation efficacy is their indirectness. Hydrocarbon biodegradation is not measured but rather projected from the increase in microbial numbers.

Oxygen consumption rates have been used as a measure of microbial utilization of hydrocarbons (Gibbs et al., 1975; Venosa et al., 1992). Such measurements, however, may also reflect the utilization of nonhydrocarbon organics in the sample. This is especially critical since the addition of oil to the environment may result in the death of some organisms, and these would constitute a ready source of carbon for aerobic microbial respiration. Since the consumption of oxygen can produce erroneous results, the production of carbon dioxide from radiolabeled hydrocarbon substrates has been used as a more definitive measure of rates of microbial hydrocarbon metabolism (Caparello and LaRock, 1975; Atlas, 1979). If experiments are performed using simulated field conditions, the measurement of such $^{14}CO_2$ evolution rates can be extrapolated to rates of hydrocarbon metabolism likely to occur at contaminated sites.

Undoubtedly, the most direct measure of bioremediation efficacy is the monitoring of hydrocarbon disappearance rates. When using this approach, the appropriate controls and the proper choice of analytical techniques become especially critical. The "disappearance" of hydrocarbons may occur not only by biodegradation but also by evaporation, photodegradation, and leaching. In a laboratory setting, the latter two are easily controlled, but the accurate control of evaporative losses is troublesome. Sealed incubation systems are incompatible with the high oxygen demand of hydrocarbon degradation. Poisoned controls in open systems notoriously underestimate biodegradation (Song *et al.*, 1990). Normally, biodegradation and evaporation compete for the same hydrocarbons. If biodegradation is suppressed by metabolic poisons (usually $HgCl_2$), hydrocarbons that would otherwise be degraded eventually evaporate. Theoretically, the best mass balance would be derived from flow-through systems with traps for volatilized hydrocarbon. In practice, such systems have many problems concerning their trapping efficiency, unobserved breakthrough, low hydrocarbon recovery from the absorbent, and flow rate fluctuation. Hydrocarbon trapping periods on activated carbon or tenax are typically measured for minutes only, but are projected for time periods of days or weeks. Obviously, any change in flow rates can lead to very large errors.

The meaning of hydrocarbon disappearance data also strongly depends on the analytical techniques employed. Gravimetric determination of residual oil may overestimate biodegradation when volatile components are lost during evaporation of the extracting solvent. Conversely, biodegradation may be underestimated when nonhydrocarbon materials are coextracted by the solvent. Biodegradation intermediates that have incorporated oxygen also increase the residual weight and may contribute to the underestimation of biodegradative losses.

Because of the outlined problems with residual weight, most studies have turned to more definitive analytical procedures (Venosa *et al.*, 1991a, 1992a; Prince *et al.*, 1990; Pritchard and Costa, 1991).

The recommended standard analysis for total hydrocarbon residues employs infrared (IR) absorption (Standard Methods, 1985). The water or soil sample is extracted with carbon tetrachloride or Freon and the IR absorption of the extract is measured at 2930 cm^{-1}. This absorption band reflects the C–H stretching vibrations of hydrocarbons and consequently the measurement has to be performed in solvents that are free of C–H bonds. It also stands to reason that saturated hydrocarbons absorb more strongly at this band than do aromatics, and for best quantitative results, the standard curve should be prepared with a hydrocarbon mixture that in its composition approximates the unknown sample. The IR method gives no information about the fate of individual hydrocarbons. On the positive side, however, it is applicable to hydrocarbons regardless of their volatility and molecular size. It will measure hexane as well as C_{40}–C_{50} waxes as long as they remain extractable by the appropriate solvents.

To obtain maximal information about individual components of hydrocarbon mixtures, many investigators have turned to gas chromatography and mass spectrometry (Cook and Westlake, 1974; Walker *et al.*, 1975; Walker and Colwell, 1976; Fedorak and Westlake, 1981b; Schwall and Herbes, 1979; Atlas *et al.*, 1981). Gas chromatographic analyses of the aliphatic fraction, often following column chromatographic separation of this fraction from other hydrocarbon fractions, is used most frequently. Such analyses permit the determination of specific hydrocarbon losses so that the degradation of individual hydrocarbons and individual classes of hydrocarbons can be determined. These detailed analyses, particularly when performed using capillary chromatography columns, allow for the inclusion of recovery standards so that the efficiency of hydrocarbon extraction and analysis can be determined. The aromatic hydrocarbon fraction can similarly be analyzed using capillary column gas chromatography. Most often these analyses are coupled with mass spectrometry using the selected ion monitoring mode to

determine the fate of individual aromatic hydrocarbons and classes of aromatic hydrocarbons

One problem with such analyses, however, is that not all compounds in an oil
mixture can be resolved, and thus there is a significant unresolved hydrocarbon complex
that must be dealt with. Also, high-molecular-weight alkanes and PAHs around and
above C_{30} cannot be analyzed by this technique for lack of sufficient volatility. In some
studies, high-pressure liquid chromatography has been used to assay the biodegradation
of such compounds (Heitkamp and Cerniglia, 1989).

In order to promote biotechnology and bioremediation, the U.S. EPA and the
University of Pittsburgh Trust have entered into a multiyear cooperative agreement to
establish the National Environmental Technology Applications Corporation (NETAC).
NETAC's purpose is to facilitate the commercialization of technologies being developed
by the government and the private sector that will positively affect the nation's most
pressing environmental problems. NETAC's efforts encompass encouraging new technologies with promising commercialization potential, as well as innovations aimed
solely at modifying and improving existing technologies or processes (USEPA, 1990).
Under the agreement with the EPA, NETAC convenes a panel of experts to review
proposals for products that have been developed for use as bioremediation. The panel
recommends those products that offer the most promise for success in the field. The
recommended products are subjected to laboratory testing at the EPA laboratory in
Cincinnati, Ohio. The objective of the laboratory protocol is to determine if commercial
bioremediation products can enhance the biodegradation of weathered crude oil to a
degree significantly better than that achievable by simple fertilizer application. The
laboratory tests consist of electrolytic respirometers set up to measure oxygen uptake
over time and shake flask microcosms to measure oil degradation and microbial growth
(Venosa, 1991; Venosa et al., 1992a). Oil constituents remaining are analyzed by
measuring the aliphatic and aromatic fractions of oil extracts. Aliphatic fractions are
measured by gas chromatography using a flame ionization detector. The aromatic fractions are characterized by gas chromatography/mass spectrometry (GC/MS). Products
that demonstrate potential efficacy are screened for toxicities and products passing the
toxicity tests are then considered for field testing.

3.2. Field Evaluations

The evaluation of hydrocarbon biodegradation in situ is far more difficult than in
laboratory studies. Analyses that require enclosure, such as respiration measurements,
typically are precluded from field evaluations of the effectiveness of hydrocarbon biodegradation. Field evaluations, therefore, have relied on the enumeration of hydrocarbon-degrading microorganisms and the recovery and analysis of residual hydrocarbons.
This is especially complicated since the distribution of oil in the environment typically is
patchy; therefore, a very high number of replicate samples must be obtained in order to
obtain statistically valid results. Even in partially enclosed containers the patchiness of
hydrocarbon distribution requires the analysis of multiple replicates (Haines and Atlas,
1982). Movement of macroorganisms, such as polychaete worms, through sediments

creates zones where oxygen incorporation favors biodegradation, while at the same time adding to the physical patchiness of the oil distribution. In open waters it is difficult to ascertain that appropriate sites are being resampled, especially when time-course determinations are being made for measuring rate of hydrocarbon biodegradation.

Because of the problems with quantitation of hydrocarbon recovery from field sites, ratios of hydrocarbons within the complex hydrocarbon mixture have been used to assess the degree of biodegradation (Atlas et al., 1981). In particular, the fact that hydrocarbon-degrading microorganisms usually degrade pristane and phytane at much lower rates than straight-chain alkanes has permitted the use of pristane or phytane as internal recovery standards (Atlas, 1981; Kennicutt et al., 1988). These measurements assume that pristane and phytane remain undegraded and, therefore, by determining the ratio of straight-chain alkanes to these highly branched alkanes, it is possible to estimate the extent to which microorganisms have attacked the hydrocarbons in the petroleum mixture (Pritchard and Costa, 1991). In situations, however, where pristane or phytane is degraded at similar rates to straight-chain alkanes, this assumption is invalid and alternative internal standards, such as hopanes, are required (Atlas et al., 1981; Pritchard, 1990; Prince et al., 1990).

An experimental design that includes appropriate controls is essential for determining the appropriate measures to be used in assessing the effectiveness of a bioremediation treatment (Fox, 1991). Often in a field bioremediation situation the necessity for cleaning up the pollutants overshadows the need for leaving an untreated reference site that is comparable to the site being treated. Thus, at the end of many bioremediation efforts all areas have been treated leaving no basis for comparison as to what would have happened if no bioremediation treatment had been employed. Given the natural degradation capacity of the indigenous microorganisms, this leaves in question the effectiveness of many bioremediation treatment strategies.

3.3. Ecological Effects Testing

In addition to demonstrating efficacy, it is essential to demonstrate that bioremediation treatments do not produce any untoward ecological effects (Colwell, 1971; Doe and Wells, 1978; O'Brien and Dixon, 1976). The focus of ecological effects testing of bioremediation has been on the direct toxicity of chemical additives, such as fertilizers, to indigenous organisms. Standardized toxicological tests are used to determine the acute toxicities of chemicals. Chronic toxicities and sublethal effects may also be determined. Generally, toxicity tests are run using the microcrustacean Daphnia bivalve, such as oyster larvae, and a fish, such as rainbow trout. Sometimes, regionally important species, such as salmon or herring, are included. Additionally, tests are run to determine effects on algal growth rates. These tests are aimed at determining levels of fertilizer application that will stimulate oil biodegradation without causing algal blooms (Atlas and Bartha, 1973b).

No test protocols have been developed or implemented for testing the potential pathogenicity of seed cultures. Concerns have sometimes been voiced that seed cultures could cause disease among humans or plant and animal populations. These concerns have been put aside when indigenous microbes—to which these populations are naturally exposed—are employed (Tabak *et al.*, 1991).

Chemical analysis detects only residues that are specifically analyzed for. To exclude the possibility that some unsuspected toxic or mutagenic residue of hydrocarbon degradation remains undetected, it is sometimes desirable to complement residue analysis with bioassays. As a rapid and convenient measure of acute toxicity, the reduction of light emission by *Photobacterium phosphoreum* (Microtox assay) has been used in the verification of land-treatment efficacy for fuel-contaminated soil (Wang and Bartha, 1990, Wang *et al.*, 1990). These measurements showed that the moderate acute toxicity of the intact fuel increased in the early phase of biodegradation, but upon the completion of the biodegradation process, it returned to the background level of uncontaminated soil. Bioremediation accelerated both the transient increase and the ultimate disappearance of toxicity. The Microtox assay has been used also to determine treatability, i.e., a need to dilute the soil prior to bioremediation when high concentrations of toxic residues interfered with biodegradation activity (Matthews and Hastings, 1987).

Mutagenic residues, especially those of PAHs, are assayed for by the well-known Ames test (Maron and Ames, 1983). In a case of a soil contaminated by diesel fuel, the initially moderate mutagenic activity of the residue increased sharply with the onset of microbial degradation, especially when the assay was run without activating microsomal enzymes (S-9 mix). However, as biodegradation progressed, the mutagenic activity returned to the background level of uncontaminated soil (Wang *et al.*, 1990).

In the case of soil, the progress of bioremediation and the decrease in toxicity was sometimes documented also by seed germination and plant growth bioassays (Bossert and Bartha, 1985; Dibble and Bartha, 1979a). As compared to microbial tests, seed and plant bioassays have moderate sensitivities and show effects usually only above 0.5–1.0% hydrocarbon of the soil dry weight. Their main function is to determine when the revegetation of an oil-inundated site can be attempted.

4. Approaches to Bioremediation

4.1. Oxygenation

The initial steps in the biodegradation of hydrocarbons by bacteria and fungi involve the oxidation of the substrate by oxygenases for which molecular oxygen is required (Atlas, 1984). While anaerobic degradation of petroleum hydrocarbons by microorganisms occurs (Ward and Brock, 1978; Grbic-Gallic and Vogel, 1987; Zeyer *et al.*, 1986, 1990), the rates of anaerobic hydrocarbon biodegradation are very low (Bailey *et al.*, 1973; Jamison *et al.*, 1975, 1976; Ward *et al.*, 1980; Atlas, 1981; Bossert and Bartha, 1984; Cooney, 1984; Floodgate, 1984). Aerobic conditions are, therefore, necessary for effective use of microbial oxidation of hydrocarbons to remove oil pollutants from the environment. Conditions of oxygen limitation normally do not exist in the upper levels of the water column in marine and freshwater environments (Floodgate, 1984; Cooney, 1984). The availability of oxygen in soils, sediments, and aquifers is often limiting and dependent on the type of soil and whether the soil is waterlogged (Jamison *et al.*, 1975; Huddleston and Cresswell, 1976; von Wedel *et al.*, 1988; Bossert and Bartha, 1984; Lee and Levy, 1991). The microbial degradation of petroleum in some groundwater and soil environments is severely limited by oxygen availability.

In surface soil, oxygenation is best assured by providing adequate drainage. Air-filled pore spaces in the soil facilitate the diffusion of oxygen to hydrocarbon-utilizing microorganisms, whereas in waterlogged soil oxygen diffusion is extremely slow and cannot keep up with the demand of heterotrophic decomposition processes. Substantial concentrations of decomposable hydrocarbons create a very high oxygen demand in soil, and the rate of diffusion is inadequate to satisfy it even in well-drained and light-textured soils. Cultivation (ploughing, rototilling) has been used to turn the soil and assure its maximal access to atmospheric oxygen (Kincannon, 1972; CONCAWE, 1989a,b). In laboratory soil columns, microbial proliferation in response to jet fuel contamination and bioremediation was three to five orders to magnitude close to the surface of the columns, but was less than one order of magnitude in the deeper portions of the columns (Song and Bartha, 1990). Reduced oxygen availability was the only explanation for this large difference.

Unsaturated subsurface (vadose) soil is normally aerobic, but strong hydrocarbon biodegradation activity may exhaust oxygen faster than it can be resupplied by diffusion. In such a situation, a periodic raising and lowering of the groundwater table can facilitate air exchange (Beraud *et al.*, 1989). Since bioremediation is often preceded by recover of free hydrocarbon by pumping, the means for manipulation of the groundwater table may be already in place.

When hydrocarbons have reached the water table and have contaminated aquifers, oxygen availability is the major problem in bioremediation. Oxygen solubility in water is low (at saturation around 8 mg/liter), and the oxygen demand for hydrocarbon degradation is very high. It may be calculated that the oxidation of 1 liter hydrocarbon will exhaust the dissolved oxygen (8 mg/liter) in 385,000–400,000 liters of water. This fact severely restricts the self-purification capacity of aquifers. It also follows that the injection of very large volumes of oxygenated water is necessary for the biodegradation of even moderate amounts of hydrocarbon pollutants. This contributes to the high expense of groundwater bioremediation.

To overcome oxygen limitation it is possible to add hydrogen peroxide in appropriate and stabilized formulations (American Petroleum Institute, 1987; Yaniga and Smith, 1984; Brown *et al.*, 1984, 1985; Thomas *et al.*, 1987; Berwanger and Barker, 1988). The decomposition of hydrogen peroxide releases oxygen which can support aerobic microbial utilization of hydrocarbons. At concentrations that are too high, however, hydrogen peroxide is toxic to microorganisms and will actually lower rates of microbial hydrocarbon biodegradation. Also, hydrogen peroxide is not stable and decomposes rapidly upon addition to contaminated soil environments.

Too rapid hydrogen peroxide decomposition creates gas pockets that interfere with subsequent pumping operations. For this reason, hydrogen peroxide is applied in conjunction with stabilizers that slow down its decomposition (Brown *et al.*, 1984). Stabilizer formulations are proprietary and their composition is not published. Some compounds with stabilizing properties such as phosphates may do double duty as stabilizers and fertilizers.

To avoid gas pockets and microbial toxicity, the practical concentration of hydrogen peroxide in injected water is kept around 100 ppm (Brown *et al.*, 1984; Yaniga and Smith, 1984). Two molecules of hydrogen peroxide decompose to form one molecule of oxygen and two molecules of water. Thus, the addition of 100 ppm hydrogen peroxide raises the dissolved oxygen concentration in water to 50 ppm instead of the 8 ppm achieved by air saturation alone. Stoichiometrically, it takes $1\frac{1}{2}$ O_2 to oxidize a -CH_2-unit. Because of additional dissolved oxygen or incomplete hydrocarbon degradation, in an actual bioremediation test 1.2–2.2 kg H_2O_2 was required to eliminate 1 kg hydrocarbon. The cost of treatment was estimated to be $20–30 per kg hydrocarbon (American Petroleum Institute, 1987). This high cost includes the installation and operation of injection and recovery wells.

As an example of hydrogen peroxide use in subsurface bioremediation, Berwanger and Barker (1988) investigated *in situ* biorestoration involving stimulating aerobic biodegradation in a contaminated anaerobic, methane-saturated groundwater situation using hydrogen peroxide as an oxygen source. Batch biodegradation experiments were conducted with groundwater and core samples obtained from a Canadian landfill. Hydrogen peroxide, added at a nontoxic level, provided oxygen which promoted the rapid biodegradation of benzene, toluene, ethyl benzene, and *o-*, *m-*, and *p*-xylene. Frankenberger *et al.* (1989) studied a 1000-gallon spillage of diesel fuel from a leaking underground diesel fuel storage tank. Hydrocarbon quantities ranged up to 1500 mg/kg soil. A laboratory study indicated relatively high numbers of hydrocarbon-oxidizing organisms relative to glucose-utilizing microorganisms. Bioreclamation was initiated in April 1984 by injecting nutrients (nitrogen and phosphorus) and hydrogen peroxide and terminated in October 1984 upon detection of no hydrocarbons (<1 mg/kg). A verification boring within the vicinity of the contaminated plume confirmed that residual contamination had reached background levels.

4.2. Nutrient Supplementation

Since microorganisms require nitrogen and phosphorus for incorporation into biomass, the availability of these nutrients within the same area as the hydrocarbons is critical. Under conditions where the rate of petroleum biodegradation is limited by nutrient deficiencies, the beneficial effect of fertilization with nitrogen and phosphorus has been conclusively demonstrated and offers great promise as a countermeasure for combating oil spills (Atlas and Bartha, 1972b; Atlas, 1981; Delaune *et al.*, 1980; Olivieri *et al.*, 1976; Pritchard, 1990; Pritchard and Costa, 1991). As early as 1967, bioremediation was used to clean the bilge water of the *Queen Mary* when it was moored at Long Beach Harbor (Applied Biotreatment Association, 1989).

Atlas and Bartha (1973b) developed an oleophilic nitrogen and phosphorus fertilizer which Atlas and Busdosh (1976), Atlas and Schofield (1975), and Atlas (1975) tested for its ability to stimulate petroleum degradation by indigenous microorganisms in several environments. The chemical properties of an oleophilic fertilizer place the nitrogen and phosphorus at the oil–water interface, the site of active oil biodegradation. Because the fertilizer is oleophilic, it remains with the oil and is not rapidly diluted from the site where it is effective. The fertilizer designed by Atlas and Bartha (1973b) contains paraffinized urea and octyl phosphate, but a range of other oleophilic nitrogen and phosphorus could serve equally well (Atlas and Bartha, 1976). Atlas and Bartha tested the effectiveness of oleophilic fertilizers for stimulating oil biodegradation in nearshore areas off the coast of New Jersey (Atlas and Bartha, 1973b), in Prudhoe Bay, and in several ponds near Barrow, Alaska (Atlas and Schofield, 1975; Atlas and Busdosh, 1976); tests included *in situ* as well as *in vitro* experiments in each case. Also the fertilizer was tested in microcosms for potential Arctic applications (Horowitz and Atlas, 1977). In each case there was a naturally occurring microbial population that was capable of petroleum biodegradation when this oleophilic fertilizer was added to an oil slick, and in each case, addition of oleophilic fertilizer stimulated biodegradative losses. The amount of stimulation varied for the different crude oils tested, but oil degradation generally was 30 to 40% higher in oleophilic-fertilized oil slicks compared to unfertilized slicks. Application of oleophilic fertilizer was not found to lead to undesirable algal blooms or to produce effects toxic to invertebrate bioassay organisms.

Olivieri *et al.* (1976) described a slow-release fertilizer containing paraffin-supported magnesium ammonium phosphate as the active ingredient for stimulating petroleum biodegradation. They reported that the biodegradation of Sarir crude oil in seawater was considerably enhanced by addition of the paraffin-supported fertilizer. After 21 days, 63% of the oil had disappeared when fertilizer was added, compared with 40% in a control area. Kator *et al.* (1972) suggested the use of paraffinized ammonium and phosphate salts for enhancing oil biodegradation in seawater. Bergstein and Vestal (1978) studied the biodegradation of crude oil in Arctic tundra ponds. They concluded that oleophilic fertilizer may provide a useful tool to enhance the biodegradation of crude oil spilled on such oligotrophic waters. Olivieri *et al.* (1978) tested the effect of potential oleophilic fertilizers on crude oil degradation in seawater. They found a combination of soybean lecithin and ethyl allophane to be good oleophilic sources of phosphorus and nitrogen, respectively.

Dibble and Bartha (1976) found additional stimulation of crude oil biodegradation when oleophilic iron was added as ferric octoate along with nitrogen and phosphorus. Greater stimulation was observed only in sediment-free offshore seawater, but not in sediment-rich nearshore seawater. Addition of oleophilic iron appears to be useful only in open ocean areas where iron concentrations are particularly low.

An attempt has also been made to combine an oleophilic fertilizer with a dispersant formulation (Bronchart *et al.*, 1985). This approach is based on the fact that increased surface contact between oil-degrading microorganisms, oil, oxygenated water, and nutrients provides the optimal environment for oil biodegradation.

In the aftermath of the *Amoco Cadiz* oil spill of 1978, a commercial oleophilic fertilizer was developed by Elf Aquitaine (Sirvins and Angles, 1986; LaDousse *et al.*, 1987; Sveum and LaDousse, 1989; Tramier and Sirvins, 1983; LaDousse and Tramier, 1991). The product called Inipol EAP 22 contains urea as a nitrogen source, laureth phosphate as a phosphate source, and oleic acid as a carbon source to boost the populations of hydrocarbon-degrading microorganisms. It is formulated as a microemulsion. Laboratory experiments have demonstrated significant enhancement of oil biodegradation; in some experiments 60% of added oil was biodegraded in fertilized flasks compared to 38% in unfertilized ones within 60 days (LaDousse *et al.*, 1987). Even greater enhancement, 70% fertilized compared to 20% unfertilized, was found in high-energy, oxygen saturation, tests (LaDousse *et al.*, 1987). Field tests also showed enhanced rates of oil biodegradation when Inipol EAP 22 fertilizer was applied, even in cold Arctic tests (Sirvins and Angles, 1986; Sveum and LaDousse, 1989).

Some studies comparing Inipol EAP 22 with nonoleophilic fertilizers, however, have indicated that the presence of oleic acid in Inipol may lessen the effectiveness of the fertilizer's application (Lee and Levy, 1987, 1989a,b). These studies demonstrated that in experimental field trials periodic applications of agricultural fertilizers (prilled ammonium nitrate and granular tripled superphosphate) significantly enhanced oil biodegradation so that within several months after heavy oiling of beaches no resolvable alkanes could be detected. Repetitive application of Inipol EAP 22 did not support as much oil removal. Pritchard and Costa (1991) found that Inipol EAP 22 was not as effective as water-soluble nitrogen- and phosphorus-containing fertilizers for enhancement of biodegradation of subsurface oil. They reported that 50–60% of the ammonia and phosphate in Inipol EAP 22 was released within a few minutes of application, followed by slower release over the following several weeks. Safferman (1991) tested several slow-release nitrogen formulations for the treatment of shorelines contaminated in the *Exxon Valdez* spill. In his tests, isobutyraldehyde diurea briquettes gave the best results in terms of gradual ammonia release.

4.3. Seeding

Some investigators have proposed that hydrocarbon-degrading microorganisms and their enzymatic capabilities may be critical limiting factors in the rates of hydrocarbon biodegradation (Atlas, 1977). Clearly, there is an adaptive process following the introduction of oil into the environment and if metabolically active hydrocarbon utilizers capable of utilizing hydrocarbons in the petroleum pollutant could be added quickly, the lag period before the indigenous population could respond would be reduced. Biodegradation of oil can be enhanced by addition of nutrients only after indigenous populations have adapted to the contaminated sediments (Lee and Levy, 1987, 1989a,b).

Since bioremediation relies on the hydrocarbon-degradation capacity of the microorganisms in contact with the oil pollutants, some have proposed seeding with hydrocarbon-degrading bacteria. Seeding involves the introduction of microorganisms into the natural environment for the purpose of increasing the rate or extent, or both, of biodegradation of pollutants. The rationale for this approach is that indigenous microbial populations may not be capable of degrading the wide range of potential substrates present in such complex mixtures as petroleum.

Even if the seed microorganisms are subsequently replaced by competition with indigenous hydrocarbon utilizers, there might be some benefit to such seeding operations, particularly in aquatic systems where reducing lag times before indigenous microbial populations could adapt to the presence of hydrocarbons could greatly reduce the impact of petroleum pollutants. However, if freeze-dried or otherwise metabolically inactive organisms were to be added or if mealy were necessary in order to culture such organisms, the benefit of reducing the lag period before the onset of rapid hydrocarbon degradation might be negated. Additionally, there is the problem of finding microorganisms with the right metabolic capabilities to augment the activities of the indigenous populations and also, of adding microorganisms that could survive and favorably compete with the indigenous organisms. Thus, the premises that the microorganisms naturally present in an environment subjected to contamination with oil would be incapable of extensively degrading petroleum and that added microorganisms would be able to do a superior job need to be examined carefully. The criteria to be met by effective seed organisms include ability to degrade most petroleum components, genetic stability, viability during storage, rapid growth following storage, a high degree of enzymatic activity and growth in the environment, ability to compete with indigenous microorganisms, nonpathogenicity, and inability to produce toxic metabolites (Atlas, 1977). Inoculation or "seeding" experiments have repeatedly demonstrated that specific cultures of oil-degrading bacteria fail to enhance the hydrocarbon degradation capability of natural environments because they are typically displaced by indigenous dominant microbiota (Lee and Levy, 1989a). On the other hand, the indigenous microbiota show a capacity for the adaptation to petroleum degradation within days (Bartha and Atlas, 1977; Lee and Levy, 1987; Tagger *et al.*, 1983).

Many investigators have suggested that complex mixtures of hydrocarbon degraders would be necessary in order to effectively degrade all of the hydrocarbons in a complex petroleum mixture (Atlas, 1977). Others have attempted to isolate organisms, which could be stockpiled for use in case of an oil spill or in the treatment of oily wastes, that are particularly effective at degrading hydrocarbons. In particular, some investigators have sought organisms capable of degrading specific components within an oil that usually are only slowly degraded. For example, some investigators have sought organisms that specifically degrade four-ring aromatic hydrocarbons which are among the more resistant compounds found in petroleum (Heitkamp and Cerniglia, 1989).

Experimental microbial seeding of petroleum-contaminated aquatic environments has been attempted, with mixed results. Tagger *et al.* (1983) observed no increase in petroleum degradation in seawater inoculated with a mixed culture of hydrocarbon-degrading bacteria. Atlas and Busdosh (1976) reported increased degradation of oil in a saline Arctic pond after inoculation with an oil-degrading *Pseudomonas* sp., but no improvement in a freshwater pond. Horowitz and Atlas (1980) found that greater losses of oil in seawater in an open flow-through system occurred when octadecane-coated bacteria were applied 2 weeks after the addition of an oleophilic fertilizer to the system than when the fertilizer alone was added. In the same study, no significant increases in the loss of gasoline from freshwater sediment were produced by seeding.

One approach for providing the enzymatic capability for degrading the diverse hydrocarbons found in petroleum is to use genetic engineering to create microorganisms with the capacity to degrade a wide range of hydrocarbons. The potential for creating, through genetic manipulation, microbial strains able to degrade a variety of different types of hydrocarbons has been demonstrated by Friello *et al.* (1976). They successfully produced a multiplasmid-containing *Pseudomonas* strain capable of oxidizing aliphatic, aromatic, terpenic, and polyaromatic hydrocarbons. The genetic information for at least some enzymes involved in alkane and simple aromatic hydrocarbon transformation occurs on plasmids (Chakrabarty, 1974; Dunn and Gunsalus, 1973; Chakrabarty *et al.*, 1973). The use of such a strain as an inoculum during seeding would preclude the problems associated with competition between strains in a mixed culture.

A hydrocarbon-degrading pseudomonad was engineered by Chakrabarty and was the organism that the Supreme Court of the United States in a landmark decision ruled could be patented (Anonymous, 1975). The organism engineered by Chakrabarty is capable of degrading a number of low-molecular-weight aromatic hydrocarbons, but does not degrade the higher-molecular-weight persistent polynuclear aromatics and thus has not been used in the bioremediation of oil spills. However, there is considerable controversy surrounding the release of such genetically engineered microorganisms into the environment, and field testing of these organisms must therefore be delayed until the issues of safety, containment, and potential for ecological damage are resolved (Sussman *et al.*, 1988).

Given the current regulatory framework for the deliberate release of genetically engineered microorganisms, it is unlikely that any such organism would gain the necessary regulatory approval in time to be of much use in treating an oil spill. Such organisms, however, could be useful in enclosed oily waste treatment systems that could be used to replace landfarming as an option for disposing of such residual oils.

Mixed cultures of non-genetically engineered microorganisms have been most commonly proposed as inocula for seeding because of the relative ease with which microorganisms with different and complementary hydrocarbon-degrading capabilities can be isolated. A special culture collection was begun as a depository for hydrocarbon-utilizing microorganisms (Cobet, 1974). Several commercial enterprises began to market microorganism preparations for removing petroleum pollutants.

Commercial mixtures of microorganisms are being marketed for use in degrading oil in waste treatment lagoons (Applied Biotreatment Association, 1989, 1990). These commercial microbial seed mixtures are also intended for use in other situations for the removal of oil pollutants. The seeding of selected bacteria and fungi into oil spills has been patented by Azarowicz (1973) and Bioteknika International, Inc. The literature supplied with seed bioremediation products is often the only information available about them. The full claims of their effectiveness remain to be proven. Atlas and Bartha (1973c) tested several commercial mixtures of oil-degrading bacteria and found that none were superior to the indigenous microorganisms in coastal marine waters. Dott *et al.* (1989) compared nine commercial mixed bacterial cultures to activated sludge microorganisms for their ability to degrade fuel oil in laboratory microcosms. They found that fuel oil degradation by the naturally occurring bacteria in activated sludge did not depend on nor was it enhanced by the application of highly adapted commercially available cultures. Most success has been achieved when chemostats or fermentors are used to control conditions or reduce competition from indigenous microbiota (Wong and Goldsmith, 1988).

In the initial effort by NETAC to identify cultures that might be applied to the cleanup effort in Prince William Sound following the *Exxon Valdez* accidental oil spillage, products from ten companies were selected for laboratory phase testing (Venosa, 1991; Venosa *et al.*, 1991a, 1992a). The manufacturers of these products were Alpha Environmental, Bioversal, Elf Aquitaine, ERI-Microbe Masters, Imbach, Microlife Technics, Polybac, Sybron, Waste Microbes, and Woodward Clyde. Some products actually delayed biodegradation of oil compared to fertilized controls. Most degradation, when it occurred, started after a 3- to 5-day lag period and reached significant levels after 20–30 days. Cultures that showed equal or even greater enhancement when tested after sterilization were considered to be acting solely as sources of nutrients and were not recommended for field testing. Of the products tested, two were selected for further field testing in Prince William Sound on shorelines impacted by the *Exxon Valdez* spill based on enhanced oxygen consumption rates by live cultures and removal of hydrocarbons compared to nutrient-supplemented natural Alaskan bacterial populations of oil-degrading microorganisms.

In the field trials a randomized complete block experimental design was employed (Venosa *et al.*, 1991b, 1992b). Four small plots consisting of a no-nutrient control plot, a mineral-nutrient-alone plot, and two plots receiving mineral nutrients and the seed culture were established in Prince William Sound oil-contaminated shoreline. Triplicate samples of beach sediments were collected at four equally spaced time intervals and analyzed for oil residue weight and alkane hydrocarbon profile changes over time. The object was to determine if either of the two commercial microbiological seed products was able to enhance biodegradation of oil to a greater extent than that achievable by fertilizer application alone. These field trials failed to demonstrate enhanced oil biodegradation by these products (Venosa *et al.*, 1991b, 1992b). There were no significant differences between the four plots during a 27-day trial period. It must be noted, however, that the oil was already highly degraded by the time these field trials were conducted and that environmental variability makes it difficult to observe statistically significant differences between experimental and reference sites when relatively few samples are collected and analyzed.

5. Applications of Hydrocarbon Biodegradation for Bioremediation

There are a number of sites where bioremediation is being applied for removal of hydrocarbon pollutants (Table I). These sites include soils, sediments, and waters contaminated with various oils and refined fuels. In some cases treatment is *in situ* and in others the contaminated material is treated in an aboveground bioreactor. Treatments range from addition of microbial cultures to nutrient addition and oxygenation.

5.1. Biodegradation of Oily Wastes—Landtreatment

Effluent treatment by refineries and petrochemical plants generates large amounts of oily sludges, including gravity (API) separator sludges, air flotation sludges, centrifugation residues, filter cakes, and biotreatment sludges. Tank bottoms and sludges

Table I. Sites Where Bioremediation Is Being Tested in the United States for Hydrocarbon-Contaminated Sites

Contaminant	Medium	Treatment/Comments
Petroleum	Marine shoreline	Bacterial seeding—visual changes observed very shortly after application
	Marine water	Bacterial seeding—visual changes observed very shortly after application
	Marine rocky shorelines	Fertilizer oleophilic + slow release or water soluble— enhanced rate of oil biodegration
	Marine sandy shoreline	Fertilizer water soluble—enhanced rate of oil biodegradation
	Soil	Excavate/culture—60–80% removal to < 1 ppm
	Soil	Landtreatment—multiple sites
Gasoline	Soil	Landtreatment—multiple sites
	Soil/groundwater	Groundwater extraction and nutrient addition—multiple sites
	Soil/groundwater	*In situ*—multiple sites
	Groundwater	Fixed film bioreactor
	Soil/groundwater	Oxygenation without nutrients
	Soil	Aboveground bioreactor treatment
Diesel fuel	Groundwater	*In situ* nutrients + oxygenation
	Soil	Aboveground bioreactor treatment—multiple sites
	Soil	Landtreatment—multiple sites
Jet fuel	Soil/groundwater	Aeration
	Soil/groundwater	Groundwater extraction and nutrient addition

from cleaning operations and, occasionally, used lubricating and crankcase oils that are considered non-recyclable are additional sources of oily wastes (Bartha and Bossert, 1984; CONCAWE, 1980b). From the available disposal alternatives, the use of soil as a "biological incinerator" is the most economical. The process is referred to as "land-treatment" or "landfarming," and constitutes a deliberate disposal process in which the place, the time, and the rates can be controlled. The deliberate disposal of oily wastes by landtreatment evolved on a trial-and-error basis. Its scientific monitoring started in the early 1970s (Kincannon, 1972; Francke and Clark, 1974). Later, the process was systematically optimized in field and laboratory experiments (Lehtomake and Niemela, 1975; Maunder and Waid, 1973, 1975; Raymond *et al.*, 1976a; Huddleston and Meyers, 1978; Dibble and Bartha, 1979b; Arora *et al.*, 1982; Brown and Donnelly, 1983; Sandvik *et al.*, 1986; Shailubhai, 1986; Amaral, 1987; Tesan and Barbosa, 1987). Practical recommendations concerning landtreatment were summarized by the American Petroleum Institute (1980) in the USA and by CONCAWE (1980b) in Europe.

In landtreatment, the chosen site has to meet certain criteria and needs to undergo preparation to assure that floods, runoff, and leaching will not spread the hydrocarbon contamination in an uncontrolled manner (Bartha and Bossert, 1984). Oily sludges are applied to soil at rates to achieve approximately 5% hydrocarbon concentration in the upper 15–20 cm layer of the soil. Hydrocarbon concentrations above 10% are definitely inhibitory to the biodegradation process. This limit translates to approximately 100,000 liters hydrocarbon per ha, usually in 3–4 times as high sludge volume (Dibble and Bartha, 1979b). The soil pH is adjusted to a value between 7 and 8 or to the nearest practical value, using agricultural limestone. Nitrogen and phosphorus fertilizers are applied in ratios of hydrocarbon : N = 200 : 1 and hydrocarbon : P = 800 : 1. Adequate drainage is essential, but irrigation is necessary only in very arid and hot climates. Hydrocarbon degradation is optimal around 25–30°C (Dibble and Bartha, 1979b; Brown and Donnelly, 1983; Hogan *et al.*, 1989). Higher temperatures are inhibitory to biodegradation. This behavior seems to be particular to hydrocarbon degradation and differs from other organic materials that decompose faster in the moderately thermophilic range (45–65°C). Mixing and aeration is provided by periodic ploughing, discing, or rototilling.

The microbial community of soils usually includes a significant hydrocarbon-utilizing component, which readily increases in response to hydrocarbon contamination (Atlas *et al.*, 1981; Jensen, 1975; Llanos and Kjoller, 1976; Pinholt *et al*, 1979; Lode, 1986). A sandy loam soil with no previous oil exposure history was found to have about 30,000 hydrocarbon degraders per g (Song and Bartha, 1990). On exposure to jet fuel without or with fertilizer, this number increased by 3 and 5 orders of magnitude, respectively (Song and Bartha, 1990). The presence of indigenous microbial populations which are highly adapted to a particular soil environment would be expected to influence negatively the ability of seed microorganisms to survive and compete successfully. Therefore, soils are not widely considered to be amenable to improvements in rates of biodegradation through seeding alone (Atlas, 1977; Bossert and Bartha, 1984). Other potential problems associated with the inoculation of soils, as reviewed by Goldstein *et al.* (1985), include inadequate (i.e, extremely low) concentrations of the chemical of interest, the presence of inhibitory substances, predation, preferential metabolism of competing organic substrates, and insufficient movement of the seed organisms within the soil. Although Shailubhai (1986) reported some positive results after inoculating an oily sludge with the yeast *Rhodotorula rubra,* these experiments were conducted in laboratory fermentors in a liquid slurry phase and are difficult to project to landtreatment.

Hydrocarbon degradation rates are dependent on the degree of optimization and on climatic conditions. In a temperate climate and with optimization, 50,000 to 100,000 kg hydrocarbon may be degraded per ha during one growing season. Typically, hydrocarbon degradation is incomplete and high-molecular-weight saturates and polycyclic aromatics above five rings remain in the soil. These relatively immobile residues do not interfere with biodegradation upon reapplication of sludge (Bossert *et al.,* 1984) but phytotoxicity (Bossert and Bartha, 1985) and heavy metal accumulation limit the ultimate use options for the landtreatment sites.

Losses of hydrocarbons to the atmosphere during landtreatment are currently raising some regulatory concerns. Losses undoubtedly occur, although their proportion depends heavily on the product and the application conditions and are difficult to quantify reliably. Volatilization can be minimized though not eliminated by subsoil injection. In this process, blade one of the machine cuts a furrow, the sludge is dispensed into this furrow, and a second blade immediately covers the sludge with soil. A more expensive option is to move the landtreatment operation into polyethylene film-covered temporary buildings and treat the exhaust air by activated carbon or biofilters.

Undegraded hydrocarbons do not leach readily into the groundwater from the landtreatment sites (Dibble and Bartha, 1979c) and the environmental impact of properly operated sites appears to be minimal (Arora *et al.*, 1982). Currently, open-air landtreatment is practiced in the USA (Phung and Ross, 1978; American Petroleum Institute, 1980; Arora *et al.*, 1982), in various European countries (CONCAWE, 1980b; Shailubhai, 1986), in Brazil (Amaral, 1987; Tesan and Barbosa, 1987), and most likely in many other countries where documentation is not readily available. In its current or improved form, the practice is likely to continue.

5.2. Bioremediation of Hydrocarbon-Contaminated Surface Soils

Essentially the same process as landtreatment has been used also for bioremediation of surface soils contaminated by crude oil or by refined hydrocarbon fuels due to accidental spills and leaks. Because of their accidental nature, the location and rate of these contamination events cannot be controlled, but it is important to know whether or not biodegradation can be applied as an effective cleanup measure at such sites, and how to optimize the process. To distinguish the cleanup of accidental spills from deliberate hydrocarbon waste disposal, the term *bioremediation* will be used for this process.

Accidental contamination of soil with hydrocarbons occurs primarily through producing, transportation, and storage accidents, such as the blowout of producing wells, rupture of pipelines, overfilling or failure of storage tanks, road and railroad accidents involving tank cars, and, occasionally, deliberate but illegal dumping of hydrocarbon wastes (CONCAWE, 1980a; Bossert and Bartha, 1984; Bartha, 1986; Morgan and Watkinson, 1989). During the same period when landtreatment was studied and optimized, scientists either reacted to and studied accidental spills (McGill and Rowell, 1977; Odu, 1978; Dibble and Bartha, 1979a; Pinholt *et al.*, 1979; Jones and Greenfield, 1991) or deliberately created laboratory-scale or small outdoor oil product spills to study their fate and bioremediation potential (Song *et al.*, 1990; Wang and Bartha, 1990; Wang *et al.*, 1990).

The behavior of a hydrocarbon spill on land depends on the quantity and viscosity of the product, porosity and moisture content of the soil, the prevailing temperatures and weather conditions, the contour of the land, and the depth of the water table. Mathematical equations were developed to describe the horizontal and vertical movement of oil on land (Raisbeck and Mohtadi, 1974; Somers, 1974; McKay and Mohtadi, 1975; Vanlooke *et al.*, 1975; McGill *et al.*, 1981) but were found to have only modest predictive value for the actual behavior of a spill. Low-viscosity hydrocarbon distillates (gasoline, kerosine, jet fuel, diesel oil, No. 2 heating oil), i.e., most of the high-volume fuel products, infiltrate into soil rapidly and deeply, unless a very tight texture, water saturation, or frozen state of the soil prevent this. After infiltration, the product is subject to minimal or no evaporative and photodegradative losses, and thus undergoes less "weathering" than oil on a water surface. The spill contaminates an irregular column-shaped mass in the unsaturated (vadose) soil. When it reaches the water table, it forms a lens or "pancake" that may be concentric or may spread out in the direction of ground-water flow (Somers, 1974; Bossert and Bartha, 1984; Morgan and Watkinson, 1989). More viscous distillates such as No. 6 (residual) fuel oil and lubricating oils infiltrate into soil much more slowly, and unless buried later, stay close to the surface of the contaminated soil.

Emergency response to large terrestrial oil spills usually consists of directing the flow of oil into temporary catchments where it can be collected by vacuum trucks. Prior to any comprehensive remediation plans, one needs to assess what product and how much of it was spilled and what the characteristics of the contaminated site are (CON-CAWE, 1980a). If data on the spill are not available from records, the contaminant is determined by matching gas chromatograms of contaminated soil extracts to those of fresh or weathered fuel samples. The quantity of the spilled fuel may be estimated by determining, via core samples, the volume of the contaminated soil and the average concentration of the contaminant in the soil. The biodegradation characteristics of some fuels are available from the scientific literature (Song et al., 1990) or may be determined in preliminary studies.

If fuel and site characteristics are favorable, "on-site" bioremediation is an eco-nomically and environmentally sound decision. The contaminated soil is dug out and spread out in a 15- to 20-cm-thick layer. Although toxicity to microorganisms is rarely a problem in the case of hydrocarbon spills, if necessary, the contaminated soil can be "diluted" with uncontaminated soil to overcome any inhibitory effects of excessive contaminant concentrations (Matthews and Hastings, 1987). Bioremediation measures are the same as the ones described in the landtreatment of oily sludge, but since the aim is to restore the contaminated site to its "original condition," the cleanup goals are usually more ambitious.

As bioremediation is frequently criticized as a too slow and too incomplete ap-proach to soil cleanup, it is necessary to define and compare the cost-effectiveness of cleanup approaches. An essentially toxicological approach (Stockman and Dime, 1986) calculated residual benzene and PAH concentrations in soils contaminated by various petroleum products and a lifetime human exposure to soil by inhalation-ingestion. To achieve a less than one in a million cancer risk from this source, they calculated that hydrocarbon residues in soil should be reduced to 100 ppm or less. Acceptable car-cinogenic PAH and benzene residues were calculated to be 0.03 and 6.9 ppm, respec-tively. The authors point out large uncertainties concerning these calculations and under-standably lean toward the more conservative assumptions. Perhaps the greatest uncertainty is the biological availability of PAH residues in soil, an issue that was not addressed in this chapter. Yet soil adsorption was reported to reduce the biological availability of toxicants like tetrachloro-dibenzo-dioxin (TCDD) by more than 20-fold (Umbreit et al., 1986).

Another approach is to measure the actual residue levels that can be attained by bioremediation within a reasonable time period (one or two growing seasons) and to test at that time for remaining toxicants by chemical analysis and by bioassays. Laboratory and field experience shows that hydrocarbon levels in surface soils heavily contaminated by medium distillate fuels such as jet fuel, No. 2 heating oil, or diesel oil can be reduced by bioremediation to 500 ppm or less during one growing season (Dibble and Bartha, 1979a; Song et al., 1990; Wang and Bartha, 1990). Microtox and Ames tests, for acute toxicity and for mutagenic–carcinogenic activities, respectively, were at this time equal to those of uncontaminated soil. A total PAH concentration of about 1100 ppm, resulting from diesel oil contamination, was reduced to less than 2 ppm (Wang and Bartha, 1990; Wang et al., 1990).

The residues left by bioremediation are not well characterized and require further research. They appear to be at least in part high-molecular-weight, immobile, and low-toxicity waxy hydrocarbons with little environmental and health significance. However, if the fuel contained PAH compounds of five or more rings, these tend to be part of the residue. There is a pronounced inverse relationship between biodegradation and the PAH ring number (McKenna and Heath, 1976; Bossert and Bartha, 1986). For this reason, the bioremediation of materials high in five- to seven-ring PAH such as coal tar does not appear to be feasible at present.

While bioremediation is slow and has its limitations, the alternatives are more expensive and often environmentally inferior (Jones and Greenfield, 1991). Transport to "secure" chemical landfills displaces the problem in space and time at great expense, but does not resolve it permanently. Incineration destroys hydrocarbon residues more quickly and completely, but contributes to air pollution and leaves the incinerated and lifeless soil residue with which to deal. Consequently, bioremediation remains in many cases not only the least costly but also the environmentally least destructive cleanup alternative.

Investigating the bioremediation potential of common fuels, Song et al. (1990) concluded that the process is most suitable for the medium fuel distillates. While gasoline responds to bioremediation, in surface soils biodegradation cannot keep up with evaporation rates and most of the product is lost to the atmosphere. In laboratory experiments, Song et al. (1990) had very limited success with No. 6 (residual) fuel oil. However, Jones and Greenfield (1991) reported quite promising results in an on-site bioremediation effort in Florida. Soil contaminated by an average of 10,000 ppm of No. 6 fuel oil was treated with fertilizer and a commercial microbial inoculum. The soil was turned, cultivated, and kept moist by sprinklers when necessary. In 300 days about 90% of the containment was eliminated, leaving approximately 1000 ppm residue that included multiring PAHs. The inoculum without fertilizer was ineffective, but in combination with fertilizer it significantly improved degradation rates. Climate factors and photodegradation may have contributed to the relative success of their bioremediation effort with a difficult product.

An alternative to on-site landtreatment of contaminated soil is composting or treatment in solid-phase or slurry reactors. These types of bioremediations are usually more costly, but require less space and offer more opportunity for process control (CONCAWE, 1980a; Morgan and Watkinson, 1989). Oiled shoreline waste from a marine crude oil spill was successfully treated in an aerated compost heap (Labrie and Cyr, 1990). Oily sand, mud, and organic debris were placed on an impermeable sheet at a slight slope to allow leachate collection. A gravel layer below the oily material contained perforated pipes connected to a reversible air compressor. An activated carbon filter was placed in the air line when the compressor was operated in the suction mode in order to control the emission of volatiles. A sprinkler system kept the pile moist. This system was connected both to a collection sump and to a fermentor unit. In the aerated fermentor, the leachate was supplemented with nutrients, cosubstrates, and surfactants. After treatment, the microbially enriched liquid was redistributed over the compost heap via the sprinkler system. In addition to compactness, the advantage of this system was that it operated above ambient temperature in the cool Canadian climate. Addition of fertilizers, nutrients, and air could be regulated and optimized. After 180 days of operation, initial oil concentrations of up to 30% were reduced below 1%. At the stage, the residue was landfilled. During the same treatment, the contaminant's PAH content was reduced from an initial 283 ppm to 8 ppm.

Because of a strong setling tendency, slurry-type bioreactors for soil are difficult to design and to operate, but supernatants from soil washing processes can be effectively bioremediated in activated sludge-type aerobic sewage treatment units (CONCAWE, 1980a; Morgan and Watkinson, 1989). It should be possible to process hydrocarbon-contaminated soils in solid-phase composting-type bioreactors (Pavoni et al., 1975) but the typically very long residence times required for hydrocarbon biodegradation and the unfavorable effects of elevated temperature on the process at present do not favor this approach.

All reactor forms of on-site bioremediation require the excavation of the contaminated soil. Not infrequently, buildings, roads, utilities, etc. render excavation impractical. Also often the great depth of the contamination precludes the excavation approach. In these cases, in situ bioremediation remains the only possible remedy.

5.3. In Situ Bioremediation of Hydrocarbon-Contaminated Subsurface Soils and Aquifers

About 50% of the United States relies on groundwater for its potable water supply (Brown et al., 1985). This vital resource is increasingly threatened by pollution (Pye and Patrick, 1983). Leading causes of groundwater pollution are leaky underground fuel tanks. To outline the magnitude of this problem, it has been estimated that as many as 300,000 leaky underground fuel tanks now exist in the United States (Dowd, 1984; Feliciano, 1984; Brown et al., 1985). The majority of gas stations tanks are made of steel, have no corrosion protection, and have been in the ground for more than 20 years. Slow leaks may go undetected for years and all too often the tanks are tested only when fuel shows up in adjacent wells or basements. By then, the contamination of the aquifer is usually massive.

Catastrophic failures of aboveground tanks and pipeline, human error in overfilling or false connections (Vanlooke et al., 1975; Dibble and Bartha, 1979a; Wilson and Ward, 1987; Beraud et al., 1989; Jones and Greenfield, 1991) can cause massive contamination of subsurface soils and aquifers, especially when low-viscosity pollutants are involved. The petroleum fraction most frequently involved in groundwater pollution is gasoline (McKee et al., 1972; Jamison et al., 1975, 1976; Kramer, 1982; Yaniga and

Smith, 1984; Beraud *et al.*, 1989) followed by jet fuel (Ehrlich *et al.*, 1985; Hutchins *et al.*, 1991; Aelion and Bradley, 1991) and diesel oil (Kappeler and Wuhrmann, 1978a,b; Frankenberger *et al.*, 1989). Aromatic solvents such as benzene and alkylbenzenes, toluene and xylene (BTX), chlorinated aromatics, haloethanes and halomethanes leak into aquifers from landfills, manufacturing and waste storage sites (Kuhn *et al.*, 1985; Wilson *et al.*, 1986; Berwanger and Barker, 1988). The common feature in these pollution incidents was that the contaminated soil, because of its depth or because of surface structures, was inaccessible to excavation, yet the continued pollution of the aquifers was not tolerable and required intervention.

In situ bioremediation techniques for hydrocarbon-contaminated subsurface systems have been reviewed and evaluated in several reports (Vanlooke *et al.*, 1975; Raymond *et al.*, 1976b; Brown *et al.*, 1985; Wilson and Ward, 1987; Lee *et al.*, 1987; Wilson *et al.*, 1986; Thomas *et al.*, 1987). Aquifer bioremediation depends very strongly on local geological and hydrological conditions and the engineering aspects of the process are beyond the scope of this review. In broad outline, usually an attempt is made to isolate the contamination plume from wells and other sensitive areas. This may be accomplished by physical barriers such as cement, bentonite, or grout injection, or dynamically by pumping the polluted portion of the aquifer. In the latter case, groundwater flow is redirected toward rather than away from the contaminated plume, and thus the spreading of the contamination is prevented.

Besides containment, the pumping process recovers free-flowing hydrocarbon and contaminants dissolved in water. In theory, prolonged pumping could eventually flush out all the contaminant, but the solubility characteristics of hydrocarbons make reliance on physical flushing alone prohibitively slow and expensive. Hydrocarbons have much higher affinities to soil particles than water (Verstraete *et al.*, 1976). To clean an aquifer by simple water flushing may take 15–20 years and several thousand times the volume of water in the contaminated portion of the aquifer. Physical flushing may be facilitated by the addition of dispersants and emulsifiers through injection wells around the periphery of the contamination plume, while continuing to withdraw water from the center of the plume. However, the use of combined biodegradation and emulsification by hydrocarbon-utilizing microorganisms is usually more efficient and economic (Brown *et al.*, 1985; Thomas *et al.*, 1987; Beraud *et al.*, 1989).

The requirements for *in situ* hydrocarbon biodegradation on subsurface soils and aquifers are similar to those described in landtreatment and on-site bioremediation, but the means of providing these necessary conditions for enhanced biodegradation activity are much more difficult. Numbers and diversity of microorganisms in subsoil are typically much lower than in surface soils. Long lag periods prior to measurable microbial activity following the pollution event and the start of bioremediation are quite typical. Inoculation in such environments would have more theoretical foundation than in surface soils, but the selection of appropriate microorganisms for each task and their effective distribution in the aquifer to be treated are formidable problems. Clear-cut benefit of inoculation by nonindigenous but naturally occurring microorganisms has not been demonstrated convincingly (Lee and Ward, 1985). Jain and Sayler (1987) and Jain *et al.* (1987) discuss the possibility and the implications of using genetically engineered microorganisms in aquifer bioremediation. Although they are optimistic about such applications in the future, the present political and regulatory environment is not as yet ready for this practice. It is common and successful, however, to augment the *in situ* microbial numbers and activity of indigenous microorganisms in connection with aboveground treatment of recovered polluted water.

When a polluted aquifer is pumped in order to keep the pollution from spreading, the recovered water is supplemented with mineral nutrients (nitrogen and phosphorus) and aerated. The combination of biodegradation and air stripping frees the recovered water from the dissolved pollutants. This water, containing now substantial numbers of hydrocarbon-degrading microorganisms, is reinjected into the aquifer around the perimeter of the polluted plume. This "pump and treat" cleanup operation is then aided by the *in situ* activity of the injected microorganisms (Lee and Ward, 1985; Brown *et al.*, 1985; Thomas *et al.*, 1987).

To maximize *in situ* activity, prior to injection, the water may be supplemented with additional mineral nutrients and materials serving as electron sinks for hydrocarbon oxidation. Positively charged ammonium ions have low mobility in soil. Similarly, phosphates precipitate readily, and are also difficult to distribute effectively. Negatively charged nitrate ions have relatively high mobility in soil and, in addition to being mineral nutrients, could also serve as electron sinks (Ehrlich *et al.*, 1985). Although the biodegradation of some aromatic hydrocarbon is clearly stimulated under denitrifying conditions, in aquifer material contaminated with jet fuel, Hutchins *et al.* (1991) found an overall inhibitory effect on hydrocarbon degradation by nitrate. The cause for this phenomenon was not clear.

As discussed earlier, hydrocarbon biodegradation is very restricted under anaerobic conditions and the biggest problem of *in situ* bioremediation is to get sufficient oxygen into the contaminated aquifers. Because of the low water solubility of oxygen, hydrogen peroxide was found to be a useful agent for increasing dissolved oxygen in contaminated aquifers (Brown *et al.*, 1984; American Petroleum Institute, 1987; Thomas *et al.*, 1987; Lee *et al.*, 1987). The use of hydrogen peroxide for this purpose was first suggested by Raymond (1974) and Raymond *et al.* (1976c) who patented his process. With a lower frequency, ozone has also been employed for this purpose (Thomas *et al.*, 1987; Lee *et al.*, 1987). Rapid decomposition and oxidation of nontarget materials such as reduced iron and manganese are problems in the use of these oxidants.

Although oxygen is quite critical in initial oxidation of intact hydrocarbons, the resulting fatty acids can be degraded further by anaerobic mechanisms (Jobson *et al.*, 1979). Could one regulate the use of oxygen only for initial oxygenation of hydrocarbons, one could make much more efficient use of these relatively expensive chemicals. Unfortunately, such regulation is not possible at present; the oxidation of intermediates competes for oxygen very effectively and restricts oxidant availability for the metabolism of intact hydrocarbons.

Bioremediation of aquifers contaminated with halogenated aromatics, haloethanes, and halomethanes presents additional complex problems (Kuhn *et al.*, 1985; Wilson *et al.*, 1986; Berwanger and Barker, 1988). While some of these materials are dehalogenated anaerobically, others cannot serve as substrates under either aerobic or anaerobic conditions and are attacked only cometabolically in the presence of methane or toluene, and only under oxidative conditions.

The U.S. Coast Guard and the U.S. EPA performed two field evaluations of bioreclamation on fuel spills at the USCG Air Station at Traverse City, Michigan in which peroxide and mineral nutrients were injected into a spill of aviation gasoline (Wilson, 1991). Eleven gallons per minute with peroxide concentrations near 750 mg/liter were injected into a series of wells across the interval contaminated with gasoline. Clean water from another part of the aquifer was injected deep below the contaminated interval at 22 gallons/min in order to raise the water table and flood the entire vertical interval contaminated with gasoline. After 18 months of operation, the concentration of benzene in monitoring wells up to 100 feet from the injection wells was less than 0.1 μg/liter. The concentrations of the other alkylbenzenes were below 5 μg/liter in wells out to 50 feet from the injection wells. However, core material only 7 feet from the injection well still contained 700 mg/kg total petroleum hydrocarbons.

A spill of JP-4 was remediated with nitrate and mineral nutrients (Wilson, 1991). A study area 30 feet by 30 feet was flooded with 200 gallons per min of water from underneath the spill. The water took 8 hr to move across the contaminated interval, then a week to move to the large production wells that supplied water to the infiltration gallery above the study area. Unamended water was circulated for 2 months to bring the water and oil to chemical equilibrium. Then 10 mg/liter of nitrate as N was circulated for an additional 2 months. Benzene was brought below 0.1 mg/liter before nitrate was added. After addition of nitrate, the other alkylbenzenes were brought below 5 μg/liter.

The *in situ* bioremediation of aquifers is a relatively new and promising technique. Its difficulties are at present more in the engineering than in the microbiological area. If methods for distributing mineral nutrients and oxidants in aquifers can be improved, the full potential of microorganisms for the biodegradation of polluting hydrocarbons will be realized.

5.4. Bioremediation of Marine Oil Spills

The use of bioremediation for treating marine oil spills has recently been examined by an Officer of Technology Workshop (Office of Technology Assessment, 1991). The evidence for effective oil spill bioremediation in actual field applications presented at the workshop was scarce and sometimes of dubious scientific validity (Fox, 1991). In particular, the conclusion that seeding enhances oil biodegradation at sea is based on visual rather than statistically valid scientific analysis. The application of fertilizers to enhance degradation by as much as an order of magnitude, while initially also based largely on "visual science," now is supported by a body of valid analytical data from industry, government, and academic scientists.

On March 24, 1989 the tanker *Exxon Valdez* ran aground on Bligh Reef of Prince William Sound in Alaska, spilling approximately 40,000 tons of crude oil into the sound (United States Environmental Protection Agency, 1989; Kelso and Kendziorek, 1991). In the enclosed waters of the sound, the spill had a tremendous impact on beaches and wildlife (Maki, 1991).

The *Exxon Valdez* spill formed the basis for a major study on bioremediation and the largest application of this emerging technology (Pritchard, 1990). The initial approach to the cleanup of the oil spilled from the *Exxon Valdez* was physical. Washing of oiled shorelines with high-pressure water was expensive and cleaned shorelines became reoiled forcing recleaning. Bioremediation, therefore, was considered as a method to augment other cleanup procedures. The EPA and Exxon entered into an agreement to jointly explore the feasibility of using bioremediation. The project focused on determining whether nutrient augmentation could stimulate rates of biodegradation by the indigenous natural populations. Three type of nutrient supplementation were considered: water-soluble (23 : P garden fertilizer formulation), slow release (isobutylenediurea), and oleophilic (Inipol EAP 22 = oleic acid, urea, lauryl phosphate). Each fertilizer was tested in laboratory simulations (Tabak *et al.*, 1991) and in field demonstration plots (Glaser *et al.*, 1991) to show the efficacy of nutrient supplementation. Consideration was also given to potential adverse ecological effects, particularly eutrophication due to algal blooms and toxicity to fish and invertebrates.

In approximately 2–3 weeks, oil on the surfaces of cobble shorelines treated with Customblen (slow-release calcium and ammonium phosphate and ammonium nitrate within a polymerized vegetable oil coating) and Inipol EAP 22 was degraded so that shorelines were visibly cleaner than non-bioremediated shorelines (Pritchard and Costa, 1991). Decreases in the C-18 : phytane ratio occurred on the slow-release fertilizer-treated beach but to a lesser extent (approximately a 30% decrease from the original value in 4 weeks). Thus, the Inipol enhanced biodegradation to a greater extent than did the briquettes, accounting for the substantial visual difference in the treated beaches. The application of the oleophilic fertilizer produced very dramatic results, stimulating biodegradation so that the surfaces of the oil-blackened rocks on the shoreline turned white and were essentially oil-free within 10 days after treatment (Fox, 1989, 1990; Pritchard, 1990; Pritchard and Costa, 1991) (Fig. 1). The striking results strongly supported the idea that oil degradation in Prince William Sound was limited by the amounts of available nutrients and that fertilizer application was a useful bioremediation strategy.

The use of Inipol was approved for shoreline treatment and was used as a major part of the cleanup effort. A joint Exxon–EPA–State of Alaska monitoring effort followed the effectiveness of the bioremediation treatment which was estimated to increase the rates of biodegradation at least threefold. Tests demonstrated that fertilizer application sustained higher numbers of oil-degrading microorganisms in oiled shorelines and that rates of biodegradation were enhanced as evidenced by the chemical changes detected in recovered oil from treated and untreated reference sites (Chianelli *et al.*, 1991). Monitoring by a joint Exxon, EPA, and State of Alaska Department of Conservation team of the oil-degrading microbial populations and measuring the rates of oil degradation activities showed that a fivefold increase in rates of oil biodegradation typically followed fertilizer application (Prince *et al.*, 1990). Owing to its effectiveness, bioremediation became the major treatment method for removing oil pollutants from the impacted shorelines of Prince William Sound.

Despite sampling and interpretation complications resulting from the high vari-

Figure 1. Photograph showing results of Inipol application to a shoreline in Prince William Sound. The "white window" square in the photograph was treated with the oleophilic fertilizer 10 days earilier. While the surrounding untreated area remained black and oil-covered, the treated area was relatively free of oil. Tests indicated that simple physical removal was not responsible and that biological degradation of oil was occurring.

ability in oil distribution on the beaches, it was possible to show statistically that oil biodegradation (as measured by changes in residue weights and oil chemistry) was significantly greater on the beach treated with the fertilizer solution than it was on the control beach (Prince *et al.*, 1990; Pritchard and Costa, 1991). After 45 days, approximately three to four times more oil remained on the control tests beach than on the fertilizer solution-treated beach. This corresponded to an enhanced biodegradation rate of about two- to threefold. Results were similar on the Inipol–Customblen-treated beach except that statistically significant differences were more difficult to establish. However, it appeared that accelerated biodegradation (approximately a two- to three-fold increase) occurred early in the test when nutrient concentrations were highest. These results imply that fertilizer reapplication (maintaining nutrient concentrations at high levels for long periods) is important.

When subsurface oil was treated by oleophilic fertilizer in combination with a slow-release fertilizer (6–12 inches deep in the mixed sand and gravel), the oil was degraded to a greater extent compared to untreated reference beaches (Pritchard and Costa, 1991). However, the use of fertilizer solutions was the most effective nutrient application technique in terms of rate and extent of oil degradation but it was more operationally complex. Results from the use of fertilizer solutions unequivocally demonstrate that oil biodegradation rates in Prince William Sound were limited by the availability of nitrogen and phosphorus and that the clean appearance of rock surfaces following fertilizer bioremediation treatment was directly caused by biodegradation.

As a result of the EPA–Exxon project, bioremediation of oil-contaminated beaches was shown to be a safe cleanup technology; no adverse ecological effects were observed (Fox, 1990; Office of Technology Assessment, 1991). The addition of fertilizers caused no eutrophication, no acute toxicity to sensitive marine test species, and did not cause the release of undegraded oil residues from the beaches. The success of the field demonstration program has now set the stage for the consideration of bioremediation as a key component (but not the sole component) in any cleanup strategy developed for future oil spills.

Biotreatment of the *Mega Borg* spill off the Texas coast consisted of applying a seed culture with a secret catalyst produced by Alpha Corporation to the oil at sea (Mangan, 1990) and has led to more dubious conclusions (Fox, 1991; Office of Technology Assessment, 1991). Claims were made that the treatment was successful at completely removing the oil, but the effectiveness of the Alpha seeding to stimulate biodegradation has not been verified, nor has the effectiveness of the culture been confirmed by the EPA or NOAA in laboratory effectiveness of the culture been confirmed by the EPA or NOAA in laboratory tests. Without adequate scientific data and because the experimental bacterial seeding did not include controls, it is impossible to make conclusions that biodegradation was at all stimulated (Fox, 1991). The Texas General Land Office has reported that the use of Alpha on the *Mega Borg* spill and also on a spillage from the *Apex* barge that impacted the Marrow marsh was effective at removing significant amounts of oil (Mauro, 1990a,b; Mauro and Wynne, 1990). Independent observations indicated that treated oil changed in physical appearance and may have been emulsified as a result of addition of the Alpha product (D. Kennedy and H. Pritchard, personal communication). Chemical analyses on samples from impacted and reference sites failed to demonstrate that treatment with the Alpha product enhanced rates of petroleum biodegradation; no significant differences in C18:phytane ratios that would indicate biodegradation enhancement were detected between Alpha-treated and untreated sites (A. Mearns, personal communication). Thus, scientifically valid conclusions cannot be reached substantiating the effectiveness of seeding of open water spills. Equally true, however, is that no harmful effects occurred. Clearly well-designed and extensive experiments will be needed if the efficacy of seeding open water oil spills is ever to be resolved.

6. Concluding Remarks

Environmental rates of hydrocarbon degradation are limited by the enzymatic capabilities of the indigenous hydrocarbon-degrading microbial populations and by environmental factors, particularly concentrations of molecular oxygen, fixed forms of nitrogen, and phosphate. Bioremediation of oil pollutants involves overcoming the rate-limiting factors. Biodegradation of oily sludges and bioremediation of oil-contaminated sites has been achieved by oxygen addition—e.g., by tilling soils in landfarming and by adding hydrogen peroxide or pumping oxygen into oiled aquifers along with addition of nitrogen- and phosphorus-containing fertilizers. Seeding with a special microbial preparation was used to treat the Texas *Mega Borg* spill but the success of this treatment is ambiguous. Exxon successfully used bioremediation, principally based on addition of an oleophilic nitrogen and phosphorus fertilizer, to degrade oil in rocky shorelines impacted by the 1989 Alaskan oil spill. Bioremediation has become a major method employed in restoration of oil-polluted environments that makes use of natural microbial biodegradative activities.

References

Abbott, B. J., and Gledhill, W. G., 1971, The extracellular accumulation of metabolic products by hydrocarbon-degrading microorganisms, *Adv. Appl. Microbiol.* **14:**249–388.

Aelion, C. M., and Bradley, P. M., 1991, Aerobic biodegradation potential of subsurface microorganisms from jet fuel contaminated aquifer, *Appl. Environ. Microbiol.* **57:**57–63.

Amaral, S. P., 1987, Landfarming of oily wastes: Design and operation, *Water Sci. Technol.* **19:**75–86.

American Petroleum Institute, 1980, *Manual on Disposal of Petroleum Wastes,* American Petroleum Institute, Washington, D.C.

American Petroleum Institute, 1987, Field Study of Enhanced Subsurface Biodegradation of Hydrocarbons Using Hydrogen Peroxide as an Oxygen Source, American Petroleum Institute Publ. 4448, American Petroleum Institute, Washington, D.C.

Amund, O. O., and Igiri, C. O., 1990, Biodegradation of petroleum hydrocarbons under tropical estuarine conditions, *World J. Microbiol. Biotechnol.* **6:**255–262.

Anonymous, 1975, G. E. superbug created to clean up oil spills, *Sci. News* **180:**108.

Anonymous, 1989, Mishaps cause three oil spills off U.S., *Oil Gas J.* **87:**22.

Applied Biotreatment Association, 1989, *Case History Compendium,* Applied Biotreatment Association, Washington, D.C.

Applied Biotreatment Association, 1990, *The Role of Biotreatment of Oil Spills,* Applied Biotreatment Association, Washington, D.C.

Arora, H. S., Cantor, R. R., and Nemeth, J. C., 1982, Land treatment: A viable and successful method of treating petroleum industry wastes, *Environ. Int.* **7:**285–292.

Atlas, R. M., 1975, Effects of temperature and crude oil composition on petroleum biodegradation, *Appl. Microbiol.* **30:**396–403.

Atlas, R. M., 1977, Stimulated petroleum biodegradation, *Crit. Rev. Microbiol.* **5:**371–386.

Atlas, R. M., 1979, Measurement of hydrocarbon biodegradation potentials and enumeration of hydrocarbon-utilizing microorganisms using carbon-14 hydrocarbon-spiked crude oil, Special Technical Report from American Society for Testing and Materials, Philadelphia.

Atlas, R. M., 1981, Microbial degradation of petroleum hydrocarbons: An environmental perspective, *Microbiol. Rev.* **45:**180–209.

Atlas, R. M. (ed.), 1984, *Petroleum Microbiology,* Macmillan Co., New York.

Atlas, R. M., and Bartha, R., 1972a, Degradation and mineralization of petroleum by two bacteria isolated from coastal water, *Biotechnol. Bioeng.* **14:**297–308.

Atlas, R. M., and Bartha, R., 1972b, Degradation and mineralization of petroleum in seawater: Limitation by nitrogen and phosphorus, *Biotechnol. Bioeng.* **14:**309–317.

Atlas, R. M., and Bartha, R., 1972c, Biodegradation of petroleum in seawater at low temperatures, *Can. J. Microbiol.* **18**:1851–1855.

Atlas, R. M., and Bartha, R., 1973a, Inhibition by fatty acids of the biodegradation of petroleum, *Antonie van Leeuwenhoek J. Microbiol. Serol.* **39**:257–271.

Atlas, R. M., and Bartha, R., 1973b, Stimulated biodegradation of oil slicks using oleophilic fertilizers, *Environ. Sci. Technol.* **7**:538–541.

Atlas, R. M., and Bartha, R., 1973c, Effects of some commercial oil herders, dispersants and bacterial inocula on biodegradation of oil in seawater, in: *The Microbial Degradation of Oil Pollutants* (D. G. Ahearn and S. P. Meyers, eds.), Publ. No. LSU-SG-73-01, Center for Wetland Resources, Louisiana State University, Baton Rouge, pp. 283–289.

Atlas, R. M., and Bartha, R., 1973d, Abundance, distribution, and oil biodegradation potential of microorganisms in Raritan Bay, *Environ. Pollut.* **4**:291–300.

Atlas, R. M., and Bartha, R., 1973e, Fate and effects of oil pollution in the marine environment, *Residue Rev.* **49**:49–85.

Atlas, R. M., and Bartha, R., 1976, Biodegradation of oil on water surfaces, United States Patent 3939127.

Atlas, R. M., and Busdosh, M., 1976, Microbial degradation of petroleum in the Arctic, in: *Proceedings of the Third International Biodegradation Symposium* (J. M. Sharpley and A. M. Kaplan, eds.), Applied Science, London, pp. 79–86.

Atlas, R. M., and Pramer, D., 1990, Focus on bioremediation, *ASM News* **56**:7.

Atlas, R. M., and Schofield, E. A., 1975, Petroleum biodegradation in the Arctic, in: *Impact of the Use of Microorganisms on the Aquatic Environment* (A. W. Bourquin, D. G. Ahearn, and S. P. Meyers, eds.), EPA 660-3-75-001, Environmental Protection Agency, Corvallis, Oreg., pp. 183–198.

Atlas, R. M., Roubal, G., Bronner, A., and Haines, J., 1980a, Microbial degradation of hydrocarbons in mousse from IXTOC-1 Cruises, in: *Proceedings of Conference on Researcher/Pierce IXTOC-I Cruises,* National Oceanographic and Atmospheric Administration, Atlantic Oceanographic and Meteorological Laboratories, Miami, pp. 1–24.

Atlas, R. M., Sexstone, A., Gustin, P., Miller, O., Linkins, P., and Everett, K., 1980b, Biodegradation of crude oil by tundra soil microorganisms, in: *Proceedings of the Fourth International Biodeterioration Symposium* (T. A. Oxley, G. Becker, and D. Allsop, eds.), Pitman, London, pp. 21–28.

Atlas, R. M., Boehm, P. D., and Calder, J. A., 1981, Chemical and biological weathering of oil from the Amoco Cadiz oil spillage in the littoral zone, *Estuarine Coastal Mar. Sci.* **12**:589–608.

Austin, B., Calomiris, J. J., Walker, J. D., and Colwell, R. R., 1977a, Numerical taxonomy and ecology of petroleum degrading bacteria, *Appl. Environ. Microbiol.* **34**:35–44.

Austin, B., Colwell, R. R., Walker, J. D., and Calomiris, J. J., 1977b, The application of numerical taxonomy to the study of petroleum degrading bacteria isolated from the aquatic environment, *Dev. Ind. Microbiol.* **18**:685–696.

Azarowicz, R. M., 1973, Microbial degradation of petroleum, *Off. Gaz. US Patent Off.* **915**:1835.

Bailey, N. J. L., Jobson, A. M., and Rogers, M. A., 1973, Bacterial degradation of crude oil: Comparison of field and experimental data, *Chem. Geol.* **11**:203–221.

Ballerini, D., 1978, IFP process for protein production from paraffins, *Rev. Inst. Fr. Pet.* **33**:101–110.

Barnsley, E. A., 1975, The bacterial degradation of fluoranthane and benzo(a)pyrene, *Can. J. Microbiol.* **21**:1004–1008.

Bartha, R., 1986, Biotechnology of petroleum pollutant biodegradation, *Microb. Ecol.* **12**:155–172.

Bartha, R., and Atlas, R. M., 1973, Biodegradation of oil in seawater: Limiting factors and artificial stimulation, in: *The Microbial Degradation of Oil Pollutants* (D. G. Ahearn and S. P. Meyers, eds), Publ. No. LSU-SG-73-01, Center for Wetland Resources, Louisiana State University, Baton Rouge, pp. 147–152.

Bartha, R., and Atlas, R. M., 1977, The microbiology of aquatic oil spills, *Adv. Appl. Microbiol.* **22**:225–266.

Bartha, R., and Atlas, R. M., 1987, Transport and transformations of petroleum: Biological processes, in: *Long-term Environmental Effects of Offshore Oil and Gas Development* (F. Boesch and N. N. Rabalais, eds.), Elsevier Applied Science, New York, pp. 287–341.

Bartha, R., and Bossert, I., 1984, The treatment and disposal of petroleum wastes, in: *Petroleum Microbiology* (R. M. Atlas, ed.), Macmillan Co., New York, pp. 553–578.

Bazylinski, D. A., Wirsen, C. O., and Jannasch, H. W., 1989, Microbial utilization of naturally occurring hydrocarbons at the Guaymas basin hydrothermal vent site, *Appl. Environ. Microbiol.* **55:**2832–2836.

Beam, H. W., and Perry, J. J., 1973, Co-metabolism as a factor in microbial degradation of cycloparaffinic hydrocarbons, *Arch. Mikrobiol.* **91:**87–90.

Beam, H. W., and Perry, J. J., 1974a, Microbial degradation and assimilation of *n*-alkyl-substituted cycloparaffins, *J. Bacteriol.* **118:**394–399.

Beam, H. W., and Perry, J. J., 1974b, Microbial degradation of cycloparaffinic hydrocarbons via co-metabolism and commensalism, *J. Gen. Microbiol.* **82:**163–169.

Beardsley, T., 1989, No slick fix: Oil spill research is suddenly back in favor, *Sci. Am.* **261**(3):43.

Beraud, J.-F., Ducreux, J. D., and Gatellier, C., 1989, Use of soil–aquifer treatment in oil pollution control of underground waters, in: *Proceedings of the 1989 Oil Spill Conference,* American Petroleum Institute, Washington, D.C., pp. 53–59.

Bergstein, P. E., and Vestal, J. R., 1978, Crude oil biodegradation in Arctic tundra ponds, *Arctic* **31:**158–169.

Berridge, S. A., Dean, R. A., Fallows, R. G., and Fish, A., 1968, The properties of persistent oils at sea, in: *Scientific Aspects of Pollution of the Sea by Oil* (P. Hepple, ed.), Institute of Petroleum, London, pp. 2–11.

Bertrand, J. C., Rambeloarisoa, E., Rontani, J. F., Giusti, G., and Mattei, G., 1983, Microbial degradation of crude oil in sea water in continuous culture, *Biotechnol. Lett.* **5:**567–572.

Berwanger, D. J., and Barker, J. F., 1988, Aerobic biodegradation of aromatic and chlorinated hydrocarbons commonly detected in landfill leachate, *Water Pollut. Res. J. Can.* **23**(3):460–475.

Bluestone, M., 1986, Microbes to the rescue, *Chem. Week* **139**(17):34–35.

Bodennec, G. J., Desmarquest, P., Jensen, B., and Kantin, R., 1987, Evolution of hydrocarbons and the activity of bacteria in marine sediments contaminated with discharges of petroleum, *Int. J. Environ. Anal. Chem.* **29:**153–178.

Bossert, I., and Bartha, R., 1984, The fate of petroleum in soil ecosystems, in: *Petroleum Microbiology* (R. M. Atlas, ed.), Macmillan Co., New York, pp. 434–476.

Bossert, I., and Bartha, R., 1985, Plant growth in soils with a history of oily sludge disposal, *Soil Sci.* **140:**75–77.

Bossert, I., and Bartha, R., 1986, Structure–biodegradability relationships of polycyclic aromatic hydrocarbons in soil, *Bull. Environ. Contam. Toxicol.* **37:**490–495.

Bossert, I., Kachel, W. M., and Bartha, R., 1984, Fate of hydrocarbons during oily sludge disposal in soil, *Appl. Environ. Microbiol.* **47:**763–767.

Boylan, D. B., and Tripp, B. W., 1971, Determination of hydrocarbons in seawater extracts of crude oil and crude oil fractions, *Nature* **230:**44–47.

Bronchart, R. E. E., Carbon, J., Chanlier, A., Jillot, A. A. R., and Verstraete, W., 1985, A new approach in enhanced biodegradation of spilled oil: Development of an oil dispersant containing oleophilic nutrients, in: *Proceedings 1985 Oil Spill Conference,* February 25–28, Los Angeles, American Petroleum Institute, Washington, D.C., Publ. No. 4385, pp. 453–462.

Brown, E. J., and Braddock, J. F., 1990, Sheen screen: A miniaturized most probable number method for enumeration of oil-degrading microorganisms, *Appl. Environ. Microbiol.* **56:**3895–3896.

Brown, K. W., and Donnelly, K. S., 1983, Influence of soil environment on biodegradation of a refinery and a petrochemical sludge, *Environ. Pollut. Ser. B* **6:**119–132.

Brown, R. A., Norris, R. D., and Raymond, R. L., 1984, Oxygen transport in contaminated aquifers, in: *Proceedings of the Conference on Petroleum Hydrocarbons and Organic Chemicals in Ground*

Water—Prevention, Detection, and Restoration, National Water Well Association, Worthington, Ohio, pp. 441–450.

Brown, R. A., Norris, R. D., and Brubaker, G. R., 1985, Aquifer restoration with enhanced bioreclamation, *Pollut. Eng.* **17:**25–28.

Buckley, E. N., Pfaender, F. K., Kylber, K. L., and Ferguson, R. L., 1980, Response of the pelagic microbial community to oil from the Ixtoc I blowout: Model ecosystem studies, in: *Proceedings of a Symposium on Preliminary Results from the September 1979 RESEARCHER/PIERCE IXTOC-I Cruise,* National Oceanic and Atmospheric Administration, Boulder, Colo., pp. 563–586.

Burlage, R. S., Sayler, G. S., and Larimer, F., 1990, Monitoring of naphthalene catabolism by bioluminescence with *nah–lux* transcriptional fusions, *J. Bacteriol.* **172:**4749–4757.

Cain, R. B., 1980, Transformations of aromatic hydrocarbons, in: *Hydrocarbons in Biotechnology* (D. E. F. Harrison, I. J. Higgins, and R. Watkinson, eds.), Heyden, London, pp. 99–132.

Calomiris, J. J., Austin, B., Walker, J. D., and Colwell, R. R., 1976, Enrichment for estuarine petroleum-degrading bacteria using liquid and solid media, *J. Appl. Bacteriol.* **42:**135–144.

Caparello, D. M., and LaRock, P. A., 1975, A radioisotope assay for the quantification of hydrocarbon biodegradation potential in environmental samples, *Microb. Ecol.* **2:**28–42.

Cerniglia, C. E., 1984, Microbial transformation of aromatic hydrocarbons, in: *Petroleum Microbiology* (R. M. Atlas, ed.), Macmillan Co., New York, pp. 99–128.

Cerniglia, C. E., and Gibson, D. T., 1977, Metabolism of naphthalene by *Cunninghamella elegans, Appl. Environ. Microbiol.* **34:**363–370.

Cerniglia, C. E., and Gibson, D. T., 1978, Metabolism of naphthalene by cell extracts of *Cunninghamella elegans, Arch. Biochem. Biophys.* **186:**121–127.

Cerniglia, C. E., Hebert, R. L., Szaniszlo, P. J., and Gibson, D. T., 1978, Fungal transformation of naphthalene, *Arch. Microbiol.* **117:**135–143.

Chakrabarty, A. M., 1974, Microorganisms having multiple compatible degradative energy-generating plasmids and preparation thereof, *Off. Gaz. US Patent Off.* **922:**1224.

Chakrabarty, A. M., Chou, G., and Gunsalus, I. C., 1973, Genetic regulation of octane dissimilation plasmid in *Pseudomonas, Proc. Natl. Acad. Sci. USA* **70:**1137–1140.

Champagnat, A., 1964, Proteins from petroleum fermentations: A new source of food, *Impact* **14:**119–133.

Champagnat, A., and Llewelyn, D. A. B., 1962, Protein from petroleum, *New Sci.* **16:**612–613.

Chianelli, R. R., Aczel, T., Bare, R. E., George, G. N., Genowitz, M. W., Grossman, M. J., Haith, C. E., Kaiser, F. J., Lessard, R. R., Liotta, R., Mastracchio, R. L., Minak-Bernero, V., Prince, R. C., Robbins, W. K., Stiefel, E. I., Wilkinson, J. B., Hinton, S. M., Bragg, J. R., McMillan, S. J., and Atlas, R. M., 1991, Bioremediation technology development and application to the Alaskan spill, in: *Proceedings of the 1991 International Oil Spill Conference,* American Petroleum Institute, Washington, D.C., pp. 549–558.

Cobet, A. B., 1974, Hydrocarbonoclastic repository, in: *Progress Report Abstracts,* Microbiology Program, Office of Naval Research, Arlington, Va., p. 131.

Colwell, E. B. (ed.), 1971, *The Ecological Effects of Oil Pollution on Littoral Communities,* Applied Science, London.

Colwell, R. R., and Walker, J. D., 1977, Ecological aspects of microbial degradation of petroleum in the marine environment, *Crib. Rev. Microbiol.* **5:**423–445.

Colwell, R. R., Mills, A. L., Walker, J. D., Garcia-Rello, P., and Campos-P. V., 1978, Microbial ecology studies of the Metula spill in the Straits of Megallan, *J. Fish. Res. Board Can.* **35:**573–580.

CONCAWE, 1980a, *Disposal Techniques for Spilt Oil,* Rep. 9/80, CONCAWE, The Hague.

CONCAWE, 1980b, *Sludge Farming: A Technique for the Disposal of Oily Refinery Wastes,* Rep. 3/80, CONCAWE, The Hague.

Cook, F. D., and Westlake, D. W. S., 1974, *Microbial Degradation of Northern Crude Oils,* Information Canada Cat. No. R72–12774, Ontario, Canada.

Cooney, J. J., 1984, The fate of petroleum pollutants in fresh-water ecosystems, in: *Petroleum Microbiology* (R. M. Atlas, ed.), Macmillan Co., New York, pp. 399–434.

Cooney, J. J., 1990, Microbial ecology and hydrocarbon degradation, in: *The Alaska Story Symposium,* September 17–18, Cincinnati, OH.

Cooney, J. J., and Summers, R. J., 1976, Hydrocarbon-using microorganisms in three freshwater ecosystems, in: *Proceedings of the Third International Biodegradation Symposium* (J. M. Sharpley and A. M. Kaplan, eds.), Applied Science, London, pp. 141–156.

Cooney, C. L., Rha, C., and Tannenbaum, S. R., 1980, Single cell protein: Engineering, economics and utilization in foods, *Adv. Food Res.* **26:**1–52.

Cripps, R. E., and Watkinson, R. J., 1978, Polycyclic aromatic hydrocarbons: Metabolism and environmental aspects, in: *Developments in Biodegradation of Hydrocarbons—1* (J. R. Watkinson, ed.), Applied Science, London, pp. 113–134.

Davies, J. A., and Hughes, D. E., 1968, The biochemistry and microbiology of crude oil degradation, in: *The Biological Effects of Oil Pollution on Littoral Communities,* Supplement to Field Studies Vol. 2 (J. D. Carthy and D. R. Arthur, eds.), Classey, Hampton, Middlesex, England, pp. 139–144.

Davis, J. B., 1956, Microbial decomposition of hydrocarbons, *Ind. Eng. Chem.* **48:**1444–1448.

Dean-Raymond, D., and Bartha, R., 1975, The effect of iron on the biodegradation of petroleum in seawater, *Appl. Environ. Microbiol.* **31:**544–550.

Delaune, R. D., Hambrick, G. A., and Patrick, W. H., 1980, Degradation of hydrocarbons in oxidized and reduced sediments, *Mar. Pollut. Bull.* **11:**103–106.

Dibble, J. T., and Bartha, R., 1976, The effect of iron on the biodegradation of petroleum in sea-water, *Appl. Environ. Microbiol.* **31:**544–550.

Dibble, J. T., and Bartha, R., 1979a, Rehabilitation of oil-inundated agricultural land: A case history, *Soil. Sci.* **128:**56–60.

Dibble, J. T., and Bartha, R., 1979b, Effect of environmental parameters on the biodegradation of oil sludge, *Appl. Environ. Microbiol.* **37:**729–739.

Dibble, J. T., and Bartha, R., 1979c, Leaching aspects of oil sludge biodegradation in soil, *Soil Sci.* **127:**365–370.

Doe, K. G., and Wells, P. G., 1978, Acute toxicity and dispersing effectiveness of oil spill dispersants: Results of a Canadian oil dispersant testing program (1973 to 1977), in: *Chemical Dispersants for the Control of Oil Spills* (L. T. McCarthy, Jr., G. P. Lindblom, and H. F. Walter, eds.), American Society for Testing and Materials, Philadelphia, pp. 50–65.

Donoghue, N. A., Griffin, M., Morris, D. G., and Trudgill, P. W., 1976, The microbial metabolism of cyclohexane and related compounds, in: *Proceedings of the Third International Biodegradation Symposium* (J. M. Sharpley and A. M. Kaplan, eds.), Applied Science, London, pp. 43–56.

Dott, W., Feidieker, D., Kaempfer, P., Schleibinger, H., and Strechel, S., 1989, Comparison of autochthonous bacteria and commercially available cultures with respect to their effectiveness in fuel oil degradation, *J. Ind. Microbiol.* **4:**365–374.

Dowd, R. M., 1984, Leaking underground storage tanks, *Environ. Sci. Technol.* **18:**309–312.

Dunn, N. W., and Gunsalus, I. C., 1973, Transmissible plasmid coding early enzymes of naphthalene oxidation in *Pseudomonas putida, J. Bacteriol.* **114:**974–979.

Ehrlich, G. G., Schroeder, R. A., and Martin, P., 1985, *Microbial Populations in a Jet-Fuel Contaminated Aquifer in Tustin, California,* U.S. Geological Survey Report 85-335, Washington, D.C.

Fall, R. R., Brown, J. L., and Schaeffer, T. L., 1979, Enzyme recruitment allows the biodegradation of recalcitrant branched hydrocarbons by *Pseudomonas citronellolis, Appl. Environ. Microbiol.* **38:**715–722.

Fedorak, P. M., and Westlake, D. W. S., 1981, Degradation of aromatics and saturates in crude oil by soil enrichments, *Water Air Soil Pollut.* **16:**367–375.

Fedorak, P. M., and Westlake, D. W. S., 1981b, Microbial degradation of aromatics and saturates in Prudhoe Bay crude oil as determined by glass capillary gas chromatography, *Can. J. Microbiol.* **27:**432–443.

Feliciano, D., 1984, Leaking underground storage tanks: A potential environmental problem, *Congressional Research Service Report,* Library of Congress, Washington, D.C.

Ferris, J. P., MacDonald, L. H., Patrie, M. A., and Martin, M. A., 1976, Aryl hydrocarbon hydroxylase activity in the fungus *Cunninghamella bainierii*. Evidence of the presence of cytochrome P450, *Arch. Biochem. Biophys.* **175**:443–452.

Floodgate, G. D., 1973, A threnody concerning the biodegradation of oil in natural water, in: *The Microbial Degradation of Oil Pollutants* (D. G. Ahearn and S. P. Meyers, eds.), Publ. No. LSU-SG-73-01, Center for Wetland Resources, Louisiana State University, Baton Rouge, pp. 17–24.

Floodgate, G. D., 1979, Nutrient limitation, in: *Microbial Degradation of Pollutants in Marine Environments* (A. W. Bourquin and P. H. Pritchard, eds.), EPA-66019-79-012, Environmental Research Laboratory, Gulf Breeze, Fla., pp. 107–119.

Floodgate, G., 1984, The fate of petroleum in marine ecosystems, in: *Petroleum Microbiology* (R. M. Atlas, ed.), Macmillan Co., New York, pp. 355–398.

Foght, J. M., Fedorak, P. M., and Westlake, D. W., 1990, Mineralization of ^{14}C-hexadecane and ^{14}C-phenanthrene in crude oil: Specificity among bacterial isolates, *Can. J. Microbiol.* **36**:169–175.

Foster, J. W., 1962a, Bacterial oxidation of hydrocarbons, in: *Oxygenases* (O. Hayaishi, ed.), Academic Press, New York, pp. 241–271.

Foster, J. W., 1962b, Hydrocarbons as substrates for microorganisms, *Antonie van Leeuwenhoek J. Microbiol. Serol.* **28**:241–274.

Fox, J. E., 1989, Native microbes role in Alaska cleanup, *Bio/Technology* **7**:852.

Fox, J. E., 1990, More confidence about degrading work, *Bio/Technology* **8**:604.

Fox, J. E., 1991, Confronting doubtful oil cleanup data, *Bio/Technology* **9**:14.

Francke, H. C., and Clark, F. E., 1974, Disposal of oil wastes by microbial assimilation, Report Y-1934, U.S. Atomic Energy Commission, Washington, D.C.

Frankenberger, W. T., Jr., Emerson, K. D., and Turner, D. W., 1989, *In situ* bioremediation of an underground diesel fuel spill—a case history, *Environ. Manage.* **13**(3):325–332.

Frankenfeld, J. W., 1973, Factors governing the fate of oil at sea; variations in the amounts and types of dissolved or dispersed materials during the weathering process, in: *Proceedings of Joint Conference on Prevention and Control of Oil Spills*, pp. 485–495, American Petroleum Institute, Washington, D.C., pp. 485–495.

Friello, D. A., Mylroie, J. R., and Chakrabarty, A. M., 1976, Use of genetically-engineered multiplasmid microorganisms for rapid degradation of fuel hydrocarbons, in: *Proceedings of the Third International Biodegradation Symposium* (J. M. Sharpley and A. M. Kaplan, eds.), Applied Science, London, pp. 205–214.

Gatellier, C. R., 1971, Les facteurs limitant la biodegradation des hydrocarbures dans l'epuration des eaux, *Chim. Ind. (Paris)* **104**:2283–2289.

Gatellier, C. R., Oudin, J. L., Fusey, P., Lacase, J. C., and Priou, M. L., 1971, Experimental exosystems to measure fate of oil spills dispersed by surface active products, in: *Proceedings of Joint Conference on Prevention and Control of Oil Spills*, American Petroleum Institute, Washington, D.C., pp. 497–507.

Gibbs, C. F., Pugh, K. B., and Andrews, A. R., 1975, Quantitative studies on marine biodegradation of oil. II. Effect of temperature, *Proc. R. Soc. London Ser. B* **188**:83–94.

Gibson, D. T., 1968, Microbial degradation of aromatic compounds, *Science* **161**:1093–1097.

Gibson, D. T., 1971, The microbial oxidation of aromatic hydrocarbons, *Crit. Rev. Microbiol.* **1**:199–223.

Gibson, D. T., 1975, Oxidation of the carcinogens benzo(a)pyrene and benzo(a)anthracene to dihydrodiols by a bacterium, *Science* **189**:295–297.

Gibson, D. T., 1977a, Microbial degradation of polycyclic aromatic hydrocarbons, in: *Proceedings of the Third International Biodegradation Symposium* (J. M. Sharpley and A. M. Kaplan, eds.), Applied Science, London, pp. 57–66.

Gibson, D. T., 1977b, Biodegradation of aromatic petroleum hydrocarbons, in: *Fate and Effects of Petroleum Hydrocarbons in Marine Ecosystems and Organisms* (D. Wolfe, ed.), Pergamon Press, Elmsford, N.Y., pp. 36–46.

Gibson, D. T., and Yeh, W. K., 1973, Microbial degradation of aromatic hydrocarbons, in: *The Microbial Degradation of Oil Pollutants* (D. G. Ahearn and S. P. Meyers, eds.), Publ. LSU-SG-73-01, Center for Wetland Resources, Louisiana State University, Baton Route, pp. 33–38.

Glaser, J. A., Venosa, A. D., and Opatken, E. J., 1991, Development and evaluation of application techniques for delivery of nutrients to contaminated shoreline in Prince William Sound, in: *Proceedings of the 1991 International Oil Spill Conference*, American Petroleum Institute, Washington, D.C., pp. 559–562.

Goldstein, R. M., Mallory, L. M., and Alexander, M., 1985, Reasons for possible failure of inoculation to enhance biodegradation, *Appl. Environ. Microbiol.* **50:**977–983.

Grbic-Gallic, D., and Vogel, T. M., 1987, Transformation of toluene and benzene by mixed methanogenic-cultures, *Appl. Environ. Microbiol.* **53:**254–260.

Gregorio, F. M., 1991, Key environmental factors to consider in the biotreatment of oil spills, *Genet. Eng. News* **Jan:**3–4.

Gudin, C., and Syratt, W. J., 1975, Biological aspects of land rehabilitation following hydrocarbon contamination, *Environ. Pollut.* **8:**107–112.

Guire, P. E., Friede, J. D., and Gholson, R. K., 1973, Production and characterization of emulsifying factors from hydrocarbonoclastic yeast and bacteria, in: *The Microbial Degradation of Oil Pollutants* (D. G. Ahearn and S. P. Meyers, eds.), Publ. No. LSU-SG-73-01, Center for Wetland Resources, Louisiana State University, Baton Rouge, pp. 229–231.

Gunkel, W., 1967, Experimentell-okologische Untersuchungen uber die limitierenden Faktoren des mikrobiellen Olabbaues in marinen Milieu, *Helgol. Wiss. Meeresunters.* **15:**210–224.

Hagar, R., 1989, Huge cargo of North Slope oil spilled, *Oil Gas J.* **87:**26–27.

Haines, J. R., and Alexander, M., 1974, Microbial degradation of high-molecular weight alkanes, *Appl. Microbiol.* **28:**1084–1085.

Haines, J. R., and Atlas, R. M., 1982, *In situ* microbial degradation of Prudhoe Bay crude oil in Beaufort Sea sediment, *Mar. Environ. Res.* **7:**91–102.

Hambrick, G. A., III, Delaune, R. D., and Patrick, W. H. Jr., 1980, Effect of estuarine sediment pH and oxidation–reduction potential on microbial hydrocarbon degradation, *Appl. Environ. Microbiol.* **40:**365–369.

Harrison, W., Winnik, M. A., Kwong, P. T. U., and Mackay, D., 1975, Crude oil spills: Disappearance of aromatic and aliphatic components from small sea-surface slicks, *Environ. Sci. Technol.* **9:**231–234.

Hatch, R. T., 1975, Fermenter design, in: *Single Cell Protein II* (S. R. Tannenbaum and D. I. C. Wang, eds.), MIT Press, Cambridge, Mass., pp. 46–68.

Heitkamp, M. A., and Cerniglia, C. E., 1989, Polycyclic aromatic degradation by a *Mycobacterium* sp. in microcosms containing sediment and water from a pristine ecosystem, *Appl. Environ. Microbiol.* **55:**1968–1973.

Heitkamp, M. A., Freeman, J. P., Miller, D. W., and Cerniglia, C. E., 1988, Pyrene degradation by a *Mycobacterium* species: Identification of ring oxidation and ring fission products, *Appl. Environ. Microbiol.* **54:**2556–2565.

Herbes, S. E., and Schwall, L. R., 1978, Microbial transformation of polycyclic aromatic hydrocarbons in pristine and petroleum-contaminated sediments, *Appl. Environ. Microbiol.* **35:**306–316.

Higgins, I. J., and Gilbert, P. D., 1978, The biodegradation of hydrocarbons, in: *The Oil Industry and Microbial Ecosystems* (K. W. A. Chater and H. J. Somerville, eds.), Hayden, London, pp. 80–117.

Hogan, J. A., Toffoli, G. R., Miller, F. C., Hunter, J. V., and Finstein, M. S., 1989, Composting physical model demonstration: Mass balance of hydrocarbon and PCBs, in: *Physicochemical and Biological Detoxification of Hazardous Wastes* (Y. C. Wu, ed.), Vol. 2, Technomic, Lancaster, Pa., pp. 742–758.

Hopper, D. J., 1978, Microbial degradation of aromatic hydrocarbons, in: *Developments in Biodegradation of Hydrocarbons—1* (J. R. Watkinson, ed.), Applied Science, London, pp. 85–112.

Horowitz, A., and Atlas, R. M., 1977, Continuous open flow-through system as a model for oil degradation in the Arctic Ocean, *Appl. Environ. Microbiol.* **33**:647–684.

Horowitz, A., and Atlas, R. M., 1980, Microbial seeding to enhance petroleum hydrocarbon biodegradation in aquatic Arctic ecosystems, in: *Proceedings of the Fourth International Biodeterioration Symposium* (T. A. Oxley, G. Becker, and D. Allsopp, eds.), Pitman, London, pp. 15–20.

Huddleston, R. L., and Cresswell, L. W., 1976, Environmental and nutritional constraints of microbial hydrocarbon utilization in the soil, in: *Proceedings of the 1975 Engineering Foundation Conference: The Role of Microorganisms in the Recovery of Oil*, NSF/RANN, Washington, D.C., pp. 71–72.

Huddleston, R. L., and Meyers, J. D., 1978, Treatment of refinery oily wastes by landfarming, *Paper presented at the 85th National Meeting of AICHE*, Philadelphia, American Institute of Chemical Engineers, New York.

Hutchins, S. R., Sewell, G. W., Kovacs, D. A., and Smith, G. A. 1991, Biodegradation of aromatic hydrocarbons by aquifer micro-organisms under denitrifying conditions, *Environ. Sci. Technol.* **25**:68–76.

Jain, R. K., and Sayler, G. S., 1987, Problems and potential for *in situ* treatment of environmental pollutants by engineered microorganisms, *Microbiol. Sci.* **4**:59–63.

Jain, R. K., Sayler, G. S., Wilson, J. T., Houston, L., and Pacia, D., 1987, Maintenance and stability of introduced genotypes in groundwater aquifer material, *Appl. Environ. Microbiol.* **53**:996–1002.

Jamison, V. M., Raymond, R. L., and Hudson, J. O., Jr., 1975, Biodegradation of high-octane gasoline in groundwater, *Dev. Ind. Microbiol.* **16**:305–312.

Jamison, V. M., Raymond, R. L., and Hudson, J. O., 1976, Biodegradation of high-octane gasoline, in: *Proceedings of the Third International Biodegradation Symposium* (J. M. Sharpley and A. M. Kaplan, eds.), Applied Science, London, pp. 187–196.

Jensen, V., 1975, Bacterial flora of soil after application of oily waste, *Oikos* **26**:152–158.

Jobson, A., McLaughlin, M., Cook, F. D., and Westlake, D. W. S., 1974, Effect of amendments on the microbial utilization of oil applied to soil., *Appl. Microbiol.* **27**:166–171.

Jobson, A., Cook, F. D., and Westlake, D. W. S., 1979, Interaction of aerobic and anaerobic bacteria in petroleum biodegradation, *Chem. Geol.* **24**:355–365.

Jones, M., and Greenfield, J. H., 1991, In situ comparison of bioremediation methods for a Number 6 residual fuel oil spill in Lee County, Florida, in: *Proceedings of the 1991 International Oil Spill Conference*, pp. 533–540, American Petroleum Institute, Washington, D.C., pp. 533–540.

Kanazawa, M., 1975, Production of yeast from n-paraffins, in: *Single Cell Protein*, vol. 2 (S. R. Tannenbaum and D. I. C. Wang, eds.), MIT Press, Cambridge, Mass., pp. 438–453.

Kappeler, T., and Wuhrmann, K., 1978a, Microbial degradation of the water-soluble fraction of gas oil—I, *Water Res.* **12**:327–334.

Kappeler, T., and Wuhrmann, K., 1978b, Microbial degradation of the water-soluble fraction of gas oil—II. Bioassays with pure strains, *Water Res.* **12**:335–342.

Kator, H., 1973, Utilization of crude oil hydrocarbons by mixed cultures of marine bacteria, in: *The Microbial Degradation of Oil Pollutants* (D. G. Ahearn and S. P. Meyers, eds.), Publ. No. LSU-SG-73-01, Center for Wetland Resources, Louisiana State University, Baton Route, pp. 47–66.

Kator, H., and Herwig, R., 1977, Microbial responses after two experimental oil spills in an eastern coasts plain estuarine ecosystem, in: *Proceedings of the 1977 Oil Spill Conference*, American Institute of Petroleum, Washington, D.C., pp. 517–522.

Kator, H., Oppenheimer, C. H., and Miget, R. J., 1971, Microbial degradation of a Louisiana crude oil in closed flasks and under simulated field conditions, in: *Joint Conference on Prevention and Control of Oil Spills*, American Petroleum Institute, Washington, D.C., pp. 287–296.

Kator, H., Miget, R. J., and Oppenheimer, C. H., 1972, Utilization of paraffin hydrocarbons in crude oil by mixed cultures of marine bacteria, in: *Symposium on Environmental Conservation*, Paper No. SPE 4206, Society of Petroleum Engineers, Dallas.

Keck, J., Sims, R. C., Coover, M., Park, K., and Symons, B., 1989, Evidence for cooxidation of polynuclear aromatic hydrocarbons in soil, *Water Res.* **23**:1467–1476.

Kelso, D. D., and Kendziorek, M., 1991, Alaska's response to the Exxon Valdez oil spill, *Environ. Sci. Technol.* **25**:16–23.

Kennicutt, M. C., 1990, Oil spillage in Antartica, *Environ. Sci. Technol.* **24**:620–624.

Kennicutt, M. C., Brooks, J. M., Atlas, E. L., and Giam, C. S., 1988, Symposium on Toxic Chemicals and Aquatic Life: Research and Management, *Aquat. Toxicol.* **11**:191–212.

Kincannon, C. B., 1972, Oily waste disposal by soil cultivation process, EPA-R2-72-100, Environmental Protection Agency, Washington, D.C.

King, D. H., and Perry, J. J., 1975, The origin of fatty acids in the hydrocarbon-utilizing microorganism, *Mycobacterium vaccae, Can. J. Microbiol.* **21**:85–89.

Kinney, P. J., Button, D. K., and Schell, D. M., 1969, Kinetics of dissipation and biodegradation of crude oil in Alaska's Cook Inlet, in: *Proceedings of 1969 Joint Conference on Prevention and Control of Oil Spills,* American Petroleum Institute, Washington, D.C., pp. 333–340.

Klug, M. J., and Markovetz, A. J., 1967a, Degradation of hydrocarbons by members of the genus *Candida, J. Bacteriol.* **93**:1847–1852.

Klug, M. J., and Markovetz, A. J., 1967b, Thermophilic bacteria isolated on *n*-tetradecane, *Nature* **215**:1082–1083.

Kramer, W. H., 1982, Ground-water pollution from gasoline, *GWMR* **(2)**(2):18–22.

Kuhn, E. P., Colberg, P. J., Schnoor, J. L., Wanner, O., Zehnder, A. J. B, and Schwartzenbach, R. P., 1985, Microbial transformations of substituted benzenes during infiltration of river water to groundwater: Laboratory column studies, *Environ. Sci. Technol.* **19**:961–968.

Labrie, P., and Cyr, B., 1990, Biological remediation of shoreline oily waste from marine spills, in: *Proceedings of the Thirteenth Annual Arctic and Marine Oil Spill Program Technical Seminar,* Environment Canada, Ottawa, pp. 387–389.

LaDousse, A., and Tramier, B., 1991, Results of 12 years of research in spilled oil bioremediation: Inipol EAP 22, in: *Proceedings of the 1991 International Oil Spill Conference,* American Petroleum Institute, Washington, D.C., pp. 577–581.

LaDousse, A., Tallec, C., and Tramier, B., 1987, Progress in enhanced oil degradation, in: *Proceedings of the 1987 Oil Spill Conference,* Abstract 142, American Petroleum Institute, Washington, D.C.

Leahy, J. G., and Colwell, R. R., 1990, Microbial degradation of hydrocarbons in the environment, *Microbiol. Rev.* **54**(3):305–315.

Lee, K., and Levy, E. M., 1987, Enhanced biodegradation of a light crude oil in sandy beaches, in: *Proceedings of the 1987 Oil Spill Conference,* American Petroleum Institute, Washington, D.C., pp. 411–416.

Lee, K., and Levy, E. M., 1989a, Enhancement of the natural biodegradation of condensate and crude oil on beaches of Atlantic Canada, in: *Proceedings of the 1989 Oil Spill Conference,* American Petroleum Institute, Washington, D.C., pp. 479–486.

Lee, K., and Levy, E. M., 1989b, Biodegradation of petroleum in the marine environment and its enhancement, in: *Aquatic Toxicology and Water Quality Management,* Wiley, New York, pp. 217–243.

Lee, K., and Levy, E. M., 1991, Bioremediation: Waxy crude oils stranded on low-energy shorelines, in: *Proceedings of the 1991 International Oil Spill Conference,* American Petroleum Institute, Washington, D.C., pp. 541–547.

Lee, M. D., and Ward, C. H., 1985, Biological methods for the restoration of contaminated aquifers, *Environ. Toxicol. Chem.* **4**:743–750.

Lee, M. D., Wilson, J. T., and Ward, C. H., 1987, *In situ* restoration techniques for aquifers contaminated with hazardous wastes, *J. Hazard. Mater.* **14**:71–82.

Lee, R. F., and Ryan, C., 1976, Biodegradation of petroleum hydrocarbons by marine microbes, in:

Proceedings of the Third International Biodegradation Symposium (J. M. Sharpley and A. M. Kaplan, eds.), Applied Science, London, pp. 119–126.

Lehtomake, M., and Niemela, S., 1975, Improving microbial degradation of oil in soil, *Ambio* **4:**126– 129.

LePetit, J., and Barthelemy, M. H., 1968, Les hydrocarbures en mer: le probleme de l'epuration des zones littorales par les microorganismes, *Ann. Inst. Pasteur Paris* **114:**149–158.

LePetit, J., and N'Guyen, M.-H., 1976, Besoins en phosphore des bacteries metabolisant les hydrocarbures en mer, *Can. J. Microbiol.* **22:**1364–1373.

Llanos, C., and Kjoller, A., 1976, Changes in the flora of soil fungi following oil waste application, *Oikos* **27:**377–382.

Lode, A., 1986, Changes in the bacterial community after application of oily sludge to soil, *Appl. Microbiol. Biotechnol.* **25:**295–299.

McAuliffe, C., 1966, Solubility in water of paraffin, cycloparaffin, olefin, acetylene, cycloolefin, and aromatic hydrocarbons, *J. Phys. Chem.* **70:**1267–1275.

McGill, W. B., and Rowell, M. J., 1977, The reclamation of agricultural soils after oil spills: I. Research, in: *Publication No. M-77-11* (J. A. Toogood, ed.), Alberta Institute of Pedology, Edmonton, Canada, pp. 69–132.

McGill, W. B., Rowell, M. J., and Westlake, D. W. S., 1981, Biochemistry, ecology, and microbiology of petroleum components in soil, in: *Soil Biochemistry,* Vol. 5 (E. A. Paul and J. N. Ladd, eds.), Dekker, New York, pp. 229–296.

MacKay, D., and Mohtadi, M., 1975, The area affected by oil spills on land, *Can. J. Chem. Eng.* **53:**140–143.

McKee, J. E., Laverty, F. B., and Hertel, R. M., 1972, Gasoline in ground water, *J. Water Pollut. Control Fed.* **44:**293–302.

McKenna, E. J., and Heath, R. D., 1976, *Biodegradation of Polynuclear Aromatic Hydrocarbon Pollutants by Soil and Water Microorganisms,* WRC Res. Rep. No. 113, University of Illinois, Urbana.

McKenna, E. J., and Kallio, R. E., 1964, Hydrocarbon structure: Its effect on bacterial utilization of alkanes, in: *Principles and Applications in Aquatic Microbiology* (H. Heukelian and N. C. Dondero, eds.), Wiley, New York, pp. 1–14.

McKenna, E. J., and Kallio, R. E. 1965, The biology of hydrocarbons, *Annu. Rev. Microbiol.* **19:**183– 208.

McKenna, E. J., and Kallio, R. E., 1971, Microbial metabolism of the isoprenoid alkane, pristane, *Proc. Natl. Acad. Sci. USA* **68:**1552–1554.

Maki, A. M., 1991, The Exxon Valdez oil spill: Initial environmental impact assessment, *Environ. Sci. Technol.* **25:**24–29.

Mangan, K. S., 1990, University of Texas microbiologist seeks to persuade skeptical colleagues that bacteria could be useful in cleaning up major oil spills, *Chron. Higher Educ.* **37**(3)**:**A5–A9.

Markovetz, A. J., 1971, Subterminal oxidation of aliphatic hydrocarbons by microorganisms, *Crit. Rev. Microbiol.* **1:**225–237.

Maron, D. M., and Ames, B. N., 1983, Revised methods for the *Salmonella* mutagenicity test, *Mutat. Res.* **113:**173–215.

Mateles, R. I., Baruah, J. N., and Tannenbaum, S. R., 1967, Growth of a thermophilic bacteria on hydrocarbons: A new source of single-cell protein, *Science* **157:**1322–1323.

Mattei, G., Rambeloarson, E., Giusti, G., Rontani, G. F., and Bertrand, J. C., 1986, Fermentation procedure of a crude oil in continuous culture on seawater, *Appl. Microbiol. Biotechnol.* **23:**302– 304.

Matthews, E., and Hastings, L., 1987, Evaluation of toxicity test procedure for screening treatability potential of waste in soil, *Toxicity Assessment* **2:**265–281.

Maunder, B. R., and Waid, J. S., 1973, Disposal of waste oil by land spreading, in: *Proceedings of the*

Pollution Research Conference, Wairakei, New Zealand, Information Series No. 97, New Zealand Department of Scientific and Industrial Research, Wellington, pp. 142–160.

Maunder, B. R., and Waid, J. S., 1975, Disposal of waste oil by land spreading, in: *Proceeding of the Third International Biodeterioration Symposium,* University of Rhode Island, Kingston, XXV-5.

Mauro, G., 1990a, Combating oil spills along the Texas coast: A report on the effects of bioremediation, Paper presented at the Bioremediation Symposium Oct. 9, Lamar University, Beaumont, Tex.

Mauro, G., 1990b, Mega Borg spill off the Texas coast: An open water bioremediation test, Paper presented at the Bioremediation symposium Oct. 9, Lamar University, Beaumont, Tex.

Mauro, G., and Wynne, B. J., 1990, *Mega Borg Oil Spill: An Open Water Bioremediation Test,* Texas General Land Office, Austin.

Miller, R. M., and Bartha, R., 1989, Evidence from liposome encapsulation for transport-limited microbial metabolism of solid alkanes, *Appl. Environ. Microbiol.* **55:**269–274.

Miller, T. L., and Johnson, M. J., 1966, Utilization of normal alkanes by yeasts, *Biotechnol. Bioeng.* **8:**549–565.

Morgan, P., and Watkinson, R. J., 1989, Hydrocarbon biodegradation in soils and methods for soil biotreatment, *CRC Crit. Rev. Biotechnol.* **8**(4):305–333.

Mulkins-Philips, G. J., and Stewart, J. E., 1974, Effect of four dispersants on biodegradation and growth of bacteria on crude oil, *Appl. Microbiol.* **28:**547–552.

National Academy of Sciences, 1975, Petroleum in the marine environment, National Academy of Sciences, Washington, D.C.

National Academy of Sciences, 1985, Oil in the sea—inputs, fates, and effects, National Academy Press, Washington, D.C.

O'Brien, P. Y., and Dixon, P. S., 1976, The effects of oil and oil components on algae: A review, *Br. Phycol. J.* **11:**115–142.

Odu, C. T. I., 1978, The effect of nutrient application and aeration on oil degradation in soil, *Environ. Pollut.* **15:**235–240.

Office of Technology Assessment, 1991, *Bioremediation for Marine Oil Spills,* United States Congress, Washington, D.C.

Olivieri, R. P., Bacchin, P., Robertiello, A., Oddo, N., Degen, L., and Tonolo, A., 1976, Microbial degradation of oil spills enhanced by a slow-release fertilizer, *Appl. Environ. Microbiol.* **31:**629–634.

Olivieri, R., Robertiello, A., and Degen, L., 1978, Enhancement of microbial degradation of oil pollutants using lipophilic fertilizers, *Mar. Pollut. Bull.* **9:**217–220.

Ooyama, J., and Foster, J. W., 1965, Bacterial oxidation of cycloparaffinic hydrocarbons, *Antonie van Leeuwenhoek J. Microbiol. Serol.* **31:**45–65.

Pavoni, J. L., Heer, J. E., Jr., and Hagerty, D. J., 1975, *Handbook of Solid Waste Disposal, Materials and Energy Recovery,* Van Nostrand–Reinhold, Princeton, N.J.

Perry, J. J., 1977, Microbial metabolism of cyclic hydrocarbons and related compounds, *Crit. Rev. Microbiol.* **5:**387–412.

Perry, J. J., 1979, Microbial cooxidations involving hydrocarbons, *Microbiol. Rev.* **43:**59–72.

Perry, J. J., 1985, Isolation and characterization of thermophilic, hydrocarbon-utilizing bacteria, *Adv. Aquat. Microbiol.* **3:**109–139.

Perry, J. J., and Cerniglia, C. E., 1973, Studies on the degradation of petroleum by filamentous fungi, in: *The Microbial Degradation of Oil Pollutants* (D. G. Ahearn and S. O. Meyers, eds.), Publ. No. LSU-SG-73-01, Center for Wetland Resources, Louisiana State University, Baton Rouge, pp. 89–94.

Pfaender, F. K., Buckley, E. N., and Ferguson, R. L., 1980, Response of the pelagic microbial community to oil from the IXTOC-I blowout, *in situ* studies, in: *Proceedings from a Symposium on Preliminary Results from the September 1979 Research/Pierce IXTOC-I Cruise,* National Oceanic and Atmospheric Administration, Boulder, pp. 545–562.

Phung, H. T., and Ross, D. E., 1978, Soil incorporation of petroleum wastes, Paper presented at the 85th National Meeting of AICHE, Philadelphia, American Institute of Chemical Engineers, New York.

Pinholt, Y., Struwe, S., and Kjoller, A., 1979, Microbial changes during oil decomposition in soil, *Holarct. Ecol.* 2:195–200.

Pirnik, M. P., 1977, Microbial oxidation of methyl branched alkanes, *Crit. Rev. Microbiol.* 5:413–422.

Pirnik, M. P., Atlas, R. M., and Bartha, R., 1974, Hydrocarbon metabolism by *Brevibacterium erythrogenes:* Normal and branched alkanes, *J. Bacteriol.* 119:868–878.

Prince, R., Clark, J. R., and Lindstrom, J. E., 1990, *Bioremediation Monitoring Program,* Joint Report of EXXON, the US EPA, and the Alaskan Dept. of Environmental Conservation, Anchorage.

Pritchard, H. P., 1990, Bioremediation of oil contaminated beach material in Prince William Sound, Alaska, Paper presented at the 199th National Meeting of the American Chemical Society, Boston, Abstract Environment 154.

Pritchard, H. P., and Costa, C. F., 1991, EPA's Alaska oil spill bioremediation report, *Environ. Sci. Technol.,* 25:372–379.

Pritchard, H. P., and Starr, T. J., 1973, Microbial degradation of oil and hydrocarbons in continuous culture, in: *The Microbial Degradation of Oil Pollutants* (D. G. Ahearn and S. O. Meyers, eds.), Publ. No. LSU-SG-73-01, Center for Wetland Resources, Louisiana State University, Baton Rouge, pp. 39–46.

Prokop, A., and Sobotka, H., 1975, Insoluble substrate and oxygen transport in hydrocarbon fermentation, in: *Single Cell Protein II* (S. R. Tannenbaum and D. I. C. Wang, eds.), MIT Press, Cambridge, Mass., pp. 127–157.

Pye, V. I., and Patrick, R., 1983, Groundwater pollution in the United States, *Science* 221:713–718.

Raisbeck, J. M., and Mohtadi, M. F., 1974, The environmental aspects of oil spills on land in the Arctic regions, *Water Air Soil Pollut.* 3:195–208.

Ratledge, C., 1978, Degradation of aliphatic hydrocarbons, in: *Developments in Biodegradation of Hydrocarbons—1* (J. R. Watkinson, ed.), Applied Science, London, pp. 1–46.

Raymond, R. L., 1974, Reclamation of hydrocarbon contaminated ground waters, *Off. Gaz. US Patent Off.* 928:260.

Raymond, R. L., and Jamison, V. W., 1971, Biochemical activities of *Nocardia, Adv. Appl. Microbiol.* 14:93–122.

Raymond, R. L., Jamison, V. W., and Hudson, J. O., 1967, Microbial hydrocarbon co-oxidation. I. Oxidation of mono- and dicyclic hydrocarbons by soil isolates of the genus *Nocardia, Appl. Microbiol.* 15:857–865.

Raymond, R. L., Hudson, J. O., and Jamison, J. W., 1976a, Oil degradation in soil, *Appl. Environ. Microbiol.* 31:522–535.

Raymond, R. L., Jamison, V. W., and Hudson, J. O., 1976b, Beneficial stimulation of bacterial activity in ground waters containing petroleum products, in: *Water—1976,* American Institute of Chemical Engineers, New York, pp. 319–327.

Raymond, R. L., Brown, R. A., Norris, R. D., and O'Neill, E. T., 1976c, Stimulation of biooxidation process in subterranean formations, U.S. Patent 4,588,506.

Reisfeld, A., Rosenberg, E., and Gutnick, D., 1972, Microbial degradation of oil: Factors affecting oil dispersion in seawater by mixed and pure cultures. *Appl. Microbiol.* 24:363–368.

Robichaux, T. J., and Myrick, H. N., 1972, Chemical enhancement of the biodegradation of crude oil pollutants, *J. Pet. Technol.* 24:16–20.

Rogoff, M. H., 1961, Oxidation of aromatic compounds by bacteria, *Adv. Appl. Microbiol.* 3:193–221.

Rontani, J. F., Bosser-Joulak, F., Rambeloarisoa, E., Bertrand, J. E., Giusti, G., and Faure, R., 1985, Analytical study of Asthart crude oil asphaltenes biodegradation, *Chemosphere* 14:1413–1422.

Safferman, S. I., 1991, Selection of nutrients to enhance biodegradation for remediation of oil spilled on beaches, in: *Proceedings of the 1991 International Oil Spill Conference,* American Petroleum Institute, Washington, D.C., pp. 571–576.

Sandvik, S., Lode, A., and Pedersen, T. A., 1986, Biodegradation of oily sludge in Norwegian soil, *Appl. Microbiol. Biotechnol.* **23**:297–301.

Sayler, G., 1991, Contribution of molecular biology to bioremediation, Paper presented *Bioremediation: Fundamentals and Effective Applications Symposium,* February 22, Lamar University, Beaumont, Tex.

Sayler, G. S., Shields, M. S., Tedford, E. T., Breen, A., Hooper, S. W., Sirotkin, K. M., and Davis, J. W., 1985, Application of DNA–DNA colony hybridization to the detection of catabolic genotypes in environmental samples, *Appl. Environ. Microbiol.* **49**:1295–1303.

Schaeffer, T. L., Cantwell, S. G., Brown, J. L., Watt, D. S., and Fall, R. R., 1979, Microbial growth on hydrocarbons: Terminal branching inhibits biodegradation, *Appl. Environ. Microbiol.* **38**:742–746.

Schwall, L. R., and Herbes, S. E., 1979, Methodology for the determination of rates of microbial transformation of polycyclic aromatic hydrocarbons in sediments, in: *Methodology for Biomass Determinations and Microbial Activities in Sediments* (C. D. Litchfield and P. L. Seyried, eds.), American Society for Testing and Materials, Philadelphia.

Sexstone, A., and Atlas, R. M., 1977, Response of populations in arctic tundra soils to crude oil, *Can. J. Microbiol.* **23**:1327–1333.

Shailubhai, K., 1986, Treatment of petroleum industry oil sludge in soil, *Trends Biotechnol.* **4**:202–206.

Shennan, J. L., 1984, Hydrocarbons as substrates in industrial fermentation, in: *Petroleum Microbiology* (R. M. Atlas, ed.), Macmillan Co., New York, pp. 643–683.

Shiaris, M. P., 1989, Seasonal biotransformation of naphthalene, phenanthrene, and benzo[a]pyrene in surficial estuarine sediments, *Appl. Environ. Microbiol.* **55**:1391–1399.

Shiaris, M. P., and Cooney, J. J., 1983, Replica plating method for estimating phenanthrene-utilizing and phenanthrene-cometabolizing microorganisms, *Appl. Environ. Microbiol.* **45**:706–710.

Sirvins, A., and Angeles, M., 1986, *Biodegradation of Petroleum Hydrocarbons,* NATO ASI Series, Vol. G9.

Soli, G., 1973, Marine hydrocarbonoclastic bacteria: Types and range of oil degradation, in: *The Microbial Degradation of Oil Pollutants* (D. G. Ahearn and S. O. Meyers, eds.), Publ. No. LSU-SG-73-01, Center for Wetland Resources, Louisiana State University, Baton Rouge, pp. 141–146.

Somers, J. A., 1974, The fate of spilled oil in the soil, *Hydrol. Sci. Bull.* **19**:501–521.

Song, H.-G., and Bartha, R., 1990, Effects of jet fuel spills on the microbial community of soil, *Appl. Environ. Microbiol.* **56**:646–651.

Song, H.-G., Pedersen, T. A., and Bartha, R., 1986, Hydrocarbon mineralization in soil: Relative bacterial and fungal contribution, *Soil Biol. Biochem.* **18**:109–111.

Song, H.-G., Wang, X., and Bartha, R., 1990, Bioremediation potential of terrestrial fuel spills, *Appl. Environ. Microbiol.* **56**:652–656.

Sorkhoh, N. A., Ghannoum, M. A., Ibrahim, A. S., Stretton, R. J., and Rdaman, S. S., 1990, Crude oil and hydrocarbon degrading strains of *Rhodococcus: Rhodococcus* strains isolated from soil and marine environments in Kuwait, *Environ. Pollut.* **65**:1–18.

Standard Methods for the Examination of Water and Wastewater, 1985, *APHA-AWWA-WPCF* pp. 496–503.

Stirling, L. A., Watkinson, R. J., and Higgins, I. J., 1977, Microbial metabolism of alicyclic hydrocarbons: Isolation and properties of a cyclohexane-degrading bacterium, *J. Gen. Microbiol.* **99**:119–125.

Stockman, S. K., and Dime, R., 1986, Soil cleanup criteria for selected petroleum products, in: *Proceedings of the National Conference on Hazardous Wastes and Hazardous Materials,* Environmental Protection Agency, Washington, D.C., pp. 442–445.

Sussman, M., Collins, C. H., Skinner, F. A., and Stewart-Tull, D. E. (eds.), 1988, *Release of Genetically-Engineered Microorganisms,* Academic Press, New York.

Sveum, P., and LaDousse, A., 1989, Biodegradation of oil in the Arctic: Enhancement by oil-soluble fertilizer application, in: *Proceedings of the 1989 Oil Spill Conference,* American Petroleum Institute, Washington, D.C., pp. 439–446.

Tabak, H. H., Haines, J. R., Venosa, A. D., Gloser, J. A., Desai, S., and Nisamaneepong, W., 1991, Enhancement of biodegradation of Alaskan weathered crude oil components by indigenous microbiota with the use of fertilizers and nutrients, in: *Proceedings of the 1991 International Oil Spill Conference,* American Petroleum Institution, Washington, D.C., pp. 583–590.

Tagger, S., Bianchi, A., Julliard, M., LePetit, J., and Roux, B., 1983, Effect of microbial seeding of crude oil in seawater in a model system, *Mar. Biol.* **78:**13–20.

Tesan, G., and Barbosa, D., 1987, Degradation of oil by land disposal, *Water Sci. Technol.* **19:**99–106.

Thomas, J. M., Lee, M. D., Bedient, P. B., Borden, R. C., Carter, L. W., and Ward, C. H., 1987, Leaking underground storage tanks: Remediation with emphasis on *in situ* bioreclamation, Rep. No. EPA/600/S2-87/008, Environmental Protection Agency, Ada, Okla.

Tramier, B., and Sirvins, A., 1983, Enhanced oil biodegradation: A new operational tool to control oil spills, in: *Proceedings of the 1983 Oil Spill Conference,* American Petroleum Institute, Washington, D.C.

Traxler, R. W., 1973, Bacterial degradation of petroleum materials in low temperature marine environments, in: *The Microbial Degradation of Oil Pollutants* (D. G. Ahearn and S. P. Meyers, eds.), Publ. No. LSU-SG-73-01, Center for Wetland Resources, Louisiana State University, Baton Rouge, pp. 163–170.

Treccani, V., 1964, Microbial degradation of hydrocarbons, *Prog. Ind. Microbiol.* **4:**3–33.

Trudgill, P. W., 1978, Microbial degradation of alicyclic hydrocarbons, in: *Developments in Biodegradation of Hydrocarbons—1* (J. R. Watkinson, ed.), Applied Science, London, pp. 47–84.

Umbreit, T. H., Hesse, E. J., and Gallo, M. A., 1986, Bio-availability of dioxin in soil from a 2,4,5-T manufacturing site, *Science* **232:**497–499.

United States Environmental Protection Agency, 1989, Alaskan Oil Spill Bioremediation Project, EPA 160018-891073.

United States Environmental Protection Agency, 1990, *ORD/NETAC: Bringing Innovative Technologies to the Market, EPA Alaskan Oil Spill Bioremediation Project Update,* Office of Research and Development, Washington, D.C.

Van der Linden, A. C., and Thijsse, G. J. E., 1965, The mechanisms of microbial oxidations of petroleum hydrocarbons, *Adv. Enzymol.* **27:**469–546.

Van Eyk, J., and Bartels, T. J., 1968, Paraffin oxidation in *Pseudomonas aeruginosa.* I. Induction of paraffin oxidation, *J. Bacteriol.* **96:**706–712.

Vanlooke, R., DeBorger, R., Voets, J. P., and Verstraete, W., 1975, Soil and groundwater contamination by oil spills: Problems and remedies, *Int. J. Environ. Stud.* **8:**99–111.

Venosa, A. D., 1991, Protocol for testing bioremediation products against weathered Alaskan crude oil, Paper presented at *Bioremediation: Fundamentals and Effective Applications Symposium,* February 22, Lamar University, Beaumont, Tex.

Venosa, A. D. Haines, J. R., and Allen, D. M., 1991a, Effectiveness of commercial microbial products in enhancing oil degradation in Prince William Sound field plots, *17th Annual EPA Hazardous Waste Research Symposium,* April 9–11, Cincinnati.

Venosa, A. D., Haines, J. R., Nisamaneepong, W., Govind, R., Pradhan, S., and Siddique, B., 1991b, Protocol for testing bioremediation products against weathered Alaskan crude oil, in: *Proceedings of the 1991 International Oil Spill Conference,* American Petroleum Institute, Washington, D.C., pp. 563–570.

Venosa, A. D., Haines, J. R., Nisamaneepong, W., Govind, R., Pradhan, S., and Siddique, B., 1992a, Efficacy of commercial inocula in enhancing oil biodegradation in closed laboratory reactors, *J. Ind. Microbiol.* in press.

Venosa, A. D., Haines, J. R., and Allen, D. M., 1992b, Efficacy of commercial products in enhancing biodegradation of weathered crude oil contaminating a Prince William Sound beach, *J. Ind. Microbiol.*, in press.

Verstraete, W., Vanlooke, R., deBorger, R., and Verlinde, A., 1976, Modelling of the breakdown and the mobilization of hydrocarbons in unsaturated soil layers, in: *Proceedings of the Third International Biodegradation Symposium* (J. M. Sharpley and A. M. Kaplan, eds.), Applied Science, London, pp. 98–112.

Vogel, T. M., and Grbic-Gallic, D., 1986, Incorporation of oxygen from water into toluene and benzene during anaerobic fermentative transformation, *Appl. Environ. Microbiol.* **52**:200–202.

von Wedel, R. J., Mosquera, J. F., Goldsmith, C. D., Hater, G. R., Wong, A., Fox, T. A., Hunt, W. T., Paules, M. S., Quiros, J. M., and Wiegand, J. W., 1988, Bacterial biodegradation and bioreclamation with enrichment isolates in California, *Water Sci. Technol.* **20**:501–503.

Wade, T. L., Kennicutt, M. C., and Brooks, J. M., 1989, Gulf of Mexico hydrogen seep communities. Part III. Aromatic hydrocarbon concentrations in organisms, sediments and water, *Mar. Environ. Res.* **27**:19–30.

Walker, J. D., and Colwell, R. R., 1974a, Microbial petroleum degradation: Use of mixed hydrocarbon substrates, *Appl. Microbiol.* **27**:1053–1060.

Walker, J. D., and Colwell, R. R., 1974b, Microbial degradation of model petroleum at low temperatures, *Microbiol. Ecol.* **1**:63–95.

Walker, J. D., and Colwell, R. R., 1976, Measuring the potential activity of hydrocarbon-degrading bacteria, *Appl. Environ. Microbiol.* **31**:189–197.

Walker, J. D., Colwell, R. R., and Petrakis, L., 1975, Microbial petroleum degradation: Application of computerized mass spectrometry, *Can. J. Microbiol.* **21**:1760–1767.

Walker, J. D., Colwell, R. R., and Petrakis, L., 1976, Biodegradation rates of components of petroleum, *Can. J. Microbiol.* **22**:1209–1213.

Wang, X., and Bartha, R., 1990, Effects of bioremediation on residues: Activity and toxicity in soil contaminated by fuel spills, *Soil Biol. Biochem.* **22**(4):501–506.

Wang, X., Yu, X., and Bartha, R., 1990, Effect of bioremediation on polycyclic aromatic hydrocarbon residues in soil, *Environ. Sci. Technol.* **24**(7):1086–1089.

Ward, D. M., and Brock, T. D., 1978, Anaerobic metabolism of hexadecane in marine sediments, *Geomicrobiol. J.*, **1**:1–9.

Ward, D., Atlas, R. M., Boehm, P. D., and Calder, J. A., 1980, Microbial biodegradation and the chemical evolution of Amoco Cadiz oil pollutants, *Ambio* **9**:277–283.

Wilson, B. H., Smith, G. B., and Rees, J. F., 1986, Biotransformations of selected alkylbenzenes and halogenated aliphatic hydrocarbons in methanogenic aquifer material: A microcosm study, *Environ. Sci. Technol.* **20**:997.

Wilson, J., 1991, Performance evaluations of *in situ* bioreclamation of fuel spills at Traverse City Michigan, in: *Proceedings of the In Situ and On-Site Bioreclamation: An International Symposium*, Butterworths, London.

Wilson, J. T., and Ward, C. H., 1987, Opportunities for bioreclamation of aquifers contaminated with petroleum hydrocarbons, *Dev. Ind. Microbiol.* **27**:109–116.

Wodzinski, R. S., and Coyle, J. E., 1974, Physical state of phenanthrene for utilization by bacteria. *Appl. Microbiol.* **27**:1081–1084.

Wong, A. D., and Goldsmith, C. D., 1988, The impact of a chemostat discharge containing oil degrading bacteria on the biological kinetics of a refinery activated sludge process, *Water Sci. Technol.* **20**:131–136.

Yaniga, P. M., and Smith, W., 1984, Aquifer restoration *via* accelerated *in situ* biodegradation of organic contaminants, in: *Proceedings of the Conference on Petroleum Hydrocarbons and Organic Chemicals in Ground Water—Prevention, Detection, and Restoration*, National Water Well Association, Worthington, Ohio, pp. 451–470.

Yen, K.-M., and Serdar, C. M., 1988, Genetics of naphthalene catabolism in pseudomonads, *CRC Crit. Rev. Microbiol.* **15:**247–268.

Zajic, J. E., and Steffens, W., 1984, Biosurfactants, *CRC Crit. Rev. Biotechnol.* **1:**87.

Zajic, J. E., Supplisson, B., and Volesky, B., 1974, Bacterial degradation and emulsification of No. 6 fuel oil, *Environ. Sci. Technol.* **8:**664–668.

Zeyer, J., Kuhn, E. P., and Schwarzenbach, R. P., 1986, Rapid microbial mineralization of toluene and 1,3-dimethylbenzene in the absence of molecular oxygen, *Appl. Environ. Microbiol.* **52:**944–947.

Zeyer, J., Eicher, P., Dolfing, J., and Schwarzenbach, P. R., 1990, Anaerobic degradation of aromatic hydrocarbons, in: *Biotechnology and Biodegradation* (D. Kamely, A. Chakrabarty, and G. S. Omenn, eds.), Gulf Publ., Houston, pp. 33–40.

Zitrides, T. G., 1990, Bioremediation comes of age, *Pollut. Eng.* **12:**59–60.

ZoBell, C. E., 1946, Action of microorganisms on hydrocarbons, *Bacteriol. Rev.* **10:**1–49.

ZoBell, C. E., 1950, Assimilation of hydrocarbons by microorganisms, *Adv. Enzymol.* **10:**443–486.

ZoBell, C. E., 1971, Sources and biodegradation of carcinogenic hydrocarbons, in: *Proceedings of Joint Conference on Prevention and Control of Oil Spills,* American Petroleum Institute, Washington, D.C., pp. 441–451.

ZoBell, C. E., 1973a, Bacterial degradation of mineral oils at low temperatures, in: *The Microbial Degradation of Oil Pollutants* (D. G. Ahearn and S. P. Meyers, eds.), Publ. No. LSU-SG-73-01, Center for Wetland Resources, Louisiana State University, Baton Rouge, pp. 153–161.

ZoBell, C. E., 1973b, Microbial degradation of oil: Present status, problems and perspectives, in: *The Microbial Degradation of Oil Pollutants* (D. G. Ahearn and S. P. Meyers, eds.), Publ. No. LSU-SG-73-01, Center for Wetland Resources, Louisiana State University, Baton Rouge, pp. 3–16.

7

Ecology of Polyprosthecate Bacteria

ALEXANDRE SEMENOV and JAMES T. STALEY

Several reviews have been written about the hyphomicrobia and caulobacters, the prosthecate bacteria with which bacteriologists are most familiar (Dow *et al.*, 1976; Whittenbury and Dow, 1977; Dow and Lawrence, 1980; Dow and Whittenbury, 1980; Harder and Attwood, 1978; Hirsch, 1974b; Moore, 1981a,b; Poindexter, 1964, 1981a,b). In contrast, the multiple-appendaged or polyprosthecate bacteria have not been so often reviewed (Schmidt, 1971). There are two reasons for this lack of attention. First, these organisms were discovered and isolated later than most other prosthecate bacteria. And second, members of this group have been, in general, more difficult to isolate in pure culture and to cultivate and study in the laboratory. Recently, however, a number of new genera and species have been isolated and named (Vasilyeva and Semenov, 1984, 1986; Bauld *et al.*, 1983; Schlesner, 1983, 1987a,b; Staley, 1984; Vasilyeva *et al.*, 1991), and these bacteria have become the subjects of greater investigation. This review briefly considers the biological characteristics of these bacteria and discusses in greater detail what is known about their ecological role(s).

1. Diversity and Classification of Heterotrophic Prosthecate Bacteria

The term *prostheca* (pl. *-ae*) is derived from the Greek root meaning *appendage* (the same root used for prosthetic device) and is defined as a semirigid appendage, bound by the cell wall, extending from a prokaryotic cell (Staley, 1968). Therefore, the cell wall and membrane of these gram-negative bacteria extends around the prostheca.

The prosthecate bacteria can be differentiated into several morphological subgroups (Table I), three of which contain several genera. Not only are there differences among the subgroups, but there are also significant differences among the genera within each subgroup.

The hyphomicrobia are budding bacteria, all of which produce buds at the tip of a

ALEXANDRE SEMENOV • Institute of Microbiology, USSR Academy of Sciences, Moscow, USSR.   JAMES T. STALEY • Department of Microbiology, University of Washington, Seattle, Washington 98195.

Advances in Microbial Ecology, Vol. 12, edited by K.C. Marshall. Plenum Press, New York, 1992.

Table I. Subgroups of Prosthecate Bacteria

Subgroup	Genera
Hyphomicrobia	*Hyphomicrobium*
	Hyphomonas
	Hirschia
	Filomicrobium
	Pedomicrobium
	Dichotomicrobium
Caulobacters	*Caulobacter*
	Asticcaulis
	Prosthecobacter
Prosthecomicrobia or	*Prosthecomicrobium*
polyprosthecate bacteria	*Ancalomicrobium*
	Stella
	Labrys
Verrucomicrobium	

polar to subpolar prostheca, a feature unique to this group. The hyphomicrobia comprise the genera *Hyphomicrobium, Hyphomonas, Filomicrobium,* and *Hirschia* which typically produce a single polar to subpolar prostheca per cell whereas the others in this group, *Pedomicrobium* and *Dichotomicrobium,* produce more than one appendage. Although the hyphomicrobia are similar morphologically, they range metabolically from the methylotrophic genus, *Hyphomicrobium,* to ordinary heterotrophs.

Another subgroup, the caulobacters, comprise organisms with a single prostheca, sometimes called a "stalk," that divide more or less by binary transverse fission (Poindexter, 1981a). Included in this group are the genera *Caulobacter* with a polar prostheca, and *Asticcaulis* with a subpolar to lateral prostheca (one species produces two prosthecae per cell) and *Prosthecobacter,* also with a polar prostheca. The caulobacters all produce holdfasts that enable them to attach to detritus and other particulate material in the environment.

The third subgroup, and the primary topic of this review, is the polyprosthecate bacteria, characterized by having cells with numerous prosthecae. Also, they completely lack holdfast structures. Included here are the genera *Ancalomicrobium* (Figs. 1 and 2), *Prosthecomicrobium* (Figs. 3 and 4), *Labrys,* and *Stella. Ancalomicrobium* and *Prosthecomicrobium* are similar morphologically in that they contain several to many prosthecae that radiate from the cell from all locations. Only one species of *Ancalomicrobium, A. adetum,* is currently known. It differs from *Prosthecomicrobium* spp. in that it is fermentative. Sugars such as glucose and lactose are fermented by mixed acid fermentation to yield formic, acetic, lactic, and propionic acids, as well as ethanol, hydrogen, and carbon dioxide. Also, all strains that have been studied produce gas vacuoles.

There are several species of *Prosthecomicrobium* which differ morphologically (Table II) and physiologically from one another. Most have been isolated from fresh-

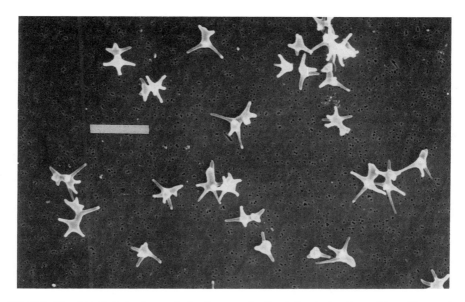

Figure 1. Scanning electron micrograph showing several cells of *Ancalomicrobium adetum*. (Bar equals 5 μm). Courtesy of A. van Neerven.

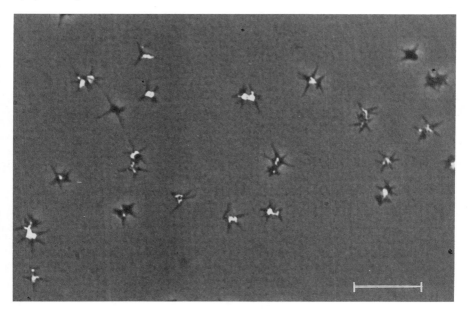

Figure 2. Phase photomicrograph of *Ancalomicrobium adetum*. The bright areas within cells are gas vacuoles. (Bar equals 10 μm.) Courtesy of A. van Neerven.

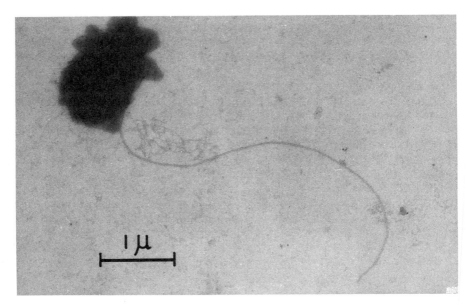

Figure 3. Electron micrograph of a cell of *Prosthecomicrobium enhydrum*. Note the short appendages and the single subpolar flagellum.

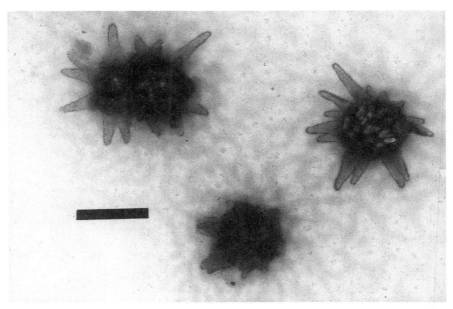

Figure 4. Electron micrograph of a cell of *Prostecomicrobium pneumaticum*. The bright areas within the cell are the gas vesicles of this species. (Bar equals 1 μm.)

Table II. some Morphological Characteristics of Bacteria
of the Genus *Prosthecomicrobium*

Organism	Cell size (μm)	Prostheca length (μm)	Ratio of prostheca length to cell length	Gas vesicles	Motility	GC content in DNA (mole %)
P. polysheroidum	0.5–0.8 × 0.85	0.1	0.5–0.8	−	+	64–66
"*P. consociatum*"	0.8–1.35 × 0.5–1.0	0.25	0.2–0.4	−	−	66–69
"*P. mishustinii*"	0.8–1.5 × 0.6–1.2	0.3–0.65	0.15–0.3	−	−	64–65
P. enhydrum	(diam.) 1.0	0.25	<0.5	−	+	66–68
P. hirschii	0.8–1.2 × 1.0–2.0	<1–>2	1–2	−	Motile stage	68–70
P. species	1.0–1.5 × 1.0	0.1–0.5	0.5	−	+	65 ± 3
P. pneumaticum	0.75–1.0	0.75–1.0	1	+	+	69–70
P. litoralum	(diam.) 1.0	<1.0	<1.0	−	+	66–67

water and soil habitats, but one marine species, *P. litoralum,* has also been described. The simplest members of this group have short appendages which are difficult to detect by light microscopy. Some of these are motile by polar to subpolar flagella, i.e., *P. polyspheroidum, P. enhydrum* (Fig. 3), *P. litoralum,* and an unidentified species, *P.* sp.; some are nonmotile, *P. consociatum* and *P. mishustinii;* and one has gas vacuoles, *P. pneumaticum* (Fig. 4). *P. hirschii* has cells with short appendages (i.e., < 1.0 μm long) as well as cells with long appendages (> 1.0 μm). The short-appendaged cells are motile by a single flagellum (Fig. 5).

Stella and *Labrys* are unique morphologically among the bacteria in having radial rather than axial cell symmetry. *Stella* spp. appear as six-pointed stars (Figs. 14–16) and divide by binary transverse fission. The species *S. vacuolata* is gas vacuolate whereas *S. humosa* is not. Two new species have been proposed, *S. pusilla* and *S. equatica* (H. Schlesner, personal communication). A number of strains are now available and the range of DNA base composition is 68 to 74 (Table III). Only one strain of *Labrys* has been isolated. It has several prosthecae tapering from one pole of the cell (Figs. 6–9).

The final genus, *Verrucomicrobium,* that has been recently described (Schlesner, 1987a) is morphologically similar to *Prosthecomicrobium* in that it, too, produces several prosthecae per cell. However, it also has a holdfast and many fimbriae which radiate from the prosthecae, features not found in the other polyprosthecate bacteria. It is placed in a new, separate group of the eubacteria based on the unique sequence of its 16 S rRNA (Albrecht *et al.,* 1987).

There are also phototrophic members of the prosthecate bacteria. Representatives of the purple nonsulfur genera included here are the genus *Rhodomicrobium* (Duchow and Douglas, 1949) and some species of *Rhodopseudomonas* (Whittenbury and McLee, 1967; Pfennig and Trüper, 1989). These resemble most closely the hyphomicrobia in that they produce buds from the tips of their prosthecae. In contrast, some of the green sulfur photosynthetic bacteria are multiple-appendaged prosthecate bacteria and there-

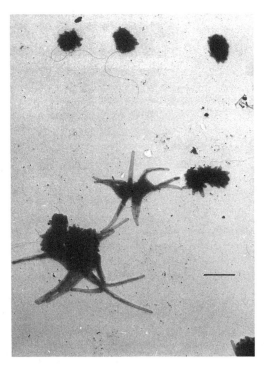

Figure 5. Electron micrograph of several cells of *Prosthecomicrobium hirschii*. This strain has two cell types: one with long and the other with short prosthecae. Note that some of the short-appendaged cells have a single flagellum. (Bar equals 1 μm.)

Table III. DNA Base Composition of *Stella* Strains

Strain	Mole % G + C
BKM B	
1137	72.7
228	69.3
227	70.0
15	70.4
142	70.8
141	70.0
10P	71.4
12B	71.4
143	71.8
12P	72.5
229	73.5
S. equatica[a]	68.0
S. pusilla[a]	67.7

[a]Strains isolated by Schlesner. (These data have not been included in the 9th edition of *Bergey's manual of Determinative Bacteriology*.)

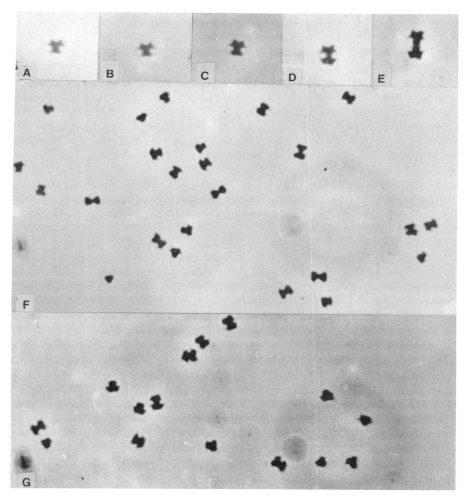

Figure 6. Cells of *Labrys monachus* during batch cultivation on media with glucose concentration up to 0.03% (phase contrast): (a–e) Morphological cell types corresponding to different stages of proliferation; (f, g) overall view of culture during the whole cultivation period (×1864).

fore resemble the polyprosthecate bacteria. These are the genera *Prosthecochloris* and *Ancalochloris* (Gorlenko, 1968; Gorlenko and Lebedeva, 1971).

These various groups of prosthecate bacteria differ from one another genotypically and phenotypically, except for the production of prosthecae. Not only are there differences among the various groups, but there are also significant differences among genera within the groups.

Although the prostheca is a distinctive and unique morphological feature, prosthecobacteria often have other unusual properties. For example, bud formation may

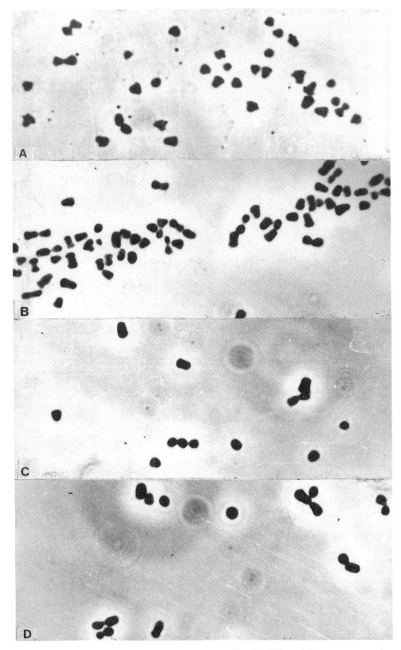

Figure 7. *L. monachus* cells during batch cultivation on media with different glucose concentrations. Phase contrast, × 1957. (a) 0.05% (64 hr); (b) 0.1% (64 hr); (c) 0.1% (111 hr); (d) 0.4% (111 hr); (e) 0.2% (159 hr); (f) 0.3% (159 hr); (g) 0.4% (159 hr); (h) 0.5% (159 hr).

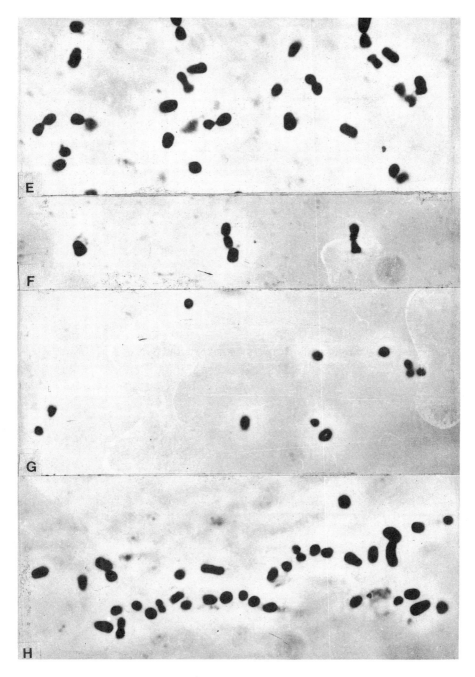

Figure 7. (*Continued*)

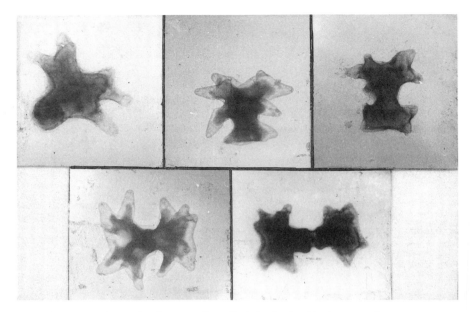

Figure 8. Electron micrographs of *L. monachus* cells during batch cultivation on media with glucose concentration up to 0.03% during the entire growth period (×1000).

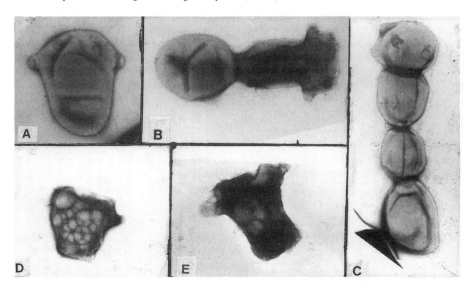

Figure 9. Electron micrographs of *L. monachus* cells during batch cultivation on media with different glucose concentrations. (a) 0.2–0.5% (98 hr, ×13,200); (b, c) 0.2–0.5% (140 hr, ×10,560); (d, e) cells with polyhydroxybutyrate (×14,080; ×12,600).

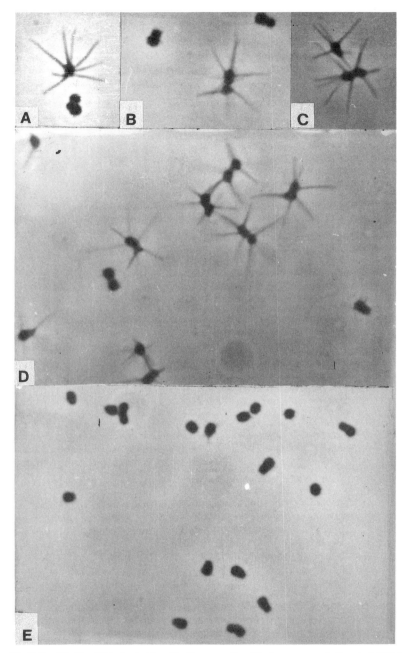

Figure 10. Cells of *P. hirschii* during batch cultivation on media with glucose concentrations to 0.03% (phase contrast). (a–c) Morphological cell types corresponding to different proliferation stages of the cell cycle; (d, e) the total view of cells under the microscope. Cells with long prosthecae (d) or motile and stationary cells with short prosthecae (e) dominate (×2330).

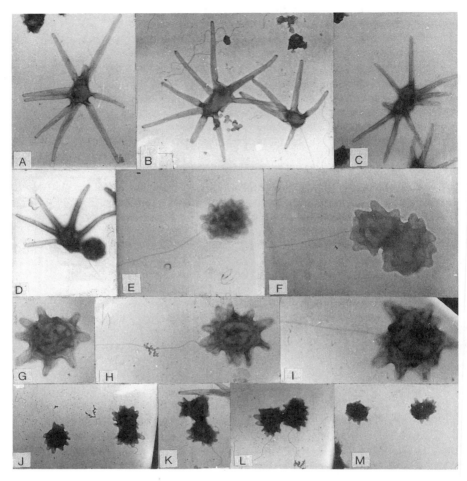

Figure 11. Electron micrograph of *P. hirschii* cells during batch cultivation on media with glucose concentration up to 0.03%. (a–d) ×4680; (e) ×7800; e–i: morphological cell types corresponding to different stages of the cell cycle; f (×11,700) and g (×15,600): the motile stage at two magnifications; j–m (×4680): different cell cycle stages showing the daughter cell with short prosthecae.

occur at the tip of the prostheca as in the case of the hyphomicrobia. Also, some of the prosthecate bacteria (e.g., *Stella*) are radially but not axially symmetrical, a feature not found in any other bacterial group.

Several classifications have been prepared for the prosthecate bacteria based on their distinctive properties (Dow and Lawrence, 1980; Dow and Whittenbury, 1979; Hirsch, 1974b; Staley, 1989). Vasilyeva (1980) has proposed a classification based on their morphological features which we have updated here (Table IV). Based on their

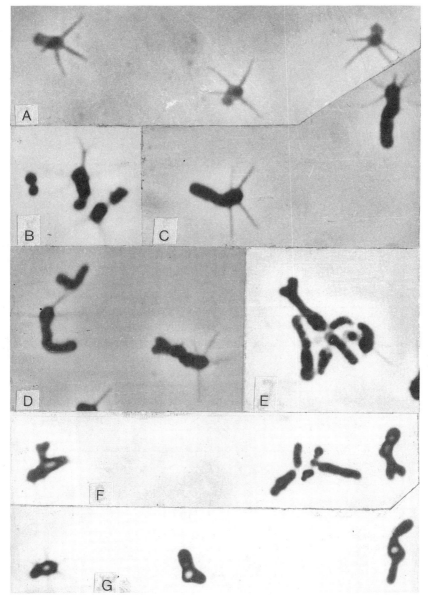

Figure 12. *P. hirschii* cells during batch cultivation on media with different glucose concentrations. (a) 0.05% (84 hr); (b) 0.2% (the cell with the branched prostheca); (c–e) 0.3% (117 hr); (f, g) 0.4% (117 hr). Polyhydroxybutyrate granules are seen in the cells (×2330).

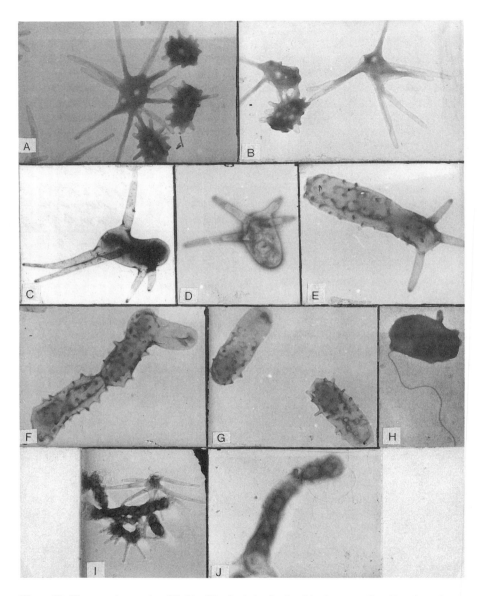

Figure 13. Electron micrographs of *P. hirschii* cells during batch cultivation on media with various glucose concentrations. a, b (×7700): 0.05%; c, d (×6160), e (×7700), f, g (×6160): 0.4% (84 hr); h (×11,550): 0.2% (stationary stage); i (×3850); j (×6160): 0.05% (117 hr, cells with poly-β-hydroxybutyrate).

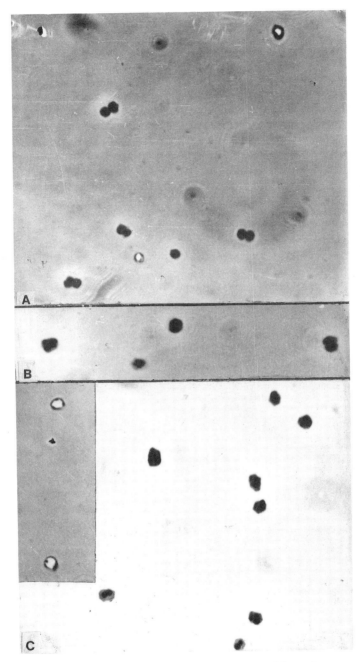

Figure 14. Cells of *Stella vacuolata* during batch cultivation on media with different glutamate concentrations (phase contrast). aL 0.025%; b, c: 0.2% (×1864).

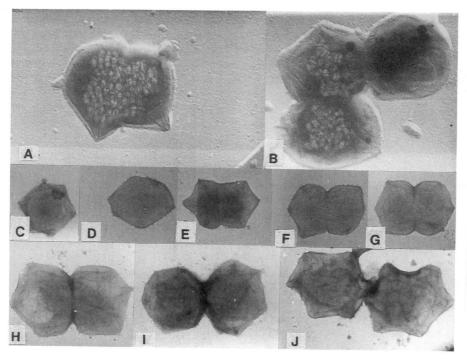

Figure 15. Electron micrographs of *S. vacuolata* cells under batch cultivation on medium with 0.025% glutamate. a, b (× 12,900): cells with gas vesicles and polyhydroxybutyrate (black spots); c–g (×8600), h–j (×12,900): morphological cell types corresponding to different developmental stages.

combined properties the prosthecobacteria are placed in four morphological subgroups of the bacteria: II, IV, VI, and VIII. Physiological and genotypic features have not been considered in this grouping.

Recent genotypic characterization of these bacteria, derived from a variety of procedures including DNA base composition, genome size determination, DNA/DNA hybridization, DNA/rRNA hybridization, 5 S rRNA and 16 S rRNA analyses and sequence determinations, have indicated that, with the sole exception of *Verrucomicrobium*, the heterotrophic prosthecate bacteria are related to one another (Staley and Mandel, 1973; Moore and Hirsch, 1972; Moore and Staley, 1976; Moore, 1977; Gebers *et al.*, 1981a,b, 1984, 1985; Lysenko *et al.*, 1984; Kölbel-Boelke *et al.*, 1985; Albrecht *et al.*, 1987; Stackebrandt *et al.*, 1988a,b; Chernykh *et al.*, 1990). They are all eubacteria that are related to the Proteobacteria, and more specifically are members of the alpha division of the Proteobacteria (Stackebrandt *et al.*, 1988a; Schlesner *et al.*, 1989; Fischer *et al.*, 1985).

Thus, the evidence, obtained from ribosomal sequence analyses which is quite independent of phenotypic (i.e., morphological) features, serves to independently con-

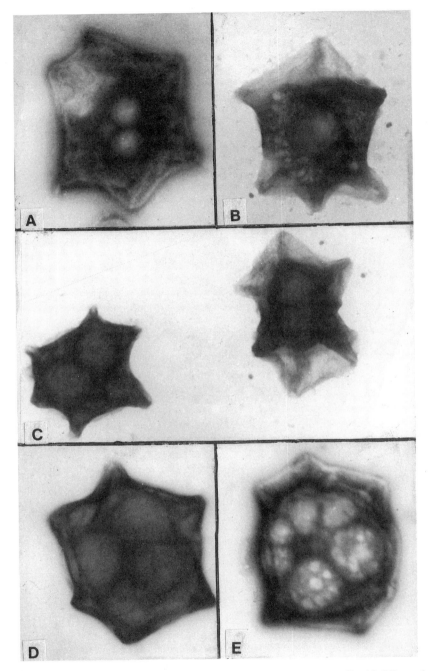

Figure 16. Electron micrographs of *S. vacuolata* cells during batch cultivation on media with different gluta-mate concentrations: (a, b) 0.1% (×20,000); (c) 0.25% (×10,000), (d, e) 0.4% (×20,000).

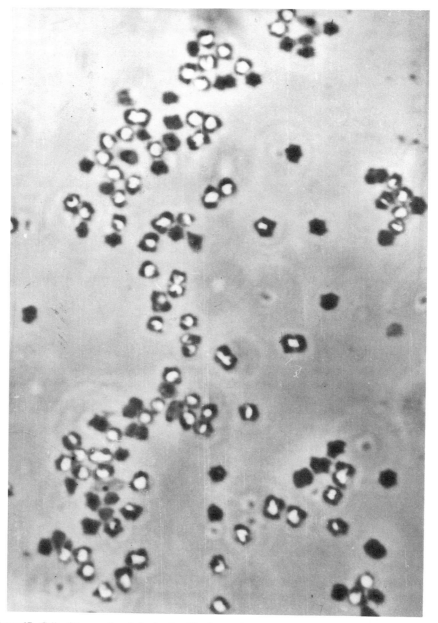

Figure 17. Cells of *S. vacuolata* during batch cultivation, stationary phase, on medium with 0.025% glutamate (phase contrast) (×2330).

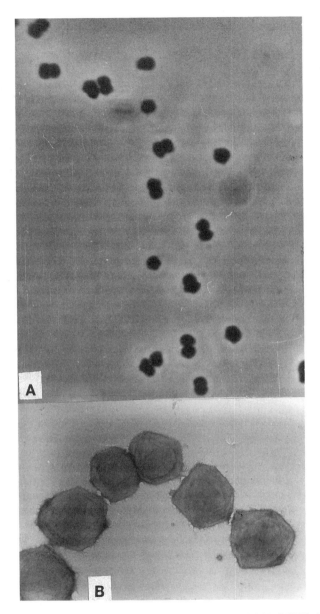

Figure 18. Cells of *S. vacuolata* during chemostat cultivation on media with 0.01–0.025% glutamate. (a) At a dilution rate of 0.04 hr^{-1} (light microscopy, phase contrast, ×2330); (b) at a dilution rate of 0.06 hr^{-1} (electron microscopy, ×10,000).

Table IV. Morphological Grouping of Bacterial Genera

| Cell shape | | Mode of reproduction | | Appendage | | Group, and numerical | Organisms |
Round 1	Flat 2	Division 3	Budding 4	Absent 5	Prostheca 6	properties 7	8
+	+	+		+		I-1,3,5	Banal: *E. coli*, *Pseudomonas*, et al.
+	+	+			+	II-1,3,6	*Caulobacter*, *Asticcacaulis*, *Prosthecobacter*
+			+	+		III-1,4,5	*Blastobacter*, *Nitrobacter*, *Rhodopseudomonas*, et al.
+			+		+	IV-1,4,6	*Hyphomicrobium*, *Hyphomonas*, *Pedomicrobium*, *Filomicrobium*, *Dichotomicrobium*, *Prosthecomicrobium*, *Ancalomicrobium*, *Verrucomicrobium*, *Rhodomicrobium*, *Ancalochloris*
	+	+		+		V-2,3,5	*Haloarcula*, *Methanoplanus*, *Pyrodictium*
	+	+			+	VI-2,3,6	*Stella*
	+		+	+		VII-2,4,5	*Angulomicrobium*
	+		+		+	VIII-2,4,6	*Labrys*

firm that the occurrence of a prostheca on an organism is a significant phylogenetic feature for determination of relatedness among bacteria. 16 S rRNA analyses have not yet been reported for the green sulfur genera *Ancalochloris* and *Prosthecochloris*, so it is not known whether they are related to other green sulfur bacteria, to *Verrucomicrobium*, or to the Proteobacteria. The photosynthetic representatives of prosthecate bacteria will not be considered further in this review.

2. Discovery and Isolation of Polyprosthecate Bacteria

From a historical perspective, it is interesting to note that both the caulobacters (Loeffler, 1890, see his Fig. 7) and polyprosthecate bacteria (Jennings, 1899) appear to have been observed by microbiologists using ordinary stained smears during the late 19th century prior to the development of modern microscopy. Indeed, even extensive ecological studies of *Caulobacter* were made in the 1930s by Henrici and his co-workers (see Henrici and Johnson, 1935) before they obtained cultures, even though Mabel Jones (1905) had clearly obtained isolates from the Chicago drinking water system before 1905. However, the true cellular nature of the prostheca was not understood at that time and the lack of cultures precluded meaningful laboratory studies of the biological properties of these bacteria until the latter half of the 20th century.

Two important events in microbiology led to the rediscovery and successful cultivation of polyprosthecate bacteria. The first was the development of improved microscopic techniques, including phase-contrast light microscopy as well as transmission electron microscopy. Improved microscopic procedures enabled microbiologists to better visualize the appearance of bacteria and to determine the true cellular nature of prosthecae.

The second event which enabled the isolation and cultivation of prosthecate bacteria was the development of dilute organic media, both for enrichment as well as growth of pure cultures. Thus, Houwink (1951) introduced the dilute peptone broth medium (containing 0.01% peptone) which led to a simple and reproducible enrichment procedure and isolation medium for growing *Caulobacter* spp. A more extensive discussion of the development of dilute media for oligotrophic bacteria is provided by Hirsch and Schlesner (1981).

Observations of natural samples with the electron microscope revealed the presence of polyprosthecate bacteria before procedures were developed for their isolation. They were observed in soil samples along with numerous other morphologically unusual organisms (Nikitin *et al.*, 1966) as well as in aquatic habitats (Nikitin and Kuznetsov, 1967; Staley, 1968; Vasilyeva, 1970).

Once pure cultures were obtained, it was clear that some of them divided by budding division (Staley, 1968) whereas others divided by binary transverse fission (Vasilyeva, 1970). The five genera currently known—*Prosthecomicrobium, Ancalomicrobium, Labrys, Stella,* and *Verrucomicrobium*—encompass all logical possible morphological varieties (Zavarzin, 1973).

3. Distribution of Polyprosthecate Bacteria in Nature

Though the heterotrophic prosthecate bacteria typically occur in low numbers in environments, they are indigenous to many habitats and are widely distributed in soils and water. Therefore, they are normal components of the microbial coenosis, and along with other ecological groups are involved in the production of soil fertility and in the biogeochemical cycles of elements (Zavarzin, 1970, 1984; Mishustin, 1975, 1981, 1982; Vasilyeva, 1984).

The genera *Prosthecomicrobium* and *Ancalomicrobium* are found in a variety of soil habitats (Vasilyeva, 1975; Vasilyeva *et al.*, 1974; Nikitin and Vasilyeva, 1967, 1968; Nikitin *et al.*, 1966; Nelidov *et al.*, 1986), in seawater as well as fresh water (Nikitin and Kuznetsov, 1967; Bauld *et al.*, 1983; Staley, 1968, 1971, 1984; Staley *et al.* 1980), in cow's tripe, (Tarakanov, 1971) and even in the intestines of insects (Cruden and Markovetz, 1981; Ostrovskaya, 1986).

Representatives of *Stella* have been reported from several locations including various soil types, sand filters of water treatment facilities, stream sediments, brackish water of the Baltic sea, and silt from Peter the Great Bay in the Far East (Vasilyeva *et al.*, 1974; Lysenko *et al.*, 1984; Nikitin *et al.*, 1966; Nelidov *et al.*, 1986; Hirsch and Schlesner, 1981; Schlesner, 1983; Staley, 1968; Vasilyeva, 1970, 1984; Vasilyeva and Semenov, 1986).

In contrast, only one strain of the genus *Labrys*, *L. monachus*, has been obtained in pure culture. It was isolated from sediments from Lake Mustyarl collected at a depth of 7 m (Vasilyeva, 1980; Vasilyeva and Semenov, 1984).

Thus, as a group, the polyprosthecate bacteria are globally distributed on all continents examined as well as in the Atlantic and Pacific oceans. Less information is available on their abundance in these various habitats. Some information is available concerning the concentration of *Prosthecomicrobium* and *Ancalomicrobium* species from freshwater habitats. During an annual survey their average numbers in a eutrophic stream (the Red Cedar River in central Michigan, USA) were 0.1 to 1 organism per ml where they comprised a small percentage (<1–5%) of the total viable concentration of heterotrophic bacteria (Staley, 1971). In contrast, they numbered up to 10^6 cells per ml in one aerated pulp mill sample (Stanley *et al.*, 1979). In a study of Australian lakes of various trophic states, their numbers ranged from <1 to 130 per ml and they comprised from <1 to 10% of the total viable heterotrophic count during the spring and summer (Staley *et al.*, 1980). Their highest concentrations and proportions to viable counts were found in a mesotrophic lake. Lower concentrations were found in eutrophic ponds (up to 24 per ml) where they comprised less than 0.01% of the total viable count. The highest concentration found in the oligotrophic lakes studied was 0.08 per ml which was 0.1% of the total viable count.

These bacteria have also been quantified in alkaline soils from flooded rice paddies in Kazakhstan. Because of the physiological peculiarity of these rice paddy strains which grow best in consortia with cellulose-degrading bacteria, they were enumerated along with them. They were also found growing in colonies of *Herpetosiphon*. The predominant species appeared to be *Prosthecomicrobium polyspheroidum* and *P. enhydrum;* however, strains resembling *Verrucomicrobium* which bear fimbriae at the tips of their prosthecae, were also common. Those from the rice paddies have 12 fimbriae per prostheca. The prosthecae are up to 0.35 μm in diameter and 0.25 to 0.6 μm in length and the cell body, without prosthecae, measures 0.6×0.9 μm (Vasilyeva, 1984). *P. hirschii* has also been isolated from the same soils (Semenov and Vasilyeva, 1986a). The concentration of these bacteria varies dramatically depending on the season and the input of different organic fertilizers, i.e., straw or compost prepared from straw. The lowest concentrations of *P. polyspheroidum* and *P. enhydrum* were found in June, i.e., 5.6 and 3000 cells per g of unamended soil, respectively. After the addition of fertilizers, especially straw compost, the numbers of these two species increased manyfold so that by October they exceeded 2.6×10^7 and 6.9×10^7 cells per g, respectively.

Stella spp. did not undergo such wide fluctuations in the rice paddy soils. In unamended soils their numbers ranged from 270 to 400 per g of soil during the year. Straw had no effect on their numbers. In soils amended with compost, however, their concentrations reached 69,000 cells per g (Nelidov et al., 1986). Similar studies (Table V) have been carried out in the black meadow soils of the Kranodar Territory of the USSR after prolonged rice paddy cultivation (Blagoveschenskaya, 1989).

4. Substrates Used by Prosthecate Bacteria as Sources of Carbon and Energy

Studies of the nutritional requirements of prosthecate bacteria in pure culture provide important information on the potential ecological niche of these organisms. Of interest in this regard is the spectrum of carbon sources used by individual species of

Table V. Concentration of Different Polyprosthecatelbacteria in Meadow-Black Soil under Paddy Culure

Kind of treatment	Concentration of Polyprosthecobacteria (cells/g dry soil)			
	Prosthecomicrobium polyspheroidum	Prosthecomicrobium species	Prosthecobacteria with fimbriae (Verrucomicrobium)	Stella strains
Virgin soil (no treatment)	≤ 100	Not detected	Not detected	Not detected
Soil used for a long time under the paddy culture (without addition of any fertilizers)	9×10^4	$\leq 1 \times 10^3$	$\leq 1\text{--}1 \times 10^8$	Not detected
Soil used for the paddy culture with added fertilizers (N,P,K = 180, 120 @ 9 kg/ha, respectively)	1.6×10^3	$6\text{--}373 \times 10^3$	$8 \times 10^2\text{--}3 \times 10^8$	≤ 100
Soil used for paddy culture with addition of crushed bean/grass mixture (28–30 ton/ha)	$0.7\text{--}4000 \times 10^3$	$> 1 \times 10^3$	$> 1 \times 10^6$	$\leq 1 \times 10^5$

prosthecate bacteria, their optimum concentration, as well as their requirements for other nutritional components such as vitamins. These features are also useful taxonomically in differentiating one species from another.

Early success in enriching for and isolating the polyprosthecate bacteria involved using media with low concentrations of organic compounds such as the Houwink (1951) dilute peptone medium for *Caulobacter* species, which contains 0.01% peptone (Staley, 1968). In some cases, low concentrations of ammonium sulfate (0.025–0.1%) and 0.04% phosphate and carbohydrates (L-rhamnose, glucose, or fructose) (−0.1%) were added to the medium, or yeast extract was included at a final concentration of 0.025 to 0.1% (Staley, 1968). For the isolation of *Prosthecomicrobium hirschii* a medium containing (g/liter) peptone (0.15), yeast extract (0.15), glucose (1.0), ammonium sulfate (0.25), and solutions of modified Hutner's salts and vitamins was used (Staley, 1984).

Vasilyeva and co-workers (Vasilyeva, 1970, 1972a,b, 1975; Vasilyeva *et al.*, 1974; Nikitin and Vasilyeva, 1967, 1968) also used media with low concentrations of nutrients for the enrichment of prosthecate bacteria because they select against the growth of common or banal copiotrophic eubacteria. These media contain a mixture of fulvic acids or horse manure extract. The polyprosthecate bacteria do not utilize fulvic acids as carbon sources (Nikitin, 1985), but use other components that are found with them or are produced in the enrichment cultures by other organisms.

The prosthecate bacteria grow well on dissolved organic compounds. *Prosthecomicrobium* and *Ancalomicrobium* species use mono-, di-, and some trisaccharides as carbon sources and can also use certain organic acids (Staley, 1968). *P. polysphaeroidum* resembles other species in the genus in its carbohydrate utilization pattern; however, it, and an as yet unidentified *Prosthecomicrobium* sp. (*P. sp.*), do not use organic acids for growth (Vasilyeva, 1975; Vasilyeva *et al.*, 1974).

Few *Prosthecomicrobium* and *Ancalomicrobium* species use polysaccharides although *P. litoralum* and *A. adetum* are moderately agarolytic in that they produce cavities in agar on prolonged cultivation (1 month or longer) and some may use dextrin and glycogen.

L-Amino acids are rarely used by most *Prosthecomicrobium* spp. and *A. adetum* (Staley, 1968); however, *P. polysphaeroidum* uses cysteine and histidine as sole carbon sources and the unidentified species mentioned previously, *P. sp.*, uses glutamic acid, cysteine, and cystine.

Each of the described species has its own spectrum of carbon sources that it utilizes. For example, all strains of the new species, *P. mishustinii,* use lactose, maltose, trehalose, cellobiose, sucrose, and mannose and are mixed in their utilization of other sugar alcohols, other monosaccharides, and alcohols.

Labrys monachus uses as carbon sources for growth a wide array of monosaccharides, sugar alcohols, and the disaccharides, maltose and trehalose but does not use other di-, tri-, and polysaccharides and has only a limited ability to use organic acids (lactate and gluconate) and amino acids (proline and hydroxyproline).

One of the distinctive features of the polyprosthecate bacteria is that many species have specific vitamin requirements. For example, all strains of *Prosthecomicrobium hirschii* that have been examined have a specific requirement for four B vitamins—

biotin, nicotinic acid, pantothenic acid, and thiamine (Staley, 1984). Furthermore, the deprivation of a vitamin may lead to a drastic change of morphology as was noted by accident once when a culture of *Ancalomicrobium adetum* was deprived of biotin for several transfers and developed unusual cell shapes while growing poorly (J. T. S, personal observation). Though it may seem surprising that oligotrophic bacteria would require vitamins for growth, many algae which are primary producers in the aquatic environments in which they grow also require vitamins, and vitamins are found in high concentrations in many of the environments in which they grow (Hutchinson, 1943, 1967; Wetzel, 1975).

5. Effect of Carbon and Energy Source Concentration on the Morphology of Polyprosthecate Bacteria

Early studies of pure cultures of polyprosthecate bacteria indicated that their growth and morphology were greatly influenced by the concentration of carbon sources. For example, Vasilyeva *et al.* (1974) found that an increase in yeast extract in the medium resulted in increased yield only up to a certain concentration before growth ceased and the cell morphology altered. The threshold concentration for *Prosthecomicrobium polyspheroidum* was 0.5% and for *Stella humosa* and another *Prosthecomicrobium* sp. was only 0.4%. At higher concentrations, growth was inhibited and the cells became swollen in appearance and devoid of prosthecae. Increases in temperature resulted in similar morphological changes.

A comparable effect has been noted using peptone in the growth medium of a polyprosthecate bacterium, putatively identified as *Ancalomicrobium adetum* (Whittenbury and Dow, 1977; Dow and Whittenbury, 1980). When the concentration of peptone exceeded 200 μg/ml, the cells lost their prosthecae, acquired a Y-shaped morphology, and growth slowed before ceasing completely. Similar effects were observed when *Prosthecomicrobium hirschii* was grown in the presence of peptone (AS, unpublished); however, it grows well in a medium with glucose and vitamins (Staley, 1984; Semenov and Vasilyeva, 1986a) even when the glucose concentration is 200 μg/ml (0.02%). This bacterium has a dimorphic life cycle with a long-appendaged nonmotile stage and a short-appendaged motile stage (Fig. 5). When the concentration of glucose exceeds 0.02%, their morphology is drastically altered—the prosthecae shorten and the cells lose their motility.

Similar effects have been found with *Labrys monachus* and *Stella vacuolata* (Semenov and Vasilyeva, 1985, 1986b). These radially symmetrical cells become swollen and rounded and there is a concomitant loss of prosthecae and cell symmetry. The cells form chains and many distorted involution forms occur. The cells of these organisms also fill with poly-β-hydroxybutyrate (PHB) granules. Indeed, the accumulation of PHB may actually account for the swelling and rounding process and lead to a disturbance in the normal compartmentalization of intracellular structures and functions as has been reported for some eutrophic bacteria (Pedros-Alio *et al.*, 1985).

Generally with the polyprosthecate bacteria the first noticeable morphological changes in cells occur when the substrate concentration approaches 0.025 to 0.03%, a concentration at which there is not a proportional increase in growth rate with increased substrate concentration. Marked morphological effects are noted when the substrate concentration reaches 0.25 to 0.3% where there is an actual decrease in culture yield (Semenov and Vasilyeva, 1985, 1986a,b).

All polyprosthecate bacteria that have been grown in the chemostat under conditions of limited substrate concentration exhibit normal cell morphology with prominent prosthecae (Semenov and Vasilyeva, 1985, 1986a,b). At increasing dilution rates, the predominant cells of *P. hirschii* cultures had long appendages and were nonmotile; very few cells had short prosthecae and were motile. This is consistent with observations of batch cultures in which the highest proportion of long-appendaged, nonmotile cells occurred during the log growth phase, whereas the short-appendaged, motile cells were most common when the cell density was greatest (J.T. S., unpublished). Perhaps the motile stage is a dispersal form for the bacterium. Furthermore, this effect suggests that the alternation between nonmotile and motile forms may be controlled by an autoinducer which increases in concentration during culture growth. *Stella vacuolata* does not fully differentiate all of its prosthecae at subcritical and critical high dilution rates resulting in the formation of rounded cells, which nonetheless maintain their flat radial symmetry (see Fig. 18).

There is also an effect caused by lowered concentrations of phosphate which may be analogous to that observed for *Caulobacter* spp. (Poindexter, 1964, 1981a). *Prosthecomicrobium pneumaticum* strains grown on a rich medium containing excess carbon source are bloated and without prominent prosthecae, but regain their native shape when grown on a medium low in inorganic phosphate (J. T. S., unpublished observation).

The morphology of various polyprosthecate bacteria grown under different substrate conditions is shown in Figs. 6–16.

6. Role of Prosthecae in Substrate Transport of Polyprosthecate Bacteria

Since the polyprosthecate bacteria live in oligotrophic environments, most microbiologists have regarded the prostheca as a structure whereby the cell can increase its surface area to enhance the uptake of inorganic and organic nutrients. However, this is only one of several ways in which polyprosthecate bacteria could enhance their nutrient uptake:

A. Increase in nutrient absorption without a change in cell surface area
   1. An increase in the density of transport systems per unit of cell surface
   2. An increase in substrate affinity without a change in the density of transport systems
   3. An increase in the density of transport systems and an increase in substrate affinity
B. Increase of absorption of nutrients due to an increase in surface area
   1. An increase in the number of transport systems by virtue of the increased surface area provided by the prostheca

2. An increase in the number of transport systems by the prostheca and an increase in affinity of the transport system

Some of these variations were presented by Poindexter (1981b). It is evident that an increase in the density of transport systems on the cell surface would require significant changes in cell surface structure and further, that these may adversely affect cell physiology. Unfortunately, little is yet known about this possibility.

More is known about the kinetics of the transport systems which affect substrate uptake. Considerable information is available concerning the K_m (transport system affinities) and V_{max} of various organic substrates by both eutrophic and oligotrophic bacteria (Table VI; see also Button, 1985). Generally speaking, the K_m values for most eutrophic bacteria range from about 1 μM to 100 mM for organic substrates. The K_m of bacteria considered by various authors as oligotrophs is generally lower; however, it overlaps with that of the eutrophic bacteria, ranging from about 5 nM to 150 μM. Despite the overlap, the results support the view that oligotrophs have high-affinity substrate uptake systems.

Less information is available about the effect of prosthecae on the kinetic parameters associated with substrate uptake. However, in Pate's laboratory (Jordan et al., 1974; Porter and Pate, 1975; Larson and Pate, 1975; Tamm and Pate, 1985) several studies have examined the uptake of sugars and amino acids by *Asticcacaulis biprosthecum*. They found that the K_m for isolated prosthecae was similar to that of intact cells or membrane vesicles.

Some data are also available on the polyprosthecate bacteria (Semenov *et al.*, 1986, 1988). Thus, it has been found that the glucose transport system of *Labrys monachus* is energy-, pH-, and temperature-dependent. [^{14}C]-Glucose uptake occurred between pH 4.5 and 8.5, with an optimum at 7.0–7.5. The maximum rate of uptake occurred at 40°C, but the rate was so rapid that it was not possible to calculate the initial uptake rate at low glucose concentrations. Therefore, studies were performed at 10 and 20°C. Glucose uptake was inhibited by cyanide and azide. The protonophoric uncoupling agent FCCP (carbonyl cyanide *p*-trifluoromethoxyphenylhydrazone) was the most powerful inhibitor. Almost complete inhibition was observed at 2.5×10^{-5} M under which conditions the activity corresponded to the glucose uptake in killed controls incubated at 0°C.

In contrast, the ATPase inhibitor DCCD (dicyclohexyl carbodiimide) had no effect on glucose uptake at $2–10 \times 10^{-5}$ M. Likewise, arsenate (20×10^{-3} M) had only a minor effect (it inhibited glucose uptake at a 60% level for 1 min only).

Almost all prosthecate bacteria obtain their energy by aerobic respiration. The transmembrane electrochemical potential, $\Delta\bar{\mu}H^+$, may rise because of respiration. It has been shown that there is a strong inhibitory effect of FCCP on glucose uptake in the isolated prosthecae of *Asticcacaulis biprosthecum* (Larson and Pate, 1975) as well as by intact cells of *Labrys monachus* (Semenov *et al.*, 1986), indicating the dependence of this process on the transmembrane electrochemical potential in these bacteria.

The concentration dependence of the rate of glucose uptake has been investigated using *L. monachus* (Semenov *et al.*, 1986, 1988) when grown in chemostat cultures with

Table VI. K_m and V_{max} for Substrate Transport in Some Eutrophic Bacteria

K_m	V_{max}	Substrate	Organism	Additional characteristics	References
1.55 μM	11.49 nmole/min/mg cells	Glucose	*Cytophaga johnsonae*	D = 0.03hr^{-1}	Hofle (1982)
8.54 μM	1.09 nmole/min/mg cells	Glucose	*Cytophaga johnsonae*	D = 0.20hr^{-1}	Hofle (1982)
13.8 μM	13.2 nmole/min/mg chlorophyll	Glutamine	*Anabaena variabilis*		Chapman and Meeks (1983)
100 μM	14.4 nmole/min/mg chlorophyll	Glutamine	*Anabaena variabilis*		
1.1 mM	125 nmole/min/mg chlorophyll	Glutamine	*Anabaena variabilis*		
1.4 mM	100 nmole/min/mg chlorophyll	Glutamine	*Anabaena variabilis*		
1.9 μM	36 nmole/min/mg protein	Succinate	*Rhizobium leguminosarum*		Finan *et al.* (1981)
2.6 μM	78 nmole/min/mg protein	Succinate	*Rhizobium leguminosarum*		
16 μM	2.7 μM/min/g cells	L-Isoleucine	*Streptococcus thermophilus*		Akpemado and Bracquart (1983)
46 μM	2.8 μM/min/g cells	L-Isoleucine	*Streptococcus thermophilus*		

Concentration	Activity	Substrate	Organism	Notes	Reference
36 µM	3.4 µM/min/g cells	L-Valine	Streptococcus thermophilus		Dijkhuizen et al. (1982)
20–25 µM	—	Methylamine	Arthrobacter PI		
0.045 mM	1.45 µM oxidized NADH/min/mg nitrogen	Glucose	Streptococcus salavarius		Vadebancoeur and Trahan (1982)
0.40 mM	3.1 mkM oxidized NADH/min/mg nitrogen	Glucose	Streptococcus salavarius		
3.2 µM	—	Glucose	Heterotrophic marine bacterium, P 303		Akagi and Taga (1980)
1.8 µM	—	L-Proline	Heterotrophic marine bacterium, P 303		Akagi and Taga (1980)
67 µM	—	Aspartate	Bacillus subtilis	Membrane vesicles	Whiteman et al. (1978)
66 µM	—	Aspartate	Bacillus subtilis		
70–100 nM	12.5 nmole/min/mg cells	Methylamine	Hyphomicrobium X		Brooke and Attwood (1984)
26 nM	—	Arginine	E. coli		Morita (1982)
20 nM	—	Histidine	Salmonella typhimurium		Morita (1982)
0.5 µM	—	Galactose	Salmonella typhimurium		Morita (1982)

0.25 and 2.5 g/liter of glucose. Results plotted by the Lineweaver–Burke method indicate either the existence of two separate transport systems for glucose uptake or a complex regulation of uptake. In addition, the minimal value of K_m was 40 nM which is significantly lower than that reported for other bacteria, including oligotrophs (Table VII). The high affinity of glucose transport expressed by this bacterium ensures its competitive advantage over that of eutrophic and most other oligotrophic bacteria.

The transport of substrates into cells is the initial event in microbial metabolism. For this reason an understanding of the mechanism by which energy is provided for substrate transport is an important aspect of microbial physiology. An analysis of the literature on transport indicates that most oligotrophs derive energy for transport from transmembrane electrochemical potential. Although not all authors have mentioned this process specifically, it can be deduced from data they have presented on the types of inhibitors of the process (Nicholls, 1982). For example, the uptake of glucose and amino acids by isolated prosthecae of *Asticcacaulis biprosthecum* is inhibited by proton motive force inhibitors, therefore implicating transmembrane potential in this process. The use of transmembrane electrochemical potential rather than ATP means that ATP obtained by respiration in prosthecate bacteria can be conserved for other metabolic purposes.

Another important aspect of transport systems is substrate specificity. Unfortunately, little is known about substrate specificity for prosthecate bacteria. However, Tamm and Pate (1985) have shown that the prosthecae of *Asticcacaulis biprosthecum* have three different amino acid transport systems: (1) a general (G system) transport system that transports 18 of the 20 amino acids they studied, (2) a P system which was able to transport proline and six other amino acids (some, such as proline, were also transferred by the G system), and (3) a final A system that transports the dicarboxylic amino acids, aspartate and glutamate. This work indicates that these prosthecate bacteria have transport systems of rather broad specificity.

T. V. Stepanovich (personal communication) has found that some oligotrophic bacteria, including species in the prosthecate genus, *Hyphomicrobium*, show increased respiration of substrates they cannot use as carbon sources for growth. This indicates that these substrates must be transported across the cell, and further that they can be respired as sources of energy, again suggesting rather broad specificity in transport.

7. Poly-β-hydroxybutyrate Storage and Exopolymer Production

The ability of bacteria to store carbon sources may be very important for them in an environment in which energy sources occur transiently. Three major types of storage polymers are known for heterotrophic bacteria: polysaccharides, poly-β-hydroxybutyrate (PHB) and other polyacids, and polyphosphate. Many prosthecate bacteria are known to store PHB including *Hyphomicrobium, Caulobacter, Labrys, Prosthecomicrobium, Ancalomicrobium,* and *Stella.*

In *Caulobacter* species, PHB is stored when cells are grown on media containing excess carbon source and limited in nitrogen and phosphorus (Poindexter, 1964). The storage of PHB is known to prevent turnover of protein and RNA during periods of starvation (Dawes and Senior, 1973; Poindexter, 1981a,b).

PHB is the sole known carbon storage polymer of polyprosthecate bacteria. They can store considerable amounts of PHB ranging from 36 to 38% of the dry weight of *Prosthecomicrobium pneumaticum* and *Stella humosa*, 28% of *S. vacuolata*, and 26 and 23% of *P. hirschii* and *Labrys monachus*, respectively (Semenov *et al.*, 1989a,b). The following reasons may account for the storage of PHB by these bacteria:

(1) PHB synthesis does not require ATP.
(2) PHB utilization does not require that it first be phosphorylated, and phosphate is commonly limiting in oligotrophic habitats (Poindexter, 1984a,b).
(3) PHB itself is inert, but β-hydroxybutyrate is readily metabolized.

Because PHB is now produced commercially by eutrophic bacteria (Sonnleitner *et al.*, 1979), its synthesis has been a topic of considerable research activity. During growth of eutrophic bacteria, PHB is synthesized preferably during oxygen limitation when the C/N ratio of the substrate is high (Jackson and Dawes, 1976; Nur et al., 1982; Ward *et al.*, 1977). Under such conditions, reduced equivalents such as NADH+ and NADPH+ can accumulate in the cells. This situation would be expected to occur commonly in prosthecate bacteria because their effective transport systems could often result in excess carbon uptake. In addition, these bacteria respire slowly and live in environments in which the utilizable nitrogen sources are often in very low concentration. It is for this reason that the polyprosthecate bacteria are able to store PHB even during growth at low substrate concentrations.

Curiously, the polyprosthecate bacteria are not known to store polyphosphate whereas this is commonly stored by oligotrophic bacteria. Not only might this serve as a storage polymer for phosphorus which could be used during periods of phosphorus limitation, but it might also serve as an energy source for some bacteria (Nikitin, 1985; Nikitin *et al.*, 1979; Poindexter, 1981b).

Some polyprosthecate bacteria, namely *Ancalomicrobium adetum* and some *Prosthecomicrobium* spp., can also produce extracellular polysaccharides. The exoglycan of *P. pneumaticum* is a high-molecular-weight (200,000) glycan of galactose with acidic pyruvateketal and *O*-acetyl groups (Semenov and Botvinko, 1988). The exoglycan of *Hyphomicrobium* strain JTS 811 consists of glucose, mannose, 2-*o*-methylmannose, and pyruvic acid residues (Kanamaru *et al.*, 1982). The physiological function of extracellular polysaccharides of bacteria is not known. For *P. pneumaticum*, the polymer is highly adhesive and may enable it to attach in appropriate places in the habitat. They may also be a means by which surplus energy and carbon can be disposed of during periods when growth is unbalanced, which seems the more likely reason in the case of the oligotrophic prosthecate bacteria.

8. Growth and Physiological Characteristics of Oligotrophs and Prosthecobacteria

There are several growth kinetic features that typify the polyprosthecate bacteria. First, they exhibit low growth rates even under optimum growth conditions. Second, they have high affinities for substrate. Third, they have low maintenance coefficients.

Table VII. K_m and V_{max} for Transport of Substrates Known for Some Oligotrophic Nonprosthecate and Prosthecate Bacteria

K_m	V_{max}	Substrate	Organism	Additional characteristics	References
7nm and 100 nM	— —	Glucose Glucose	Heterotrophic marine bacterium St. LN B-155	The bacterium growing at low concentrations of nutrients	Hodson et al. (1979)
56 nM and 200 nM	— —	Glutamate Glutamate	Vibrio sp. "	"	Ishida et al. (1979)
13 μM	—	Glucose	Pseudomonas sp. St. 486	Oligotrophic bacterium	Akagi and Taga (1980)
200 nM	—	L-Proline	"	"	
220 nM	—	Glucose	Oligotrophic bacteria	St. LW2	Moaledj and Overbeck (1980)
1.2 μM	—	Glucose	"	St. N^{-6}	
1 μM	—	Acetate	"	St. B,B	
2.4 μM	—	Acetate	"	St. LW2	
11.1 μM	385 pmole/min/mg protein	Proline	Asticcacaulis biprosthecum	Isolated prosthecae	Porter and Pate (1975)
1.8 μM	358 pmole/2 min/mg protein	Glucose	A. biprosthecum	Isolated prosthecae	Larson and Pate (1976)

34 μM	1250 pmole/2 min/mg protein				
40 nM	4.1 nmole/min/mg dry mass of cells	Glucose	L. monachus	Cells grown in chemostat at glucose concn 0.25 g/liter	Semenov et al. (1986, 1988)
1.25 μM	12.5 nmole/min/mg dry mass of cells				
0.1 μM	2.0 nmole/min/mg dry mass of cells	Glucose	L. monachus	Cells grown in chemostat at glucose concn 0.25 g/liter	Semenov et al. (1986, 1988)
1.25 μM	2.0 nmole/min/mg dry mass of cells	"	"	"	"
15 μM	58 pmole/2 min/mg protein	Histidine	A. biprosthecum	Isolated prosthecae	Tamm and Pate (1985)
14 μM	30 "	Glycine	"	"	
2.5 μM	52 "	Proline	"	"	
134 μM	15 "	"	"	"	

The data supporting these attributes will be briefly reviewed and then their implications will be discussed.

The growth of an organism, especially its growth rate, is the integrated expression of the intensity of its metabolism and, as such, is an important and fundamental characteristic of an organism (Jannasch, 1963).

Both intra- as well as extracellular limiting or inhibiting factors can be responsible for a decrease in the growth rate of a microorganism (Pirt, 1975; Panikov and Zvyagintsev, 1983b). The growth rates for eutrophic bacteria are largely determined by external factors, namely nutrient concentrations. When nutrients are available in high concentrations, their growth rate increases correspondingly, and vice versa for low concentrations. In contrast, the low maximum growth rates of oligotrophic polyprosthecate bacteria cannot be explained by external factors.

A central theory can be developed that helps explain the slow growth of oligotrophs and eutrophs. This theory is based on Monod's concept (1949) of a key rate-limiting step in metabolism that could internally control the growth of an organism (such as an oligotroph) and Ierusalimsky's idea (1966) of environmental limiting factors which could act externally to control growth rate (such as in eutrophs). Golovlev (1985) mentioned three levels at which growth rate could be controlled internally: (1) synthesis of major macromolecules, (2) transport of organic substrates into the cell, and (3) the state of metabolic processes responsible for generating energy.

Several parameters can be measured in assessing the growth of a microbial population. These include the specific growth rate (μ), the specific maximum growth rate (μ_{max}), the coefficient of economy (y), the saturation constant (K_s), and the maintenance energy coefficient (m) as well as others (Panikov and Zvyagintsev, 1983a,b; Pirt, 1975, 1982).

According to Zavarzin's (1970) definition, the "microbiota of dispersion" is a group of microorganisms characterized by growth kinetics, not by substrates utilized. These are organisms with low K_s values. However, it might also include organisms with moderate K_s values and high μ_{max} inasmuch as these organisms are sometimes found associated with the microbiota of dispersion. Thus, the microbiota of dispersion includes both oligotrophs and some banal eutrophs.

The polyprosthecate bacteria have long been regarded as oligotrophic members of the microbiota of dispersion because of their utilization of low-molecular-weight compounds and their poor growth on rich laboratory media (Vasilyeva et al., 1974). However, only recently have the kinetic parameters associated with oligotrophic growth been determined for representatives of the polyprosthecate bacteria using batch cultures and chemostats (Semenov and Vasilyeva, 1985, 1986a,b; Semenov, 1987b). Experiments have been conducted with *Prosthecomicrobium hirschii, P. mishustinii, P. polyspheroidum,* and *Labrys monachus* using different glucose concentrations (0.01 to 0.05%) and *Stella vacuolata* with glutamate at the same concentrations (Table VIII).

At all tested substrate concentrations, each organism exhibited the same lag period regardless of the initial substrate concentration. *P. mishustinii, P. hirschii,* and *L. monachus* all had a very short exponential growth phase with prolonged stationary phase. *S. vacuolata* and *P. polyspheroidum* did not undergo exponential growth at all.

Table VIII. Kinetic Growth Characteristics of Several Oligotrophic polyprosthecatelbacteria

Growth parameters	L. monachus			P. hirschii		P. polyspheroidum	P. mishustinii	S. vacuolata	
	Glucose			Glucose		Glucose	Glucose	Glutamate	
Substrate concentrations during bacterial growth, mg/liter	100	250	2.5×10^{-3}	250	2.5×10^{-3}	100	100	100	250
Specific maximal growth rate, hr^{-1}	0.15	0.13	0.13	0.09	0.09	0.149	0.08	0.06	0.05
Minimal generation time, hr	4.62	5.33	5.33	7.70	7.70	4.65	8.66	11.6	13.9
Substrate constant (K_s), mg/liter	2.4×10^{-1}	—	—	5.4×10^{-2}	—	6.9×10^{-1}	2.2×10^{-1}	$< 1 \times 10^{-2}$	
Economic coefficient, %	76	62.1	—	52.0	—	—	—	65.0	53.0

Instead they grew at a linear rate which ended with a prolonged stationary phase. There was a proportionate increase in biomass with increase in substrate concentration for only a limited concentration range (0.01% to 0.1%), depending on the species (*L. monachus*, *P. mishustinii*, and *S. vacuolata*, 0.025 to 0.03%, and *P. hirschii*, 0.1%). In *P. hirschii* an increase in substrate concentration to 0.25–0.3% resulted in a decrease in biomass in batch cultures indicative of some unknown limiting and/or inhibiting growth factors, either external or internal. The morphological changes of these organisms in response to increased carbon source concentrations have been discussed previously.

Kinetic parameters have been determined by computer analysis of growth curves. The specific growth rate of *L. monachus* and *P. hirschii* is dependent on substrate concentration in an inhibitory fashion. The μ_{max} values from these growth curves are similar to those obtained in chemostat culture, but K_s values were greatly overestimated (Fig. 19). Therefore, batch cultivation is of limited utility in determining growth kinetic parameters of polyprosthecate bacteria. Furthermore, the inability of these bacteria to grow at such high (for oligotrophs) concentrations of substrate (in this case at >700 mg/liter) may be explained physiologically by growth inhibition.

As mentioned heretofore, the growth of microorganisms in nature is frequently limited by nutrient availability. The condition of nutrient limitation can be easily established by limitation of the carbon and energy source. Thus, the data obtained from chemostats should relate closely to the kinetics that would be expected in the natural habitat. The growth curves of *L. monachus*, *P. hirschii*, *P. polyspheroidum*, *P. mishustinii*, and *S. vacuolata* obtained with 0.01 and 0.025% of substrate produced classical chemostat curves (Fig. 20). When *L. monachus* and *P. hirschii* were grown using

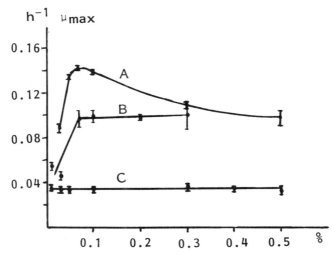

Figure 19. Dependence of the maximal specific growth rate on the substrate concentration in the medium (A) *L. monachus* and (B) *P. hirschii*: growth on the glucose-containing medium; (C) *S. vaculoata:* growth on the glutamate-containing medium.

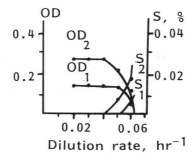

Figure 20. Chemostat growth curves of *S. vacuolata*. $OD_{1,2}$: the biomass at 0.01 and 0.025% glutamte concentrations in the medium; $S_{1,2}$: the residual substrate concentrations.

0.25% glucose under these conditions, glucose was no longer limiting (Fig. 21). Other growth parameters of polyprosthecate bacteria determined during these continuous cultivation experiments are shown in Table VIII.

Thus, the low specific maximum growth rates typical of polyprosthecate bacteria are compensated for by their higher affinity for substrate, i.e., their K_s values are one to two orders of magnitude lower than the K_s values reported for other bacteria grown with the same or an analogous substrate (Pirt, 1975).

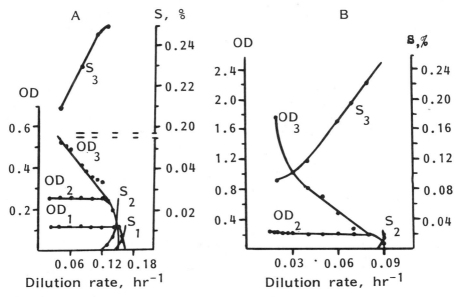

Figure 21. Chemostat curves on *L. monachus* (a) and *P. hirschii* (b) growth on media with different glucose concentrations. $OD_{1,2,3}$: the biomass in the case of growth on medium with 0.01, 0.025, and 0.25% glucose, respectively; $S_{1,2,3}$: the residual substrate concentrations.

The polyprosthecate bacteria respond to a decrease in the substrate concentration (from 0.025% to 0.01%) by an increase of their specific maximum growth rate and an increase in their coefficient of economy (Table VIII). Furthermore, when grown at low substrate concentrations the polyprosthecate bacteria have extremely low (close to zero) maintenance energy requirements. A marked increase of substrate concentration (from 0.025% to 0.25%) leads to a change in the limiting growth factor. Moreover, there is evidence of either growth inhibition due to the substrate and/or possibly to the products of metabolism. Unlike eutrophs, the oligotrophic polyprosthecate bacteria are incapable of using all of the substrate when it is supplied at high concentrations; instead they use only a necessary but small amount, indicating their unique and economical metabolic capabilities.

In conclusion, oligotrophic polyprosthecate bacteria cannot compete with eutrophs at high substrate concentrations because (1) eutrophs have higher specific growth rates and (2) polyprosthecate bacteria undergo substrate inhibition and nutrient limitation at high substrate concentrations. This inhibitory effect may be due to an interference of the excess substrate or other metabolites in normal cell reproductive processes.

Polyprosthecate bacteria have an advantage over eutrophic bacteria at low substrate concentrations because: (1) they have lower K_s values, (2) their metabolism is more economical, and (3) they can grow with a high maximal growth rate when substrate concentrations are low.

One final physiological feature may also play an important role in the survival of the polyprosthecate bacteria, namely respiratory activity. Respiratory activity of *L. monachus, P. hirschii, P. mishustinii,* and *S. vacuolata* always occurs regardless of the substrate, but is lowest when the cultures are grown under conditions of nutrient limitation (Semenov, 1986, 1987a). The respiratory activity of *L. monachus, P. hirschii,* and *S. vacuolata* ranges between 6.4 and 21.0 nmole O_2 per min per mg dry cell biomass; that of *P. mishustinii* is somewhat higher, between 23 and 50 nmole O_2. Thus, although the polyprosthecate bacteria are strict aerobes, they take up oxygen in amounts close to that of microaerophilic/facultative anaerobic bacteria such as *Propionibacterium acnes* and *Pediococcus halophilus* (Midgley *et al.,* 1984; Kanbe and Uchida, 1985). The low total respiratory activity, and their low response in respiration to an increase in substrate, combined with their ability to synthesize PHB lead us to suggest that the respiratory chain may be the key limiting step in the metabolism of these bacteria, or according to Monod and Ierusalimsky, their "master, rate-limiting reaction" in metabolism.

References

Akagi, Y., and Taga, N., 1980, Uptake of D-glucose and L-proline by oligotrophic and heterotrophic marine bacteria, *Can. J. Microbiol.* **26:**454–459.

Akpemado, K. M., and Bracquart, P. A., 1983, Uptake of branched-chain amino acids by *Streptococcus thermophilus, Appl. Environ. Microbiol.* **45:**136–140.

Albrecht, W., Fischer, A., Smida, J., and Stackebrandt, E., 1987, *Verrucomicrobium spinosum,* a eubacterium representing an ancient line of descent, *Syst. Appl. Microbiol.* **10:**57–62.

Bauld, J., Bigford, R., and Staley, J. T., 1983, *Prosthecomicrobium litoralum*, a new species from marine habitats, *Int. J. Syst. Bacteriol.* **33:**613–617.

Blagoveschenskaya, G. G., 1989, Microbial Cenoses of the Meadow-Black Soils During the Long-Term Rice Growing, Thesis, Moscow (in Russian).

Brooke, A. G., and Attwood, M. M., 1984, Methylamine uptake by the facultative methylotroph *Hyphomicrobium* X, *J. Gen. Microbiol.* **130:**459–463.

Button, D. K., 1985, Kinetics of nutrient limited transport and microbial growth, *Microbiol. Rev.* **156:**122–129.

Chapman, J. S., and Meeks, J. S., 1983, Glutamine and glutamate transport by *Anabaena variabilis, J. Bacteriol.* **156:**122–129.

Chernykh, N. A., Vasilyeva, L. V., Ginijatullina, A. I., and Semenov, A. M., 1990, DNA–DNA hybridization of new Prosthecomicrobium strains, *Microbiology* **59:**127–132 (in Russian).

Cruden, D. C., and Markovetz, A. J., 1981, Relative numbers of selected bacterial forms in different regions of the cockroach hindgut, *Arch. Microbiol.* **121:**129–134.

Dawes, E. A., and Senior, P. J., 1973, The role and regulation of energy reserve polymers, *Adv. Microb. Physiol.* **10:**135–266.

Dijkhuizen, L., de Boek, L., Boers, R. H., Harder, W., and Konings, W. H., 1982, Uptake of methylamine via an inducible energy-dependent transport system in the facultative methylotroph Arthrobacter P. 1, *Arch. Microbiol.* **133:**261–266.

Dow, C. S., and Lawrence, A., 1980, Microbial growth and survival in oligotrophic freshwater environments, Microbial growth and survival in extremes of environment, Autumn, Demonstr., Meet, London, pp. 1–20.

Dow, C. S., and Whittenbury, R., 1979, Prosthecate bacteria, in: *Developmental Biology of Prokaryotes,* Oxford, pp. 139–165.

Dow, C. S., and Whittenbury, R., 1980, Prokaryotic form and function, in: *Contemporary Microbial Ecology* (D. C. Ellwood, J. M. Hedger, M. J. Latham, J. M. Lynch, and J. H. Slater, eds.), Academic Press, New York, pp. 391–417.

Dow, C. S., Westmacott, D., and Whittenbury, R., 1976, Ultrastructure of budding and prosthecate bacteria, in: *Microbial Ultrastructure* (R. Fuller and D. W. Loverlock, eds.), Academic Press, New York, pp. 187–221.

Duchow, E., and Douglas, H. S., 1949, *Rhodomicrobium vannielii,* a new photoheterotrophic bacterium, *J. Bacteriol.* **58:**409–416.

Finan, T. M., Wood, J. M., and Jordan, D. C., 1981, Succinate transport in *Rhizobium leguminosarum, J. Bacteriol.* **148:**193–202.

Fischer, A., Roggentin, T., Schlesner, H., and Stackebrandt, E., 1985, 16S ribosomal RNA oligonucleotide cataloguing and the phylogenetic position of *Stella humosa, Syst. Appl. Microbiol.* **6:**43–47.

Gebers, R., Moore, R. L., and Hirsch, P., 1981a, DNA/DNA reassociation studies on the genus Pedomicrobium, *FEMS Microbiol. Lett.* **11:**283–286.

Gebers, R., Moore, R. L., and Hirsch, P., 1981b, Deoxyribonucleic acid base composition and nucleotide distribution of Pedomicrobium spp., *Zentralbl. Bakteriol. Parasitenkd, Infektionskr. Hyg. Abt. 1 Orig. Reihe C* **2:**332–338.

Gebers, R., Moore, R. L., and Hirsch, P., 1984, Physiological properties and DNA/DNA homologies of *Hyphomonas polymorpha* and *Hyphomonas neptunium, Syst. Appl. Microbiol.* **5:**510–517.

Gebers, R., Wehmeyer, U., Roggentin, T., Schlesner, H., Kölbel-Boelke, J., and Hirsch, P., 1985, Deoxyribonucleic acid base compositions and nucleotide distribution of 65 strains of budding bacteria, *Int. J. Syst. Bacteriol.* **35:**260–269.

Golovlev, E. L., 1985, The metabolic limitation of microbiological synthesis, in: *Problems of Biochemistry and Physiology of Microorganisms,* Puschino on Oka, pp. 76–84 (in Russian).

Gorlenko, V. M., 1968, A new species of green thiobacteria, *Rep. USSR Acad. Sci.* **179:**1229–1231 (in Russian).

Gorlenko, V. M., and Lebedeva, E. V., 1971, New green sulphur bacteria with apophyses, *Microbiology* **40:**1035–1039.

Harder, W., and Attwood, M. M., 1978, Biology, physiology, and biochemistry of *Hyphomicrobium, Adv. Microb. Physiol.* **17:**303–359.

Henrici, A. T., and Johnson, D. E., 1935, Studies of freshwater bacteria. II. Stalked bacteria, a new order of schizomycetes, *J. Bacteriol.* **30:**61–93.

Hirsch, P., 1974a, Budding and/or appendaged bacteria, in: *Bergey's Manual of Determinative Bacteriology,* 8th ed. (R. E. Buchanan and N. E. Gibbons, eds.), Williams & Wilkins, Baltimore, pp. 148–151.

Hirsch, P., 1974b, Budding bacteria, *Annu. Rev. Microbiol.* **28:**391–444.

Hirsch, P., and Schlesner, H., 1981, The genus *Stella,* in: *The Prokaryotes: A Handbook on Habitats, Isolation and Identification of Bacteria,* Vol. 1 (M. P. Starr and H. Stolp, eds.), Springer-Verlag, Berlin, pp. 461–465.

Hodson, R. E., Carlucci, A. F., and Azam, F., 1979, Glucose transport in a low nutrient marine bacterium, *Abstr. 79th Annu. Meet. ASM,* Los Angeles, p. 189.

Hofle, M. G., 1982, Glucose uptake of *Cytophaga johnsonae* studied in batch and chemostat culture, *Arch. Microbiol.* **133**(4):289–294.

Houwink, A. L., 1951, *Caulobacter* versus *Bacillus* spec. div., *Nature* **168:**654–655.

Hutchinson, G. E., 1943, Thiamine in lake waters and aquatic organisms, *Arch. Biochem.* **2:**143–150.

Hutchinson, G. E., 1967, *A Treatise on Limnology. II. Introduction to Lake Biology and the Limnoplankton,* Wiley, New York.

Ierusalimsky, N. D., 1966, Principles of regulation of microorganisms' growth rate, in: *Controlling Biosynthesis,* Nauka, pp. 5–19 (in Russian).

Ishida, Y., Imai, J., and Kadota, H., 1979, Growth and activity of an aquatic bacterium in low nutrient media, *Abstr. 79th Annu. Meet. ASM,* Los Angeles, p. 195.

Jackson, F., and Dawes, E., 1976, Regulation of the tricarboxylic acid cycle and poly-β-hydroxybutyrate metabolism in *Azotobacter beijerinckii* grown under nitrogen or oxygen limitation, *J. Can. Microbiol.* **97:**303–312.

Jannasch, H. W., 1963, Bacteriales Wachstum bei geringen substraktkonzentrationen, *Arch. Mikrobiol.* **45**(2):323–342.

Jennings, A. V., 1899, On a new genus of bacteria *(Astrobacter), Proceedings of the Royal Irish Academy,* Third Series, Vol. 5, No. 2, pp. 312–316.

Jones, M., 1905, A peculiar microorganism showing rosette formation, *Zentralbl. Bakteriol. Parasitenkd. Abt. II* **14:**459–463.

Jordan, T. L., Porter, J. S., and Pate, J. L., 1974, Isolation and characterization of prosthecae of *Asticcacaulis biprosthecum, Arch. Microbiol.* **96**(2):1–16.

Kanamaru, K., Hieda, T., Iwamura, Y., Mikami, Y., Kisaki, T., 1982, Isolation and characterization of *Hyphomicrobium* sp. and its polysaccharide formation from methanol, *Agric. Biol. Chem.* **46**(10):2411–2417.

Kanbe, C., and Uchida, K., 1985, Oxygen consumption by *Pediococcus halophilus, Agric. Biol. Chem.* **49**(10):2931–2937.

Kölbel-Boelke, J., Gebers, R., and Hirsch, P., 1985, Genome size determinations for 33 strains of budding bacteria, *Int. J. Syst. Bacteriol.* **35:**270–273.

Larson, R. J., and Pate, J. L., 1976, Glucose transport in isolated prosthecae of *Asticcacaulis biprosthecum, J. Bacteriol.* **126**(1):282–293.

Loeffler, F., 1890, Weitere Untersuchungen über die Beizung und Färbung der Geisselen bei den Bakterien, *Centralbl. Bakteriol.* **7:**625–639.

Lysenko, A. M., Semenov, A. M., and Vasilyeva, L. V., 1984, DNA nucleotide composition of prosthecate bacteria with radial cell symmetry, *Microbiology* **53**(5):859–861 (in Russian).

Midgley, M., Noor, M. A., and Mohd, A., 1984, The interaction of oxygen with *Propionibacterium acnes*, *FEMS Microbiol. Lett.* **23**(2–3):183–186.

Mishustin, E. N., 1975, Associations of soil microorganisms, Nauka, p. 107 (in Russian).

Mishustin, E. N., 1981, Current problems in investigations of the soil microbial populations, in: *Microbial Communities and Their Functioning in the Soils*, Kiev, pp. 3–13 (in Russian).

Mishustin, E. N., 1982, The development of studies on the cenoses of the soil microorganisms, *Advances in Microbiology*, Nauka, No. 17, pp. 117–136 (in Russian).

Moaledj, K., and Overbeck, J., 1980, Studies on uptake kinetics of oligotrophic carbophilic bacteria, *Arch. Hydrobiol.* **89**(3):303–312.

Monod, J., 1949, The growth of bacterial cultures, *Annu. Rev. Microbiol.* **3**:371–394.

Moore, R. L., 1977, Ribosomal ribonucleic acid cistron homologues among *Hyphomicrobium* and various other bacteria, *Can. J. Microbiol.* **23**:478–481.

Moore, R. L., 1981a, The genera *Hyphomicrobium*, *Pedomicrobium*, and *Hyphomonas*, in: *The Prokaryotes. A Handbook on Habitats, Isolation and Identification of Bacteria* (M. P. Starr and H. Stolp, eds.), Springer-Verlag, Berlin, Vol. 1, pp. 480–487.

Moore, R. L., 1981b, The biology of *Hyphomicrobium* and other prosthecate, budding bacteria, *Annu. Rev. Microbiol.* **35**:567–594.

Moore, R. L., and Hirsch, P., 1972, Deoxyribonucleic acid base sequence homologies of some budding and prosthecate bacteria, *J. Bacteriol.* **110**(1):256–261.

Moore, R. L., and Staley, J. T., 1976, Deoxyribonucleic acid homology in *Prosthecomicrobium* and *Ancalomicrobium* strains, *Int. J. Syst. Bacteriol.* **26**:283–285.

Morita, R. Y., 1982, Starvation-survival of heterotrophs in the marine environment, in: *Adv. Microb. Ecol.* (K. C. Marshall, ed.), Plenum Press, New York, Vol. 6, pp. 171–198.

Nelidov, S. N., Vasilyeva, L. V., and Mishustin, E. N., 1986, Application of crop residues for increased rice yield in alkaline soils under amelioration, *Proc. USSR Acad. Sci. Biol. Ser.* **1**:43–57 (in Russian).

Nicholls, D. G., 1982, *Bioenergetics: An Introduction to the Chemiosmotic Theory*, Academic Press, New York.

Nikitin, D. I., 1985, The biology of oligotrophic bacteria, Doctoral thesis, Inst. Microbiol., Acad. Sci. USSR, Moscow (in Russian).

Nikitin, D. I., and Kuznetsov, S. I., 1967, Water microflora studied by electron microscopy, *Microbiology* **36**(5):938–941 (in Russian).

Nikitin, D. I., and Vasilyeva, L. V., 1967, Rod-shaped organisms with spherical inflations, *Proc. USSR Acad. Sci. Biol. Ser.* **2**:296–301 (in Russian).

Nikitin, D. I., and Vasilyeva, L. V., 1968, The new species of the soil organism *Agrobacterium polyspheroidum*, *Proc. Acad. Sci. USSR, Biol. Ser.* **3**:443–444 (in Russian).

Nikitin, D. I., Vasilyeva, L. V., and Lokhmacheva, R. A., 1966, New and rare forms of the soil microorganisms, Nauka (in Russian).

Nikitin, D. I., Andreeva, L. V., and Kotova, O. M., 1979, Conditions of medium and the cycles of development of oligotrophic soil microorganisms, in: *Ontogenesis of Microorganisms*, Nauka, pp. 217–234 (in Russian).

Nur, I., Okon, Y., and Henis, Y., 1982, Effect of dissolved oxygen tension on production of carotenoids, poly-β-hydroxybutyrate, succinate oxidase and superoxide dismutase by *Azospirillum brasilense* Cd grown in continuous culture, *J. Gen. Microbiol.* **128**(12):2937–2943.

Ostrovskaya, T. A., 1986, The number and morphological peculiarities of water bacteria—the indications of lake eutrophication, in: *Structure and Function of Communities of Water Microorganisms*, Nauka, pp. 85–88 (in Russian).

Panikov, N. S., and Zvyagintsev, D. G., 1983a, Kinetic approach to the evaluation of the diversity of microbial habitat types in soil, *Rep. USSR Acad. Sci.* **268**(5):1241–1244 (in Russian).

Panikov, N. S., and Zvyagintsev, D. G., 1983b, The role of different cultivation conditions for physiological studies of microorganisms, *Microbiology* **52**(1):161–166 (in Russian).

Pedros-Alio, C., Mas, J., and Cinezzero, R., 1985, The influence of poly-β-hydroxybutyrate accumulation on cell volume and buoyant density in *Alcaligenes eutrophus*, *Arch. Microbiol.* **143**(2): 178–184.

Pfennig, N., and Trüper, H. G., 1989, Anoxygenic phototrophic bacteria, in: *Bergey's Manual of Systematic Bacteriology* (J. T. Staley, M. Bryant, and N. Pfennig, eds.), Williams & Wilkins, Baltimore, Vol. III, pp. 1635–1709.

Pirt, S. J., 1975, *Principles of Microbe and Cell Cultivation,* Blackwell, Oxford.

Pirt, S. J., 1982, Maintenance energy: A general model for energy-limited and energy-sufficient growth, *Arch. Microbiol.* **133**(4):300–302.

Poindexter, J. S., 1964, Biological properties and classification of the *Caulobacter* group, *Bacteriol. Rev.* **28**:231–295.

Poindexter, J. S., 1981a, The caulobacters: Ubiquitous unusual bacteria, *Microbiol. Rev.* **45**(1): 123–179.

Poindexter, J. S., 1981b, Oligotrophy. Feast and famine existence, *Adv. Microb. Ecol.* **5**:63–89.

Poindexter, J. S., 1984a, The role of calcium in stalk development and in phosphate acquisition in *Caulobacter crescentus*, *Arch. Microbiol.* **138**(2):140–152.

Poindexter, J. S., 1984b, The role of prostheca development in oligotrophic aquatic bacteria, in: *Current Perspectives in Microbial Ecology* (M. J. Klug and C. A. Reddy, eds.), ASM, pp. 33–40.

Porter, J. S., and Pate, J. L., 1975, Prosthecae of *Asticcacaulis biprosthecum:* System for the study of membrane transport, *J. Bacteriol.* **122**(3):976–986.

Schlesner, H., 1983, Isolierung und Beschreibung knospender und prostecater Bacterien aus der Kiel Forde, dissertation zur Ellanging des Doctorgrades, Der Christianalbrechta-Universität, Kiel.

Schlesner, H., 1987a, *Verrumicrobium spinosum* gen. nov., sp. nov.: A fimbriated prosthecate bacterium, *Syst. Appl. Microbiol.* **10**:54–56.

Schlesner, H., 1987b, *Filomicrobium fusiforme* gen. nov., sp. nov., a slender budding hyphal bacterium from brackish water, *Syst. Appl. Microbiol.* **10**:63–67.

Schlesner, H., Kath, T., Fischer, A., and Stackebrandt, E., 1989, Studies on the phylogenetic position of *Prosthecomicrobium pneumaticum, P. enhydrum, Ancalomicrobium adetum,* and various *Prosthecomicrobium*-like bacteria, *Syst. Appl. Microbiol.* **12**:150–155.

Schmidt, J. M., 1971, Prosthecate bacteria, *Annu. Rev. Microbiol.* **25**:92–110.

Semenov, A. M., 1986, The respiration activity of oligotrophous prosthecate bacteria, *Microbiology* **55**(6):929–932 (in Russian).

Semenov, A. M., 1987a, The morpho-physiological characteristics of a group of *Polyprosthecobacteria,* Thesis, Inst. Microbiol., Acad. Sci. USSR, Moscow, p. 203 (in Russian).

Semenov, A. M., 1987b, Characteristics of soil *Prosthecobacteria, Proc. 9th Int. Symp. Soil Biol. Conserv. Biosphere* (J. Szegi, ed.), Acad. Kiado, Budapest, pp. 697–702.

Semenov, A. M., and Botvinko, J. V., 1988, Exoglycan by *Prosthecomicrobium pneumaticum, Microbiology* **57**(3):511–512 (in Russian).

Semenov, A. M., and Vasilyeva, L. V., 1985, Morpho-physiological characteristics of budding Prosthemicrobium *Labrys monachus* with radial symmetry of cell under periodical and uninterrupted cultivation, *Proc. USSR Acad. Sci. Biol. Ser.* **2**:288–293 (in Russian).

Semenov, A. M., and Vasilyeva, L. V., 1986a, The morphological and physiological characteristics of the oligotrophic prosthecobacterium *Prosthecomicrobium hirschii* grown under the conditions of batch and continuous cultivation, *Microbiology* **55**(2):248–252 (in Russian).

Semenov, A. M., and Vasilyeva, L. V., 1986b, *Stella vacuolata* growth upon batch and continuous cultivation, *Proc. USSR Acad. Sci. Biol. Ser.* **6**:959–963 (in Russian).

Semenov, A. M., Okorokov, L. A., and Vasilyeva, L. V., 1986, Discovery of the extremely high affinity to substrate of Prosthecobacteria, *Rep. USSR Acad.' Sci.* **291**(1):225–227 (in Russian).

Semenov, A. M., Okorokov, L. A., and Vasilyeva, L. V., 1988, Glucose uptake by *Labrys monachus,* a budding prosthecate bacterium with radial cell symmetry, *Microbiology* **6**:912–916 (in Russian).

Semenov, A. M., Hanzlikova, A., and Jandera, A., 1989a, Quantitative estimation of poly-β-hydroxybutyric acid in some oligotrophic polyprosthecate bacteria, *Folia Microbiol.* **34**(3):267–270.

Semenov, A. M., Hanzlikova, A., and Tenov, N., 1989b, Accumulation of poly-β-hydroxybutyrate by some oligotrophic polyprosthecate bacteria, *Microbiology* **58**(6):923–926 (in Russian).

Sonnleitner, B., Heinzle, E., Braunegg, G., and Lafferty, R. M., 1979, Formation kinetics of poly-β-hydroxybutyric acid (PHB) production in *Alkaligenes eutrophus* H 16 and *Mycoplana;* the dissolved oxygen tension in ammonium-limited batch culture, *Eur. J. Appl. Microbiol. Biotechnol.* **7**(1): 1–10.

Stackebrandt, E., Fischer, A., Roggentin, T., Wehmeyer, U., Bomaz, D., and Smida, J., 1988a, A phylogenetic survey of budding and/or prosthecate, non-phototrophic eubacteria; membership of *Hyphomicrobium, Hyphomonas, Pedomicrobium, Filomicrobium, Caulobacter,* and *"Dichotomicrobium"* to the alpha-subdivision of purple-non-sulfur bacteria, *Arch. Microbiol.* **149**: 547–556.

Stackebrandt, E., Murray, R. G. E., and Trüper, H. G., 1988b, Proteobacteria classis nov., a name for the phylogenetic taxon that includes the "Purple Bacteria and their Relatives," *Int. J. Syst. Bacteriol.* **38**:321–325.

Staley, J. T., 1968, *Prosthecomicrobium* and *Ancalomicrobium:* New prosthecate freshwater bacteria, *J. Bacteriol.* **95**(5):1921–1942.

Staley, J. T., 1971, Incidence of prosthecate bacteria in a polluted stream, *J. Appl. Microbiol.* **22**(4): 496–502.

Staley, J. T., 1984, *Prosthecomicrobium hirschii,* a new species in a redefined genus, *Int. J. Syst. Bacteriol.* **34**(3):304–308.

Staley, J. T., and Fuerst, J. A., 1989, The budding and/or appendaged bacteria, in: *Bergey's Manual of Systematic Bacteriology, Vol. III* (J. T. Staley, M. Bryant, and N. Pfennig, eds.), Williams & Wilkins, Baltimore.

Staley, J. T., and Mandel, M., 1973, Deoxyribonucleic acid base composition of *Prosthecomicrobium* and *Ancalomicrobium* strains, *Int. J. Syst. Bacteriol.* **23**(3):271–273.

Staley, J. T., Marshall, K. C., and Skerman, V. B. D., 1980, Budding and prosthecate bacteria from freshwater habitats of various trophic states, *Microb. Ecol.* **5**(4):245–252.

Stanley, P. M., Ordal, E. J., and Staley, J. T., 1979, High numbers of prosthecate bacteria in pulp mill waste aeration lagoons, *Appl. Environ. Microbiol.* **37**(5):1007–1011.

Stepanovich, T. V., 1985, Physiologo-biochemical peculiarities of oligotrophic bacteria, Thesis, Inst. Microbiol., Acad. Sci. USSR, Moscow (in Russian).

Tamm, E., and Pate, J. L., 1985, Amino acid transport by prosthecae of *Asticcacaulis biprosthecum.* Evidence of a broad-range transport system, *J. Gen. Microbiol.* **131**(10):2687–2699.

Tarakanov, B. V., 1971, Fimbria and unusual appendages in microorganisms inhabiting cattle rumen, *Microbiology* **40**(2):335–341 (in Russian).

Vadeboncoeur, C., and Trahan, L., 1982, Glucose transport in *Streptococcus salivarius.* Evidence for the presence of a distinct phosphoenolpyruvate: glucose phosphotransferase system which catalyses the phosphorylation of α-methylglucoside, *Can. J. Microbiol.* **28**(2):190–199.

Vasilyeva, L. V., 1970, A starshaped soil microorganism, *Proc. USSR Acad. Sci. Biol. Ser.* **2**:308–309 (in Russian).

Vasilyeva, L. V., 1972a, The peculiarities of the ultrastructure and the cycle of development of the bacterium *Stella humosa, Proc. USSR Acad. Sci. Biol. Ser.* **5**:782–785 (in Russian).

Vasilyeva, L. V., 1972b, On the cycle of development and cytological properties of a new soil microorganism possessing prosthecae, *Proc. USSR Acad. Sci. Biol. Ser.* **6**:860–864 (in Russian).

Vasilyeva, L. V., 1975, The soil Prosthecobacteria, *Thesis, Inst. Microbiol.*, Acad. Sci. USSR, Moscow (in Russian).

Vasilyeva, L. V., 1980, Morphological grouping of Prosthecobacteria, *Proc. USSR Acad. Sci. Biol. Ser.* **5:**719–737 (in Russian).

Vasilyeva, L. V., 1984, Oligotrophs as components of biocenosis, in: *Soil Organisms as Components of Biogeocenosis,* Nauka, pp. 232–241 (in Russian).

Vasilyeva, L. V., and Semenov, A. M., 1984, *Labrys monachus,* a genus of budding and prosthecate bacteria with radial cell symmetry, *Microbiology* **53**(1):85–92 (in Russian).

Vasilyeva, L. V., and Semenov, A. M., 1986, Prosthecobacteria of the genus *Stella* and description of a new species, *Stella vacuolata, Proc. USSR Acad. Sci. Biol. Ser.* **4:**534–540 (in Russian).

Vasilyeva, L. V., Lafitskaya, T. N., Aleksandrushkina, N. J., and Krasilnikova, E. N., 1974, Physiologo-biochemical peculiarities of Prosthecobacteria *Stella humosa* and *Prosthecomicrobium* sp., *Proc. USSR Acad. Sci. Biol. Ser.* **5:**699–714 (in Russian).

Vasilyeva, L. V., Semenov, A. M., and Giniyatullina, A. J., 1991, A new species of soil bacteria of *Prosthecomicrobium* genus, *Microbiology* **60**(2):350–359 (in Russian).

Ward, A. C., Rawley, B. I., and Dawes, E. A., 1977, Effect of oxygen and nitrogen limitation on poly-β-hydroxybutyrate biosynthesis in ammonium growth of *Azotobacter beijerinckii, J. Gen. Microbiol.* **102**(1):61–68.

Wetzel, R. G., 1975, *Limnology,* Saunders, Philadelphia, pp. 310–312.

Whiteman, P. A., Iijima, T., Diesterhaft, M., and Freese, E., 1978, Evidence for a low affinity but high velocity aspartate transport system needed for rapid growth of *Bacillus subtilis* and aspartate as sole carbon source, *J. Gen. Microbiol.* **107**(2):297–307.

Whittenbury, R., and Dow, C. S., 1977, Morphogenesis and differentiation in *Rhodomicrobium vanniellii* and other budding and prosthecate bacteria, *Bacteriol. Rev.* **41**(2):754–808.

Whittenbury, R., and McLee, A. G., 1967, *Rhodopseudomonas palustris* and *Rhodopseudomonas viridis*—Photosynthetic budding bacteria, *Arch. Microbiol.* **59**(1–3):324–334.

Zavarzin, G. A., 1970, The notion of microflora of dispersion in the carbon cycle, *J. Gen. Biol.* **31**(4):386–393 (in Russian).

Zavarzin, G. A., 1973, Incompatibility of characters in the systems of bacterial genera, *J. Gen. Biol.* **34**(4):530–538 (in Russian).

Zavarzin, G. A., 1984, Bacteria and composition of atmosphere, Nauka, Moscow (in Russian).

8

Genetic Exchange in Natural Microbial Communities

DUNCAN A. VEAL, H. W. STOKES, and GRANT DAGGARD

1. Introduction

Genetic exchange between bacteria was first observed over 60 years ago (Griffith, 1928). In recent years, considerable advances have been made in the understanding of the molecular mechanisms involved in bacterial gene transfer. We now have a clear understanding of the three basic mechanisms of genetic exchange in bacteria: conjugation, transformation, and transduction. Most of these studies were, however, performed using pure cultures of bacteria and genetic transfer was regarded largely as a laboratory phenomenon (De Flaun *et al.*, 1990). More recently, genetic exchange by each of these mechanisms has been demonstrated in a variety of natural environments (Table I).

Interest in the development of genetically engineered microorganisms (GEMs) for use in the environment has greatly accelerated our investigations into the significance of gene transfer in natural microbial communities. The concern of many is that, when released into the environment, GEMs may transfer their recombinant genes to native bacteria creating potentially harmful hybrids (McKenna, 1989). Certainly reports made over the past few years leave little doubt that horizontal gene transfer among bacteria can and does occur in the natural environment (De Flaun *et al.*, 1990; Table I). What is unknown is the frequency and significance of these transfer events. While the debate over the environmental release of GEMs has certainly focused attention on genetic transfer in natural environments, it should not be forgotten that gene flux in microbial communities is of fundamental importance to the study of both microbial taxonomy and ecology. The subject of gene transfer in natural microbial communities has been extensively reviewed in a number of publications (De Flaun *et al.*, 1990; Fry and Day, 1990; Levy and Miller, 1989; Levy and Marshall, 1988; Marshall and Levy, 1990; Reanney *et al.*, 1983; Slater, 1985; Stotzky *et al.*, 1990).

DUNCAN A. VEAL, H. W. STOKES, and GRANT DAGGARD • School of Biological Sciences, Macquarie University, Sydney NSW 2109, Australia.
Advances in Microbial Ecology, Vol. 12, edited by K.C. Marshall. Plenum Press, New York, 1992.

Table I. Selected Demonstrations of Gene Transfer *in Situ* or in Laboratory Microcosms

Mechanism	DNA source/ phenotype	Environment	Organisms	Reference
Conjugation	Plasmid DNA			
	Ab-resistance[a]	Wastewater	Enterobacteriaceae	Mach and Grimes (1982)
	Hg-resistance	River water	Fluorescent pseudomonads	Bale *et al.* (1988)
	Ab-resistance	Lake water	*P. aeruginosa*	O'Morchoe *et al.* (1988)
	Ab-resistance	Pond water	*E. coli*	Gowland and Slater (1984)
	Ab-resistance	Rhizosphere	Pseudomonads	van Elsas *et al.* (1988)
	Symbiotic	Rhizosphere	*Rhizobium*	Broughton *et al.* (1987)
	N$_2$-fixation	Soil	*Enterobacter*	Klingmueller (1991b)
	Ab-resistance	Soil	*E. coli*	Trevors and Starodub (1987)
	Ab-resistance	Soil	*Streptomyces*	Wellington *et al.* (1990a,b)
	Ab-resistance	Cheese	*Lactococcus lactis*	Gabin-Gauthier *et al.* (1991)
	Xenobiotic catabolism	Human intestine	*E. coli*	Anderson (1975)
		Fresh water	Pseudomonads	Fulthorpe and Wyndham (1991)
	Chromosomal			
	Ab-resistance	Soil	*E. coli*	Krasovsky and Stotzky (1987)
Mobilization	Plasmid			
	Ab-resistance	Soil	*E. coli and* soil pseudomonads	Henschke and Schmidt (1990)

Transduction	Ab-resistance	E. coli	Wastewater	Mancini et al. (1987)
	Thymidine kinase	Enterobacteriaceae	Drinking water	Sandt and Herson (1991)
	Plasmid			
	Ab-resistance	P. aeruginosa	Lake water	Saye et al. (1987)
	Ab-resistance	E. coli	Soil	Zeph et al. (1988)
	Chromosomal			
	Ab-resistance	P. aeruginosa	River water	Amin and Day (1988)
	Ab-resistance	P. aeruginosa	Lake water	Morrison et al. (1978)
	Agarase	V. parahaemolyticus	Seawater	Baross et al. (1974)
	Ab-resistance	E. coli	Soil	Germida and Khachatourians (1988)
	Aa-biosynthesis[b]			
Transformation	Plasmid			
	Ab-resistance	Vibrio	Seawater	Paul et al. (1991)
	Chromosomal			
	Ab-resistance	Vibrio	Seawater	Paul et al. (1991)
	Ab-resistance	P. stutzeri	Seawater	Stewart and Sinigalliano (1990)
Unknown	Plasmid			
	Ab-resistance	Enterobacteriaceae	Wastewater	Alther and Kasweck (1982)
	Ab-resistance	Enterobacteriaceae	River water	Grabow et al. (1975)
	Ab-resistance	E. coli	Seawater	Stewart and Koditschek (1980)
	Ab-resistance	E. coli	Marine sediment	Stewart and Koditschek (1980)

[a]Ab, antibiotic
[b]Aa, amino acid

The purpose of this chapter is not to produce a balanced review of existing literature in this large field, but to summarize the current state of knowledge on the mechanisms of gene transfer and how they relate to gene flux in the natural environment. We also wish to draw the attention of the reader to the variety of mechanisms of gene transfer and discuss why these may be more prominent than hitherto envisioned.

2. Significance of Gene Transfer

Gene transfer has been studied in a number of different situations. Significant conclusions about the consequences of gene transfer have been reached in both clinical and natural environments.

2.1. Medical

The presence of antibiotic-resistant microorganisms has been a clinical problem since the introduction of antibiotics in the 1940s. While perhaps a somewhat "unnatural" environment, hospitals provide a useful model for understanding microbial gene flow. Indeed, many of the important discoveries in bacterial genetics, including plasmids and transposons, have come about through study of the acquisition of antibiotic resistance. There have been several reviews of this area; one which is particularly topical is that of multiple-antimicrobial-resistant *Staphylococcus aureus* (MRSA) (Al-Masaudi *et al.*, 1991), which has been a recurring problem in hospitals around the world.

Another less prominent problem in medicine is that of enterotoxigenic organisms, most commonly *Escherichia coli,* which cause disease in both man and animals (Tzipori, 1985). The toxins responsible for disease symptoms are encoded on enterotoxigenic (Ent) plasmids (Betley *et al.*, 1986). These plasmids may also carry the genes important in colonization, e.g., genes which allow adhesion to the intestinal wall (Singer *et al.*, 1986) or for antibiotic resistances (Martinez *et al.*, 1987). Ent plasmids are conjugative and are transferred to a wide range of gram-negative bacteria including strains of *Salmonella, Vibrio, Klebsiella, Enterobacter,* and *Citrobacter* (Evans and Evans, 1983). Thus, like antibiotic resistance, pathogenicity is found in a variety of different strains isolated from different locations (McConnell *et al.*, 1981).

2.2. Environmental

A number of environmentally and agriculturally important phenotypes are encoded on transmissible replicons (Table II). With the exception of a few examples, the environmental significance of transfer of these replicons is unclear. However, these limited studies, and analogies with the spread of antibiotic-resistance genes, would indicate that their transmission may be very significant. For example, in the major classes of fast-growing rhizobia, the genes responsible for symbiosis with the legume host are encoded on large, sometimes conjugative, symbiotic (Sym) plasmids. Interspecific transfer of a Sym plasmid from *Rhizobium leguminosarum* to a nonnodulating strain of *R. meliloti* generated transconjugants which were capable of nodulating legumes (Broughton *et al.*, 1987). Such interspecific transfer of Sym plasmids has been demonstrated both in the

Table II. Examples of Transmissible Plasmid-Encoded Phenotypes

	Phenotype	Plasmid	Transfer	Reference
Catabolic	Hydrogen oxidation	pHG1	C	Friedrich et al. (1981)
	Denitrification	pHG1	C	Roemermann and Friedrich (1985)
	Citrate	pOH3122	C	Ishigaro and Sato (1979)
	Toluates	Tol	C	Williams and Murray (1974), Wong and Dunn (1974)
	Salicylates	Sal	C	Chakrabarty (1972)
	Naphthalene	Nah	C	Dunn and Gunsalus (1973)
	Octane	Oct	C	Chakrabarty et al. (1973)
	Camphor	Cam	C	Rheinwald et al. (1973)
	2,4-Dichlorophenoxy acetic acid	pJP1	C	Pemberton and Fischer (1977)
	4-Chlorobiphenyl	pAC21	C	Kamp and Chakrabarty (1979)
Synthetic	Nitrogen fixation	nif	C	Klingmueller et al. (1989)
	Carbon dioxide fixation	pHG1	C	Klintworth et al. (1985)
Morphological	Capsule	pSRQ2202	C	Vedamuthu and Neville (1986)
	Fimbriae	—	C/M	Hales and Amyes (1986)
Resistance	Copper	pT23	C	Bender and Cooksey (1986)
	Chromate	pLHB1	C	Bopp et al. (1983)
	Nickel	pMOL28	C	Mergeay et al. (1985)
	Mercury	pMOL28	C	Mergeay et al. (1985)
	Cobalt	pMOL28	C	Mergeay et al. (1985)
	Zinc	pMOL30	C	Mergeay et al. (1985)
	Cadmium	pMOL30	C	Mergeay et al. (1985)
	Tellurite	RP4^r	C	Taylor and Bradley (1987)
	UV	pQM1	C	Bale et al. (1987)
Interactions				
Phage	Phage resistance	pTR2030	C	Steenson and Klaenhammer (1985)
	Restriction modification	R56 & R64	C	Hedges (1972)
	Phage F1 sensitivity	F	C	Jacobson (1972)
Bacterial	Bacteriocin	pPM52	C	Muriana and Klaenhammer (1987)
	Agrocin 84	pAgK84	C	Farrand et al. (1985)
Animal	Enterotoxins	Ent	C	Betley et al. (1986)
	Adherence	pMAR2	C	Baldini et al. (1983)
	Phagocytosis resistance	F	C	Aguero et al. (1984)
	Invasiveness	pBL001	M	Barrow and Lovell (1988)
	Iron uptake	ColV	C	Williams (1979)
	Microbial insecticide	Cry	C	Gonzalez et al. (1983)

(*continued*)

Table II. (*Continued*)

	Phenotype	Plasmid	Transfer	Reference
Plant	Legume symbiosis	pRL6JI	M[a]	Brewin *et al.* (1980a)
	Tumour inducing	Ti	C[b]	Van Larebeke *et al.* (1975), Watson *et al.* (1975)
	Phytopathogenicity	pEA29	M	Falkenstein *et al.* (1989)
Miscellaneous	Chromosome-mobilizing ability (cma)	F	C	Ippen-Ihler and Minkley (1986)

[a]C, conjugative
[b]M, mobilizable

host legume rhizosphere (Broughton *et al.*, 1987) and in the field (Schofield *et al.*, 1987). Further retrospective studies indicate that recombination of Sym plasmids has occurred in the field (Schofield *et al.*, 1987). The study of these transfer and recombination events may help explain the apparent temporal loss of inoculant strains in the soil and could also be particularly useful in the development of superior inoculant strains of *Rhizobium* (Schofield *et al.*, 1987) and inoculation strategies.

In *Agrobacterium,* another genus of the Rhizobiaceae, the tumor-inducing (Ti) plasmid may be transferred between strains *in planta* converting nonvirulent strains of *Agrobacterium radiobacter* into phytopathogenic strains (Kerr, 1971).

There are many examples of gene transfer events enabling microorganisms to acquire novel catabolic activities (Reanney *et al.*, 1983). In one recent study, the ability of catabolic plasmids to spread through a natural bacterial population was examined with the aim of using this approach to degrade the organic pollutant 3-chlorobenzoate (Fulthorpe and Wyndham, 1991). Transconjugants of the native biota capable of degrading 3-chlorobenzoate were recovered, although their rate of catabolism of the substrate was slower than that of the original strain.

3. Homologous Recombination

To a eukaryotic biologist the concept of homologous recombination is a relatively simple one and its role in generating genetic diversity is both obvious and unquestioned. Bacteria, however, are haploid and that very fact perversely complicates any assessment of the importance of homologous recombination in these organisms. Forty years ago, questions of gene exchange in bacteria would not have been asked. Since that time though, a range of mechanisms have been identified which allow horizontal gene transfer between bacterial cells. The ability to homologously recombine DNA is probably ubiquitous among microorganisms as evidenced by the widespread presence of genes such as *recA* (Miller and Kokjohn, 1990). The only question to answer, then, is to what extent does homologous recombination contribute to the spread of genes in microbial communities? The answer to this is still not known despite an explosion in interest in recent years, particularly with regard to the recombinant DNA debate.

4. Conjugation

Conjugation is a process of gene exchange whereby DNA is passed from one bacterial cell to another by cell–cell contact. It is mediated by some, but not all, bacterial plasmids. For the purposes of discussing bacterial gene transfer, therefore, plasmids can be divided into two major groups: conjugative and nonconjugative.

The ability to conjugate is determined by a significant number of genes. The best studied example is the F plasmid of *E. coli,* which encodes in excess of 20 conjugation or transfer (*tra*) genes (Ippen-Ihler and Minkley, 1986). This appears to be the case for all conjugative plasmids and, consequently, they are never less than about 30 kb in size. The ability and extent of plasmid transfer, by conjugation, is influenced by two major factors. These are the transfer efficiency, of the plasmid, and its host range. In the laboratory, transfer efficiency is usually expressed as the number of transconjugants per donor cell, or simply the probability that a donor cell will donate its plasmid to a recipient. Depending on the conjugative plasmid involved, this may vary from near undetectable levels (ca. 10^{-8}) to 1. In addition, the transfer frequency for any given plasmid may depend substantially on environmental factors. An obvious example is temperature (Singleton and Anson, 1981), but other more subtle influences are also important. Conjugative ability is also an inherent property of the plasmid itself. The F plasmid is unusual in that its transfer genes are expressed constitutively and it is capable of transfer at near 100% efficiency. Most plasmids isolated directly from nature have considerably lower rates of transfer. In many cases this is due to regulation via a repressor of transfer function, as derepressed mutants, with much higher transfer rates, can often be isolated (Chandler and Krishnapillai, 1977). Another important factor, in natural populations, where multiple plasmid-containing organisms are common, is the phenomenon of fertility inhibition. This is a process whereby the presence of one conjugative plasmid in a cell can inhibit the ability of a second plasmid to conjugate (Atwood *et al.,* 1951). It has been suggested that fertility inhibition may be a strategy for enabling a plasmid to dominate a natural population (Gasson and Willetts, 1975). Another process which may represent a strategy with a similar role in natural populations is that of entry or surface exclusion. In this case a resident conjugative plasmid reduces, by up to several orders of magnitude, the efficiency with which a second conjugative plasmid can enter a cell possessing that resident (Ippen-Ihler and Minkley, 1986). A third property possessed by all plasmids, not just those that are conjugative, and important in understanding plasmid biology in natural populations is that of incompatibility. This is a phenomenon whereby plasmids of the same incompatibility group are unable to coexist in a growing cell through a mutual inhibition of plasmid replication (Novick, 1987). In contrast, plasmids of different incompatibility can coexist in the same cell.

The major determinant of the extent to which a plasmid may transfer in the environment is its host range or the spectrum of species and genera to which it can transfer and maintain itself. For example, the F plasmid can transfer at nearly 100% efficiency between strains of *E. coli*. It is, however, virtually confined to this species since, while it can transfer intergenerically, it cannot replicate in other than *E. coli* cells. It is thus considered to have a narrow host range. Other plasmids may have a narrow host range through an inability to transfer. In contrast, many plasmids exhibit a broad host range being able to both transfer to and replicate within a remarkable array of gram-negative bacteria. Of plasmids from the gram-negatives, members of the incompatibility groups IncC, N, P, Q, and W are generally regarded as broad host range with members of the IncP group being particularly promiscuous (Guiney and Lanka, 1989). The basis of broad host range is poorly understood but probably involves a range of factors including the nature of the plasmid's transfer genes, the type and number of plasmid-encoded replication functions, and the ability to evade host restriction systems (Thomas, 1989). Conjugal transfer at low frequency between gram-positive and gram-negative organisms has also been demonstrated (Trieu-Cuot *et al.*, 1987, 1988). This work was carried out using genetically engineered chimeric plasmids. Whereas it could be argued that this is a relatively artificial situation, evidence for natural exchange involving antibiotic-resistance genes has also been found (Brisson-Noel *et al.*, 1988).

Plasmids lacking transfer (Tra) functions may still transfer via conjugation if they are coresident in a cell with a Tra$^+$ plasmid (Falkow, 1975). This ability to be mobilized is relatively common, even in plasmids that are very small, and is essentially the result of the mobilized plasmid "borrowing" most of the transfer functions of a conjugative plasmid to effect their own transfer. That the ability to be mobilized is so common, probably reflects that it represents a mechanism of plasmid dissemination, without the need to carry the genetic machinery required for conjugal transfer. Many broad-host-range plasmids are mobilizable. For example, the broad-host-range IncQ plasmid RSF1010 can be mobilized by other plasmids of varying host range in several organisms (Willetts and Crowther, 1981). Indeed, the ability to be mobilized intergenerically is the basis for many cloning systems in gram-negative organisms other than *E. coli* (Ditta *et al.*, 1980) and mobilization of a plasmid from a genetically engineered organism to indigenous soil bacteria has been demonstrated (Henschke and Schmidt, 1990).

Plasmids as a group represent a widely dispersed class of genetic element. While they are not found in every bacterial cell, they nonetheless are probably present in some individuals of all representatives of the prokaryotes in all environments. Although they do not contain genes essential for the survival of the host cell in all environments, they do possess a remarkable array of functions that may be advantageous in certain environments. Some environmentally significant phenotypes are listed in Table II. Apart from the fact that all of these phenotypes have the potential to be disseminated by self-transfer or by mobilization, one characteristic that is worth particular mention in the context of genetic exchange is that of chromosome mobilization ability or *cma*. This is a genotype associated with some conjugative plasmids which enables transfer of part of the host chromosome to a recipient cell. Once transferred, homologous recombination may occur with the recipient chromosome. The best known example of this is the F plasmid of *E. coli*, but such plasmids exist in both gram-positive and gram-negative organisms (Helinski *et al.*, 1985). Such plasmids have made possible the development of genetic maps in a number of bacterial species.

Normally, genetic transfer is unidirectional, i.e., from donor to recipient. Recently, however, gene transfer in the opposite direction, or retrotransfer, has been identified

(Mergeay *et al.*, 1987). The basis of retrotransfer is not well understood, but appears to be due, in part, to mating aggregates involving multiple donor and recipient cells. The ability of natural conjugative plasmids to retrotransfer mobilizable plasmids, and chromosomal genes may be more common than previously thought (McClure, personal communication).

4.1. Conjugation in Natural Environments

There is no doubt that the dissemination of genes via conjugation does occur in natural environments. Studies demonstrating this date back at least 20 years (Weinberg and Stotzky, 1972). Measuring the rates and extent of gene transfer in natural environments, particularly for comparative studies, however, is more difficult. For example, even in laboratory studies there are several definitions of conjugal transfer rates which may involve relating transconjugants to the number of donors, recipients, plasmid-containing cells in the population, or other parameters. As pointed out by Simonsen (1990), even under controlled conditions, the choice of calculation can yield vastly different values. Consequently, these authors have proposed a relatively simple end-point method based on a single estimate of the donor, recipient, transconjugant population, and knowledge of the exponential growth rate of the total population. This is likely to be a useful method for standardizing transfer rates under defined experimental conditions; however, its accuracy in natural populations, as with all other methods, needs to be assessed carefully.

A number of studies have been carried out in recent years that have examined rates of conjugative transfer in natural communities. Clearly, such work has been stimulated by the need for risk assessment in relation to GEMs. Much of this work is difficult to compare since the test conditions vary enormously between studies. A general underlying theme, however, is that most workers can indeed detect transfer.

4.2. Conjugation in Terrestrial Environments

In considering terrestrial environments for example, conjugative plasmid transfer has been demonstrated within streptomycetes (Wellington *et al.*, 1990a,b), *Rhizobium* (Jarvis *et al.*, 1989), and between *E. coli* and pseudomonads (Berg and Trevors, 1990). All of these studies were done in soil, and indicated that transfer often occurs very quickly, within hours, and at high transfer rates. Studies have also been done with animals. For example, plasmid-mediated antibiotic resistance was found in a baboon population, with increased prevalence for those baboons feeding on human refuse (Rolland *et al.*, 1985). All of these findings have to be interpreted carefully, however. For example, all of the experiments mentioned only examined isolates over short periods of time; up to 10 days. To what extent then do such plasmid genes persist in a population? One recent study, involving inter- and intraspecies transfer on a farm over a 4-month period, showed that while an *E. coli* strain could be disseminated and persist in the population for the full course of the study, transfer of a conjugative plasmid to the resident biota was not detected (Marshall *et al.*, 1990). This study perhaps underlies the importance of strain variation since, while one of the two *E. coli* strains persisted in the population, the second declined very rapidly. Thus, the inability to detect transfer of the conjugative plasmid used may reflect the properties of that particular plasmid. The method of screening for transconjugants may also bias data pertaining to rates of conjugative transfer in natural environments. For example, the rate of transfer is determined by the selective media used for matings (Smit and Van Elsas, 1990). It is not surprising therefore that other natural processes can affect the outcome. Simonsen (1990) has considered in detail the dynamics of plasmid transfer on surfaces and found that on solid surfaces transfer rates were only similar to those obtained in liquid culture at high initial cell densities. At lower cell densities, transfer rates were markedly less on solid surfaces whereas the rate was less affected by lowered densities in liquid. Interestingly, the reduction on solid surfaces was less marked for a repressed plasmid than for a de-repressed mutant, suggesting that in many natural environments, where cell densities are probably low, plasmids inherently more efficient in their ability to conjugate may not be disseminated more rapidly than those with lower rates of transfer.

4.3. Conjugation in Aquatic Environments

Apart from soil, the other commonly studied environment is water. Most of the problems discussed in relation to soil also apply here. It is clear that conjugative transfer can be readily detected in aquatic environments, a significant observation in itself, since it could be envisaged that this type of environment has the potential to disseminate genes over quite large distances. Using the broad-host-range plasmid RP4, Trevors *et al.* (1990a) found that the presence of nutrients, which led to high cell numbers, or surfaces, which provided an opportunity for cell adhesion, both led to higher recoveries of transconjugants. This work is consistent with previous findings (Bale *et al.*, 1987, 1988; Rochelle *et al.*, 1989b; Trevors and Starodub, 1987). The impact of nutrient levels is important in considering runoff from agricultural land or aquatic environments receiving wastewater. Studies involving wastewater do indeed demonstrate relatively high levels of transfer (Gealt *et al.*, 1985; Mancini *et al.*, 1987). Other studies have nonetheless shown that conjugative plasmids can be recovered from more pristine environments (Cruz-cruz *et al.*, 1988; Weinberg and Stotzky, 1972) and both groups of authors believe their findings have implications warranting consideration in relation to the release of GEMs. The study of Weinberg and Stotzky (1972) is of particular interest in that it demonstrates that the copper-resistant plasmid studied, pFBA20, was still present up to a year after any obvious selective pressure was removed. Some studies have also been done to examine the potential for plasmids to be mobilized in natural aquatic environments. It is known that naturally occurring aquatic bacteria harbor plasmids that can mobilize a nonconjugative plasmid (Smith *et al.*, 1981). The mobilization of a recombinant plasmid out of *E. coli* into *Enterobacter cloacae* has been observed in drinking water (Sandt and Herson, 1991). This is perhaps a particularly significant observation since mobilization occurred in the absence of a surface epilithon to concentrate cells and thereby facilitate mobilization.

5. Transduction

Transduction is defined as the transfer of genetic information between bacterial cells mediated by a bacteriophage (Masters, 1985). Both chromosomally and plasmid-encoded genes may be transduced (Saye *et al.*, 1990). In transduction a bacteriophage incorporates a portion of the bacterial genome into the viral capsid and then infects a new host, transferring the bacterial DNA in the process. Phage particles will incorporate only a limited amount of DNA and the maximum amount of DNA which they can transduce is roughly equivalent to the size of the phage genome. In the case of phage P1, an amount of DNA equivalent to approximately 2% of the *E. coli* genome is packageable (Masters, 1985). Thus, only small numbers of genes whose loci are physically close can be cotransduced in a single phage particle (Stewart and Koditschek, 1980). The packaging of DNA in phage particles provides protection from nuclease action during DNA transfer. Therefore, in the natural environment transduction provides an attractive model for gene transfer (De Flaun *et al.*, 1990).

Two distinct types of transduction have been recognized, generalized and specialized. In generalized transduction, any allele may be incorporated into the phage at essentially equal frequency. In the case of specialized transduction, which is a consequence of integration of a temperate phage into the chromosome, only those genes which are close to the site of phage integration are transduced.

5.1. Generalized Transduction

Generalized transduction occurs during the lytic growth cycle of both lytic and temperate phage. Here, phage-encoded nucleases cleave the bacterial chromosome into small fragments some of which escape complete degradation and may be packaged in place of phage DNA in the viral capsid (Lin *et al.*, 1984). Such packaging is a rare event; typically, less than 1 in 10^6 viral capsids contain bacterial DNA. It is thought that certain sites in the bacterial DNA mimic the phage *pac* site; this is a particular site in the phage DNA cut by nucleases prior to packaging into the capsid. This can result in spurious incorporation of host DNA into the prophage head (Kokjohn, 1989). Generalized transducing phage carrying bacterial instead of viral DNA cannot establish a lytic growth cycle; however, such phage are still able to attach to and inject DNA into a new host cell. In recombination-proficient hosts, incorporation of the injected DNA may occur if the DNA shares homology with a region of the host chromosome. Such homologous recombination can result in the acquisition of novel genetic material.

5.2. Specialized Transduction

Specialized transduction is mediated by temperate phage which are able to incorporate single or multiple copies of their genome into the host bacterial chromosome at specific sites. The incorporation of phage DNA into the chromosome is by a site-specific recombination event. The integrated phage genome is termed prophage DNA and the bacteria that contain it are termed lysogenic (Lin *et al.*, 1984). When induced, phage DNA is excised from the bacterial chromosome, reestablishing the lytic cycle of phage replication. If during phage excision, an illegitimate recombination event occurs, between the phage DNA and nearby host DNA, a segment of phage DNA will be replaced by a segment of bacterial DNA and packaged into phage particles (Campell, 1977). These events occur at a very low frequency. Typically, bacterial DNA is packaged in about one bacterial cell per 10^6–10^7 lysogens (Stotzky *et al.*, 1990).

5.3. Lysogeny and Induction

Only between 1 and 10% of temperate phage particles will lysogenize (Stotzky *et al.*, 1990). Lysogeny is favored under conditions of physiological stress, e.g., nutrient limitation (Herskowitz and Hagen, 1980; Ogunseitan *et al.*, 1990). Theoretically, this response will aid the survival of the phage and its host organism (Kokjohn, 1989). In the lysogenic state, temperate phage only allow expression of a small subset of their genes. Most of the expressed genes cause the host bacterium to provide a variety of mechanisms, such as repressor-dependent immune systems, which are designed to protect the cell against infection by other phage (Kokjohn, 1989; Schmieger, 1990). Lysogeny can also change the properties of cells in a variety of ways which are known collectively as phage conversion. For example, *Corynebacterium diphtheriae* gain their pathogenic potential through lysogenization with corynebacteriophage β which carries the genes for the diphtheria toxin (Freeman, 1951). Similarly, the *Streptococcus pyogenes* exotoxin gene forms part of the genome of the temperate phage T12 (Zabriskie, 1964). The significance of such lysogenic conversions within microbial communities has not been assessed; however, there are some indications that such conversions can lead to increased fitness (Saye *et al.*, 1990). The frequency of lysogeny in natural populations varies substantially. In *Pseudomonas putida* prophage DNA is relatively rare; in *P. aeruginosa* it can approach 100%, and in *E. coli* prophage DNA may constitute up to 30% of the total DNA (Holloway and Krishnapillai, 1975). Moreover, many bacteria are polylysogenic, carrying several unrelated phage genomes per cell (Holloway and Krishnapillai, 1975).

The lysogenic state is maintained by a phage-encoded repressor. Inactivation of this repressor, which induces the lytic cycle, occurs at a spontaneous frequency of approximately one in 10^5 to 10^6 DNA replication cycles in phage (Stotzky *et al.*, 1990). Considerably higher frequencies of induction of lytic reproduction occur when cells are exposed to UV light (Lwoff *et al.*, 1950) or mutagenic chemicals (Goze *et al.*, 1975). Thus, it is possible that xenobiotic chemicals present in pollution could induce prophages of the microbial biota in natural environments (Schmieger, 1990).

5.4. Transduction in Natural Environments

Transducing phages have so far been found in over 57 bacterial species contained within 24 eubacterial genera (Kokjohn, 1989). It seems likely, therefore, that the potential for transductional gene exchange is universal within the eubacteria. Little is known, however, about transduction as a mechanism of gene transfer in natural microbial communities.

5.5. Transduction in Aquatic Environments

In an aquarium designed to simulate natural marine environments, *Vibrio parahaemolyticus* located inside oysters was transduced by the bacteriophage P4 for the gene encoding agar degradation (Baross *et al.*, 1974). Rates of transduction in the order of 10^{-2}–10^{-3} per cell were recorded. In marine environments, rates of transduction may be expected to be higher within the specialized environment of an oyster, since these filter feeders will tend to concentrate marine bacteria and they may contain high levels of *V. parahaemolyticus* bacteriophages (Baross *et al.*, 1974).

In fresh water, transduction of *Pseudomonas aeruginosa* chromosomally encoded streptomycin resistance by the generalized transducing phage F116 has been demonstrated using environmental chambers suspended in a lake (Goldberg *et al.*, 1974). Mean transduction frequencies ranged from 1.4×10^{-5} to 8.3×10^{-2} per cell during a 10-day incubation. Both cell-free lysates, grown on the donor strain, and F116 lysogens were shown to mediate transduction despite the nutritive, thermal, and ionic conditions encountered *in situ*. The test chambers used in these studies contained autoclaved lake water and, in order to optimize transduction, population densities were higher than those typically found in lake water.

In similar studies, transduction of the *P. aeruginosa* nonconjugative plasmid Rms149 by the generalized transducing phage Ω DS1 was demonstrated in a freshwater lake (Saye *et al.*, 1987). Transduction was demonstrated in both the absence and presence of the natural microbial community, at levels of *P. aeruginosa* equivalent to natural aquatic populations (Saye *et al.*, 1987). The presence of the natural community did, however, cause a rapid decrease in the numbers of introduced donors and recipients and in the number of transductants recovered. Greatest numbers of transductants were detected in the test chambers when the concentrations of donor and recipient cells were highest. Interestingly, transductants were detected in environmental chambers containing a nonlysogenic plasmid donor strain and a lysogenic recipient strain. For transduction to occur in this system, spontaneous induction of phage from the lysogen is required. These phage particles must then infect, propagate, and lyse the plasmid-containing donor. Transducing phage particles produced must then transfer donor DNA to the original lysogen.

In a more recent study by the same authors (Saye *et al.*, 1990), transduction of chromosomal DNA, by phage F116L, carrying a single locus, and cotransduction of closely linked loci was observed between *P. aeruginosa* cells in a freshwater reservoir. Transduction was observed (1) from a genetic donor lysogenic for mediating phage to a nonlysogenic recipient, (2) from a nonlysogenic donor to a lysogenic recipient, and (3) between two lysogens. Transductants were recovered at frequencies of 10^{-6} to 10^{-5} transductant per CFU. These results indicate that both primary infection of the nonlysogen and induction of the prophage from lysogens generated sufficient numbers of transducing particles to allow transduction. Induction of the prophage may have been spontaneous or in response to an unidentified inducing stimulus present in the natural environment. Transductants of lysogenized strains were recovered 10- to 100-fold more frequently than were transductants of nonlysogenic parents. The reason for this may be that lysogens may be more easily recovered owing to their immunity to superinfection and thus killing by phage (Kokjohn, 1989; Schmieger, 1990). Certainly, lysogeny can lead to increased fitness of bacteria in natural environments (Saye *et al.*, 1990) probably through lysogenic conversions which result in immunity from superinfection (Kokjohn, 1989; Schmieger, 1990). Consistent with this hypothesis, approximately 45% of the *Pseudomonas* isolates from a freshwater reservoir tested positive in colony hybridization with DNA of a naturally occurring phage from the field site (Ogunseitan *et al.*, 1990).

Clays and other particulate matter can affect bacteria–phage interactions in aquatic systems. Ripp and Miller (1991) found rates of transduction 100-fold greater in water taken from the bottom of a lake, containing large concentrations of particulate matter, than in surface waters, containing small concentrations of particulate matter. These authors speculated that the production of mixed colonies on the surface of these particles increases the effective concentration of bacteria and phages, thus increasing the probability of positive interactions between them.

5.6. Transduction in Terrestrial Environments

Generalized transduction by coliphage P1 of auxotrophic and tetracycline-resistance markers on the chromosome of *E. coli* in a sandy and silty clay loam soil has been observed (Germida and Khachatourians, 1988). Considerably greater numbers of transductants were isolated from the sandy soil than from the silty clay loam soil used. The frequency of transduction of these markers to added recipient strains of *E. coli* was 10^{-6} per cell, similar to the frequency obtained *in vitro*. Thus, conditions in nonsterile soil were apparently not detrimental to transduction by phage P1.

Zeph *et al.* (1988) have studied transduction of *E. coli* plasmid DNA in soil, by the generalized transducing coliphage P1. Presumptive transformation of nonlysogenic *E. coli* by lysates of P1 and by *E. coli* lysogenic for P1 was observed both in sterile and in nonsterile soil. In a subsequent study, presumptive transductants isolated from soils were confirmed to be lysogenic for P1 by hybridization with a biotinylated probe specific for phage P1 (Zeph and Stotzky, 1989). Using lysates of P1, approximately 10^8 transductants per gram dry weight of soil were detected in sterile soil and approximately 10^6 transductants per gram dry weight of soil were detected in nonsterile soil 4 days after inoculation. In nonsterile soil the numbers of transductants fell to approximately 10^3 per gram dry weight of soil after 28 days, whereas in sterile soil the number of transduced *E. coli* remained high. Thus, transduction occurs in the presence of the natural microbial populations. However, the rate of transduction and the survival of transductants are considerably reduced in the nonsterile soil. Amendments of nonsterile soil with nutrients did not significantly affect the number or survival of *E. coli* transductants during the 28-day experiment, even though the total numbers of *E. coli* increased by one order of magnitude in the nutrient-amended soil. The phage thus appeared capable of infecting cells and establishing lysogeny under the relatively low nutritional conditions that exist in soil. Transduction was not significantly affected by the type or amount of clay added.

Using P1 lysogenic *E. coli* the number of transductants was considerably lower than for cell-free lysates and the indigenous microbiota appeared to have a greater inhibitory effect on transduction (Zeph *et al.,* 1988). In sterile soils, $\sim 10^5$ transductants per gram of dry soil and $\sim 10^3$ PFU of free phage were recovered throughout the 22-day experiment. In nonsterile soil, $\sim 10^4$ transductants per gram of dry soil and $\sim 10^{14}$ PFU were observed. The numbers of both the lysogen and the recipient decreased from the original inoculum levels, of $\sim 10^6$ CFU per gram of soil, to undetectable levels within 20 days. Transductants and phage were only detected on the first day after inoculation. Interestingly, in all of these experiments no P1 lysogens of indigenous soil bacteria were found (Zeph *et al.,* 1988; Zeph and Stotzky, 1989) even though the host range of phage P1 includes phage-sensitive mutants of the normal soil inhabitants *Klebisella* and *Enterobacter* (Goldberg *et al.,* 1974). This may have been due to host restriction barriers and/or the rarity of P1-sensitive mutants. In these experiments, exact determination of the frequency of transduction was not possible, except shortly after the start of the experiment, because it was impossible to distinguish between changes in the number of transductants, resulting from multiplication, or lack of survival of the *E. coli* transduced early in the incubation from sequential infection by the phage (Stotzky, 1989). These studies did, however, conclusively demonstrate transduction of *E. coli* in soil. *E. coli* is not, however, an indigenous soil bacterium, although it may be found in soils treated with sewage effluent. Thus, there appear to be no studies demonstrating natural transduction of indigenous soil bacteria in nonsterile soils. Moreover, bacteriophage P1 used in these studies is not a typical phage in that it is maintained extrachromosomally as a self-replicating circular DNA, whereas most phage DNA is integrated into the chromosome (Stotzky, 1989). Furthermore, P1 is unusually large and can accommodate both the phage genome together with bacterial DNA resulting in phage particles which are self-sufficient for replication. Most phage containing bacterial DNA are defective and not self-sufficient for replication, and therefore their increase in soil would be considerably restricted compared to a nondefective phage (Stotzky, 1989).

5.7. Conclusions

Based on early work with phage such as λ and T4, it has been argued that the potential for extensive transduction will be restricted by host range (Reanney *et al.,* 1983). It is becoming clear, however, that many transducing phages have a relatively broad host range (Baross *et al.,* 1974; Colon *et al.,* 1972; Greene and Goldberg, 1985; Voeykova *et al.,* 1980). Additionally, if host range is restricted by factors other than failure to attach, then it is possible that transduction may occur beyond the recognized host range of the phage. Further, through mutation, phage host range may be extended; such mutants have been generated in the laboratory (Goldberg *et al.,* 1974). Environmental conditions may also influence host range. For example, the growth of *P. aeruginosa* PAO at elevated temperature inactivates the restriction enzyme system of this strain (Rolfe and Holloway, 1966).

Saye *et al.* (1987) have found that phage F116L is rapidly inactivated in natural aquatic environments. While it could be argued that short half lives will limit the opportunity for transduction, it is not known how representative this phage is of those in natural environments. This is an important point, since, if bacteriophages persist in the environment, the probability of transduction occurring will be high even in environments where the cell density is low. Furthermore, in soils and sediments bacteriophages may adsorb to clay minerals, especially montmorillonite, and possibly other particles, which appear to protect them against inactivation over long periods of time (Stotzky, 1980; Weinberg and Stotzky, 1972). In fact, bacteriophages adsorbed on clay minerals may serve as reservoirs of bacterial DNA in soil and other natural habitats and the packaging of genetic material in a transducing bacteriophage probably represents an evolutionary survival strategy for bacterial genes (Stotzky, 1989; Stotzky and Babich, 1986; Zeph *et al.*, 1988). It has been argued that most bacteriophage genomes exist in nature integrated into their host DNA (Reanney *et al.*, 1983). We believe, however, that the evidence presented for this is tenuous. First, not all bacteriophages are capable of lysogeny, but in any event the detailed experiments required to show the distribution of phage genomes in natural environments have not been performed.

Sufficient evidence has recently accumulated to suggest that transduction as a mechanism of genetic exchange in natural habitats is more significant than has been traditionally envisioned. However, here again, not enough is known about the prevalence, survival, and host ranges of indigenous phage in natural environments, or their ability to transduce genetic information, to assess the significance of transduction to genetic flux.

6. Transformation

Transformation embraces a wide range of biochemical mechanisms which involve the uptake and incorporation of naked DNA into the genome.

6.1. Competence

For transformation to occur in natural microbial communities, naked DNA must both persist in the environment and be taken up by cells which are competent (i.e., cells which have the ability to take up DNA), then the DNA must be maintained within these cells. Competence is a definite physiological state which is transitory in the recipient population, and its duration is restricted to a small fraction of the growth cycle (Hayes, 1968). Interest in transformation as a tool of molecular biology has resulted in the development of a variety of chemical, enzymatic, and/or physical techniques to artificially transform the majority of bacteria with foreign DNA (Saunders and Saunders, 1988). The conditions used to artificially transform bacteria are, however, unlikely to occur in natural microbial habitats.

For natural transformation to be biologically significant, bacteria which are naturally competent need to be present. These are cells which have the ability to take up DNA as part of their normal metabolic processes. Natural competence has been demonstrated in a number of gram-positive and gram-negative bacteria (Carlson *et al.*, 1983; Frischer *et al.*, 1990; Graham and Ibstock, 1978; Saunders and Saunders, 1988; Stewart,

1989; Stewart and Carlson, 1986; Stewart and Sinigalliano, 1990). However, it should be emphasized that both competent and noncompetent strains of the same species have been isolated (Carlson *et al.*, 1983; Juni, 1978; Rochelle *et al.*, 1988). In naturally transformable species, competence appears to be induced during particular stages in the growth cycle or after shifts in the nutritional status of the culture (Saunders and Saunders, 1988). For example, competence is maximal in *Pseudomonas stutzeri* (Carlson *et al.*, 1983) and *Bacillus subtilis* (Contente and Dabnau, 1979) just as the culture enters stationary phase. In *Haemophilus influenzae* and *H. parainfluenzae*, competence is stimulated by transferring an exponentially growing culture to a medium which does not support growth: if these cells are then returned to a rich medium, competence is quickly lost (Smith *et al.*, 1981). In *Streptococcus*, competence is induced by an extracellular protein termed competence factor which is produced in response to the population density and initial pH of the medium (McCarty, 1980). Addition of this exogenous competence factor can provoke competence in noncompetent streptococci (Chen and Morrison, 1987).

Spontaneous mutation of *Vibrio* strain DI-9 can result in the conversion of an apparently noncompetent strain to a naturally competent high-frequency-of-transformation (HfT) strain. Depending on the type of DNA used, increases in the transformation efficiency between 10 and 50,000 times those of the parental strain were observed (Frischer *et al.*, 1990). The HfT strains transformed at frequencies ranging from 1.1×10^{-8} to 1.3×10^{-4} transformant per recipient with plasmid DNA and at an average frequency of 8.3×10^{-5} transformant per recipient with homologous chromosomal DNA. The physiological differences between the HfT strain and the parental strain which allow more efficient transformation were not identified. However, the HfT strains bound ^{3}H-labeled bacteriophage λ DNA 2.1 times more rapidly than the parental strain. Such a small increase in the binding rate alone probably does not account for the increase in the transformation frequency observed in the HfT strains.

The potential significance of transformation in environments can only be fully appreciated with understanding of the extent of natural transformation ability (Rochelle *et al.*, 1988). Very limited information exists on the frequency of natural competence among bacteria in natural environments. The work of Stewart and Cyr (1987) indicates that 14% of culturable marine isolates display the ability to take up and express chromosomal genes under laboratory transformation conditions. However, such studies may underestimate natural transformability in species where competence can be induced by an exogenous competence factor, since strains which are nontransformable in pure culture may be rendered competent in natural mixed microbial populations by competence factor produced by other strains within the community.

6.2. Naked DNA in Natural Environments

Unlike conjugation and transduction, transformation involves the transfer of naked DNA from one cell to another. DNA is released into the environment in large quantities from dead or moribund cells or from certain viable cells which actively excrete DNA during specific growth phases (Reanney *et al.*, 1983). In many natural environments, a high percentage of bacteria produce DNase (Rochelle *et al.*, 1988) and DNA is often rapidly degraded with turnover times as short as 6.5 hr (Paul *et al.*, 1986). The survival of naked DNA in the natural environment is clearly a major factor governing the likelihood of transformation.

Lorenz and his co-workers (Lorenz *et al.*, 1981; Lorenz and Wackernagel, 1987) have reported that nucleic acids bind noncovalently to sediments and that transforming DNA resists enzymatic degradation longer when bound to sediments than when free in solution (Aardema *et al.*, 1983). The amount of DNA which adsorbed to sand increased with the increasing salinities and salt valency ($Na^+ < Mg^{2+}$ and Ca^{2+}) (Lorenz and Wackernagel, 1987). Similarly, in soils, nucleic acids are protected from nuclease action by such binding (Graham and Ibstock, 1978). Absorbed DNA is still capable of transforming cells of *Bacillus subtilis* loaded onto sand columns (Khanna and Stotzky, 1991; Lorenz *et al.*, 1988) and between intact donors and recipients in soil (Graham and Ibstock, 1978). Transformation may thus be possible in sediments and soil despite the presence of nucleases.

6.3. Transformation in Aquatic Environments

In aquatic sediments, there is considerable indirect evidence suggesting that natural transformation is a mechanism of gene transfer (De Flaun *et al.*, 1990). Marine sediments have been shown to contain particularly high concentrations of absorbed DNA (De Flaun *et al.*, 1988; Orgram *et al.*, 1987) which is often sufficiently large to encode genes or parts of genes (De Flaun *et al.*, 1987). Furthermore, several marine bacterial isolates have been reported naturally transformable (Frischer *et al.*, 1990; Stewart and Sinigalliano, 1990). Stewart and Sinigalliano (1990) found an increase in rifampicin-resistant CFU when recipient *Pseudomonas stutzeri* ZoBell cells and transforming DNA were loaded onto columns containing either sterile or nonsterile marine sediments. Although apparent transformation frequencies were lower in the nonsterile sediments, they were still 18 times that of the spontaneous resistance. Various sediments were tested and those with the highest organic matter showed the highest rate of transformation. These authors also found transformation was highest in cells tightly associated with the sediment with no transformation in the water column, thus confirming the significance of surfaces in transformation (Stewart *et al.*, 1983). Conversely, transformation frequencies up to 4.7×10^{-7} transformant per recipient were found in marine water column microcosms containing the ambient community but no detectable transformation in nonsterile sediments when using broad-host-range plasmid multimers and an HfT *Vibrio* strain as recipient (Paul *et al.*, 1991). These authors suggested that in sediments there may be greater DNase activity than in the water column or that native sediments may be sufficiently reduced or contain metabolic poisons (e.g., sulfides) which inhibit transformation. The native microbial population reduced the observed transformation frequency possibly as a consequence of nuclease digestion of DNA or competition with the natural population for DNA uptake (Paul *et al.*, 1991). Low levels of nutrient amendments were found to increase rates of transformation suggesting that transformation is more likely in environments rich in organic nutrients rather than in oligotrophic environments.

In a riverine epilithic community, Rochelle *et al.* (1988) have identified an identical 7.8-kb nonconjugative mercury-resistance plasmid in two separate strains of *Acinetobacter calcoaceticus*. DNase-sensitive transfer of this plasmid from intact cells of both isolates to a naturally competent soil isolate of the same species was demonstrated suggesting a transformation-like process. Transformation by intact donor cells was about 10^3 times more efficient than when using crude cell lysates indicating such transfer is mediated by cell-to-cell contact (Stewart *et al.*, 1983). With plasmid DNA, relatively high transformation frequencies were obtained (6.3 × 10^{-5} at 14°C) and transformation had a broad temperature optimum leading the authors to suggest that temperature would not be a factor limiting plasmid transformation within the epilithon. However, a high percentage of epilithic isolates produced DNase activity, indicating that DNA would not survive long in the epilithon and no naturally competent strains of *Acinetobacter* were isolated. Transformation in an intact epilithic community was not demonstrated.

Paul (personal communication) has demonstrated DNase-sensitive plasmid transfer from *E. coli* to a marine *Vibrio* sp. by cell contact-dependent natural transformation. Transformation was observed in both sterile and nonsterile marine microcosms. This is the first report of intergeneric natural plasmid transformation. The transforming DNA was located on the surface of the donor cell and transformation was facilitated by the donor cell, since, with purified plasmid DNA, little or no transformation was observed.

6.4. Transformation in Terrestrial Environments

In sterile soil, Graham and Ibstock (1978, 1979) have demonstrated transformation-like gene transfer with strains of *Bacillus subtilis* each having three different chromosomally-located, linked markers. *Bacillus* spores were loaded onto sterile soil and heat shock used to induce germination. Heat shocking also resulted in the release of transforming DNA and induction of competency. After 8 days of incubation, 79% of randomly selected colonies exhibited a phenotype containing markers from both parents. Transformation was presumed to be responsible for the gene transfer observed because *B. subtilis* is known to release transforming DNA and there were no detectable plasmids or generalized transducing phages in the strains employed. However, unlike other transformation systems, transfer was not sensitive to DNase. The authors speculated that the DNase could have been adsorbed on the soil particles and inactivated or the released bacterial DNA may have formed a complex with protein or bacterial membranes making them unavailable for degradation by DNase.

Stotzky (1990) has reported natural plasmid transformation in nonsterile soil at frequencies several orders of magnitude below that found in sterile soil. We could locate no other reports of natural transformation in soil in the presence of the indigenous microbiota.

6.5. Conclusions

Transformation appears to be a likely mechanism of gene exchange in the sediments and soils where bonding of DNA to particles (Aardema *et al.*, 1983; Lorenz *et al.*, 1981; Lorenz and Wackernagel, 1987) provides protection against nuclease action and maintains DNA in a biologically active form for a sufficient time for transformation to occur.

In many bacteria the ability to accept extracellular DNA is favored when cells face survival problems (Reanney *et al.*, 1983). Thus, transformation may be an adaptation in order to acquire novel phenotypes (e.g., antibiotic resistance) during unfavorable growth conditions. Evidence of an active role for donor cells in natural transformation by homologous DNA in *Pseudomonas stutzeri* (Stewart *et al.*, 1983; Stewart and Sinigalliano, 1990) further suggests that the system evolved to promote genetic exchange between closely related species, with safeguards to protect the cells from foreign DNA (Hirsch, 1990). The finding that cells can mutate to competent phenotype (Frischer *et al.*, 1990) is of particular significance in this regard since directed mutagenesis (Hall, 1990) or expression of cryptic genes (Hall *et al.*, 1983) controlling competence may result in increased rates of transformation under stressed conditions. In *Acinetobacter calcoaceticus*, however, transformation does not appear to be favored by adverse conditions as the peak of competence is reached during early stages of exponential growth (Cruze *et al.*, 1979) and transformation is favored by rapid growth of recipient cells (Singer *et al.*, 1986) on media containing higher concentrations of organic nutrients.

The maintenance of naked DNA from diverse sources in some natural environments may provide opportunities for genetic exchange across wide phylogenetic distances (Reanney *et al.*, 1983). Paul (personal communication) has demonstrated intergeneric natural transformation of *Vibrio* species by plasmid DNA from a laboratory strain of *E. coli*. Homology in the nucleotide sequences of aminoglycoside-resistance genes indirectly provides evidence of horizontal gene transfer between gram-positive and gram-negative bacteria (Trieu-Cuot *et al.*, 1985).

7. Nonhomologous Recombination

Conjugation, transduction, and transformation are all useful genetic tools and important to varying degrees in the dissemination of genes in natural microbial populations. Whereas all of these genetic processes provide mechanisms for the horizontal transfer of genetic information, there are nonetheless constraints on the extent to which this can occur. For example, chromosomal DNA entering a new cell via any of these mechanisms will only become part of the genome of the new cell if recombination occurs with existing DNA. Since recombination is dependent on significant homology existing between the recombining molecules, homologous recombination tends to preserve gene order. A similar situation exists for plasmids as homologous recombination would be expected to place constraints on the exchange of DNA between these elements as well. In addition, such plasmid features as incompatibility and entry exclusion may further limit even the opportunity for recombination between homologous plasmids to occur. In bacteria, in particular, it is known that mechanisms exist for the horizontal transfer of DNA that are free of the constraints normally imposed by homologous recombination. These mechanisms are important in understanding gene flow since they have the potential both to alter the arrangement of genes in a DNA molecule and to increase the range of available hosts which a gene can inhabit.

7.1. Transposons

It is beyond the scope of this chapter to provide a detailed review of transposons and the transposition process. Instead a number of excellent reviews are available for this purpose with perhaps the most comprehensive being that of Berg (1989). In the context of gene transfer, however, some features should be emphasized. First, they are probably ubiquitous, being found in large numbers of both prokaryotic and eukaryotic organisms. Their most distinctive feature is their ability to move from one location to another within or between DNA molecules by nonhomologous recombination. In prokaryotes, most transposable elements range in length from about 1 to 20 kb and all encode a transposase which is essential for the transposition event. This enzyme generally recognizes short inversely repeated DNA sequences at the ends of the element. These short inverted repeats are therefore also essential for transposition. Transposition in bacteria is, for the most part, a replicative process generating an additional copy of the element at the target site. Apart from the functions necessary for transposition, transposons may also encode other genes, including those for antibiotic resistance, heavy metal resistance, catabolic functions, bacteriocins, and others.

A characteristic of some gram-positive transposable elements is their ability to conjugally transfer (Roberts and Kenny, 1987). Thus, such transposons have a built-in mechanism for horizontal gene transfer and, as such, possess properties similar to those of conjugative plasmids. Many of these transposons have a broad host range and can conjugally transfer and transpose into a wide range of both gram-negative and gram-positive hosts (Bertram and Durre, 1989; Bertram et al., 1991; Clewell and Gawron-Burke, 1986; Stratz et al., 1990). Of particular interest also is that the rate of conjugal transfer of one of these transposons, Tn925, which codes for resistance to the antibiotic tetracycline, is enhanced in the presence of this drug (Torres et al., 1991). Thus, it appears that the dissemination of this element can be enhanced when located in suitable environments. By virtue of the fact that they can integrate by nonhomologous recombination, all transposons have the potential for horizontal gene transfer by, for example, their insertion into a conjugative or mobilizable plasmid. If a gene carried by a transposon is selected, then such plasmids may form a substantial part of a bacterial population as is the case of antibiotic-resistance outbreaks in hospitals. In addition, the presence of transposons has the potential to influence the gene pool in other ways. For example, the ability of the F plasmid to integrate into the host chromosome and thus generate high-frequency-of-recombination (Hfr) donor strains is a consequence of the presence in the F genome of the transposon Tn1000 which allows integration. Interestingly, Tn1000 can also mobilize nonconjugative plasmids during transposition from F, a phenomenon that has practical applications in cloning in the laboratory (Sancar and Rupp, 1979). Other transposons can have similar effects. The plasmid R68-45, a variant of the broad-host-range plasmid R68, displays a greatly enhanced chromosome-mobilizing ability as a consequence of the insertion of the transposon IS21 into the plasmid (Willetts et al., 1981). If generated in natural environments, a plasmid of this type would have the potential to spread chromosomal as well as plasmid genes. The consequences of transposon acquisition can sometimes be quite subtle. For example, chemostat experiments have demonstrated that the transposon IS50 improves the growth rate of *E. coli* compared to non-transposon-containing strains, without otherwise changing the host phenotype (Hartl *et al.*, 1983). Cells with such a fitness advantage in natural populations would have the potential to alter the gene pool.

7.2. Integrons

Site-specific recombination is being increasingly recognized as an important mechanism for the dissemination and stable integration of DNA sequences. For example, the bacteriophage λ can stably integrate into the *E. coli* chromosome by site-specific recombination (Weisberg and Landy, 1983). The virus-like particle SSV1 can similarly integrate into the chromosome of the archaebacterium *Sulfolobus* strain B12 using transfer RNA genes as the preferred target site (Reiter *et al.*, 1989). Many plasmids in the antibiotic-producing actinomycetes are also capable of site-specific recombination (Bibb *et al.*, 1981; Brown *et al.*, 1990; Cohen *et al.*, 1985).

Integrons are a recently characterized genetic element found in many plasmids and transposons of gram-negative bacteria (Stokes and Hall, 1989). They consist of two highly conserved segments of DNA between which is found a variable segment (Fig. 1) that is different for different integrons and contains one or more antibiotic-resistance genes. Integrons are unusual in a number of respects. The genes within the variable segment can be acquired or exchanged by a process of site-specific recombination that is catalyzed by a DNA integrase encoded within the 5′-conserved segment. The DNA integrase recognizes a 59-base element (Cameron *et al.*, 1986) associated with the inserted DNA segment and a site within the integron (Hall *et al.*, 1991; Martinez and De la Cruz, 1988, 1990). The inserted genes, which are always present in the same orientation, normally do not possess their own promoter but instead are all transcribed from a promoter in the 5′-conserved segment (Stokes and Hall, 1989). Integrons thus act as natural expression cassettes for any inserted genes. Exchange of antibiotic-resistance genes between integrons appears to be common as the same gene can be found at different locations in different integrons (Hall *et al.*, 1991). A model has been proposed whereby antibiotic-resistance genes can excise from these elements as small circular sequences to be inserted within another integron by a site-specific recombination event with a single crossover point (Hall *et al.*, 1991).

Recent epidemiological studies using appropriate DNA probes have shown that sequences homologous to the conserved segments of the integron are very common in multiply resistant clinical isolates (Burnside and Groot Obbink, personal communication). Interestingly, veterinary isolates with sequences homologous to integron-specific probes are less common and not always associated with multiple antibiotic resistance (Burnside and Groot Obbink, personal communication). Thus, comparison of isolates from each of these two environments may provide another avenue for investigating the environmental spread of genes by these elements.

7.3. Cassette Exchange

Cassette or module exchange is a term devised by Campbell *et al.* (1986) to describe a phenomenon first noted in plasmids from gram-positive bacteria. In *Staphylo-*

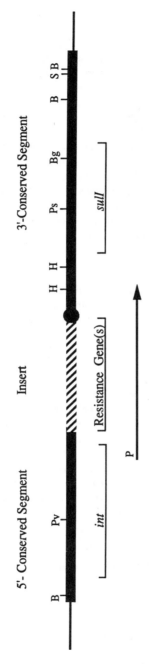

Figure 1. Idealized structure of an integron. Thick black lines represent the 5'- and 3'-conserved segments. Hatched line represented a single inserted gene cassette with its associated 59-base element shown as a solid black circle. The location of the DNA integrase (*int*) and sulfonamide resistance (*sulI*) genes ared shown. The promoter (P) for the inserted genes is shown, with the direction of transcription indicated by the arrow. Other letters represent restriction endonuclease cutting sites in the two conserved segments: B, *Bam*HI; Bg, *Bgl*II; H, *Hind*III; Ps, *Pst*I; Pv, *Pvu*II; S, *Sal*I.

coccus, in particular, it is found that Class I plasmids have blocks of sequences in common (Novick, 1989) and that these plasmids evolved by the extensive horizontal exchange of sequences. What makes cassette exchange unusual is that sequence homology between conserved regions is very high but the surrounding sequences are unrelated. Moreover, the cassette junctions are abrupt, normally definable to a base pair, as distinct from a gradual loss of homology. Cassette exchange is functionally distinct from transposons and integrons since the junctions do not appear to display the characteristic features of either of these elements. The role of cassette exchange in the horizontal transfer of DNA is unclear since it is only readily observed through the generation of DNA sequence data. One other possible example of cassette exchange may be that of the sulfonamide-resistance gene, *sulI,* where DNA sequence and restriction site map data would suggest that, while similar or identical when different isolates are compared, they can be found nonetheless in otherwise unrelated plasmids (Radstrom and Swedberg, 1988). The mechanism underlying cassette exchange is not known and perhaps provides a salutary lesson that, in assessing the likely extent of gene transfer in the environment, one needs to take into account the unexpected.

7.4. Conclusions

Given the rather sophisticated and specialized mechanisms for horizontal gene transfer by nonhomologous recombination, one may be led to question the cohesiveness of species in prokaryotes. It has nonetheless been found that species can be defined with relative ease. For example, DNA hybridization analysis reveals generally very high relatedness betwen isolates of the same species but relatively less for different species. Thus, prokaryotes have a similar species cohesiveness to eukaryotes, despite the greater barriers to horizontal gene transfer in eukaryotes (Hartl, 1985). This should not, however, be used as an argument to overlook the role of horizontal gene flow in prokaryotes. Transposons may be important in eukaryotic evolution. To name but one example, the P element, a transposon in *Drosophila,* has been implicated in contributing to speciation in that genus (Engels, 1986). Perhaps more importantly, though, is the fact that transposons and integrons, in combination with plasmids, can have a major impact on the genetic makeup of certain microbial communities under appropriate selection conditions. For example, while plasmids were common in bacteria in the "preantibiotic era," none of those which have been examined encoded antibiotic resistance (Datta and Hughes, 1983; Hughes and Datta, 1983). The impact therefore of these particular plasmids and integrons in a relatively short period of time has been quite remarkable.

8. Maintenance of Genes and Gene Flux in Microbial Communities

8.1. Selection

Microorganisms have a limited capacity to maintain homeostasis and microbial communities adapt to environmental perturbation by changes in community structure. In addition to normal methods of adaptation, microorganisms can also respond to selective pressures by horizontal gene transfer. The genetic flexibility available to bacteria in the form of high mutation rates, plasmid-borne genes, and haploidy allows bacteria to respond rapidly to changing environmental conditions in spite of the very limited genetic constitution of individual microorganisms (Day, 1987). Genetic interactions within microbial communities can be highly complex (Reanney et al., 1983). Slater (1985) has classified microbial communities into either "tight" communities (e.g., those involved in the degradation of xenobiotic compounds in which a highly interactive and interdependent community develops) or "loose" in which plasmid transfer of resistance factors (e.g., for antibiotics and heavy metals) is the predominant transfer mechanism rather than metabolic interdependence. While not attempting to review microbial community structure, we wish to focus on several aspects of importance to gene flow within such complex assemblages.

8.2. Periodic Selection

The classical model of evolution in asexual populations suggests a series of replacement cycles (periodic selection), populations essentially consisting of one clone, which when exposed to new environmental stresses undergoes a series of "replacement cycles" each clonal replacement having a higher fitness than the one it replaces (Atwood et al., 1951; Crow and Kimura, 1970). Recent work has suggested that periodic selection is a simplistic model and high levels of genetic diversity have been observed in natural populations of E. coli (Hartl and Dykhuizen, 1984). Even when an in vitro culture of E. coli was initiated with a single clone in a chemostat, after 800 generations extensive polymorphism (reflecting differences in growth rates and uptake and excretion of metabolites) developed (Helling et al., 1987). Most interestingly, Helling et al. (1987) have demonstrated that metabolites excreted by some clones were utilized by others so that perturbation of a relatively constant environment by a single clonal type is sufficient to provide opportunities for the rapid development of biodiversity.

Periodic selection can be used to explain the mechanism by which some plasmids are maintained within microbial communities. The frequency of plasmid-bearing bacteria is often significantly elevated by environmental stresses, for example in polluted environments (Eberhard, 1990; Hada and Sizemore, 1981). Plasmid load may impose a selective disadvantage to bacteria for a number of reasons (Eberhard, 1990) and may decrease competitiveness (Helling et al., 1981). However, Kelly and Reanney (1984) and Pickup (1989) have found that metal resistance plasmids may be common in both soil and water bacteria in the absence of selection pressure. This is not inconsistent with the concept of periodic selection, since if the rate of plasmid loss is relatively small, the number of plasmic-bearing cells in a population may be substantial long after the selection pressure has been removed. Similarly, catabolic plasmids (e.g., TOL plasmid) have been maintained over an 8-week period in a groundwater aquifer in the absence of any apparent selection pressure for toluene catabolism (Jain et al., 1987).

8.3. Cryptic and Mutator Genes

A problem in the modeling of the impact of gene transfer in the natural environment is that not all gene interactions will be observable. For example, cryptic genes have been defined as phenotypically silent DNA sequences, not normally expressed during the life cycle of an individual (Hall *et al.*, 1983). The characteristic feature of cryptic genes is that they are present in a subset of the population in a form in which they can be reactivated by mutation. This makes them functionally distinct from pseudogenes which are inactivated and permanently removed from the gene pool. This does not preclude their reactivation by mutation, recombination, insertion, deletion, or other genetic mechanisms. An example of a cryptic gene is the *ilvGEDA* transcription unit in *E. coli* K-12 which involves a frameshift mutation in a gene coding for α-acetohydroxyacid synthase (Hall *et al.*, 1983). The mutant gene is unaffected by product inhibition (valine) while the wild-type gene is sensitive to inhibition. Thus, depending on the concentration of valine in the environment, either the mutant or the wild-type cells can exhibit an advantageous phenotype. This mutation was found widely distributed in independent *E. coli* isolates and its spontaneous frequency of mutational activation (10^{-7}–10^{-8}) is relatively high. Other cases of cryptic genes include the phospho-β-glucosidase system of family Enterobacteriaceae and the occurrence of auxotroph "revertants" in which reversion to prototrophy for many common growth factors (e.g., isoleucine) can occur (Hall *et al.*, 1983). Another example is the spontaneous chromosomal mutation in *E. coli* K-12 allowing utilization of citrate as the sole carbon source (Hall, 1982). This is of significance since lack of citrate utilization is a primary means of distinguishing *E. coli* from other enterics. Therefore, either reactivation of cryptic genes, or acquisition of plasmid-encoded genes from an unrelated organism may result in the misidentification of environmental isolates, whether indigenous or introduced. Cryptic genes can be retained, within microbial communities, without having any selective advantage, even if selection for the reactivated gene only occurs occasionally (Wen-Hsiung, 1984). Thus, the loss of a cryptic gene from a microbial population is likely to be an extremely rare event, unless populations go through severe genetic bottlenecks. Cryptic genes have also been found on plasmids (De Vos *et al.*, 1984; Guiney *et al.*, 1984).

Periodic selection and the rate at which microbial populations can adapt to *in vitro* conditions are significantly influenced by mutation rate. Clearly, high rates of mutation will potentially allow clones of higher fitness to develop at a rapid rate and therefore a rapidity of clonal replacement in asexual populations. In *E. coli* the estimated mutation rate is somewhere between 10^{-6} and 10^{-7} per gene replication. Using a gene in *E. coli* which increases the mutaiton rate (*mut T*), Chao and Cox (1983) have demonstrated that this gene confers an evolutionary advantage in chemostat experiments compared with isogenic strains in a frequency-dependent manner. Similarly, Chao and Cox (1983) have described the maintenance of Tn5 and Tn10 in *E. coli* populations in chemostats in the absence of any known selective pressure. The advantage conferred is frequency dependent and coincides with a change in location of Tn10, new insertions converging on a site within a 3.2-kb fragment of the genome. This suggests an evolutionary role for transposable elements like Tn10 as "mutator" genes allowing rapid adaptation in microbial populations. Gross and Siegel (1981) have observed mutator strains in natural *E. coli* populations at a frequency of 0.24%.

8.4. Directed Mutation

A cornerstone of contemporary biology is that mutations occur randomly and independently of the environment. Subsequently, mutations that are by chance advantageous are selected for, therefore increasing the frequency of the new variant. Over the years, questions have been raised over the universal validity of this view, but the principle of randomly generated mutations has generally stood firm. Recently, however, the debate has reopened in a serious way with the report by Cairns *et al.* (1988) of directed mutations. These are mutations which arise selectively as a response to the environment and the concept has generated a lot of controversy (Benson *et al.*, 1988; Charlesworth *et al.*, 1988; Lenski, 1989). Most of the evidence for directed mutations comes from studies with bacteria, most notably from the work of Barry Hall. Hall has demonstrated in a series of experiments that spontaneous mutations can be more frequent when advantageous (Hall, 1990) and that multiple mutations may not occur as rare independent events when the consequences of such mutations are advantageous (Hall, 1988, 1989, 1991).

Several hypotheses have been put forward to explain, at the molecular level, how these mutations may arise. What is perhaps most relevant here, however, are the consequences of directed mutations for gene pools in the natural environment particularly in relation to GEMs. For example, such mutations arise under conditions of physiological stress (Hall, 1990) and these conditions may be quite common in natural environments. Directed mutations, which may involve point mutations or transposable elements, have been shown to activate formally functional genes inactivated either by mutation or by cryptic genes (Hall, 1988, 1990). Thus, cells possess the "potential" to acquire the desired function. Conceivably, however, an existing gene could be modified by a directed mutation to acquire a related but new function. In any event, when designing containment vectors for the release of modified genes into the environment, thought should be given to the potential for directed mutations to occur. For example, the inactivation of the transfer functions of a plasmid by transpositional insertion may generate a vector that is highly unlikely to revert on the basis of spontaneous mutations. In the appropriate environment, however, directed mutations may increase the probability of reversion substantially.

9. Distribution and Persistence: Implications for Gene Transfer

Temporal and spatial barriers are likely to be critical factors in governing the rate and extent of gene transfer in the natural environment.

9.1. Microbial Distribution and Movement

The small size of bacteria and their limited capacity for movement mean that spatial barriers are likely to be particularly important factors governing the likelihood of gene flow in the natural environment. The movement of both plant and animal pathogens via a wide range of vectors is well documented (Andorv, 1986; Atlas and Bartha, 1987).

Additionally, more direct distribution mechanisms such as water percolation (Masden and Alexander, 1982; Trevors *et al.*, 1990b), earthworm disturbance (Henschke *et al.*, 1989), and even transportation by protozoa (Heynen *et al.*, 1988) are likely to have an important impact on the movement of both bacteria and free DNA in the environment. However, in soil, using a LacZY-marked (Barry, 1986) *Pseudomonas aureofaciens*, Drahos *et al.* (1986) found that migration, in the field, was largely limited to 18 cm horizontally from the point of application and 30 cm vertically. This is consistent with root alone associated dispersal. This study, however, may reflect poor survival of this organism at distance from the root rather than any lack of migration, as soil composition is an important factor in both bacterial survival and transport (Trevors *et al.*, 1990b).

Rates of gene transfer are unlikely to be uniform in the environment. Environmental heterogeneity results in zones of intense microbial activity, e.g., in the rhizosphere, phylloplane, and epilithon. Such zones are likely to be associated with elevated rates of genetic exchange, since it is known that the rate of gene transfer is related both to the population density (Gowland and Slater, 1984; Rochelle *et al.*, 1989b) and to the physiological state of donor and recipient bacteria. Certainly, higher rates of gene exchange *in situ* have been observed in the epilithon (Rochelle *et al.*, 1989b) and in the rhizosphere (Van Elsas *et al.*, 1988, 1991). Plant roots exude a variety of low-molecular-weight compounds (Rovira *et al.*, 1979) and microorganisms exhibit a positive chemotaxis toward the rhizosphere in response to such exudates (Dowling and Broughton, 1986; Zaulin *et al.*, 1988). Roots may therefore act as attractors of bacteria and thus, potentially, be foci for genetic exchange.

The interaction of bacteria, phages, and soil particles has been extensively documented (Burns, 1980; Schiffenbauer and Stotzky, 1982; Stotzky and Babich, 1986). Lytic organisms such as phage or *Bdellovibrio* may play an important role in gene exchange by lysing bacteria resulting in the release of free DNA (Dowling and Broughton, 1986) which may be available for transformation. Additionally, physical, physiological, and genetic factors have a significant effect on the rate of bacterial gene exchange. In general, the presence of the microbial community reduces genetic exchange (Acea *et al.*, 1988; Bale *et al.*, 1987; Van Overbeek *et al.*, 1990). The nature of this inhibition has, however, not been determined.

9.2. DNA Persistence in the Environment

There are a number of mechanisms by which DNA can be stabilized in the environment. For example, bacterial cells may persist in oligotrophic environments longer than predicted by death rate kinetics (Lynch, 1990; Morita, 1982). Cells may adapt to low nutrient conditions by arresting their metabolism and obtaining maintenance energy requirements by utilizing dead cells (Morita, 1982). Such longevity was observed with *Enterobacter cloacae*, *Pseudomonas putida*, and *Azospirillum brasilense*, suggesting that this may be a common property of soil bacteria (Lynch, 1990). Soil particles can accumulate DNA, protect DNA from DNase activity (Khanna and Stotzky, 1991; Lorenz *et al.*, 1981), and influence bacterial transformation rates (Lorenz *et al.*, 1981; Richaume *et al.*, 1989; Van Elsas *et al.*, 1988). Similarly, the same effect of adsorption on clay and other particles occurs for phage (Stotzky, 1980; Weinberg and Stotzky, 1972).

Recent field trials suggest a limited persistence of released GEMs in the natural environment. For example, field planting of wheat seed coated with LacZY-marked *Pseudomonas aureofaciens* followed by harvesting of the wheat crop and a subsequent soybean crop resulted in an inability to detect marked *P. aureofaciens* in a second winter wheat crop planted on the site, emphasizing the apparent temporal limitations to persistence faced by this released bacterium (Drahos *et al.*, 1986).

10. Genetically Engineered Microorganisms

The planned release of GEMs has been the subject of considerable discussion (Domsch *et al.*, 1988; Glick and Skof, 1986; Hodgson and Sugden, 1988; Levin *et al.*, 1987; Lindow, 1987; Pickup *et al.*, 1991; Tiedje *et al.*, 1989). In assessing the ecological impact of GEMs, Brownlea and Roiko (unpublished) have posed six critical questions:
(1) Will the organism be released into the environment? (2) Will the organism survive? (3) Will the organism proliferate? (4) Will the organism spread beyond where it was intended to perform its task? (5) Will the organism cause ecological damage where it spreads? (6) Will the organism transfer any of its novel traits to another host?

It is this last question, the likelihood of transfer of recombinant DNA in the environment, rather than the establishment and environmental perturbation by GEMs, that we will examine in the following section.

10.1. Considerations Prior to Environmental Release

Once a GEM is released into the environment, we believe it must be assumed that the genes released will be available for transfer to other organisms. The question to be assessed is how likely is that transfer to occur and what are the consequences of such transfer.

Models presently being developed for predicting the spatial movement of released GEMs rely on the inability of engineered genes to transfer from the host organism to others in the environment (Molak and Stara, 1988). This, however, needs to be validated on a case-by-case basis for each GEM release to evaluate not only the ability of genes to migrate by traditional methods (conjugation, transduction, transformation) but also the stability and transfer of DNA released. The ability of clay-containing soils to protect DNA from degradation and the probable widespread release of GEMs suggest that models need to be designed which will test not only the limits of DNA stability in the natural environment but also the combinational effects of released DNA interacting with other genes.

Successful use of contained microcosms to model the fate of GEMs [*P. fluorescens* (lacZY) and *P. syringae* (Ice$^-$)] in the natural environment suggests some degree of confidence in the current case-by-case approach to GEM risk analysis (Slater, 1985). However, limitations in risk assessment of GEM releases include not only the length of

Table III. Examples of Environmental Releases of Genetically Engineered Microorganisms

Species	Gene	Country	Use	Reference
Pseudomonas syringae	Ice⁻	USA	Control of frost damage	Lindow and Panopoulos (1988)
Pseudomonas fluorescens	lacZy	USA	Field release marker	Drahos *et al.* (1988)
		Australia		Ryder (personal communication)
Agrobacterium tumefaciens	K84	Australia	Biocontrol of crown gall	Kerr (1989)
Rhizobium fredii	lacZY	Australia	Field release marker	Rolfe *et al.* (1989)

time available for evaluation and the number of possible environmental probabilities to be tested but also that such assessment is currently based on accumulated negative evidence from a limited number of trials (Table III).

10.2. Mechanisms to Prevent Transfer of Recombinant DNA

There are a number of factors which may limit genetic exchange in the natural environment. These include environmental barriers (effects of temperature, soil type, pH, etc.), entry barriers (degree of natural competence, host range of transducing phages, cellular envelope compatibility and pili formation, etc.), and barriers to stable DNA integration (restriction systems, plasmid/phage incompatibility) (Miller, 1988). Further, barriers to gene expression, for example, promoter compatibility within a foreign host, may limit the detection of such genetic exchange (Miller, 1988). The effects of these factors on gene exchange in natural environments have yet to be evaluated. Thus, genetic exchange involving recombinant organisms is unpredictable. The introduction of deletion mutants (e.g., Ice⁻) is likely to produce the least risk, as no novel DNA is released into the environment, whereas the release of GEMs containing novel genes is generally considered more hazardous.

The breakdown of genetic barriers between released GEMs and indigenous bacteria may result in the generation of new, pathogenic isolates. This has occurred in the case of non-GEMs; e.g., *Agrobacterium tumefaciens* K84, carrying a plasmid for agrocin 84, used to biologically control crown gall disease. Transfer of this plasmid to indigenous pathogenic strains resulted in the development of pathogenic, agrocin 84-resistant strains. In response to this breakdown in biological control, the transfer region (Tra) of plasmid pAgK84 was first inactivated by Tn5 insertion and subsequently deleted to prevent reversion. The result was a Tra⁻ *A. tumefaciens* strain K1026 (Kerr, 1989). This strain is as effective against pathogenic *A. tumefaciens* as the original and *in vitro* attempts to remobilize pAgK84 have demonstrated the effectiveness of the removal of the Tra region in maintaining gene isolation. However, transfer by mechanisms not dependent on the deleted *Tra* functions may lead to the breakdown of this barrier to transfer in the natural environment.

Transposons have also been used as vectors for the introduction of genes into a bacterial chromosome of microorganisms intended for release into the environment (Barry, 1986). In the case of a transposon, containment can be achieved by the removal or inactivation of the transposase gene. The defective transposon containing the engineered genes is transposed into the desired location in the laboratory by the presence of a functional helper transposon or similar element producing an active transposase, which is removed from the cell prior to release. Thus, in principle the engineered transposon is locked in position. This does not preclude the possibility, however, that the cell could acquire a functional transposon after release which could facilitate retransposition. If this occurred onto a broad-host-range conjugative plasmid, the engineered genes would be free to move.

10.3. Monitoring Released DNA

There has been considerable interest in developing techniques to monitor GEMs released into the environment (Barkay and Sayler, 1988; Ford and Olsen, 1988; Jain et al., 1988; Olsen, 1991; Pickup and Saunders, 1990; Trevors and Van Elsas, 1989; Zeph and Stotzky, 1989). These techniques differ in their fidelity and sensitivity (Table IV). Many of these techniques will be of limited value when DNA is transferred into other bacterial species in natural environments. With many of these methods, detection depends on the culturability of cells and on the ability to detect a gene product. For example, typically less than 10% of viable cells can be cultured from most natural environments. Furthermore, not all hosts will express acquired genes; e.g., the transfer of genes for arginine catabolism from *P. putida* to *E. coli* results in only 2% efficiency of the expression of that in the original strain (Clark, 1984).

In the natural environment, nutrient limitations may significantly slow bacterial growth rates and alter both their rate of loss and culturability. Arrested metabolic rates in both marine and soil bacteria, subjected to starvation conditions, may be quite a common survival strategy in the natural environment (Morita, 1982; Roszak and Colwell, 1987). For example, while the generation time of rhizobia may be as short as 9–12 hr in the rhizosphere, it can exceed 200 hr in the soil, where nutrients may be limited (Bowen and Rovira, 1976).

There is significant distinction between bacterial viability and culturability. The number of bacteria capable of forming colonies on solid media can be much less than the number metabolically active (often by orders of magnitude) in freshwater, marine, and soil environments. This "viable but nonculturable" stage has been reported for many bacteria including: *E. coli, Shigella sonni, Shigella flexeai, Salmonella enteritidis, Aeromonas salmonicida, Vibrio cholerae,* and *Pseudomonas fluorescens* (Cruz-cruz et al., 1988; Linder and Oliver, 1989; Trevors et al., 1990b) using standard laboratory conditions and media.

Using DNA isolated directly from the natural environment, amplified using the polymerase chain reaction (PCR) overcomes several of these problems. It is both very sensitive and does not require the culturing of cells (Steffan and Atlas, 1988). However, quantification of the number of target cells within a sample may then present additional

Table IV. Limits of Various Detection Systems and Methods[a]

Method	Cells per ml or per g	Indigenous background	Target	Medium	Reference
Viable nonselective plating	10^3	10^6	xylE	Lake water	Morgan *et al.* (1989)
Viable selective plating	10^1	10^6	RP4-Tol	Lake water	Pickup *et al.* (1990)
Bioassay	10^3	10^6	xylE	Lake water	Morgan *et al.* (1989)
ELISA	10^3	10^6	xylE	Lake water	Morgan *et al.* (1989)
Luminometry	10^3	ND[b]	lux	Soil	Rattray *et al.* (1990)
DNA hybridization	10^3	10^6	xylE	Lake water	Morgan *et al.* (1989)
Solution hybridizaton	10^2–10^3	ND	2,4,5-T	Soil	Steffan and Atlas (1990)
DNA hybridization MPN	10^1–10^2	ND	Tn5	Soil	Fredrickson *et al.* (1988)
Polymerase chain reaction (PCR)	10^2 (100 g)	10^{11}	2,4,5-T	Soil	Steffan and Atlas (1988)
Fluorescent oligonucleotides	3×10^5	10^8	16 S RNA	Mixed suspension	Amman *et al.* (1990b)

[a] Adapted with permission from Pickup (1991).
[b] ND, not determined.

difficulties. Thus, the use of both qualitative and quantitative analysis techniques will be important in assessing the extent of gene transfer events in the natural environment (Pickup *et al.,* 1991).

Not all microorganisms are equally amenable to DNA analysis. Viruses and protozoa may occur at low densities (Olsen, 1991) necessitating a filter/concentrating step for their detection. Furthermore, there is the problem of extracting DNA from different bacteria with equal efficiency. Most DNA extraction protocols have been developed for gram-negative bacteria and in many polluted sites the efficiency of lysis is only about 85% with as much as 100% variation in samples taken from the same location (Olsen, 1991). Thus, while using the chromosomally encoded lacZY marker system in field release experiments failed to detect functional transfer of this gene system to the indigenous microbiota, based on the identification of 10,000 lacZY-positive isolates (Kluepfel *et al.,* 1991), this does not preclude possibly phenotypically silent (nonfunctional or nonculturable) transfer events.

While there may be no apparent effect of plasmid type on bacterial survival in fresh water (Cruz-cruz *et al.,* 1988; Devanas *et al.,* 1989), changes in plasmid expression due to starvation have been reported (Caldwell *et al.,* 1989; Caulcott *et al.,* 1987). For example, the loss of plasmid expression and maintenance in the starvation survival of bacteria in well water is dependent on both plasmid type and host (Caldwell *et al.,* 1989). In the case of R388:Tn1712 (Tp^r, Tc^r), expression of plasmid-encoded antibiotic resistance in four bacterial species (*Enterobacter agglomerans, Escherichia coli, Klebsiella pneumoniae,* and *Pseudomonas cepacia*) rapidly declined to undetectable levels even though the plasmid was still maintained at quite high levels within the population (>50%). Similarly, *E. coli,* exposed to seawater, rapidly entered a nonculturable state though plasmid DNA could still be recovered (Byrd and Colwell, 1990).

The problems presented by variability in bacterial viability, culturability, and plasmid expression *in vivo* present difficulties for both modeling and assessing gene transfer in natural environments. Clearly, the current case-by-case approach to the evaluation of GEM release is essential, not only for monitoring and understanding the dispersal and impact of the released GEM on the natural environment and its ecology, but also for evaluating the genetic fidelity and stability of the released GEM in the natural environment.

11. Future Directions for Research

From the available evidence, most of which has been collected over the past decade, it can be concluded that genetic transfer does occur in a wide range of natural environments (Table I). A variety of mechanisms of genetic transfer between bacteria have been identified and the molecular mechanisms mediating such transfers are becoming increasingly well understood. These mechanisms of transfer have been studied primarily with pure cultures of bacteria in the laboratory. There is a dearth of information about gene transfer *in situ,* in the presence of the indigenous microflora, and more research effort needs to be focused in this area.

Many of the *in situ* studies which have been performed indicate that extrapolations from pure culture, laboratory studies, may not be valid within natural microbial communities. For example, transformation was considered to be unlikely as a mechanism of extensive gene transfer in the natural microbial communities because of the presence of nucleases which will denature any naked DNA and due to the apparent rarity of naturally competent bacteria. However, it now appears that transformation may be quite significant in some environments where binding of DNA to sediments or soils provides protection against nuclease action (Aardema *et al.*, 1983; Lorenz *et al.*, 1981; Lorenz and Wackernagel, 1987) or where cell-to-cell contact facilitates transformation (Stewart *et al.*, 1983; Paul, personal communication). If we are to assess the significance of transformation in any natural environment, a better understanding of the factors governing the survival of DNA in a range of different environments is required. Further, little is known about the frequency of, or factors governing, uptake of DNA by bacteria in natural environments.

Similarly, for transduction, it is now apparent that phage may persist in soils and sediments for long periods of time absorbed to clay minerals (Stotzky, 1980; Weinberg and Stotzky, 1972) and phage host ranges may not be as restricted as previously considered (Colon *et al.*, 1972; Greene and Goldberg, 1985; Rolfe and Holloway, 1966; Voeykova *et al.*, 1980). However, once again, most of these studies are laboratory based and we really know very little about bacteriophage ecology.

The majority of reports of gene transfer in the natural environment involve conjugation. Conjugation is generally considered to be the most likely mechanism of extensive genetic transfer within microbial communities. While this may be true for zones of intense microbial activity such as the epilithon (Rochelle *et al.*, 1989b) or rhizosphere (Klingmueller, 1991), these are not typical of many microbial communities where bacterial densities and growth rates are lower. Rates of conjugative transfer are dependent on the density of donors and recipients, with no transfer being detected below a critical cell density (Gowland and Slater, 1984; Rochelle *et al.*, 1989b). In many environments, low cell densities and growth rates are typical. The persistence of bacterial DNA, perhaps long after the demise of the host bacterium, either adsorbed directly onto sediments or soil or contained within a phage absorbed onto clay, suggests that transduction and transformation may make a more significant contribution to gene flux than conjugation in such environments. However, we know of no studies which have attempted to measure the relative contribution of conjugation, transduction, and transformation to gene flux.

There is currently considerable interest in the development of recombinant DNA products for use in the environment, such as bacteria with improved N_2-fixing capabilities, recombinant biological control agents, live vaccines, mineral-mobilizing bacteria, xenobiotic-catabolizing bacteria, etc. By their nature, these products will involve the release of GEMs into the environment. Much of the current work on gene transfer has been prompted by concerns over the fate of GEMs released. Based on current knowledge, we believe it cannot be assumed that recombinant DNA will not be horizontally transferred to natural microbial communities, no matter how contained within the released organism. However, what is unclear is the likelihood and factors which govern such events. There is a need, therefore, to develop suitable methods to monitor gene transfer rates in natural environments. Possibly of more significance to the GEM debate than transfer *per se,* is the role selection plays on the survival and establishment of recombinant genes, in whatever host, and the perturbation these genes cause to the environment. Thus, perhaps, we should give more consideration to the effects of novel genes introduced into the environment, whether in a GEM or nonmanipulated host, rather than to the transfer of those genes. Certainly, more basic ecological data on GEMs in natural environments and their effects are required to enable the assessment of risks arising from their environmental introduction.

Although stimulated by the debate over the release of GEMs, gene transfer is of wider academic and applied significance. The fact that bacteria exchange genetic information may be used to introduce novel phenotypes into complex microbial communities. For example, Fulthorpe and Wyndham (1991) have demonstrated the proliferation of a chlorobenzoate-degrading plasmid through a microbial community. The authors believe that the alternative hosts are better adapted *a priori* to conditions in that environment than the original introduced host. The ability of such catabolic plasmids to transfer and be expressed in indigenous bacteria is clearly of benefit from the point of view of remediating contaminated waters (Fulthorpe and Wyndham, 1991). This approach has, potentially, many applications. For example, a similar approach could be adopted, using the Sym plasmid, to improve the legume/rhizobium symbiosis in the field. Genetic flux in microbial communities is of considerable fundamental importance to the microbial ecologist studying microbial population biology and evolution. The differentiation of organisms into species depends on a degree of genetic isolation from other organisms. Interspecies gene transfer may tend to blur our concept of a species and for microbial taxonomy an understanding of the extent and barriers to gene transfer within natural microbial communities is required.

Much of the debate on the extent of genetic transfer in natural microbial communities, we feel, has been based on preconceived ideas for which there is a little experimental justification. There is a clear need to develop methodologies to test these ideas, and quantify gene transfer, in a variety of environments. Such experiments require a multidisciplinary approach, involving collaboration between microbiologists in the areas of molecular biology, ecology, and genetics. The ultimate objectives should be to produce and test quantitative models of, and determine the significance of, genetic exchange in the environment. These models need to consider not only the organisms themselves, but also the ecology of their phage and lytic organisms and the survival and uptake, by bacteria, of naked DNA in the environments. Not only are the data lacking in these areas but methods to collect the data are currently poorly developed. However, we feel that confident that current, emerging interest in the application of molecular methods to microbial ecology will not only help to provide answers to these questions but will be of mutual benefit to the advancement of both disciplines.

ACKNOWLEDGMENTS. We thank Dr. John Watson and Dr. Nick McClure for their valuable comments on the drafts of this manuscript.

References

Aardema, B. W., Lorenz, M. G., and Krumbein, W. E., 1983, Protection of sediment adsorbed transferring DNA against enzymatic inactivation, *Appl. Environ. Microbiol.* **46:**417–420.

Acea, A. J., Moore, C. R., and Alexander, M., 1988, Survival and growth of bacteria introduced into soil, *Soil Biol. Biochem.* **20:**509–515.

Aguero, M. E., Arow, L., DeLuca, A. G., Timmis, K. N., and Cabello, F. C., 1984, A plasmid-encoded outer membrane protein Tra T enhances resistance of *Escherichia coli* to phagocytes, *Infect. Immun.* **46:**740–746.

Al-Masaudi, S. B., Day, M. J., and Russell, A. D., 1991, A review: Antimicrobial resistance and gene transfer in *Stephylococcus aureus, J. Appl. Bacteriol.* **70:**279–290.

Altherr, M. R., and Kasweck, K. L., 1982, *In situ* studies with membrane diffusion chambers of antibiotic resistance transfer in *Escherichia coli, Appl. Environ. Microbiol.* **44:**838–843.

Amin, M. K., and Day, M. J., 1988, Donor and recipient effects on transduction frequency in situ, *REGEM* **1:**11.

Amman, R. I., Binder, B. J., Olsen, R. J., Chisholm, S. W., Devereux, R., and Stahl, D. A., 1990, Combination of 16S rRNA-targeted oligonucleotide probes with flow cytometry for analysing mixed microbial populations, *Appl. Environ. Microbiol.* **56:**1919–1925.

Anderson, E. S., 1975, Problems and implications of chloramphenicol resistance in typhoid bacillus, *J. Hyg.* **74:**289–299.

Andorv, D. A., 1986, Dispersal of microorganisms with emphasis on bacteria, *Environ. Manage.* **10:**470–487.

Atlas, R. M., and Bartha, R. (ed.), 1987, *Microbial Ecology,* 2nd ed., Benjamin–Cummings, Menlo Park, Calif.

Atwood, K. C., Schneider, L. K., and Ryan, F. J., 1951, Selective mechanisms in bacteria, *Cold Spring Harbor Symp. Quant. Biol.* **16:**345–354.

Baldini, M. M., Kaper, J. B., Levine, J. B., Candy, D. C., and Moon, H. W., 1983, Plasmid-mediated adhesion in enteropathogenic *Escherichia coli, J. Pediatr. Gastroent. Nutr.* **2:**534–538.

Bale, M. J., Fry, J. C., and Day, M. J., 1987, Plasmid transfer between strains of *Pseudomonas aeruginosa* on membrane filters attached to river stones, *J. Gen. Microbiol.* **133:**3099–3107.

Bale, M. J., Fry, J. C., and Day, M. J., 1988, Transfer and occurrence of large mercury resistance plasmids in river epilithon, *Appl. Environ. Microbiol.* **54:**972–978.

Barkay, T., and Sayler, G. S., 1988, Gene probes as a tool for the detection of specific genomes in the environment, in: *Aquatic Toxicology and Hazard Assessment* (W. J. Adams, G. A. Chapman, and W. G. Landis, eds.), American Society for Testing and Materials, Philadelphia, pp. 29–36.

Baross, J. A., Liston, J., and Morita, R. Y., 1974, Some implications of genetic exchange among marine *Vibrio parahaemolyticus,* naturally occurring in the Pacific oyster, *International Symposium on Vibrio parahaemolyticus* (T. Fujino, G. Sakaguchi, R. Sakazaki, and Y. Takeda eds.), Saikon, Tokyo, pp. 129–137.

Barrow, P. A., and Lovell, M. A., 1988, The association between a large molecular mass plasmid and virulence in a strain of *Salmonella pullorum, J. Gen. Microbiol.* **134:**2307–2316.

Barry, G. F., 1986, Permanent insertion of foreign genes into the chromosomes of soil bacteria, *Bio/Technology* **4:**446–449.

Bender, C. L., and Cooksey, D. A., 1986, Indigenous plasmids in *Pseudomonas syringae pv.* tomato: Conjugative transfer and role in copper resistance, *J. Bacteriol.* **165:**534–541.

Benson, S. E., Partridge, L., and Morgan, M. J., 1988, Is bacterial evolution random or selective? *Nature* **336:**21–22.

Berg, D. E., 1989, Transposable elements in prokaryotes, in: *Gene Transfer in the Environment* (S. B. Levy and R. V. Miller, eds.), McGraw–Hill, New York, pp. 99–138.

Berg, G., and Trevors, J. T., 1990, Bacterial conjugation between *Escherichia coli* and *Pseudomonas sp.* donor and recipient cells in soil, *J. Ind. Microbiol.* **5:**79–84.

Bertram, J., and Durre, P., 1989, Conjugal transfer and expression of streptococcal transposons in *Clostridium acetobutylicum,* *Arch. Microbiol.* **151:**551–557.

Bertram, J., Strätz, M., and Durre, P., 1991, Natural transfer of conjugative transposon Tn916 between Gram-positive and Gram-negative bacteria, *J. Bacteriol.* **173:**443–448.

Betley, M. J., Miller, V. L., and Mekalanos, J. J., 1986, Genetics of bacterial enterotoxins, *Annu. Rev. Microbiol.* **40:**577–605.

Bibb, M. J., Ward, J. M., Kieser, T., Cohen, S. N., and Hopwood, D. A., 1981, Excision of chromosomal DNA sequences from *Streptomyces coelicolor* forms a novel family of plasmids detectable in *Streptomyces lividans, Mol. Gen. Genet.* **184:**230–240.

Bopp, L. H., Chakrabarty, A. M., and Ehrlich, H. C., 1983, Chromate resistance plasmid in *Pseudomonas fluorescens, J. Bacteriol.* **155:**1105–1109.

Bowen, G. D., and Rovira, A. D., 1976, Microbial colonization of plant roots, *Annu. Rev. Phytopathol.* **14:**121–144.

Brewin, N. J., Beringer, J. E., Buchanou-Wollaston, A. V., Johnston, A. V., and Hirsch, P. R., 1980a, Transfer of symbiotic genes with bacteriocinogenic plasmids in *Rhizobium leguminosarum, J. Gen. Microbiol.* **116:**216–270.

Brewin, N. J., DeJong, T. M., Phillips, D. A., and Johnston, A. W. B., 1980b, Co-transfer of determinants for hydrogenase activity and nodulation ability in *Rhizobium leguminosarum, Nature* **288:**77–79.

Brisson-Noel, A., Arthur, M., and Courvalin, P., 1988, Evidence for natural gene transfer from Gram-positive cocci to *Escherichia coli, J. Bacteriol.* **170:**1739–1745.

Broughton, W. J., Samrey, U., and Stanley, J., 1987, Ecological genetics of *Rhizobium meliloti:* Symbiotic plasmid transfer in the Medicago sativa rhizosphere, *FEMS Microbiol. Lett.* **40:**251–255.

Brown, D. P., Idler, K. B., and Katz, L., 1990, Characterization of the genetic elements required for site-specific integration of plasmid pSE211 in *Saccharopolyspora erythraea, J. Bacteriol.* **172:**1877–1888.

Burns, R. G., 1980, Microbial adhesion to soil surfaces: Consequences for growth and enzyme activities, in: *Microbial Adhesion to Surfaces* (R. C. W. Berkeley, J. M. Lynch, J. Melling, P. R. Rutter, and B. Vincent, eds.), Horwood, Chichester, pp. 249–262.

Byrd, J. J., and Colwell, R. R., 1990, Maintenance of plasmids pBR322 and pUC8 in nonculturable *Escherichia coli* in the marine environment, *Appl. Environ. Microbiol.* **56:**2104–2107.

Cairns, J., Overbaugh, J., and Miller, S., 1988, The origin of mutants, *Nature* **335:**142–145.

Caldwell, B. A., Ye, C., Griffiths, R. P., Moyer, C. L., and Morita, R. Y., 1989, Plasmid expression and maintenance during long-term starvation-survival of bacteria in well water, *Appl. Environ. Microbiol.* **55:**1860–1864.

Cameron, F. H., Groot Obbink, D. J., Ackerman, V. P., and Hall, R. M., 1986, Nucleotide sequence of the AAD(2") aminoglycoside adenylyltransferase determinant aadB. Evolutionary relationship of this region with those surrounding aadA in R538-1 and dhfrII in R388, *Nucleic Acids Res.* **14:**8625–8635.

Campbell, A., Ma, D. P., Benedik, M., and Limberger, R., 1986, Reproductive isolation in prokaryotes and their accessory DNA elements, in: *Antibiotic Resistance Genes: Ecology, Transfer and Expression* (R. P. Novick and S. B. Levy, eds.), Cold Spring Harbor Laboratory, Cold Spring Harbor, N. Y., pp. 337–345.

Campell, A., 1977, Defective bacteriophages and incomplete prophages, in: *Comprehensive Virology,* Vol. 8 (H. Fraenkel-Conrat and R. R. Wagner, eds.), Plenum Press, New York, pp. 259–328.

Carlson, C. A., Pierson, L. S., Rosen, J. J., and Ingraham, J. L., 1983, *Pseudomonas stutzeri* and related species undergo natural transformation, *J. Bacteriol.* **153:**93–99.

Caulcott, C. A., Dunn, A., Robertson, H. A., Cooper, N. S., Brown, M. E., and Rhodes, P. M., 1987,

Investigation of the effect of growth environment on the stability of low copy-number plasmids in *Escherichia coli, J. Gen. Microbiol.* **133:**1881–1889.

Chakrabarty, A. M., 1972, Genetic basis of the biodegradation of salicylate in *Pseudomonas, J. Bacteriol.* **112:**815–823.

Chakrabarty, A. M., Chon, G., and Gansulas, I. C., 1973, Genetic regulation of octane dissimilation plasmid in *Pseudomonas, Proc. Natl. Acad. Sci. USA* **70:**1137–1140.

Chandler, P. M., and Krishnapillai, V., 1977, Characterization of *Pseudomonas aeruginosa* derepressed R plasmids, *J. Bacteriol.* **130:**596–603.

Chao, L., and Cox, E. C., 1983, Competition between high and low mutating strains of *Escherichia coli, Evolution* **37:**125–134.

Charlesworth, D., Charlesworth, B., Bull, J. J., Graffen, A., Holliday, R., Rosenberger, R. F., Velen, L. V. M., Danchin, A., Tessman, I., and Cairns, J., 1988, Origins of mutants disputed, *Nature* **336:**525–528.

Chen, J. D., and Morrison, D. A., 1987, Modulation of competence for genetic transformation in *Streptococcus pneumoniae, J. Gen. Microbiol.* **133:**1959–1967.

Clark, P. H., 1984, Evolution of new phenotypes, in: *Current Perspectives in Microbial Ecology* (M. J. Klugg and C. A. Reddy, eds.), American Society for Microbiology, Washington, D.C., pp. 71–78.

Clewell, D. B., and Gawron-Burke, M. C., 1986, Conjugative transposons and the dissemination of antibiotic resistance in streptococci, *Annu. Rev. Microbiol.* **40:**635–659.

Cohen, A., Bar-Nir, D., Goedeke, M., and Parag, Y., 1985, The integrated and free states of *Streptomyces griseus* plasmid pSG1, *Plasmid* **13:**41–50.

Colon, A. E., Cole, R. M., and Leonard, C. G., 1972, Intergroup lysis and transduction by *Streptococcus* bacteriophages, *J. Virol.* **9:**551–553.

Contente, S., and Dabnau, D., 1979, Characterization of plasmid transformation in *Bacillus subtilis:* Kinetic properties and the effect of DNA conformation, *Mol. Gen. Genet.* **167:**251–258.

Crow, J. F., and Kimura, M. (ed.), 1970, *An Introduction to Population Genetics Theory,* Harper & Row, New York, pp. 483–488.

Cruz-cruz, N. E., Toranzos, G. A., Ahearn, D. G., and Hazen, T. C., 1988, In situ survival of plasmid-bearing and plasmidless *Pseudomonas aeruginosa* in pristine tropical waters, *Appl. Environ. Microbiol.* **54:**2574–2577.

Cruze, J. A., Singer, J. T., and Finnerty, W. R., 1979, Conditions for quantitative transformation in *Acinetobacter calcoaceticus, Curr. Microbiol.* **3:**129–132.

Datta, N., and Hughes, V. M., 1983, Plasmids of the same Inc groups in Enterobacteria before and after the medical use of antibiotics, *Nature* **306:**616–617.

Day, M. J., 1987, The biology of plasmids, *Sci. Prog. Oxf.,* **71:**203–220.

De Flaun, M. F., Paul, J. H., and Jeffrey, W. H., 1987, The distribution and molecular weight of dissolved DNA in subtropical estuarine and oceanic environments, *Mar. Ecol. Prog. Ser.* **33:** 29–40.

De Flaun, M. F., Davis, D., and Paul, J. H., 1988, Simplified method for dissolved DNA determinations in aquatic environments, *Appl. Environ. Microbiol.* **52:**654–659.

De Flaun, M. F., Tanzer, A. S., McAteer, A. L., Marshall, B., and Levy, S. B., 1990, Development of an adhesion assay and characterization of an adhesion-deficient mutant of *Pseudomonas fluorescens, Appl. Environ. Microbiol.* **56:**112–119.

Devanas, M. A., Rafaeli-Eshkol, D., and Stotzky, G., 1986, Survival of plasmid containing strains of *Escherichia coli* in soil: Effects of plasmid size and nutrients on survival of host and maintenance of plasmids, *Curr. Microbiol.* **13:**269–277.

De Vos, G. F., Finan, T. M., Signer, E. R., and Walker, G. C., 1984, Host dependent transposon Tn-5 mediated streptomycin resistance, *J. Bacteriol.* **159:**395–399.

Ditta, G., Stanfield, S., Corbin, D., and Helinski, D. R., 1980, Broad host range DNA cloning system for Gram-negative bacteria: Construction of a gene bank of *Rhizobium meliloti, Proc. Natl. Acad. Sci. USA* **77:**7347–7351.

Domsch, K. H., Driesel, A. J., Goebel, W., Andersch, W., Lindemaier, W., Lotz, W., Reber, H., and Schmidt, F., 1988, Considerations on release of gene-technology engineered microorganisms into the environment, *FEMS Microbiol. Ecol.* **53**:261–272.

Dowling, D. N., and Broughton, W. J., 1986, Competition for nodulation of legumes, *Annu. Rev. Microbiol.* **40**:131–157.

Drahos, D. J., Hemming, B. C., and McPherson, S., 1986, Tracking recombinant organisms in the environment: β-galactosidase as a selectable non-antibiotic marker for fluorescent pseudomonads, *Bio/Technology* **4**:43–48.

Drahos, D. J., Barry, G. F., Hemming, B. C., Brandt, E. J., Skipper, H. D., Kline, E. L., Kluepfel, D. A., Hughes, T. A., and Gooden, D. T., 1988, Pre-release testing procedures: US field test of a lacZY-engineered soil bacterium, in: *The Release of Genetically Engineered Microorganisms* (M. Sussman, C. H. Collins, F. A. Skinner, and D. E. Stewart-Tull, eds.), Academic Press, New York, pp. 181–191.

Dunn, N. W., and Gunsalus, I. C., 1973, Transmissible plasmid coding early enzymes of naphthalene oxidation in *Pseudomonas putida, J. Bacteriol.* **114**:974–979.

Eberhard, W. G., 1990, Evolution in bacterial plasmids and levels of selection, *Q. Rev. Biol.* **65**:3–22.

Engels, W. R., 1986, On the evolution and population genetics of hybrid-dysgenesis-causing transposable elements in Drosophila, *Philos. Trans. R. Soc. London Ser. B* **312**:205–215.

Evans, D. J., and Evans, D. G., 1983, Classification of pathogenic *Escherichia coli* according to serotype and the production of virulence factors, with special reference to colonization factor antigens, *Rev. Infect. Dis.* **5**:5692–5701.

Falkenstein, H., Zeller, W., and Geider, K., 1989, The 29Kb plasmid, common in strains of *Erwinia amylovora,* modulates development of fireblight symptoms, *J. Gen. Microbiol.* **135**:2643–2650.

Falkow, S. (ed.), 1975, *Infectious Multiple Drug Resistance,* Pion, London.

Farrand, S. K., Slota, J. E., Shim, J. S., and Kerr, A., 1985, Tn5 insertion in the agrocin 84 plasmid: The conjugal nature of pAgK84 and the location of determinants for transfer and agrocin 84 production, *Plasmid* **13**:106–117.

Ford, S., and Olsen, B. H., 1988, Methods for detecting genetically engineered microorganisms in the environment, *Adv. Microb. Ecol.* **10**:45–79.

Fredrickson, J. K., Bezdicek, D. F., Brickman, F. J., and Li, S. W., 1988, Enumeration of Tn5 mutant bacteria in soil by using a most-probable-number DNA hybridization technique and antibiotic resistance, *Appl. Environ. Microbiol.* **54**:446–453.

Freeman, V. J., 1951, Studies on the virulence of bacteriophage infected strains of *Corynebacterium diphtheriae, J. Bacteriol.* **61**:675–688.

Friedrich, B., Hogrefe, C., and Schlegel, H. G., 1981, Naturally occurring genetic transfer of hydrogen-oxidizing ability between strains of *Alcaligenes eutrophus, J. Bacteriol.* **147**:198–205.

Frischer, M. E., Thurmond, J. M., and Paul, J. H., 1990, Natural plasmid transformation in a high-frequency-of-transformation marine Vibrio strain, *Appl. Environ. Microbiol.* **56**:3439–3444.

Fry, J. C., and Day, M. J. (ed.), 1990, *Bacterial Genetics in Natural Environments,* Chapman & Hall, London.

Fulthorpe, R. R., and Wyndham, R. C., 1991, Transfer and expression of the catabolic plasmid pBRC60 in wild bacterial recipients in a freshwater ecosystem, *Appl. Environ. Microbiol.* **57**:1546–1553.

Gabin-Gauthier, K., Gratadoux, J.-J., and Richard, J., 1991, Conjugal plasmid transfer between lactococci on solid surface matings and during cheese making, *Microbiol. Ecol.* **85**:133–140.

Gasson, M. J., and Willetts, N. S., 1975, Five control systems preventing transfer of *Escherichia coli* K12 sex factor F, *J. Bacteriol.* **122**:518–525.

Gealt, M. A., Chai, M. D., Alpert, K. B., and Boyer, J. C., 1985, Transfer of plasmids pBR322 and pBR325 in freshwater from laboratory strains of *Escherichia coli* to bacteria indigenous to the waste disposal system, *Appl. Environ. Microbiol.* **49**:836–841.

Germida, J. J., and Khachatourians, G. G., 1988, Transduction of *Escherichia coli* in soil, *Can. J. Microbiol.* **34**:190–193.

Glick, B. R., and Skof, Y. C., 1986, Environmental implication of recombinant DNA technology, *Biotechnol. Adv.* **4**:261–277.

Goldberg, R. B., Bender, R. A., and Streicher, S. L., 1974, Direct selection for P1-sensitive mutants of enteric bacteria, *J. Bacteriol.* **118**:810–814.

Gonzalez, J. M., Brown, B. J., and Carlton, B. C., 1983, Transfer of *Bacillus thuringiensis* plasmid coding for delta-endotoxin among strains of *Bacillus thuringiensis* and *Bacillus cereus*, *Proc. Natl. Acad. Sci. USA* **79**:6951–6955.

Gowland, P. C., and Slater, J. H., 1984, Transfer and stability of drug resistance plasmids in *Escherichia coli* K12, *Microb. Ecol.* **10**:1–13.

Goze, A., Sarasin, A., Moute, Y., and Devoret, R., 1975, Induction and mutagenesis of prophage lambda in *E. coli* K12 by metabolites of aflatoxin B1, *Mutat. Res.* **28**:1–7.

Grabow, W. O. K., Prozesky, O. W., and Berger, J. S., 1975, Behaviour in a river and dam of coliform bacteria with transferable or non-transferable drug resistance, *Water Res.* **9**:777–782.

Graham, S. B., and Ibstock, C. A., 1978, Genetic exchange in *Bacillus subtilis* in soil, *Mol. Gen. Genet.* **166**:287–290.

Graham, S. B., and Ibstock, C. A., 1979, Gene exchange and natural selection cause *Bacillus subtilis* to evolve in soil culture, *Science* **204**:637–639.

Greene, J., and Goldberg, R. B., 1985, Isolation and preliminary characterization of lytic and lysogenic phages with a wide host range within the Streptomycetes, *J. Gen. Microbiol.* **131**:2454–2465.

Griffith, F., 1928, The significance of pneumococcal types, *J. Hyg.* **27**:113–159.

Gross, M. D., and Siegel, E. C., 1981, Incidence of mutator strains in *Escherichia coli* and coliforms in nature, *Mutat. Res.* **91**:107–110.

Guiney, D. G., and Lanka, E., 1989, Conjugative transfer of IncP plasmids, in: *Promiscuous Plasmids of Gram-negative Bacteria* (C. M. Thomas, ed.)., Academic Press, New York, pp. 27–56.

Guiney, D. G., Jr., Hasegawa, P., and Davis, C. E., 1984, Expression in *Escherichia coli* of cryptic tetracycline resistance genes from R plasmids, *Plasmid* **11**:248–252.

Hada, H. S., and Sizemore, R. K., 1981, Incidence of plasmids in marine *Vibrio spp.* isolated from an oil field in the northwestern Gulf of Mexico, *Appl. Environ. Microbiol.* **41**:199–202.

Hales, B. A., and Amyes, S. K. B., 1986, The transfer of genes encoding production of mannose-resistant haemagglutinating fimbriae from uropathogenic Enterobacteria, *J. Gen. Microbiol.* **132**:2243–2247.

Hall, B. G., 1982, Chromosomal mutation for citrate utilization by *Escherichia coli* K-12, *J. Bacteriol.* **151**:269–273.

Hall, B. G., 1988, Adaptive evolution that requires multiple spontaneous mutations. I. Mutations involving an insertion sequence, *Genetics* **120**:887–897.

Hall, B. G., 1989, Selection, adaptation, and bacterial operons, *Genome* **31**:265–271.

Hall, B. G., 1990, Spontaneous point mutations that occur more often when advantageous than when neutral, *Genetics* **126**:5–16.

Hall, B. G., 1991, Adaptive evolution that requires multiple spontaneous mutations—mutations involving base substitutions, *Proc. Natl. Acad. Sci. USA* **18**:5882–5886.

Hall, B. G., Yokoyama, S., and Calhoun, D. H., 1983, Role of cryptic genes in microbial evolution, *Mol. Biol. Evol.* **1**:109–124.

Hall, R. M., Brookes, D. E., and Stokes, H. W., 1991, Site-specific insertion of genes into integrons: Role of the 59-base element and determination of the recombination cross-over point, *Mol. Microbiol.* **5**:1941–1959.

Hartl, D. L., 1985, Engineered organisms in the environment: Inferences from population genetics, in: *Engineered Organisms in the Environment: Scientific Issues* (H. O. Halvorson, D. Pramer, and M. Rogul, eds.), American Society for Microbiology, Washington, D.C.

Hartl, D. L., and Dykhuizen, D. E., 1984, The population genetics of *Escherichia coli*, *Annu. Rev. Genet.* **18**:31–68.

Hartl, D. L., Dykhuizen, D., Miller, R. D., Green, L., and DeFramond, J., 1983, Transposable element IS50 improves growth rate of *E. coli* cells without transposition, *Gene* **35**:503-510.

Hayes, W. (ed.), 1968, *The Genetics of Bacteria and Their Viruses: Studies in Basic Genetics and Molecular Biology,* Blackwell, Oxford.

Hedges, R. W., 1972, Phenotypic characterization of fi⁻ R-factor determining restriction modification hsp11 specificity, *Mol. Gen. Genet.* **115**:225–233.

Helinski, D. R., Cohen, S. N., Clewell, D. B., Jackson, D. A., and Hollaender, A. (ed.), 1985, *Plasmids in Bacteria,* Plenum Press, New York.

Helling, R. B., Kinney, T., and Adams, J., 1981, The maintenance of plasmid containing organisms in populations of *Escherichia coli, J. Gen. Microbiol.* **123**:129–141.

Helling, R. B., Vargas, C. N., and Adams, J., 1987, Evolution of *Escherichia coli* during growth in a constant environment, *Genetics* **116**:349–358.

Henschke, R. B., and Schmidt, F. R. S., 1990, Plasmid mobilization from genetically engineered bacteria to members of the indigenous soil flora in situ, *Curr. Microbiol.* **20**:105–110.

Henschke, R. B., Nucken, E., and Schmidt, F. R., 1989, Fate and dispersal of recombinant bacteria in a soil microcosm containing the earthworm *Lumbricus terrestris, Biol. Fertil. Soils* **7**:374–376.

Herskowitz, I., and Hagen, D., 1980, The lysis–lysogeny decision of phage lambda: Explicit programming and responsiveness, *Annu. Rev. Genet.* **14**:399–445.

Heynen, C. E., Van Elsas, J. D., and Kuikman, P. J., 1988, Dynamics of *Rhizobium leguminosarum biovar trifolii* introduced into soil; the effect of bentonite clay on predation by protozoa, *Soil Biol. Biochem.* **20**:483–488.

Hirsch, P. R., 1990, Factors limiting gene transfer in bacteria, in: *Bacterial Genetics in Natural Environments* (J. C. Fry and M. J. Day, eds.), Chapman & Hall, London, pp. 31–40.

Hodgson, J., and Sugden, A. M. (ed.), 1988, *Planned Release of Genetically Engineered Organisms. Trends in Biotechnology/Trends in Ecology and Evolution Special Publication,* Elsevier, Amsterdam.

Holloway, B. W., and Krishnapillai, V., 1975, Bacteriophages and bacteriocins, in: *Genetics and Biochemistry of Pseudomonas* (P. H. Clarke and M. H. Richmond, eds.), Wiley, New York, pp. 99–132.

Hughes, V. M., and Datta, N., 1983, Conjugative plasmids in bacteria of the "pre-antibiotic" era, *Nature* **302**:725–726.

Ippen-Ihler, K. A., and Minkley, E. G., 1986, The conjugation system of F, the fertility factor of *Escherichia coli, Annu. Rev. Genet.* **20**:593–624.

Ishigaro, N., and Sato, G., 1979, The distribution of plasmids determining citrate-positive variants of *Escherichia coli* from humans, domestic animals, feral birds and environment, *J. Hyg.* **83**:331–344.

Jacobson, A., 1972, Role of F pilus in the penetration of bacteriophage F1, *J. Virol.* **10**:835–843.

Jain, R. K., Sayler, G. S., Wilson, J. T., Houston, L., and Pacia, D., 1987, Maintenance and stability of genotypes in groundwater aquifer material, *Appl. Environ. Microbiol.* **53**:996–1002.

Jain, R. K., Burlage, R. S., and Sayler, G. S., 1988, Methods for detecting recombinant DNA in the environment, *Crit. Rev. Biotechnol.* **8**:33–84.

Jarvis, B. D. W., Ward, L. J. H., and Slade, E. A., 1989, Expression by soil bacteria of nodulation genes from *Rhizobium leguminosarum biovar trifolii, Appl. Environ. Microbiol.* **55**:1426–1434.

Juni, E., 1978, Genetics and physiology of Acinetobacter, *Annu. Rev. Microbiol.* **32**:349–371.

Kamp, P. F., and Chakrabarty, A. M., 1974, Plasmids specifying p-chlorobiphenyl degradation in enteric bacteria, in: *Plasmids of Medical, Environmental and Commercial Importance* (K. N. Timmis and A. Puhler, eds.), Elsevier/North-Holland, Amsterdam, pp. 275–285.

Kelly, W. J., and Reanney, D. C., 1984, Mercury resistance among soil bacteria: Ecology and transferability of genes encoding resistance, *Soil Biol. Biochem.* **16**:1–8.

Kerr, A., 1971, Acquisition of virulence by non-pathogenic isolates of *Agrobacterium radiobacter*, *Physiol. Plant Pathol.* **1**:241–246.

Kerr, A., 1989, Commercial release of a genetically engineered bacterium for the control of crown gall, *Agric. Sci.* **89**:41–44.

Khanna, M., and Stotzky, G., 1991, Binding of DNA to the clay minerals, montmorillonite and kaolinite and the effect of DNase on transforming ability of bound DNA, *Annual Meeting, American Society for Microbiology, Dallas,* Abstract Q17, p. 279.

Klingmueller, W., 1991, Plasmid transfer in natural soil: A case by case study with nitrogen-fixing Enterobacter, *FEMS Microbiol. Ecol.* **85**:107–116.

Klingmueller, W., Heterich, S., and Min, B. W., 1989, Molecular analysis of N_2-fixation in associative Enterobacter, in: *Nitrogen Fixation with Non-legumes* (F. A. Skinner, R. M. Boddey, and I. Fendrick, eds.), Kluwer, Dordrecht, pp. 173–178.

Klintworth, R., Husemann, M., Salnikow, J., and Bowien, B., 1985, Chromosomal and plasmid location for phosphoribulokinase genes in *Alcaligenes eutrophus, J. Bacteriol.* **164**:954–956.

Kluepfel, D. A., Kline, E. L., Skipper, H. D., Hughes, T. A., Gooden, D. T., Drahos, D. J., Barry, G. F., Hemming, B. C., and Brandt, E. J., 1991, The release and tracking of genetically engineered bacteria in the environment, *Phytopathology* **81**:348–352.

Kokjohn, T. A., 1989, Transduction: Mechanisms and potential for gene transfer in the environment, in: *Gene Transfer in the Environment* (S. B. Levy and R. V. Miller, eds.), McGraw–Hill, New York, pp. 73–98.

Krasovsky, V. N., and Stotzky, G., 1987, Conjugation and genetic recombination in Escherichia coli in sterile and nonsterile soil, *Soil Biol. Biochem.* **19**:631–638.

Lenski, R. E., 1989, Are some mutations directed? *Trends Ecol. Evol.* **4**:148–150.

Levin, M. A., Seidler, R., Borquin, A. L. W., Fowle, J. R., and Barkay, T., 1987, EPA developing methods to assess environmental release, *Bio/Technology* **5**:38–45.

Levy, S. B., and Marshall, B. M., 1988, Genetic transfer in the natural environment, in: *Release of Genetically-Engineered Microorganisms* (M. Sussman, C. H. Collins, F. A. Skinner, and D. E. Stewart-Tull, eds.), Academic Press, New York, pp. 61–76.

Levy, S. B., and Miller, R. V. (ed.), 1989, *Gene Transfer in the Environment,* McGraw–Hill, New York.

Lin, E. C. C., Goldstein, R., and Syvanen, M. (ed.), 1984, *Bacteria, Plasmids and Phages,* Harvard University Press, Cambridge, Mass.

Linder, K., and Oliver, J. D., 1989, Membrane fatty acid and virulence changes in the viable but nonculturable state of *Vibrio vulnificus, Appl. Environ. Microbiol.* **55**:2837–2842.

Lindow, S. E., 1987, Competitive exclusion of epiphytic bacteria by Ice$^-$ mutants of *Pseudomonas syringae, Appl. Environ. Microbiol.* **53**:2520–2527.

Lindow, S. E., and Panopoulos, N. J., 1988, Field tests of recombinant Ice$^-$ *Pseudomonas syringae* for biological frost control in potato, in: *The Release of Genetically Engineered Microorganisms* (M. Sussman, C. H. Collins, F. A. Skinner, and D. E. Stewart-Tull, eds.), Academic Press, New York, pp. 121–138.

Lorenz, M. G., and Wackernagel, W., 1987, Adsorption of DNA to sand and variable degradation rates of adsorbed DNA, *Appl. Environ. Microbiol.* **53**:2948–2952.

Lorenz, M. G., Aardema, B. W., and Krumbein, W. E., 1981, Interaction of marine sediment with DNA and DNA availability to nucleases, *Mar. Biol.* **64**:225–230.

Lorenz, M. G., Aardema, B. W., and Wackernagel, W., 1988, Highly efficient genetic transformation of *Bacillus subtilis* attached to sand grains, *J. Gen. Microbiol.* **134**: 107–112.

Lwoff, A., Siminovitch, L., and Kjeldgaard, N., 1950, Induction de la production de bacteriophages chez un bacterie lysogene, *Ann. Inst. Pasteur* **79**:815.

Lynch, J. M., 1990, Longevity of bacteria: Considerations in environmental release, *Curr. Microbiol.* **20**:387–389.

McCarty, M., 1980, Reminiscences of the early days of transformation, *Annu. Rev. Genet.* **14**:1–15.

McConnell, M. M., Smith, H. R., Willshaw, G. A., Field, A. M., and Rowe, B., 1981, Plasmids coding for colonization factor antigen I and heat-stable enterotoxin production isolated from enterotoxigenic *Escherichia coli:* Comparison of their properties, *Infect. Immun.* **32:**927–936.

Mach, P. A., and Grimes, D. J., 1982, R-plasmid transfer in a wastewater treatment plant, *Appl. Environ. Microbiol.* **44:**1395–1403.

McKenna, S., 1989, Genetic engineering inquiry, *Friends of the Earth Newsletter* **7:**1–2.

Mancini, P., Fertels, S., Nave, D., and Gealt, M. A., 1987, Mobilization of plasmid pHSV106 from *Escherichia coli* HB101 in a laboratory-scale waste treatment facility, *Appl. Environ. Microbiol.* **53:**665–671.

Marshall, B., and Levy, S. B., 1990, Gene exchange in the natural environment, in: *Advances in Biotechnology* (E. Heseltine, ed.), AB Boktryck HBG, Stockholm, pp. 131–143.

Marshall, B., Petrowski, D., and Levy, S. B., 1990, Inter- and intraspecies spread of *Escherichia coli* in a farm environment in the absence of antibiotic usage, *Proc. Natl. Acad. Sci. USA* **87:**6609–6613.

Martinez, E., and De la Cruz, F., 1988, Transposon Tn21 encodes a RecA-independent site-specific integration system, *Mol. Gen. Genet.* **211:**320–325.

Martinez, E., and De la Cruz, F., 1990, Genetic elements involved in Tn21 site-specific integration, a novel mechanism for the dissemination of antibiotic resistance genes, *EMBO J.* **9:**1275–1281.

Martinez, L. Y., Arenus, M. M. P., Montes, M. Y. R., Martinez, L. J., and Baca, B. E., 1987, Antibiotic resistance and plasmid pattern of enterotoxigenic ST-a strains of *Escherichia coli, Can. J. Microbiol.* **33:**816–819.

Masden, E. L., and Alexander, M., 1982, Transport of *Rhizobium* and *Pseudomonas* through soil, *Soil Sci. Soc. Am. J.* **46:**557–560.

Masters, M., 1985, Generalized transduction, in: *Genetics of Bacteria* (J. Scuife, D. Lead, and A. Galizzi, eds.), Academic Press, New York, pp. 197–216.

Mergeay, M., Nies, D., Schlegel, H. G., Gerits, J., Charles, P., and Van Grijsegem, F., 1985, Alcaligenes eutrophus CH34 is a facultative chemolithotroph with plasmid-bound resistance to heavy metals, *J. Bacteriol.* **162:**328–334.

Mergeay, M., Lejeune, P., Sadouk, A., Gerits, J., and Fabry, L., 1987, Shuttle transfer (or retrotransfer) of chromosomal markers mediated by plasmid pULB113, *Mol. Gen. Genet.* **209:**61–70.

Miller, R. V., 1988, Potential for transfer and establishment of engineered genetic sequences, in: *Planned Release of Genetically Engineered Organisms (Trends in Biotechnology/Trends in Ecology and Evolution special publication)* (J. Hodgson and A. M. Sugden, eds.), Elsevier, Amsterdam, pp. 23–26.

Miller, R. V., and Kokjohn, T. A., 1990, General microbiology of recA : Environmental and evolutionary significance, *Annu. Rev. Microbiol.* **44:**365–394.

Molak, V., and Stara, J. F., 1988, Genetically engineered microorganisms in the aquatic environment: Environmental safety assessment, in: *Aquatic Toxicology and Hazard Assessment* (W. J. Adams, G. A. Chapman, and W. G. Landis, eds.), American Society for Testing and Materials, Philadelphia, pp. 43–50.

Morgan, J. A. W., Winstanley, C., Pickup, R. W., Jones, J. G., and Saunders, J. R., 1989, Direct phenotypic and genotypic detection of a recombinant pseudomonad population released into lake water, *Appl. Environ. Microbiol.* **55:**2537–2544.

Morita, R. Y., 1982, Starvation-survival of heterotrophs in the marine environment, *Adv. Microb. Ecol.* **6:**171–198.

Morrison, W. D., Miller, R. V., and Sayler, G. S., 1978, Frequency of F116 mediated transduction of *Pseudomonas aeruginosa* in a natural freshwater environment, *Appl. Environ. Microbiol.* **36:**724–730.

Muriana, P. M., and Klaenhammer, T. R., 1987, Conjugal transfer of plasmid-encoded determinants for bacteriocin production and immunity in *Lactobacillus acidophilus* 88, *Appl. Environ. Microbiol.* **53:**553–560.

Novick, R. P., 1987, Plasmid incompatibility, *Microbiol. Rev.* **51**:381–395.

Novick, R. P., 1989, Stephylococcal plasmids and their replication, *Annu. Rev. Microbiol.* **43**:537–565.

Ogunseitan, O. A., Sayler, G. S., and Miller, R. V., 1990, Dynamic interaction of *Pseudomonas aeruginosa* and bacteriophages in lake water, *Microb. Ecol.* **19**:171–185.

Olsen, B. H., 1991, Tracking and using genes in the environment, *Environ. Sci. Technol.* **25**:604–611.

O'Morchoe, S. B., Ogunseitan, O., Sayler, G. S., and Miller, R. V., 1988, Conjugal transfer of R68.45 and FP5 between Pseudomonas aeruginosa strains in a freshwater environment, *Appl. Environ. Microbiol.* **54**:1923–1929.

Orgram, A., Sayler, G. S., and Burkay, T., 1987, The extraction and purification of microbial DNA from sediments, *J. Microbiol. Methods* **7**:57–60.

Paul, J. H., DeFlaun, M. F., and Jeffrey, W. H., 1986, Elevated levels of microbial activity in the coral surface microlayer, *Abstract, Annual Meeting American Society for Microbiology*, N72, p. 253.

Paul, J. H., Frischer, M. E., and Thurmond, J. M., 1991, Gene transfer in marine water column and sediment microcosms by natural plasmid transformation, *Appl. Environ. Microbiol.* **57**:1509–1515.

Pemberton, J. M., and Fischer, P. R., 1977, 2,4-D plasmids and persistence, *Nature* **266**:50–51.

Pickup, R. W., 1989, Related plasmids found in an English lake district stream, *Microb. Ecol.* **18**:211–220.

Pickup, R. W., 1991, Development of molecular methods for the detection of specific bacteria in the environment, *J. Gen. Microbiol.* **137**:1009–1019.

Pickup, R. W., and Saunders, J. R., 1990, Detection of genetically engineered traits among bacteria in the environment, *Biotechnology* **8**:329–334.

Pickup, R. W., Morgan, J. A. W., Winstanley, C., and Saunders, J. R., 1991, Implications for the release of genetically engineered organisms, *J. Appl. Bacteriol. Symp. Suppl.* **70**:19s–30s.

Radstrom, P., and Swedberg, G., 1988, RSF1010 and a conjugative plasmid contain sulII, one of two known genes for plasmid-borne sulfonamide resistance dihydropteroate synthase, *Antimicrob. Agents Chemother.* **32**:1684–1692.

Rattray, E. A., Prosser, J. I., Killham, K., and Glover, L. A., 1990, Luminescence-based non-extractive technique for in situ detection of *Escherichia coli* in soil, *Appl. Environ. Microbiol.* **56**:3368–3374.

Reanney, D. C., Gowland, P. C., and Slater, J. H., 1983, Genetic interactions among communities, in: *Microbes in the Natural Environment* (J. H. Slater, R. Whittenbury, and J. W. T. Wimpenny, eds.), Cambridge University Press, Cambridge, pp. 379–421.

Reiter, W. D., Palm, P., and Yeats, S., 1989, Transfer RNA genes frequently serve as integration sites for prokaryotic genetic elements, *Nucleic Acids Res.* **17**:1907–1914.

Rheinwald, J. G., Chakrabarty, A. M., and Gunsalus, I. C., 1973, A transmissible plasmid controlling camphor oxidation in Pseudomonas putida, *Proc. Natl. Acad. Sci. USA* **70**:885–889.

Richaume, A., Angle, S., and Sadowsky, M. J., 1989, Influence of soil variables on *in situ* plasmid transfer from *Escherichia coli* to *Rhizobium fredii*, *Appl. Environ. Microbiol.* **55**:1730–1734.

Ripp, S., and Miller, R. V., 1991, Importance of suspended particles in providing surfaces for genetic exchange among bacteria in fresh water environments, *Abstracts, 91st General Meeting of the American Society for Microbiology*, Dallas, Q15, p. 279.

Roberts, M. C., and Kenny, G. E., 1987, Conjugal transfer of transposon Tn916 from *Streptococcus faecalis* to *Mycoplasma hominis*, *J. Bacteriol.* **169**:3836–3839.

Rochelle, P. A., Day, M. J., and Fry, J. C., 1988, Occurrence, transfer and mobilization in epilithic strains of Acinetobacter of mercury-resistance plasmids capable of transformation, *J. Gen. Microbiol.* **134**:2933–2941.

Rochelle, P. A., Fry, J. C., and Day, M. J., 1989a, Plasmid transfer between Pseudomonas spp. within epilithic films in a rotating disc microcosm, *FEMS Microbiol. Ecol.* **62**:127–136.

Rochelle, P. A., Fry, J. C., and Day, M. J., 1989b, Factors affecting conjugal transfer of plasmics encoding mercury resistance from pure cultures and mixed natural suspensions of epilithic bacteria, *J. Gen. Microbiol.* **135**:409–424.

Röemermann, D., and Friedrich, B., 1985, Denitrification by *Alcaligenes eutrophus* is plasmid dependent, *J. Bacteriol.* **162**:852–854.

Rolfe, B., and Holloway, B. W., 1966, Alterations in host specificity of bacterial deoxyribonucleic acid after increase in growth temperature of *Pseudomonas aeruginosa, J. Bacteriol.* **92**:42–48.

Rolfe, B. G., Brockwell, J., Bolton-Gibbs, J., Clark, K., Brown, T., and Weinman, J. J., 1989, Controlled field release of genetically manipulated *Rhizobium* strains, *Aust. Microbiol.* **10**:364.

Rolland, R. M., Hausfater, G., Marshall, B., and Levy, S. B., 1985, Antibiotic-resistant bacteria in wild primates: Increased prevalence in baboons feeding on human refuse, *Appl. Environ. Microbiol.* **49**:791–794.

Roszak, D. B., and Colwell, R. R., 1987, Survival strategies of bacteria in the natural environment, *Microbiol. Rev.* **51**:365–379.

Rovira, A. D., Foster, R. C., and Martin, J. K., 1979, Note on terminology: Origin, nature and nomenclature of the organic materials in the rhizosphere, in: *The Soil–Root Interface* (J. C. Hartley and R. S. Russell, eds.), Academic Press, New York, pp. 1–4.

Sancar, A., and Rupp, W. D., 1979, Cloning of uvrA, lexC and SSB genes of *Escherichia coli, Biochem. Biophys. Res. Commun.* **90**:123–129.

Sandt, C. H., and Herson, D. S., 1991, Mobilisation of the genetically engineered plasmid pHSV106 from *Escherichia coli* HB101(pHSV106) to *Enterobacter cloacae* in drinking water, *Appl. Environ. Microbiol.* **57**:194–200.

Saunders, J. R., and Saunders, V. A., 1988, Bacterial transformation with plasmid DNA, *Methods Microbiol.* **21**:79–128.

Saye, D. J., Ogunseitan, O., Sayler, G. S., and Miller, R. V., 1987, Potential for transduction of plasmids in a natural freshwater environment: Effect of plasmid donor concentration and a natural microbial community on transduction in *Pseudomonas aeruginosa, Appl. Environ. Microbiol.* **53**:987–995.

Saye, D. J., Ogunseitan, O. A., Sayler, G. S., and Miller, R. V., 1990, Transduction of linked chromosomal genes between *Pseudomonas aeruginosa* strains during incubation in situ in a freshwater habitat, *Appl. Environ. Microbiol.* **56**:140–145.

Schiffenbauer, M., and Stotzky, G., 1982, Adsorption of coliphages T1 and T7 to clay minerals, *Appl. Environ. Microbiol.* **43**:590–596.

Schmieger, H., 1990, Phage genetics and ecology, in: *Bacterial Genetics in Natural Environments* (J. C. Fry and M. J. Day, eds.), Chapman & Hall, London, pp. 41–54.

Schofield, P. R., Gibson, A. H., Dudman, W. F., and Watson, J. M., 1987, Evidence for genetic exchange and recombination of Rhizobium symbiotic plasmids in a soil population, *Appl. Environ. Microbiol.* **53**:2942–2947.

Simonsen, L., 1990, Dynamics of plasmid transfer on surfaces, *J. Gen. Microbiol.* **136**:1001–1007.

Singer, J. T., Van Turjl, J. T., and Finnerty, W. R., 1986, Transformation and mobilization of cloning vectors in *Acinetobacter spp., J. Bacteriol.* **165**:301–303.

Singleton, P., and Anson, A. E., 1981, Conjugal transfer of R-plasmid Rldrd-19 in *Escherichia coli* below 22°C, *Appl. Environ. Microbiol.* **42**:789–791.

Slater, J. H., 1985, Gene transfer in microbial communities, in: *Engineered Organisms in the Environment* (H. O. Halvorson, D. Pramer, and M. Rogal, eds.), American Society for Microbiology, Washington, D. C., pp. 89–98.

Smit, E., and Van Elsas, J. D., 1990, Determination of plasmid transfer frequency in soil: Consequences of bacterial mating on selective agar media, *Curr. Microbiol.* **21**:151–157.

Smith, H. O., Danner, D. B., and Deich, R. A., 1981, Genetic transformation, *Annu. Rev. Biochem.* **50**:189–196.

Steenson, L. R., and Klaenhammer, T. R., 1985, *Streptococcus eremeris* M12R transconjugants carrying the conjugal plasmid pTR2030 are insensitive to attack by lytic bacteriophages, *Appl. Environ. Microbiol.* **50**:851–858.

Steffan, R. J., and Atlas, R. M., 1988, DNA amplification to enhance detection of genetically engineered bacteria in environmental samples, *Appl. Environ. Microbiol.* **54:**2185–2191.

Steffan, R. J., and Atlas, R. M., 1990, Solution hybridization assay for detecting genetically engineered microorganisms in environmental samples, *Biotechniques* **8:**316–318.

Stewart, G. J., 1989, The mechanism of natural transformation, in: *Gene Transfer in the Environment* (S. B. Levy and R. V. Miller, eds.), McGraw–Hill, New York, pp. 139–165.

Stewart, G. J., and Carlson, C. A., 1986, The biology of natural transformation, *Annu. Rev. Microbiol.* **40:**211–235.

Stewart, G. J., and Cyr, D. H., 1987, Distribution of natural transformation ability among marine bacteria, *Eos* **68:**1712.

Stewart, G. J., and Sinigalliano, C. D., 1990, Detection of horizontal gene transfer by natural transformation in native and introduced species of bacteria in marine and synthetic sediments, *Appl. Environ. Microbiol.* **56:**1818–1824.

Stewart, G. J., Carlson, C. A., and Ingraham, J. L., 1983, Evidence for an active role of donor cells in natural transformation in *Pseudomonas stutzeri, J. Bacteriol.* **156:**30–35.

Stewart, K. R., and Koditschek, L., 1980, Drug resistance transfer in *Escherichia coli* in New York Bight sediment, *Mar. Bull.* **11:**130–133.

Stokes, H. W., and Hall, R. M., 1989, A novel family of potentially mobile DNA elements encoding site-specific gene-integration functions: Integrons, *Mol. Microbiol.* **3:**1669–1683.

Stotzky, G., 1980, Surface interactions between clay minerals and microbes, viruses and soluble organics and the probable importance of these interactions to the ecology of microbes in soil, in: *Microbial Adhesion to Surfaces* (R. C. W. Berkeley, J. M. Lynch, J. Melling, P. R. Rutter, and B. Vincent, eds.), Horwood, Chichester, pp. 231–249.

Stotzky, G., 1989, Gene transfer among bacteria in soil, in: *Gene Transfer in the Environment* (S. B. Levy and R. V. Miller, eds.), McGraw–Hill, New York, pp. 165–222.

Stotzky, G., 1990, Gene transfer by conjugation, transduction and transformation in soil, *U.S. Environmental Protection Agency Publ. EPA/600/9–90/029*, pp. 82–87.

Stotzky, G., and Babich, H., 1986, Survival of, and genetic transfer by, genetically engineered bacteria in natural environments, *Adv. Appl. Microbiol.* **31:**93–138.

Stotzky, G., Devanas, M. A., and Zeph, L. R., 1990, Methods for studying bacterial gene transfer in soil by conjugation and transduction, *Adv. Appl. Microbiol.* **35:**57–169.

Stratz, M., Gottschalk, G., and Durre, P., 1990, Transfer and expression of the tetracycline resistance transposon Tn925 in *Acetobacterium woodii, FEMS Microbiol. Lett.* **68:**171–176.

Taylor, D. E., and Bradley, D. E., 1987, Location on RP4 of a tellurite resistance determinant not normally expressed in Inc P and plasmids, *Antimicrob. Agents Chemother.* **31:**823–825.

Thomas, C. M. (ed.), 1989, *Promiscuous Plasmids of Gram-negative Bacteria,* Academic Press, New York.

Tiedje, J. M., Colwell, R. K., Grossman, Y. L., Hodson, R. E., Lenski, R. E., Mack, R. N., and Regal, P. J., 1989, The planned introduction of genetically engineered organisms: Ecological considerations and recommendations, *Ecology* **70:**298–315.

Torres, O. R., Korman, R. Z., Zahler, S. A., and Dunny, G. M., 1991, The conjugative transposon Tn925: Enhancement of conjugal transfer by tetracycline in *Enterococcus faecalus* and mobilization of chromosomal genes in *Bacillus subtilis* and *E. faecalis, Mol. Gen. Genet.* **225:**395–400.

Trevors, J. T., and Starodub, M. E., 1987, R-plasmid transfer in non-sterile agricultural soil, *Syst. Appl. Microbiol.* **9:**312–315.

Trevors, J. T., and Van Elsas, J. D., 1989, A review of selected methods in environmental microbial genetics, *Can. J. Microbiol.* **35:**895–902.

Trevors, J. T., Van Elsas, J. D., Starodub, M. E., and Van Overbeek, L. S., 1990a, *Pseudomonas fluorescens* survival and plasmid RP4 transfer in agricultural water, *Water Res.* **24:**751–755.

Trevors, J. T., Van Elsas, J. D., Van Overbeek, L. S., and Starodub, M. E., 1990b, Transport of a genetically engineered *Pseudomonas fluorescens* strain through a soil microcosm, *Appl. Environ. Microbiol.* **56:**401–408.

Trieu-Cuot, P., Gerbaud, T., Lambert, T., and Courvalin, P., 1985, In vivo transfer of genetic information between Gram-positive and Gram-negative bacteria, *EMBO J.* **4:**3583–3587.

Trieu-Cuot, P., Carlier, C., Martin, P., and Courvalin, P., 1987, Plasmid transfer by conjugation from *Escherichia coli* to gram-positive bacteria, *Microbiol. Lett.* **48:**289–294.

Trieu-Cuot, P., Carlier, C., and Courvalin, P., 1988, Conjugative plasmid transfer from *Enterococcus faecalis* to *Escherichia coli*, *J. Bacteriol.* **170:**4388–4391.

Tzipori, S., 1985, The relative importance of enteric pathogens affecting neonates of domestic animals, *Adv. Vet. Sci. Comp. Med.* **29:**103–206.

Van Elsas, J. D., Trevors, J. T., and Starodub, M. E., 1988, Bacterial conjugation between pseudomonas in the rhizosphere of wheat, *FEMS Microbiol. Ecol.* **53:**299–306.

Van Elsas, J. D., Trevors, J. T., and Van Overbeek, L. S., 1991, Influence of soil properties on the vertical movement of genetically-marked *Pseudomonas fluorescens* through large soil microcosms, *Biol. Fertil. Soils* **10:**249–255.

Van Larebeke, N., Gentello, C., Schell, J., Schilperoort, R. A., Hermans, A. K., Hernalsteens, J. P., and Van Montayu, M., 1975, Acquisition of tumour-inducing ability by non-oncogenic Agrobacteria as a result of plasmid transfer, *Nature* **255:**742–743.

Van Overbeek, L. S., Van Elsas, J. D., Trevors, J. T., and Starodub, M. E., 1990, Long-term survival of and plasmid stability in *Pseudomonas* and *Klebsiella* species and appearance of nonculturable cells in agricultural drainage water, *Microb. Ecol.* **19:**239–249.

Vedamuthu, E. R., and Neville, J. M., 1986, Involvement of a plasmid in production of ropiness (mucoidness) in milk cultures of *Stephylococcus cremoris* MS, *Appl. Environ. Microbiol.* **51:**677–682.

Voeykova, T. A., Orekhov, A. V., and Rebentish, B. A., 1980, New approaches to the study of restriction and modification systems in actinomycetes, *Actinomycetes* **15:**152–166.

Watson, B., Currier, T. C., Gorden, M. P., Chilton, M. D., and Nester, E. W., 1975, Plasmid required for virulence of *Agrobacterium tumefaciens*, *J. Bacteriol.* **123:**255–264.

Weinberg, S. R., and Stotzky, G., 1972, Conjugation and genetic recombination of *Escherichia coli* in soil, *Soil Biol. Biochem.* **4:**171–180.

Weisberg, R., and Landy, A., 1983, Site-specific recombination in lambda, in: *Lambda II* (R. W. Henrix, J. W. Roberts, F. W. Stahl, and R. A. Weisberg, eds.), Cold Spring Harbor Laboratory, Cold Spring Harbor, N.Y., pp. 211–250.

Wellington, E. M. H., Cresswell, N., Herron, P. R., Clewlow, L. J., Saunders, V. A., and Wipat, A., 1990a, Gene transfer between streptomyces in soil, in: *Bacterial Genetics in Natural Environments* (J. C. Fry and M. J. Day, eds.), Chapman & Hall, London, pp. 216–230.

Wellington, E. M. H., Cresswell, N., and Saunders, V. A., 1990b, Growth and survival of streptomycete inoculants and extent of plasmid transfer in sterile and nonsterile soil, *Appl. Environ. Microbiol.* **56:**1413–1419.

Wen-Hsiung, L., 1984, Retention of cryptic genes in microbial populations, *Mol. Biol. Evol.* **1:**212–218.

Willetts, N., and Crowther, C., 1981, Mobilization of the nonconjugative IncQ plasmid RSF1010, *Genet. Res.* **37:**311–316.

Willetts, N. S., Crowther, C., and Holloway, B. W., 1981, The insertion sequence IS21 of R68.45 and the molecular basis for mobilization of the bacterial chromosome, *Plasmid* **6:**30–52.

Williams, P. A., and Murry, K., 1974, Metabolism of benzoates and the methylbenzoates by *Pseudomonas putida* (arvilla) mt-2. Evidence for the existence of a TOL plasmid, *J. Bacteriol.* **120:**416–423.

Williams, P. H., 1979, Novel iron uptake system specific by ColV plasmids: An important component in the virulence of invasive strains of *Escherichia coli*, *Infect. Immun.* **26:**925–932.

Wong, C. L., and Dunn, N. W., 1974, Transmissible plasmid coding for the degradation of benzoate and m-toluate in *Pseudomonas aravilla* mt-2, *Genet. Res.* **23:**227–230.

Zabriskie, J. B., 1964, The role of temperate bacteriophage in the production of erythrogenic toxin by group A streptococci, *J. Exp. Med.* **119:**761–780.

Zaulin, I. B., Tretyakova, S. E., and Ignatov, V. V., 1988, Chemotaxis of *Azospirillum brasilense* towards compounds typical of plant root exudates, *Folia Microbiol.* **33:**277–280.

Zeph, L. R., and Stotzky, G., 1989, Use of a biotinylated DNA probe to detect bacteria transduced by bacteriophage P1 in soil, *Appl. Environ. Microbiol.* **55:**661–665.

Zeph, L. R., Onaga, M. A., and Stotzky, G., 1988, Transduction of *Escherichia coli* by bacteriophage P1 in soil, *Appl. Environ. Microbiol.* **54:**1731–1737.

9

Ecological Aspects of Methane Oxidation, a Key Determinant of Global Methane Dynamics

GARY M. KING

1. Introduction

Methane oxidation became a subject of scientific inquiry when Alessandro Volta observed in 1776 that gas bubbles collected from a pond were combustible. Methane was subsequently exploited as a source of heat and light. However, in spite of its commercial significance, the biological and ecological aspects of methane oxidation were largely ignored until the pioneering work of Söhngen (1906), who first isolated methane-oxidizing bacteria (MOB). [Quayle (1987) notes that Lowe probably isolated the first MOB in 1892 without recognizing their ability to oxidize methane.] Little additional progress was made until the 1960s, at which time the systematic efforts of several groups provided methodological tools and details on the taxonomy, physiology, and biochemistry of C_1 metabolism. Aside from purely academic motivations, this work was stimulated by: (1) the potential use of methanotrophic bacteria as sources of "single cell protein"; (2) the role of methylotrophic bacteria in food spoilage; (3) the possible use of methanotrophs in the bioremediation of certain halogenated organic pollutants or as agents for commercial biotransformations (Higgins et al., 1980). Ecological studies were slower in development, but a number of important observations established the ubiquity of methanotrophs, the impact of methane oxidation in freshwater and some marine systems, and the potential for anaerobic as well as aerobic methane oxidation (see Hanson, 1980, and Rudd and Taylor, 1980, for earlier reviews).

The critical role of methane in the atmosphere has stimulated more recent ecological research. The roles of methane in atmospheric chemistry and the Earth's heat budget are well documented (e.g., Ehhalt, 1985). Likewise, the trend for increasing atmospheric methane concentrations is clear (e.g., Blake and Rowland, 1988), as is the association of methane with past climate changes (Chappellaz et al., 1990). As a consequence, there is considerable interest in all aspects of the production, consumption, transport, and

GARY M. KING • Darling Marine Center, University of Maine, Walpole, Maine 04573.
Advances in Microbial Ecology, Vol. 12, edited by K.C. Marshall. Plenum Press, New York, 1992.

chemistry of methane. Oremland (1988) and Cicerone and Oremland (1988) have summarized the results of many recent studies in excellent comprehensive reviews.

The interest in methane dynamics has fostered consideration of the regulatory role of biological oxidation. Even so, much more is known about methanogenesis. Perhaps the focus on methanogenesis results from the search for atmospheric methane sources (e.g., Sheppard *et al.*, 1982; Cicerone and Oremland, 1988; Wahlen *et al.*, 1989); perhaps biological oxidation has been discounted since the hydroxyl radical is the primary atmospheric methane sink (Khalil and Rasmussen, 1983; Ehhalt, 1985; Crutzen, 1991). Regardless, the available evidence indicates that biological oxidation is a major factor limiting fluxes from some of the most important methane sources (e.g., wetlands and rice paddies). In addition, biological oxidation is probably greater in magnitude than chemical oxidation if the total cycle of methane production and consumption is considered, and not just the fate of methane after transport to the atmosphere.

The present review concentrates primarily on post-1980 evidence for the key role of biological oxidation. Oxidation in soils and sediments is emphasized since these systems are probably the most significant in terms of atmospheric methane fluxes. However, pertinent observations of water column studies and anaerobic oxidation are examined. Finally, relevant advances in the microbiology of MOB, symbiotic associations based on methane oxidation, and plant-associated methane consumption are considered. Others have examined in detail microbiological and biochemical aspects of methane oxidation (e.g., Higgins *et al.*, 1981; Haber *et al.*, 1983; Anthony, 1982; Bédard and Knowles, 1989; Hanson *et al.*, 1990a, 1991).

2. Microbiology

2.1. Phylogeny

Although several new species have been described (e.g., Sieburth *et al.*, 1987; Lidstrom, 1988; Bowman *et al.*, 1990), the overall taxonomic scheme for methanotrophs has changed relatively little since the initial proposals of Whittenbury and colleagues (e.g., Whittenbury *et al.*, 1970a,b; but see Komagata, 1990, for descriptions of a new group of methylotrophs, the aerobic photosynthetic bacteria). Three groups are used to characterize the currently known isolates: type I, II, and X. These are distinguished by pathways of carbon assimilation, internal membrane structure, rosette formation, types of cysts, and catabolic enzyme suites (Table I; Hanson *et al.*, 1990a, 1991). The general validity of Whittenbury's taxonomic scheme as well as relationships among the various MOB and other prokaryotes has been confirmed in general by analyses of 5 S and 16 S RNA (Bulygina *et al.*, 1990; Tsuji *et al.*, 1990). Tsuji *et al.* (1990) have published a largely complete sequence of the 16 S rRNA for a number of methylotrophic bacteria. They conclude that "phylogenetic relationships based on 16 S rRNA sequences reflect the classical taxonomic classification systems based on phenotypic characteristics." Their analyses place type I methylotrophs in the β subgroups of

Table I. General Diagnostic Characteristics of Methanotrophic Bacteria[a]

Character	Type I	Type II	Type X
Morphology	Rods	Rods, vibrioid	Coccoid
Membrane structure			
Bundles of vesciles located centrally or marginally	Yes	No	Yes
Paired membranes aligned peripherally	No	Yes	No
Resting stages	Cysts	Exospores or cysts	Cysts
Rosettes	No	Yes	No
Carbon assimilation pathway	RMP[b]	Serine[c]	RMP/serine
Tricarboxylic acid cycle	Incomplete	Complete	Incomplete
Nitrogenase	No	Yes	Yes
Diagnostic fatty acid carbon length	16	18	16
CO_2 fixation	No	No	Yes

[a]See text and Hanson *et al.* (1991) for additional details.
[b]Incorporation of formaldehyde via the ribulose monophosphate pathway, including the diagnostic enzyme, 3-hexulose phosphate synthase.
[c]Incorporation of formaldehyde via serine, including the diagnostic enzyme, hydroxypyruvate reductase.

the Proteobacteria and type II methylotrophs in the α subgroup. A somewhat different phylogeny results from 5 S rRNA analyses. Bulygina *et al.* (1990) conclude that "the phylogenetic relations within groups of obligate methano- and methylotrophic bacteria revealed by comparative 5 S rRNA sequence analysis do not support the current rudimentary classification." Bulygina *et al.* (1990) also conclude that the obligate methanotrophs are taxonomically distinct from all other methylotrophs; both obligate methanotrophs and methylotrophs form presumably independent monophyletic groups while the facultative methylotrophs are polyphyletic. However, with few exceptions the general groupings of methylotrophs within the Proteobacteria described by Bulygina *et al.* (1990) and Tsuji *et al.* (1990) are in agreement. Differences in phylogenetic placements and interpretation may result from both the lower resolution of 5 S versus 16 S rRNA and from the use of different algorithms for phylogenetic tree construction.

Sequence analyses of methanol dehydrogenase (MDH) provide another useful perspective on genetic diversity. Machlin and Hanson (1988) have sequenced the structural gene for MDH from *Methylobacterium organophilum* XX. Comparisons of this sequence with the analogous genes of *M. extorquens* AM1 and *Paracoccus denitrificans* reveal considerably similarity, in spite of numerous other physiological and genetic dissimilarities (Harms *et al.*, 1987; Machlin *et al.*, 1987). More extensive comparisons among the methylotrophs may prove useful for establishing phylogenetic relationships and for reconstructing the evolution of methylotrophy. The genetics of methane monooxygenase, the initial catabolic enzyme in methane oxidation, have not been explored as completely (Lidstrom *et al.*, 1987; Hanson *et al.*, 1990a; Lidstrom, 1990; Cardy *et al.*, 1991) but may provide equally important taxonomic, evolutionary, and ecological insights. Recently, Stainthorpe *et al.* (1990) have shown that a gene cluster for the soluble methane monooxygenase (sMMO) can be used to prepare a probe suitable for detecting this enzyme in DNA extracts or colony hybridizations; comparative analyses of methanotrophs using such an approach are further facilitated by the highly conserved nature of the sMMO, at least among type II and X MOB (Pilkington and Dalton, 1991; Cardy *et al.*, 1991). The gene(s) which code for the particulate methane monooxygenase (pMMO) have been somewhat more elusive. However, several groups are pursuing the genetics of pMMO and a successful characterization is likely in the near future. This will be significant because the pMMO is common to all methanotrophs, unlike the sMMO.

Whereas molecular phylogenies help clarify the evolution of and taxonomic relationships among methylotrophs, the basic sequence information from which phylogenies are constructed also provides an extremely powerful tool for exploring ecological problems. At present, analyses of MOB population structure depend primarily on traditional enrichment and isolation techniques. Such methods have proven valuable in establishing the ubiquity, and to some extent the diversity, of MOB in a wide variety of habitats (e.g., Whittenbury *et al.*, 1970a; Heyer *et al.*, 1984). However, the approach has obvious limitations, even though it has provided the raw material for classical as well as molecular taxonomy. Molecular probes provide an alternative for examining the distribution of extant species as well as changes in the composition of MOB populations within or among systems. Probes derived from 5 S and 16 S rRNA sequence data or from the sequences of genes that are diagnostic for methylotrophs (e.g., MDH) allow species or even strain identification from relatively small samples in comparatively short periods of time. Numerous examples of the power of molecular approaches for the analysis of microbial populations are now available (e.g., Diels and Mergeay, 1990; Hahn *et al.*, 1990; Lee and Fuhrman, 1990; Pütz *et al.*, 1990; Torsvik *et al.*, 1990a,b). One particularly exciting possibility involves the use of sequence amplification by the polymerase chain reaction (PCR) to allow the detection of extremely small numbers of a given target sequence. This technique has been used to examine the competitiveness of strains of *Frankia* spp. for infecting the roots of *Alnus* spp. (Simonet *et al.*, 1990). Target sequences in the *nif*H gene of *Frankia* have been extracted from milligram amounts of root tissue and detected after amplification by PCR. Simonet *et al.* (1990) have reported detection limits of subnanogram quantities of target after a 30-cycle amplification. Application of this approach using primers prepared from existing sequence data (e.g., Bulygina *et al.*, 1990; Machlin and Hanson, 1988; Tsuji *et al.*, 1990) could greatly facilitate the analysis of methylotrophic populations associated with microoxygen and methane gradients in sediments or plant tissues. Indeed, Hanson and colleagues (personal communication) have used both gene and rRNA probes to characterize the methanotrophic/methylotrophic populations of various reactors and soils.

White and colleagues and others have demonstrated that methylotrophs possess diagnostic fatty acids or "biomarkers" which can be used to distinguish between type I and II organisms as well as other bacteria (Nichols *et al.*, 1985; Bowman *et al.*, 1991). Type I methylotrophs contain novel 16-carbon monoenoic acids ($16:1\omega8c$, $16:1\omega8t$, $16:1\omega7t$, $16:1\omega5c$, and $16:1\omega5t$) while type II methylotrophs contain 18-carbon monoenoic acids ($18:1\omega8c$, $18:1\omega8t$, $18:1\omega7t$, and $18:1\omega6c$). In fact, the distribution of these "signature" fatty acids among methylotrophs is concordant with rRNA phylogenies (Guckert *et al.*, 1991). These biomarkers have also been recovered from aquifer soils that were incubated with elevated methane or propane concentrations (Ringelberg *et al.*, 1989). Further, the addition of methane to a soil microcosm results primarily in accumulations of the 18:1ω8c fatty acid indicative of type II organisms (Nichols *et al.*, 1987). Should the 16- and 18-carbon monoenoic acids prove specific for methylotrophs and should these acids occur in a relatively constant ratio to cell biomass, it would be feasible to estimate total microbial biomass (from total phospholipid or fatty acid concentrations; see, e.g., Brinch-Iversen and King, 1990), the fraction of biomass attributable to methylotrophs, methylotroph biomass dynamics, and in combination with molecular probes, methylotroph population structure. However, since biomarker analyses typically require relatively large amounts of material, the technique may not be suitable for environments with microgradients or systems where sample sizes are restricted. On the other hand, soils or sediments treated with methanotrophs in bioremediation programs represent ideal systems for analysis since sample availability is not necessarily limiting and since microscale sampling is less important.

To date, a relatively small number of organisms have formed the basis for the microbiology of the MOB. Although numerous isolates have been obtained from diverse habitats (e.g., Whittenbury *et al.*, 1970a; Heyer *et al.*, 1984), the approaches used for isolation have been limited and used in common by many investigators. For example, the media most commonly employed for enrichment and isolation are based on the nitrate or ammonia mineral salts media reported by Whittenbury *et al.* (1970a); gas phase compositions of 30–50% methane have been routinely used. While such media have proven useful, they may have limited both the taxonomic and physiological diversity of the organisms isolated. Ecological studies have indicated that active MOB may be exposed to only low micromolar to submicromolar concentrations of methane and suboxic to microaerophilic oxygen concentrations (Kuivila *et al.*, 1988; Frenzel *et al.*, 1990; King, 1990b; King *et al.*, 1990; Ward, 1990). Temperatures and pH regimes can also vary substantially in natural systems (Heyer and Suckow, 1985; Born *et al.*, 1990). None of these parameters have been duplicated well in attempts to characterize the diversity of MOB. Some exceptions include the isolations by Gal'chenko and colleagues of halotolerant and thermophilic MOB (see Gal'chenko *et al.*, 1989, and references therein). In addition, Lees *et al.* (1990) have reported that some methanotrophs may not grow on solid media, a limitation that would certainly limit the diversity of typical enrichments. As a consequence, the current status of MOB microbiology may be analogous to that of the sulfate-reducing bacteria (SRB) during the 1970s. At that time, the SRB were considered a relatively simple group of organisms from both a taxonomic and physiological perspective (Widdel, 1988). The use of more varied isolation protocols by Pfenning, Widdel, Postgate, and co-workers has transformed this view almost entirely. The SRB are now considered highly diverse with characteristics and ecological roles that were unanticipated as little as 10–15 years ago (Widdel, 1988). A similar revision in the status of the MOB is not unlikely. Alternative approaches to enrichment and isolation, such as those of Lees *et al.* (1991) and Putzer *et al.* (1991), provide promising directions for exploring MOB diversity.

Future isolation programs might profitably emphasize fungi and mixotrophic MOB. Zajic *et al.* (1969) have documented methane consumption by a fungus (*Graphia* spp.) isolated from soils associated with a gas pipeline. Later reports have documented methane oxidation by several yeasts (e.g., Wolfe and Hanson, 1980). Most recently, Jones and Nedwell (1990) have isolated methylotrophic species of *Trichoderma* and *Penicillium* from landfill soils. The implications of these observations are extremely important since it is conceivable that the oxidation of atmospheric methane in soils is carried out by fungi as well as the classically described MOB. An important role for fungi might explain apparent discrepancies between the kinetics of oxidation in soils and the kinetic properties of known bacterial isolates (but see Section 4). A role for fungi or mixotrophic MOB (see Jones and Nedwell, 1990, for indications of relative importance) is also consistent with predictions from a kinetic and maintenance energy of atmospheric methane oxidation in soils (Conrad, 1984).

2.2. Kinetics

K_m values for pure cultures, enrichments, cell-free extracts and purified methane monooxygenase (Table II) range from 1 to 92 μM and 0.1 to 37 μM for methane and oxygen, respectively (e.g., Nagai *et al.*, 1973; Linton and Buckee, 1977; Lamb and Garver, 1980; Joergensen and Degn, 1983; Joergensen, 1985; Green and Dalton, 1986; Whalen *et al.*, 1990; Megraw and Knowles, 1987a,b; Oldenhuis *et al.*, 1991). These ranges have no apparent taxonomic origin in that both high and low values have been recorded for the same species and for type I, II, and X organisms. The lowest and perhaps most accurate values for both methane and oxygen are those of Joergensen (1985), who used a membrane-inlet mass spectroscopic technique in which no diffusion limitations for gas transfer were apparent. The high values reported by Oldenhuis *et al.* (1991) for the same organism used by Joergensen (1985) may result from differences in culture conditions. Oldenhuis *et al.* (1991) report kinetic parameters for cells expressing only sMMO whereas data from Joergensen (1985) reflect the kinetics of pMMO (see Section 2.3).

The half-saturation constants (K_{app}) for methane uptake in natural samples (Table II) are comparable to values for cultures and pMMO. Ward (1990) has recently calculated submicromolar K_{app}'s from a four-point Lineweaver–Burke kinetic analysis. Yavitt *et al.* (1990a) have used a similar approach and reported K_{app}'s of about 5 μM for peat samples. Lidstrom and Somers (1984) and Kuivila *et al.* (1988) have estimated K_{app}'s of 5–10 μM for sediments from Lake Washington. King (1990b) has used progress curve analyses and reported K_{app}'s of about 2–4 μM for Danish wetland sediments. The lower K_{app}'s are generally consistent with the range of methane concentrations found in the oxic zones from which samples were collected. Few estimates of K_{app} for oxygen uptake by MOB in natural samples are available; values of 10–20 μM have been obtained for sediments from Lake Washington (Lidstrom and Somers, 1984; Kuivila *et al.*, 1988).

Though few data are available, reported maximal uptake (or oxidation) rates (V_{max}) correlate well with methane flux rates. This relationship suggests that the supply of

Table II. Representative Kinetic Parameters for Methane Oxidation by Methane Monoxygenase, Various Pure and Mixed Cultures, and Natural Samples.

Sample source or organism	K_m (K_s) (μM)	V_{max}	Reference
Methane monooxygenase (soluble, *M. capsulatus*)	3	56.0[a]	Green and Dalton (1986)
Pure cultures			
Methylosinus trichosporium	2	26.0[b]	Joergensen (1985)
Strain OU-4-1	0.8		Joergensen and Degn (1983)
Landfill isolate	9.3	5.3[c]	Whalen and Reeburgh (1990)
Nitrosococcus oceanus	6.6[d]		Ward (1987)
Nitrosomonas europaea	2000		Hyman and Wood (1983)
Mixed cultures			
Sludge isolates	1.7		Lamb and Garver (1980)
Sediment isolates	32.0		Linton and Buckee (1977)
Sediments and soils			
Landfill soil	2.5	237[e]	Whalen and Reeburgh (1990)
Peat, 0–10 cm	3.7	1.9[f]	Yavitt *et al.* (1990a)
Lake Washington	8.3–10.7	38[f]	Lidstrom and Somers (1984)
	5.1–10.0	28[f]	Kuivila *et al.* (1988)
Lake Superior	4.6	0.7[f]	Remsen *et al.* (1989)
Danish wetland	2.2–3.7	662–1441[f]	King (1990b)

[a]nmole (mg protein A)$^{-1}$ min^{-1}.
[b]nmole (mg dry weight)$^{-1}$ min^{-1}.
[c]nmole (mg dry weight)$^{-1}$ min^{-1}; calculated by assuming 5×10^{-14} (g dry weight cell)$^{-1}$.
[d]But see also Ward (1990) for a discussion of methane uptake in *Nitrosomonas*.
[e]μmole liter^{-1} hr^{-1}; calculated assuming a soil density of 1 g cm^{-3}.
[f]μmole liter^{-1} hr^{-1}.

methane to the zone of oxidation may determine V_{max} (King, 1990b; King *et al.*, 1990). Since V_{max} is probably an indicator of active MOB biomass (Remsen *et al.*, 1989), such a relationship is not surprising. Regardless, more extensive comparisons are necessary for determining if a general, predictable relationship exists among diverse sites.

Additional kinetic evaluations are important because K_m (K_{app}) reflects the extent of adaptation for consumption of methane and oxygen at *in situ* concentrations. High micromolar K_m's are inconsistent with the low micromolar to nanomolar concentrations observed in most oxic sediments and waters (e.g., Ward *et al.*, 1987, 1989; Kuivila *et al.*, 1988; Frenzel *et al.*, 1990; King, 1990b); low nanomolar methane concentrations are also expected in soils at or near equilibrium with the atmosphere. Conrad (1984) has evaluated relationships among kinetic parameters, maintenance energy requirements, and population sizes and concluded that high-K_m uptake systems are not likely to sustain oxidation rates sufficient to meet growth requirements at low *in situ* methane concentrations.

2.3. Methane Monooxygenase and Dehalogenation

The MOB are unique in many respects; one of the most remarkable aspects of these organisms is the enzyme, MMO. This copper-containing complex occurs in two forms, membrane-bound or particulate (pMMO) and soluble (sMMO). The former occurs in all MOB while the latter has a more restricted distribution (see Anthony, 1982; Dalton *et al.*, 1984; Dalton and Higgins, 1987). Aside from cellular location, these two enzymes differ in a number of respects, including substrate specificity, sensitivity to inhibitors, requirements for NAD(P)H, kinetics, and tertiary structure among others (e.g., Colby *et al.*, 1977; Dalton, 1980; Stanley *et al.*, 1983; Burrows *et al.*, 1984; Green and Dalton, 1986; Dalton and Higgins, 1987; Fox *et al.*, 1989). In at least some type II and X MOB, the expression of one form or the other is determined by the availability of copper (e.g., Stanley *et al.*, 1983; Burrows *et al.*, 1984; Pilkington and Dalton, 1991). At low copper concentrations (≤ 1 μM), the soluble form dominates activity; at concentrations $>1-5$ μM, MMO is exclusively particulate. Scott *et al.* (1981) have also reported a sensitivity to other growth factors; however, their data are not inconsistent with copper regulation. Copper may also play an important role in type I MOB; Collins *et al.* (1991) have reported that copper additions increased both cell yields and MMO activity in *M. albus* BG8, an organism not known to produce sMMO. Recognition of the regulatory role of copper has provided a solution to some earlier discrepancies in the characteristics of certain MOB and clearly emphasized the need for detailed specification of growth conditions and trace metal availability in any comparative studies.

The biochemical and physiological properties of the soluble and particulate MMO have significant ecological consequences. For example, the pMMO K_m for oxygen appears considerably lower than that of the sMMO (0.1 versus 17 μM; Joergensen, 1985; Green and Dalton, 1986). This difference, if consistent among all MOB, indicates that the capacity to compete for and remain active at low oxygen concentrations is determined in part by the active form of MMO. The more narrow specificity of the pMMO limits the effects of competitive substrates on rates of methane oxidation (Burrows *et al.*, 1984). The requirement of sMMO for NAD(P)H limits the extent to which co-oxidation of other substrates (e.g., ethanol) can sustain MMO activity; this requirement also limits the energetic efficiency of the sMMO versus pMMO system (Burrows *et al.*, 1984; Green and Dalton, 1986; Leak and Dalton, 1986).

In addition, there are commercial and environmental ramifications for the location of MMO activity. Unlike pMMO, sMMO oxidizes a variety of aromatic and alicyclic compounds, including aromatic alcohols, benzene, toluene, and cyclohexanol (e.g., Colby *et al.*, 1977; Dalton, 1980; Burrows *et al.*, 1984; Mountfort *et al.*, 1990). Moreover, the sMMO, but not pMMO, of *Ms. trichosporium* also catalyzes the oxidative dehalogenation of various halomethanes, -alkanes, and -alkenes, with degradation of trichloroethylene (TCE) of particular interest for bioremediation (Oldenhuis *et al.*, 1989, 1991; Tsien *et al.*, 1989; Brusseau *et al.*, 1990; Fox *et al.*, 1990; Hanson *et al.*, 1990b). Others have reported dehalogenation by soils exposed to methane (Wilson and Wilson, 1985; Strand and Shippert, 1986; Henson *et al.*, 1988; Lanzarone and McCarty, 1990), by pure and mixed methylotrophic cultures (Fogel *et al.*, 1986; Vogel *et* al., 1987; Janssen et al., 1988; Little et al., 1988), by alkane (propane)-oxidizing mycobacteria (Wackett et al., 1989), by ammonia-oxidizing bacteria (Arciero et al., 1989), which contain an enzyme, ammonia monooxygenase, that is remarkably similar to MMO (e.g., Bédard and Knowles, 1989), and by methanogens (Vogel and McCarty, 1985). In the case of Ms. trichosporium, it is clear that copper availability plays a key role in TCE metabolism (Oldenhuis et al., 1989; Tsien et al., 1989; Brusseau et al., 1990; Fox et al., 1990), a fact consistent with involvement of sMMO (Fig. 1). Brusseau et al. (1990) have developed a rapid, sensitive assay for sMMO based on the oxidation of the polycyclic aromatic, naphthalene; this method has proven useful for optimizing

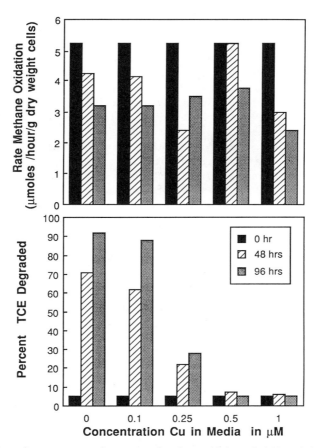

Figure 1. Effects of copper concentration on rates of methane oxidation and trichloroethylene degradation in cultures of *Methylosinus trichosporium* OB3b. Cultures were incubated with various concentrations, harvested at the times indicated, and then assayed for methane oxidation or TCE degradation rates. Illustration courtesy of H.-C. Tsien and R. S. Hanson. Form Tsien et al. (1989).

conditions for TCE degradation. In contrast, Henry and Grbic-Galic (1990) report that smMMO does not catalyze TCE dehalogenation by a *Methylomonas* sp. since the organism expresses only pMMO. They also demonstrate the sensitivity of methane oxidation, growth yield, and dehalogenation to medium composition, particularly copper and chelator concentrations. Alvarez-Cohen and McCarty (1991), Henry and Grbic-Galic (1991), and Oldenhuis *et al.* (1991) have all documented TCE toxicity, a general inactivation of cellular metabolism by TCE or TCE metabolites, and the significance of sources of reductant, such as formate, which provide NADH for smMMO without competing with TCE.

2.4. Methylotrophic Symbioses

Although MOB have been isolated routinely from a variety of sources during the last century, active symbioses involving MOB have only been described recently. Subsequent to reports of symbiotic associations between sulfide-oxidizing chemolithotrophs and the vestimniferan tube-worm, *Riftia pachyptila* (Cavanaugh *et al.*, 1981), other symbioses were reported for various invertebrates (e.g., Southward *et al.*, 1981; Ott *et al.*, 1982; Cavanaugh, 1983, 1985; Dando *et al.*, 1985; Dando and Southward, 1986). Based on stable isotope evidence, Southward *et al.* (1981) suggested a methane-based symbiosis for a pogonophoran; later efforts proved this suggestion incorrect (Southward *et al.*, 1986). However, a variety of other observations confirmed that mollusks and pogonophorans did indeed harbor methane-oxidizing symbionts (Childress *et al.*, 1986; Brooks *et al.*, 1987; Cavanaugh *et al.*, 1987; Fisher *et al.*, 1987; Schmaljohann and Flügel, 1987; Cary *et al.*, 1988, 1989; Wood and Kelly, 1989; Page *et al.*, 1990; Schmaljohann *et al.*, 1990). For instance, numbers of MOB in gill tissues of a mollusk were about 3×10^8 cells (g tissue)$^{-1}$, somewhat less than the 4×10^9 cells (g tissue)$^{-1}$ reported for sulfide-oxidizing bacteria associated with *R. pachyptila*, but still remarkable.

To date the MOB symbionts have been either coccoid or rod-shaped cells with type I internal membranes (Fig. 2) and an active hexulose phosphate synthase pathway for carbon assimilation; thus far, type II organisms have not been observed (e.g., Cavanaugh *et al.*, 1987; Wood and Kelly, 1989; Schmaljohann *et al.*, 1990). Regardless of the taxonomic affinities of the MOB, these symbioses accounted for a large fraction of host carbon and energy requirements (e.g., Cary *et al.*, 1988; Fisher *et al.*, 1987) and apparently contributed to dramatic, productive benthic communities isolated from significant phytoplanktonic organic inputs (e.g., Paull *et al.*, 1984, 1985; Kennicutt *et al.*, 1985, 1989; Hovland and Thomsen, 1989; MacDonald *et al.*, 1990; Dando *et al.*, 1991).

Symbiotic relationships between plants and MOB have received virtually no attention relative to animal symbioses, even though methanotrophs were first isolated from the leaves of the macrophyte *Elodea* (Söhngen, 1906). While MOB symbioses may be nonobligatory or even of minor benefit to plant hosts, the ecological ramifications of the relationship are substantial. DeBont *et al.* (1978) have reported methane oxidation in association with rice (*Oryza sativa*) roots. Holtzapfel-Pschorn *et al.* (1985, 1986) and Schütz *et al.* (1989a) have made similar observations and concluded that much of the

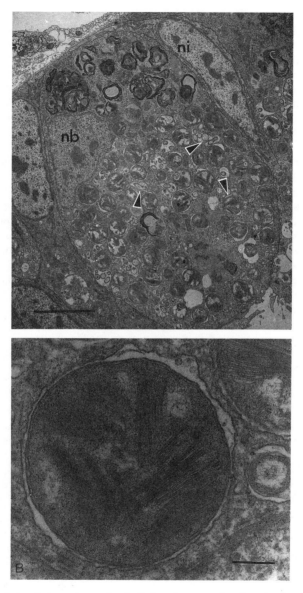

Figure 2. Transmission electron micrographs of gill tissue from mussels collected at the Florida Escarpment. (A) Transverse section of a gill filament showing bacteria-containing host cells (bacteriocytes; nb, nucleus) separated by intercalary cells (ni, intercalary cell nucleus); bacterial cells are designated by arrows. Scale bar is 5 μm. (B) Transverse section of bacterial cell showing apparently gram-negative ultrastructure and stacked internal membranes typical of type I methantrophs. Scale bar is 0.3 μm. Figure courtesy of C. Cavanaugh; from Cavanaugh *et al.* (1987).

methane which diffuses to the rice rhizosphere is oxidized. This observation is extremely important because Cicerone and Shetter (1981), Schütz *et al.* (1989b), Sass *et al.* (1990), and others have suggested that a large fraction of the methane efflux from rice paddies occurs through the plants. Consequently, methane oxidation is likely a major control of the significance of rice as a global methane source. Since rice accounts for about 25% of the current global flux estimate (Cicerone and Oremland, 1988; Wahlen *et al.*, 1989), small changes in the rhizosphere oxidation term can have a globally important impact.

Methane oxidation also occurs in association with the roots of other aquatic plants (King *et al.*, 1990; Chanton *et al.*, 1992). King *et al.* (1990) and King (unpublished data) have observed rapid methane oxidation by the sediment-free roots of a wide diversity of macrophytes, including species that are commonly distributed throughout northern wetlands. Several aspects of the observations are notable. First, methane oxidation by sediment-free roots occurs with no lag, implying that populations of MOB are exposed to conditions suitable for activity *in situ*. Second, thresholds for methane uptake are typically relatively high (>5 ppmv), implying that consumption of atmospheric methane is unlikely (King, unpublished data). A single exception for an aquatic grass has been observed, however, with threshold values <0.1 ppm; it is doubtful that the plant consumes atmospheric methane though, as its roots are exposed to high concentrations of methane in the sediments in which it grows (King, unpublished data). Third, the capacity for methane oxidation by roots shows surprising variability within a given species. For example, two species from the Florida Everglades show no root methane oxidation when growing in marls, but significant activity when growing in peats (King *et al.*, 1990); likewise, roots of *Carex rostrata* from one fen oxidize methane, but roots of the same species collected from a similar site are devoid of activity. The cause(s) of this variability are as yet unknown.

Though not as striking as animal–MOB symbioses, plant-associated methane oxidation clearly has global consequences. Aquatic plants are a well-known and significant conduit for methane flux to the atmosphere (Dacey and Klug, 1979; Dacey, 1980, 1981, 1987; Sebacher *et al.*, 1985). Oxidation in the rhizosphere may substantially limit this flux. As a result, understanding the controls of methane dynamics in wetlands requires considerably more information on plant–methanotroph interactions. Are root-associated MOB taxonomically or physiologically distinctive? Do MOB form host-specific interactions? Are the interactions mutualistic or a loose commensalism? How do root-associated methanotrophs respond to plant dormancy? These and many other questions warrant a focused research effort.

3. Methane Oxidation in Freshwater Sediments

Current budgets indicate that freshwater sediments, including those of wetlands, rice paddies, and various other aquatic systems, account for 40–50% of the annual atmospheric methane flux (e.g., Harriss *et al.*, 1985; Matthews and Fung, 1987; Aselmann and Crutzen, 1989; Cicerone and Oremland, 1988; Wahlen *et al.*, 1989). Rice paddies are also likely contributors to the temporally increasing global flux rate (see

Cicerone and Oremland, 1988). While the dynamics and controls of methane production in these systems have been well documented, surprisingly few analyses have specifically addressed aerobic oxidation. The available data suggest that oxidation at or near the sediment surface limits methane flux to only a fraction, sometimes <10%, of the methane produced (e.g., Holzapfel-Pschorn et al., 1985, 1986; Heyer and Suckow, 1985; Abramochkina et al., 1987; Kuivila et al., 1988; Frenzel et al., 1990; Remsen et al., 1989; Schütz et al., 1989a,b; King, 1990a,b; King et al., 1990, 1991; Yavitt et al., 1988, 1990a; Sweerts et al., 1991; Fechner and Hemond, 1992). In at least some cases, aerobic oxidation is confined to extremely narrow intervals only a few millimeters thick (Kuivila et al., 1988; Frenzel et al., 1990; King, 1990b; King et al., 1990). Within these highly constrained intervals, methane produced over many centimeters is consumed by a "biofilter" that can drastically reduce diffusive fluxes to the atmosphere and that converts reduced carbon from a diffuse source into a much more concentrated pool of microbial biomass.

Consider data from Frenzel et al. (1990). In a 3-mm interval of pelagic sediments in Lake Constance, methane oxidation consumes over 90% of the methane flux to the sediment–water interface. In contrast, methane production occurs over an interval of at least 10 cm in the underlying anoxic sediments. If fermentation and methanogenesis produce a 50:50 yield of CO_2 and methane below 3 mm, and if MOB in the oxic sediments incorporate methane with an efficiency of 50%, then 25% of the anaerobic carbon mineralization over a 10-cm interval is recycled through MOB biomass on a scale about 33-fold smaller than that over which methanogenesis occurs. Carbon enrichment and recycling of this magnitude has profound implications, not only for methane budgets but for sediment biogeochemistry. For instance, at a 4:1 molar C:N ratio, MOB biosynthesis in the above example requires 62.5% of the nitrogen regenerated from the fermentative mineralization of an organic substrate with a 10:1 molar C:N ratio. Obviously, these calculations are not intended as definitive estimates since they are based on approximations for assimilation and C:N ratios. However, they do illustrate the potential impact of methane oxidation on the complex trophic interactions and elemental cycles that occur in sediments. A useful model by Di Toro et al. (1990) provides an additional perspective on this complexity by quantitatively relating organic matter diagenesis, methane and ammonia production and oxidation, and diffusive transport to sediment oxygen demand. The implications of methane oxidation for water column biogeochemistry are illustrated similarly by the large fraction (62–70%) of the hypolimetic oxygen demand attributable to methanotrophic activity (Mayer et al., 1982).

To date, the distribution and concentration of oxygen have received the greatest attention as controls of sediment methane oxidation. Rudd et al. (1976) speculated that methane oxidation was significant in the oxic sediments of Lake 227, but Kuivila et al. (1988) first characterized both the distribution of oxygen and methane as well as rates of oxidation. They showed using oxygen microelectrodes that maximal rates of methane consumption occurred near the depths of maximal oxygen penetration; based on benthic flux chamber data and estimates of diffusive fluxes of methane, they calculated relative (about 50%) and absolute rates of oxidation (250–350 μmole m^{-2} day^{-1}) and the contribution of methane to total sediment oxygen demand (7–10%). Similar relationships were observed by Remsen *et al.* (1989) for sediments of Lake Superior. Frenzel *et al.* (1990) estimated relative (93%) and absolute rates of methane oxidation (447 μmole m^{-2} day^{-1}) in deep pelagic sediments of Lake Constance and established a critical water column oxygen concentration (about 18 μM), below which methane oxidation apparently ceased.

King (1990a,b) and King *et al.* (1990, 1991) expanded these observations by demonstrating the sensitivity of methane oxidation to changes in sediment oxygen penetration. Light regimes, benthic photosynthesis, algal mats, and hydrologic parameters were key factors affecting oxygen penetration. For example, illumination of a sediment surface with benthic algae increased oxygen penetration and concentrations and methane oxidation while concomitantly decreasing methane flux (Fig. 3; King, 1990a; King *et al.*, 1990). Changes in the water table height of peats also resulted in dramatic changes in oxygen distribution and methane oxidation and flux. Over a range of about 3 cm, a decrease in the water table of a Canadian fen was accompanied by decreased oxygen penetration and methane oxidation and increased methane flux; these effects were reversible with an increased water table (King *et al.*, 1991). Increased methane flux has also been reported for a 10 cm decrease in the water table at this site; decreases >10 cm had an opposite effect (Moore and Knowles, 1989; Roulet *et al.*, 1992). Seasonal decreases >10 cm in the Great Dismal Swamp and the Florida Everglades were accompanied by decreased methane fluxes, even atmospheric methane

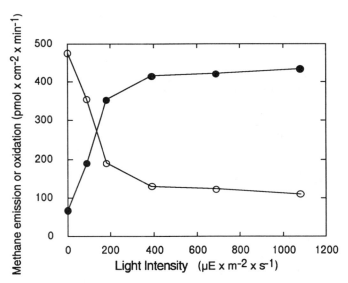

Figure 3. Effect of stepwise increases in light intensity on rates of methane flux (○) and methane oxidation (●) in triplicate cores from a Danish wetland. Each point represents a mean value determined over approximately 80 min of incubation at the intensities indicated. From King (1990a).

consumption, presumably due to enhanced oxygen input and methane oxidation (Harriss *et al.*, 1982, 1988). The relationship between hydrology and methane oxidation at any given site is probably best understood in terms of sediment compressibility and air entry, models of which have been previously reported (e.g., Hemond *et al.*, 1984).

The controls of aerobic methane oxidation are obviously related in part to the absolute requirement for molecular oxygen. Of course, the kinetics of oxygen uptake are determined by the response of MMO to methane as well as oxygen. The available K_m/K_{app}'s for oxygen and methane suggest that uptake of both substrates is saturated at concentrations approximately ≥ 10 μM. Consequently, methane oxidation is probably oxygen-saturated and methane-limited in the uppermost layers of oxic sediments and methane-saturated but oxygen-limited at depths approaching the limits of oxygen penetration. The localization of MOB biomass and activity between these extremes reflects the interaction among rates of substrate uptake, biosynthesis, and the diffusion of growth-limiting substrates from opposite directions. Koch (1990) provides a lucid and highly relevant description of gradient systems of this type as well as a model which predicts biomass (activity) distribution within substrate gradients. Analogous arguments have previously been invoked to explain the distribution of methane oxidation in the water column of Lake Mendota (Harrits and Hanson, 1980). The interaction between oxygen distribution and methane oxidation in Lake Mendota and sediments generally differs from the relationship proposed by Rudd *et al.* (1976), who suggested that the sensitivity of nitrogenase to oxygen constrained methane oxidizers in the nitrogen-limited waters of Lake 227. Though conceivable in the water column, nitrogen limitation is an unlikely factor in most sediments.

Rates of methane oxidation in sediments are also determined by the response of MOB to temporal changes in oxygen distribution. Field studies indicate that oxygen regimes change on scales of hours to days and that MOB are subjected to shifts between oxic and anoxic conditions (King, 1990a; King *et al.*, 1990, 1991). Several physiological or metabolic responses to such changes are possible, depending on the time scale involved. Long-term shifts to oxic conditions can involve activation of resting stages (spores or cysts) and growth; shifts to anoxia can involve sporulation and encystment (Whittenbury *et al.*, 1970b) or as yet undescribed catabolic pathways. Short-term shifts may elicit rather different responses. King (1990b) has suggested that the MOB in sediments consist of two functional types with respect to oxygen, or more properly, anoxia. Anoxic conditions rapidly inactivate one type which recovers slowly (>24 hr) after reexposure to oxygen. The second type survives even extended periods of anoxia while retaining a capacity for responding rapidly to oxygen. This second type appears to account for a variable, but high percentage of the methane oxidation potential in shallow sediments (see, e.g., King, 1990b, and Fig. 4). Anoxia-tolerant populations of MOB may also explain the absence of lag periods in methane consumption after addition of oxygen to anoxic sediments (Heyer and Suckow, 1985; Yavitt *et al.*, 1988; King, 1990b; King *et al.*, 1990) and account for the notable cell densities in some silty sediments (Abramochkina *et al.*, 1987). Though mechanisms for anoxia-tolerance are currently unknown, the phenomenon should provide a selective advantage in environments with fluctuating oxygen regimes. In fact, anoxia-tolerant MOB should be relatively enriched

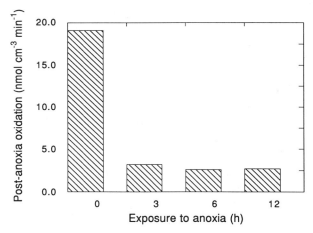

Figure 4. Effect of various intervals of anoxic preincubation on subsequent aerobic methane oxidation. Rates of oxidation of added methane were measures 1 hr after exposing slurries to air; the slurries were previously incubated with 100% nitrogen. From King (1990b).

in systems such as shallow sediments and plant rhizospheres. Though they may possess some unique physiological attributes, anoxia-tolerant MOB need not be taxonomically or phylogenetically unique. In fact, preliminary surveys indicate that both methane oxidation and growth of several "classic" MOB, including *Methylococcus capsulatus* Bath, *Methylomonas rubrum, M. albus* BG8, and *Ms. trichosporium* OB3B, resume immediately with little or no inhibition after 6 hr of anoxia (King, unpublished data). The range of responses to as well as mechanisms for tolerance of anoxia clearly merit further investigation in both natural systems and cultures.

Aside from oxygen, other determinants of methane oxidation include pH, trace metal (especially copper) availability, and ammonia concentrations. Neither these factors nor other possible controls have been examined extensively. King (1990b) has reported inhibition of methane oxidation at elevated pH; the effects of low pH have not been specifically analyzed, but Born *et al.* (1990) note that methane oxidation rates are similar in soils across a pH range from 3.5 to 8.0 and Heyer and Suckow (1985) report active oxidation for peats with a pH of 3.7–4.4. King (1990b) has also described a possible interaction between ammonia and pH. Unlike the suggested effects of ammonia in soils, ammonia inhibition in sediments presumably occurs via competitive interactions with MMO (O'Neill and Wilkinson, 1977; Dalton, 1977; Bédard and Knowles, 1989). Contrary to reports for soils, there are no suggestions that methane oxidation in sediments involves ammonia-oxidizing bacteria (AOB); in fact, Megraw and Knowles (1987a,b, 1989a,b) report that methanotrophs are the likely agents for ammonia oxidation in a humisol from which AOB could not be isolated. Harrits and Hanson (1980) have also proposed that methanotrophs contribute significantly to ammonia oxidation in Lake Mendota.

The potential diversity and complexity of sediment methane oxidation controls are illustrated by analyses of peats and marls from the Florida Everglades (King *et al.*, 1990). The capacity of peats, but not neighboring marls, to oxidize methane at significant rates is not accounted for by differences in oxygen availability or methane concentrations. A substantial direct effect of small differences in pH or nutrients is inconsistent with observations from other systems. Indirect effects of pH, perhaps related to calcium carbonate precipitation in the marl, might play a key, but as yet undefined role. Seasonality in methane oxidation can be inferred from data of Harriss *et al.* (1982, 1988); these data also raise another unanswered question about sediments. What determines the capacity of wetland sediments to consume atmospheric methane after a decrease in the water table? Since saturated sediments show no capacity for atmospheric methane consumption (King, 1990b), significant changes must occur in either the physiology or population structure of MOB. The nature of any such changes is currently unknown; however, they provide a key for understanding sediment methane oxidation in general and for predicting the response of methane oxidation to future climate changes. Whalen and Reeburgh (1990) have commented on the potential response of tundra soils to climate change; similarly significant changes may occur in many temperate wetlands if altered hydrologic cycles result in longer periods of water desaturation. It is, of course, rather premature to predict future changes in global, even regional, methane flux or oxidation based on the hydrologic predictions of global climate models, no matter how accurate, since such models provide at most a crude basis for predicting critical phenomena such as plant community dynamics, peat or sediment loss, effects of wildfires, all of which have uncertain effects and relationships to variations in hydrologic cycles.

4. Methane Oxidation in Soils

Methane oxidation has long been considered a key process in aquatic ecosystems. However, the potential importance of methane oxidation in terrestrial systems has been recognized only recently. Though regarded as improbable based on culture data (Conrad, 1984), observations of wetlands and savannah and forest soils convincingly demonstrated atmospheric methane consumption (Fig. 5; Harriss *et al.*,1982; Keller *et al.*, 1983, 1986; Seiler *et al.*, 1984). Uptake of atmospheric methane was first reported for a wetland after the water table fell below the sediment surface (Harriss *et al.*, 1982). Atmospheric methane was also consumed at significant rates by tropical savannah soils adjacent to termite mounds in South Africa; as a result, Seiler *et al.* (1984) questioned the role of termite ecosystems in the atmospheric methane budget. In sharp contrast, Hao *et al.* (1988) found no atmospheric methane consumption, but rather a small flux from tropical savannah soils in Venezuela. Differences relative to the results of Seiler *et al.* (1984) were attributed to either biogenic methane production or diffusion from subsurface natural gas deposits. Hao *et al.* (1988) did not eliminate the possibility of methane consumption at supra-atmospheric levels. Keller *et al.* (1983, 1986) documented substantial rates of atmospheric methane consumption in temperate and tropical

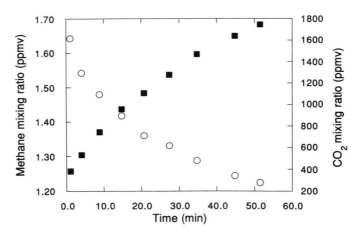

Figure 5. Consumption of atmospheric methane (○) and production of CO_2 (■) as a function of time in static chambers enclosing a tropical savannah soil. From Seiler *et al.* (1984).

forest soils. Subsequent observations (see Table III) have confirmed the generality of the process in various agricultural soils and grasslands (Mosier *et al.*, 1991), deciduous and coniferous forests (Steudler *et al.*, 1989; Born *et al.*, 1990; Keller *et al.*, 1990; Yavitt *et al.*, 1990b; Crill, 1991; Adamsen and King, unpublished data), and tundra soils (King *et al.*, 1989; Whalen and Reeburgh, 1990; Adamsen and King, unpublished data). Though possibly premature, the global significance of the soil methane sink has been estimated as 6–60 Tg year^{-1}, accounting for roughly 1–12% of the global methane flux (Born *et al.*, 1990). Mosier *et al.* (1991) have also suggested that changing land use practices, including fertilization and conversion of soils to agricultural use, have decreased the soil methane sink and thereby contributed to increasing atmospheric methane concentrations.

Soil methane oxidation is notable for its sensitivity to nitrogen addition. Steudler *et al.* (1989) have reported that nitrogen fertilization decreases rates of methane oxidation in forest soils (see Fig. 6). Keller *et al.* (1990) have proposed that changes in nitrogen availability explain decreased methane oxidation in rain forest soils after clearing and agricultural use. Mosier *et al.* (1991) have documented lower rates for methane oxidation in grassland soils subjected to fertilization. In each of these studies, the lower rates are the result of a long-term response to nitrogen enrichment since fertilization was not continuous. Steudler *et al.* (1989) present data from soil plots that were fertilized at monthly intervals during a 6-month period; Mosier *et al.* (1991) report results from soils fertilized once annually and soils fertilized once 8–9 years prior to the study. Though methane uptake is consistently decreased by fertilization, the magnitude of the effect is not obviously related to the frequency or amount of nitrogen added or total soil nitrogen, nitrate, or ammonia. For example, Mosier *et al.* (1991) note a decrease in methane oxidation at a "midslope" site 8 years postfertilization, even though there are no differences in the soil nitrogen content of fertilized plots relative to controls.

Table III. Reported Rates of Methane Oxidation for Selected Soils and Sediments

Site	Method[a]	Rate (mg m^{-2} d^{-1})	% ox.[b]	Reference
Wetland sediments and peats				
Denmark	IC	100.0[c]	10–>90	King (1990b)
Virginia	FC	<1.0–5.0		Harris et al. (1982)
West Virginia	SL	86.4	72	Yavitt et al. (1988)
	IC	0.6–2.2		Yavitt et al. (1988)
Florida	IC	0–36.1	0–91	King et al. (1990)
Lake sediments				
Lake Constance	IC	7.2	93	Frenzel et al. (1990)
Lake Washington	FC	4.0–5.6	50	Kuivila et al. (1988)
Anoxic marine sediments				
Black Sea (abyss)	IC	1.6[d]	>80	Reeburgh et al. (1992)
Skan Bay	IC	25.3		Alperin and Reeburgh (1984)
Saanich Inlet	FM	61.4		Devol et al. (1984)
Danish coast	IC	0.2–18.6		Iversen and Jørgensen (1985)
Atmospheric methane oxidation by soils				
Tundra, Alaska	FC	2.7		Whalen and Reeburgh (1990)
Tundra, Canada	FC	3.3		King et al. (1991)
Coniferous forest, Canada	FC	0.3–1.6		King et al. (1991)
Savannah, Africa	FC	1.2		Seiler et al. (1984)
Mesophytic forest, West Virginia	IC	2.0		Yavitt et al. (1990b)
Tropical forest	FC	0.5		Keller et al. (1983, 1986)
Mesophytic forest	FC	0.8		Keller et al. (1986)
Grassland, Colorado	FC	0.1–0.6		Mosier et al. (1991)
Mixed forest	FM	0.3–3.5		Born et al. (1990)
Mixed forest, New Hampshire	FC	0–3.5		Crill (1991)

[a]Estimates of oxidation were based on a variety of techniques: IC, intact cores; FC, flux chambers; SL, sediment slurries; FM, flux models.
[b]Percent oxidation refers to the reported fraction of the total potential flux oxidized.
[c]Maximum oxidation rate observed.
[d]Rate in mg m^{-2} year^{-1}.

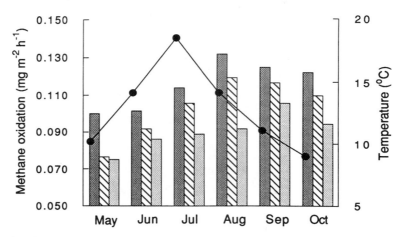

Figure 6. Effect of nitrogen fertilization on *in situ* rates of atmospheric methane uptake in soils of a pine forest. Soil temperatures (●) are from the 0–2.5 cm interval. The low-nitrogen treatment (N) represents an addition of 37 kg N ha^{-1} year^{-1} while the high-nitrogen addition plots |(□)| received 120 kg N ha^{-1} year^{-1}; rates of oxidation are compared to untreated or control plots (▨). From Steudler *et al.* (1989).

The lack of a clear relationship between nitrogen addition and rates of oxidation suggests that the observed changes are the result of shifts in population or community structure or subtle changes in the kinetics of MOB extant prior to fertilization. Steudler *et al.* (1989) and Mosier *et al.* (1991) have suggested that changes in AOB may be causative. A role for AOB is questionable, however. To date, AOB have not been shown to oxidize atmospheric methane [though concentrations as low as 12 nM are consumed (Jones and Morita, 1983)] and ammonia, nitrite, and nitrate concentrations up to 0.7 mM stimulate methane oxidation in *Nitrosococcus oceanus* and *Nitrosomonas europaea* (Jones and Morita, 1983). Concentrations of 0.7 mM for dissolved inorganic nitrogen species are considerably higher than the values for KCl-extractable ammonia and nitrate reported by Mosier *et al.* (1991) and the probable free ammonia and nitrate levels in the soils examined by Steudler *et al.* (1989). Moreover, Jones and Morita (1983) do not show net inhibition of methane oxidation by 3.5 mM ammonia relative to 0.07 mM; nitrite and nitrate additions beyond 0.7 mM also have no inhibitory effect. Thus, it might be argued that nitrogen additions could stimulate, not inhibit atmospheric methane oxidation by AOB in soils.

In contrast, inhibition of MOB by ammonia is consistent with culture data (e.g., O'Neill and Wilkinson, 1977) and offers at least a partial explanation of the field results; the response of MOB to ammonia can also be invoked to explain increased rates of nitrous oxide emission from fertilized soils (Yoshinari, 1985; Knowles and Topp, 1988), though this is probably better attributed to the activities of AOB and denitrifying bacteria. Of course, it is conceivable that the effects of nitrogen fertilization are expressed via indirect or secondary mechanisms rather than directly via substrate interactions with

MOB. In support of this possibility, Ward and Kilpatrick (1990) have found that ammonia and methane oxidation rates in the water column of Saanich Inlet were independent of methane and ammonia, respectively. Obviously, the response of soil methane oxidation to nitrogen requires considerably more detailed field and culture analyses. Future efforts might emphasize not only the controls of methane oxidation by nitrogen additions, but other interactions with the nitrogen cycle, especially the production and consumption of N_2O and NO (e.g., Krämer et al., 1990).

The use of inhibitors, especially N-serv, is a common agricultural practice that may affect methane oxidation to a greater extent than fertilization. MOB are basically sensitive to the same inhibitors as AOB (reviewed in Bédard and Knowles, 1989). N-serv and related analogues are particularly effective inhibitors of methane oxidation in culture, soil, and sediments (Topp and Knowles, 1982, 1984; Salvas and Taylor, 1984; Bédard and Knowles, 1989; King, 1990b; Megraw and Knowles, 1990). The routine application of N-serv to agricultural soils may not only inhibit methane consumption by AOB, but may severely limit methane oxidation by MOB. The extent to which this aspect of agriculture, as opposed to nitrogen fertilization, has altered the soil methane sink has not been evaluated.

In addition to emphasizing the response of MOB to nitrogen, it is important to understand basic kinetic phenomena. For example, K_m and threshold values are critical determinants of methane consumption. The threshold for consumption, i.e., that level below which no uptake occurs, has not been systematically examined for cultures. However, in a limited survey of *Methylosinus trichosporium* OB3B, *Methylomonas rubrum*, *M. albus* BG8, *Methylococcus capsulatus* Bath, and an isolate from a lake sediment, all but *M. Capsulatus* could consume atmospheric methane; thresholds were <0.1 ppm in some cases (King, unpublished data). There are also some fascinating insights available from soil and sediment studies. In particular, it appears that water-saturated sediments have thresholds incompatible with atmospheric methane consumption (King, 1990b) whereas soils generally have subatmospheric thresholds. Values of 2–3 ppm have been reported for a sediment (atmospheric = 1.7ppmv); apparent thresholds for soils are about 10-fold lower, ranging from < 0.1 to 0.4 ppmv (Born et al., 1990; Whalen and Reeburgh, 1990; Whalen et al., 1990; Yavitt et al., 1990b; Adamsen and King, unpublished data). Yavitt et al. (1990b) have also observed apparent threshold values of about 10 ppmv for a forest soil that apparently did not consume atmospheric methane. The causes of threshold variability are currently uncertain but may be related to physiological phenomena such as the expression of sMMO versus pMMO, energetic and NADH limitation at low methane partial pressures, or competitive inhibition of MMO by ammonia. Differences in threshold between soils and sediments or among sites might also reflect species-specific characteristics and distinctive population distributions. Regardless of the cause, threshold variability could substantially affect rates of atmospheric methane consumption or even determine whether a given system is a methane sink or source. Anthropogenically induced changes in thresholds could also account for decreased rates of methane oxidation in a variety of soils and thereby exacerbate anthropogenically induced increases in methane fluxes.

The apparent sensitivity to and long-term effect of disturbance on soil methane oxidation merits much more careful attention. If current global methane flux rates are about 500 Tg year^{-1} (Cicerone and Oremland, 1988) and soil methane consumption 60 Tg year^{-1} (Born *et al.*, 1990), then it is obvious that even small changes in uptake can contribute signficantly to both historical and current changes in the net accumulation of atmospheric methane. Changes in source terms, such as rice paddies and ruminants, could well dominate the trend for atmospheric methane accumulation but the potential role of soils as a sink cannot be ignored.

The process of soil methane oxidation is not just limited to the atmosphere for substrate. Endogenous methane production has been reported for a humisol and a forest soil (Megraw and Knowles, 1987a,b; Sextone and Mains, 1990). Endogenous production also occurs in the anoxic layers of landfills resulting in the transport of high concentrations of methane to the overlying oxic soils where substantial rates of consumption occur, perhaps limiting fluxes to 50% of the rate of production (Whalen *et al.*, 1990; Jones and Nedwell, 1990). Whalen *et al.* (1990) show that oxidation in landfills is very sensitive to soil moisture, that peak activity occurs in a narrow subsurface layer, that landfill soils can consume atmospheric methane, and that a methanotrophic isolate from the landfill is comparable in its characteristics to other known MOB. However, in spite of high rates of oxidation, landfills remain significant sources of methane; data of Whalen *et al.* (1990) and Jones and Nedwell (1990) imply that net consumption of atmospheric methane does not normally occur even if such a capability exists. Obviously, factors that limit the extent of methane oxidation require greater attention. What, for instance, determines the depth distribution of activity in soils? Why do landfill and tundra soils differ with respect to the distribution of activity (see Whalen and Reeburgh, 1990, versus Whalen *et al.*, 1990)? What regulates the extent of methane respiration versus incorporation into biomass? Can landfill soils be managed to enhance methane oxidation?

A final aspect of soil oxidation concerns the fate of the methane carbon. Culture data suggest a range of incorporation efficiencies (i.e., percent methane converted to biomass), depending on the organism used and growth conditions (e.g., Whittenbury *et al.*, 1970a). In general, though, incorporation varies between about 50 and 70%. Comparable values of 54, 50–68, 73, and 69% have been reported for tundra, forest, humisol, and landfill soils, respectively (Whalen and Reeburgh, 1990; Yavitt *et al.*, 1990b; Megraw and Knowles, 1987b; Whalen *et al.*, 1990). In contrast, incorporation of methane carbon is significantly lower in AOB (Jones and Morita, 1983; Ward, 1990), water-saturated peats (22%, Yavitt *et al.*, 1990a), and the water column of marine (e.g., < 2%, Griffiths *et al.*, 1982) and freshwater systems (e.g., 33%, Rudd *et al.*, 1974; 22%, Harrits and Hanson, 1980; 15–31%, Abramochkina *et al.*, 1987). The reported incorporation efficiencies of 30–80% for the water column of Saanich Inlet appear to represent an exception (Ward *et al.*, 1989). A number of parameters, including species composition and physiological status, could account for variability in incorporation. Regardless, it is striking that methane incorporation in soils, but not aquatic systems, is consistent with data from MOB in culture, even though there has been speculation that AOB were the active soil methane oxidizers. A more extensive evaluation of carbon incorporation could provide a wealth of information on MOB growth rates *in situ* and differential controls of growth and substrate partitioning in soil and aquatic ecosystems.

5. Anaerobic Methane Oxidation

From a budgetary perspective, methane oxidation is dominated on a global scale by aerobic consumption. Using a conservative assumption that aerobic oxidation in wetlands and rice paddies is equivalent to the estimated flux from these systems, about 200 Tg year^{-1}, anaerobic methane oxidation (20–100 Tg year^{-1}; Reeburgh, 1989) is at most only 10–50% of aerobic oxidation; more realistic estimates of aerobic consumption, including soil oxidation, lower this percentage much further. However, there are circumstances in which anaerobic methane consumption is conspicuous. For example, Smith *et al.* (1991) have recently reported circumstantial evidence linking methane oxidation and dissimilatory nitrate reduction (denitrification?) in anoxic groundwaters. Because of the potential significance of a nitrate-based anaerobic methane oxidation, their results need further confirmation, including a clear demonstration of mechanisms, end products, and causative organisms. In contrast to the case for nitrate as an electron acceptor, a large body of geochemical evidence supports the coupling of methane consumption to sulfate reduction (e.g., Barnes and Goldberg, 1976; Martens and Berner, 1977). This evidence is based primarily on models of sulfate and methane distribution which are best explained by a methane consumption term; in addition, there are geochemical observations which indicate that an active zone of anoxic methane consumption coincides with a zone of elevated sulfate depletion (Reeburgh, 1980; Devol and Ahmed, 1981; Devol *et al.*, 1984). Changes in the distribution of stable isotopes and dissolved methane also support a biologically mediated consumption of methane which discriminates against [^{13}C] methane, resulting in an isotopically enriched residuum (Oremland and Marais, 1983; Alperin and Reeburgh, 1984; Whiticar and Faber, 1986; Whiticar, in press). Finally, the carbonate-rich structures (pavements and chimneys) commonly associated with methane seeps (Kennicutt *et al.*, 1989; Dando *et al.*, 1991) are best explained by anoxic methane oxidation. This process generates alkalinity according to the following stoichiometry:

$$CH_4 + SO_4^{2-} + \rightarrow HCO_3^- + HS^- + H_2O$$

Increased alkalinity results in the deposition of carbonate cements which assume a morphology that depends on the nature of the methane source. Erosional events subsequently expose pavements or chimneys formed below the sediment–water interface. The ^{13}C isotopic composition of the carbonate cements strongly supports this interpretation since the carbonates are isotopically light (∂^{13}C about -36 to -51%o) as expected for carbon dioxide originating at least in part from biogenically formed methane (Dando *et al.*, 1991).

Microbiological evidence also supports anaerobic methane consumption. ^{14}CH$_4$

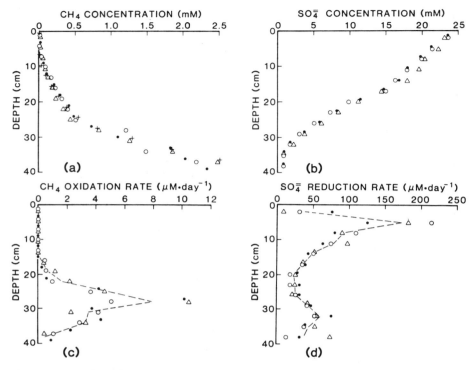

Figure 7. Depth distributions of methane (a), sulfate (b), methane oxidation (c), and sulfate reduction rates (d) in sediments from Skan Bay. $\bigcirc$, $\bullet$, and $\triangle$ represent data from individual replicate subcores; $+$ is the mean methane concetration (a); dashes denote the means for the methane oxidation and sulfate reduction rates. From Alperin and Reeburgh (1985).

oxidation to $^{14}CO_2$ has been documented for anoxic marine sediments (Fig. 7 and Reeburgh, 1980; Iversen and Blackburn, 1981; Alperin and Reeburgh, 1984, 1985; Iversen and Jørgensen, 1985; Iversen et al.,1987; Alperin et al., 1988; Reeburgh et al., 1992) and water masses (e.g., Framvaren Fjord, Lidstrom, 1983; Cariaco Trench, Ward et al., 1987, 1989; Black Sea, Reeburgh et al., 1992). Of particular interest are data from the Black Sea which show substantially higher (10^4-fold) rates of methane consumption in the anoxic water column than in either oxic waters or anoxic sediments; the turnover time of methane in the anoxic waters of the Black Sea is also remarkably fast, 3.6–18 years, relative to turnover times of 300–2000 years for the bottom water (Reeburgh et al., 1992). In contrast, aerobic methane oxidation appeared to exceed anaerobic oxidation in the water column of Saanich Inlet, whereas anoxic oxidation in sediments was 10^4-fold greater than total oxidation in the water column (Ward et al., 1987). In addition, assays of sulfate reduction using $^{35}SO_4^{2-}$ have demonstrated a secondary maximum associated with the zone of putative methane oxidation; sulfate reduction rates at the secondary maximum fit well with expectations based on modeled and measured rates of methane consumption (Devol and Ahmed, 1981; Devol *et al.*, 1984; Iversen and Jørgensen, 1985).

Though in many respects compelling, these studies remain somewhat controversial. For instance, Alperin and Reeburgh (1985) report that neither molybdate, a specific inhibitor of sulfate reduction, nor bromo-ethanesulfonic acid, a specific inhibitor of methanogenesis, affect rates of $^{14}CH_4$ oxidation in Skan Bay sediments. The former results raise questions about the role of methane as a typical substrate for sulfate reducers whereas the latter seem to exclude artifacts such as the isotopic exchange phenomenon described by Zehnder and Brock (1980). Moreover, there are at this writing no published studies of pure or mixed anaerobic cultures that conclusively oxidize methane. Thus, both the mechanism and agent for anaerobic methane oxidation await further clarification. There is little doubt, however, that a net consumption of methane does occur in both anoxic marine waters and sediments.

6. Stable Isotopes as Indices of Methane Oxidation

Stable isotopes have proven extremely valuable for understanding the dynamics of methane. Although ^{14}C tracers have long been used, methane oxidation has been routinely probed with ^{13}C tracers only during the last decade. Barker and Fritz (1981) reported fractionation factors for CO_2 production from methane of 1.0052–1.0313; these values were largely independent of temperature, rates of methane oxidation, or methane/oxygen ratios in mixed cultures enriched from a stream. Similar estimates (1.013–1.025) were calculated for methanotrophic cultures by Coleman *et al.* (1981). Comparable values (1.002–1.014) have also been reported for anaerobic methane consumption in a variety of marine sediments (Whiticar and Faber, 1986; Alperin *et al.*, 1988; Whiticar, in press). Since abiological consumption should result in little or no isotopic fractionation, these results provided strong evidence for the biological nature of anaerobic methane oxidation (Fig. 8). Based on some of the only field observations of isotopic fractionation during aerobic methane oxidation, King *et al.* (1989) concluded that fractionation factors for tundra soils were 1.016–1.026, with a possible inverse correlation with temperature.

Although isotopic fractionation during methane oxidation is considerably less than during methanogenesis, the reported fractionation factors result in signatures which aid interpretations of methane sources or postformation history (e.g., Barker and Fritz, 1981; Cicerone and Oremland, 1988; Whiticar, in press). For example, Quay *et al.* (1988) argued that the isotopic signatures of dissolved and bubble methane in the Amazon floodplain were consistent with methane oxidation. Chanton *et al.* (1988a) also recognized the potential importance of methane oxidation as a factor limiting plant-associated fluxes in the Amazon. Stevens and Engelkemeir (1988) reported a shift of about +6‰ during methane emission from a *Typha*-dominated slough in Illinois; based on isotopic evidence, they also estimated that oxidation consumed about 20% of the potential flux. Differences between sediment bubble and atmospheric isotopic composition (+5–10‰) in the Florida Everglades supported the possibility of active methane

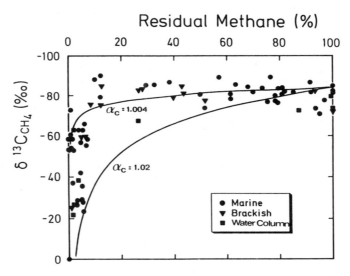

Figure 8. $\delta^{13}C$ in methane as a function of the fraction of the original pool remaining unoxidized for various marine and brackish sediments and water column samples as indicated. The curves represent expected relationships for fractionation factors (α_c) of 1.004 and 1.02. From Whiticar and Faber (1986).

oxidation (Burke *et al.*, 1988; Chanton *et al.*, 1988b; Stevens and Engelkemeir, 1988); estimates of the relative extent of oxidation were not reported. Of particular interest were discrepancies between plant methane and sediment bubble isotope values that could indicate methanotrophic activity (Chanton *et al.*, 1988b). A shift of about +4‰ was noted for bubble and atmospheric isotopic signatures in a study of tundra methane flux (Quay *et al.*, 1988), suggesting oxidation in these sites. In contrast, no differences were observed between bubble and atmospheric methane isotopic composition for samples from a Minnesota peatland (Quay *et al.*, 1988). Similarly, isotopic data indicated that oxidation was minimal in termite mounds (Tyler *et al.*, 1988), an observation which contradicts data of Seiler *et al.* (1984).

Results from these studies are important not only because they indicate the significance of methane oxidation, but because they provide a means of verifying atmospheric methane budget estimates (e.g., Stevens and Rust, 1982). Since the ^{13}C concentration of tropospheric methane and isotopic fractionation during reactions with hydroxyl radical are known (Davidson *et al.*, 1987; Cantrell *et al.*, 1990), the magnitude and ^{13}C content of an average global source can be estimated. In principle, extrapolations of global fluxes from the various sources (e.g., wetlands, rice paddies, ruminants) should, after weighting the isotopic contents of the sources, agree with the atmospheric methane ^{13}C concentration. Lack of concordance indicates the existence of unknown sources or errors in flux terms and isotopic composition. To date, flux measurements and isotope budgets are generally consistent; however, ^{13}C data do emphasize the importance of anthropogenic methane sources such as biomass burning. A similar approach based on ^{14}C

inventories emphasizes the importance of other anthropogenic methane sources such as fossil fuel consumption (Wahlen et al., 1989).

7. Summary

Methane oxidation is ubiquitous in the biosphere. It has not yet been reported in extreme environments, but this may reflect a lack of effort as much as a lack of activity. Otherwise, methane oxidation occurs in a diverse array of aquatic systems covering broad physicochemical, climatic, and biogeographic regimes. In many aquatic systems, oxidation occurs in close proximity to methane production and can consequently limit atmospheric fluxes to $< 10\%$ of the potential values. Since methane production in aquatic systems must greatly exceed the measured fluxes of about 215 Tg year^{-1} (Crutzen, 1991), the importance of oxidation as a control of global-scale atmospheric chemistry cannot be overemphasized. On a more local scale, the compression of methane oxidation into very narrow zones, either in sediments or the water column, can have substantial impacts on the trophodynamics of carbon and nitrogen cycling. Soil methane oxidation is also distributed across a wide range of conditions in polar, temperate, and tropical regions. On a global scale, it is a surprisingly robust process, equivalent to as much as 37% of the total terrestrial methane flux (60 versus 160 Tg year^{-1}; maximum soil estimate from Born et al., 1990; total terrestrial estimate from Crutzen, 1991) and 12% of the total flux from all sources (60 versus 505 Tg year^{-1}; total flux from Crutzen, 1991). However, in spite of recent advances in the microbiology and ecology of oxidation in soils and aquatic systems, much about the process remains unresolved. To what extent do methanotrophs contribute to nitification and nitrous oxide production *in situ?* Do AOB consume methane in soils or the water column? What determines the relative extent of oxidation in sediments? What physiological or ecological factors regulate the oxidation of atmospheric methane in soils? These are but a few of the key questions which must be answered before the functional role(s) of methane oxidation in ecosystem and biospheric dynamics can be understood or predicted. Predictive knowledge is especially important in view of the increasing concentrations of methane in the atmosphere and the documented susceptibility of methane oxidation to climatic fluctuations and anthropogenic disturbance. A major challenge facing microbial ecologists is to understand methane oxidation sufficiently to manipulate the process in systems under anthropogenic control (e.g., agricultural fields, rice paddies, landfills) so that the human contribution to atmospheric methane fluxes can be reduced to levels that do not affect the global atmosphere or climate.

ACKNOWLEDGMENTS. The author was inspired by the outstanding work of the many scientists who have contributed to the topic. A number of these individuals kindly provided reprints, unpublished manuscripts, data, and discussion; they are too many to mention specifically, but I am indebted to them all. This review was begun during the tenure of an appointment to the Institute of Ecology and Genetics, University of Århus; I am especially grateful to Drs. T. H. Blackburn, F. Bak, B. B. Jørgensen, and N. P.

Revsbech and to A. P. Adamsen, K. Finster, P. Roslev, and H. Skovgaard for invaluable input in a variety of ways. Drs. R. Conrad, P. Frenzel, D. Nedwell, and J.-P. Sweerts were also particularly generous with their time, hospitality, and discussion. NASA grant NAGW-1428 provided support for the review and my own research on methane oxidation.

References

Abramochkina, F. N., Bezrukova, L. V., Koshelev, A. V., Gal'chenko, V. F., and Ivanov, M. V., 1987, Microbial oxidation of methane in a body of fresh water, *Mikrobiologiya* **56**:464–471.

Alperin, M. J., and Reeburgh, W. S., 1984, Geochemical observations supporting anaerobic methane oxidation, in: *Microbial Growth on C-1 Compounds* (R. L. Crawford and R. S. Hanson, eds.), American Society for Microbiology, Washington, D.C., pp. 282–289.

Alperin, M. J., and Reeburgh, W. S., 1985, Inhibition experiments on anaerobic methane oxidation, *Appl. Environ. Microbiol.* **50**:940–945.

Alperin, M. J., Reeburgh, W. S., and Whiticar, M. J., 1988, Carbon and hydrogen isotope fractionation rseulting from anaerobic methane oxidation, *Global Biogeochem. Cycles* **2**:279–288.

Alvarez-Cohen, L., and McCarty, P. L., 1991, Effects of toxicity, aeration, and reductant supply on trichloroethylene transformation by a mixed methanotrophic culture, *Appl. Environ. Microbiol.* **57**:228–235.

Anthony, C., 1982, *The Biochemistry of Methylotrophs,* Academic Press, New York.

Arciero, D. T., Vannelli, T., Logan, M., and Hooper, A. B., 1989, Degradation of trichlorethylene by the ammonia-oxidizing bacterium *Nitrosomonas europaea, Biochem. Biophys. Res. Commun.* **159**:640–643.

Aselmann, I., and Crutzen, P. J., 1989, Global distribution of natural freshwater wetlands and rice paddies, their net primary productivity, seasonality and possible methane emissions, *J. Atmos. Chem.* **8**:307–358.

Barker, J. F., and Fritz, P., 1981, Carbon isotope fractionation during microbial methane oxidation, *Nature* **293**:289–291.

Barnes, R. O., and Goldberg, E. D., 1976, Methane production and consumption in anoxic marine sediments, *Geology* **4**:297–300.

Bédard, C., and Knowles, R., 1989, Physiology, biochemistry, and specific inhibitors of CH_4, NH_4^+, and CO oxidation by methanotrophs and nitrifiers, *Microbiol. Rev.* **53**:68–84.

Blake, D. R., and Rowland, F. S., 1988, Continuing worldwide increase in tropospheric methane, 1978–1987, *Science* **239**:1129–1131.

Born, M., Dörr, H., and Ingeborg, L., 1990, Methane consumption in aerated soils of the temperate zone, *Tellus* **42**(B):2–8.

Bowman, J. P., Skerratt, J. H., Nichols, P. D., and Sly, L. I., 1990, Phospholipid fatty acid and lipopolysaccharide fatty acid signature lipids in methane-utilizing bacteria, *FEMS Microbiol. Ecol.* **85**:15–22.

Brinch-Iversen, J., and King, G. M., 1990, Effects of substrate concentration, growth state, and oxygen availability on relationships among bacterial carbon, nitrogen and phospholipid phosphorous content, *FEMS Microbiol. Ecol.* **74**:345–355.

Brooks, J. M., Kennicutt, I. M. C., Fisher, C. R., Macko, S. A., Cole, K., Childress, J. J., Bidigare, R. R., and Vetter, R. D., 1987, Deep-sea hydrocarbon seep communities: Evidence for energy and nutritional carbon sources, *Science* **238**:1138–1142.

Brusseau, G. A., Tsien, H.-C., Hanson, R. S., and Wackett, L. P., 1990, Optimization of trichloroethylene oxidation by methanotrophs and the use of a colorimetric assay to detect soluble methane monooxygenase activity, *Biodegradation* **1**:19–29.

Bulygina, E. S., Galchenko, V. F., Govorukhina, N. I., Netrusov, A. I., Nikitin, D. I., Trotsenko, Y. A., and Chumakov, K. M., 1990, Taxonomic studies on methylotrophic bacteria by 5S ribosomal RNA sequencing, *J. Gen. Microbiol.* **136**:441–446.

Burke, R. A., Barber, T. R., and Sackett, W. M., 1988, Methane flux and stable hydrogen and carbon isotopic composition of sedimentary methane from the Florida Everglades, *Global Biogeochem. Cycles* **2**:329–340.

Burrows, K. J., Cornish, A., Scott, D., and Higgins, I. G., 1984, Substrate specificities of the soluble and particulate methane monooxygenases of *Methylosinus trichosporium* OB3b, *J. Gen. Microbiol.* **130**:3327–3333.

Cantrell, C. A., Shetter, R. E., McDaniel, A. H., Calvert, J. G., Davidson, J. A., Lowe, D. C., Tyler, S. C., Cicerone, R. J., and Greenberg, J. P., 1990, Carbon kinetic isotope effect in the oxidation of methane by the hydroxyl radical, *J. Geophys. Res.* **95**:22455–22462.

Cardy, D. L. N., Laidler, V., Salmond, G. P. C., and Murrell, J. C., 1991, The methane monooxygenase gene cluster of *Methylosinus trichosporium:* cloning and sequencing of the *mmoC* gene, *Arch. Microbiol.* **156**:477–483.

Cary, S. C., Fisher, C. R., and Felbeck, H., 1988, Mussel growth supported by methane as sole carbon and energy source, *Science* **240**:78–80.

Cary, S. C., Fry, B., Felbeck, H., and Vetter, R. D., 1989, Multiple trophic resources from a chemoautotrophic community at a cold water brine seep at the base of the Florida Escarpment, *Mar. Biol.* **100**:411–418.

Cavanaugh, C. M., 1983, Symbiotic chemoautotrophic bacteria in marine invertebrates from sulfide-rich habitats, *Nature* **302**:58–61.

Cavanaugh, C. M., 1985, Symbioses of chemoautotrophic bacteria and marine invertebrates from hydrothermal vents and reducing sediments, *Bull. Biol. Soc. Wash.* **6**:373–388.

Cavanaugh, C. M., Gardiner, S. L., Jones, M. L., Jannasch, H. W., and Waterbury, J. B., 1981, Prokaryotic cells in the hydrothermal vent tube worm *Riftia pachyptila* Jones: Possible chemoautotrophic symbionts, *Science* **213**:340–342.

Cavanaugh, C. M., Levering, P. R., Maki, J. S., Mitchell, R., and Lidstrom, M. E., 1987, Symbiosis of methylotrophic bacteria and deep-sea mussels, *Nature* **325**:346–348.

Chanton, J., Crill, P., Bartlett, K., and Martens, C. S., 1988a, Amazon capims (floating grassmats): A source of ^{13}C enriched methane to the troposphere, *Geophys. Res. Lett.* **16**:799–802.

Chanton, J. P., Pauly, G. G., Martens, C. S., Blair, N. E., and Dacey, J. W. H., 1988b, Carbon isotopic composition of methane in Florida Everglades soils and fractionation during its transport to the troposphere, *Global Biogeochem. Cycles* **2**:245–252.

Chanton, J. P., Whiting, G. J., Showers, W. J., and Crill, P. M., 1992, Methane flux from *Peltandra virginica:* stable isotope tracing and chamber effects, *Global Biogeochem. Cycles* **6**:15–32.

Chappellaz, J., Barnola, J. M., Raynaud, D., Korotkevich, Y. S., and Lorius, C., 1990, Ice-core record of atmospheric methane over the past 160,000 years, *Nature* **345**:127–131.

Childress, J. J., Fisher, C. R., Brooks, J. M., Kennicutt, I. M. C., Bidigare, R., and Andersen, A., 1986, A methanotrophic molluscan (Bivalvia: Mytilidae) symbiosis: Mussels fueled by gas, *Science* **233**:1306–1308.

Cicerone, R. J., and Oremland, R. S., 1988, Biogeochemical aspects of atmospheric methane, *Global Biogeochem. Cycles* **2**:299–327.

Cicerone, R. J., and Shetter, J. D., 1981, Sources of atmospheric methane: Measurements in rice paddies and a discussion, *J. Geophys. Res.* **86**:7203–7209.

Colby, J., Stirling, D. I., and Dalton, H., 1977, The soluble methane monooxygenase of *Methylococcus capsulatus* (Bath). Its ability to oxygenate n-alkanes, n-alkenes, ethers and alicyclic, aromatic and heterocyclic compounds, *Biochem. J.* **165**:395–402.

Coleman, D. D., Risatti, J. B., and Schoell, M., 1981, Fractionation of carbon and hydrogen isotopes by methane-oxidizing bacteria, *Geochim. Cosmochim. Acta* **45**:1033–1037.

Collins, M. L. P., Buchholz, L. A., and Remsen, C. C., 1991, Effect of copper on *Methylomonas albus* BG8, *Appl. Environ. Microbiol.* **57**:1261–1264.

Conrad, R., 1984, Capacity of aerobic microorganisms to utilize and grow on atmospheric trace gases (H_2, CO, and CH_4), in: *Perspectives on Microbial Ecology* (M. J. Klug and C. A. Reddy, eds.), American Society for Microbiology, Washington, D.C., pp. 461–467.

Crill, P. M., 1991, Seasonal patterns of methane uptake and carbon dioxide release by a temperate woodland soil, *Global Biogeochem. Cycles* **5**:319–334.

Crutzen, P. J., 1991, Methane's sinks and sources, *Nature* **350**:380–381.

Dacey, J. W. H., 1980, Internal winds in water lilies: An adaptation for life in anaerobic sediments, *Science* **210**:1017–1019.

Dacey, J. W. H., 1981, Pressurized ventilation in the yellow water lily, *Ecology* **62**:1137–1147.

Dacey, J. W. H., 1987, Knudsen-transitional flow and gas pressurization in leaves of Nelumbo, *Plant Physiol.* **85**:199–203.

Dacey, J. W. H., and Klug, M. J., 1979, Methane efflux from lake sediments through water lilies, *Science* **203**:1253–1254.

Dalton, H., 1977, Ammonia oxidation by the methane-oxidizing bacterium *Methylococcus capsulatus* strain Bath, *Arch. Microbiol.* **114**:272–279.

Dalton, H., 1980, Oxidation of hydrocarbons by methane monooxygenases from a variety of microbes, *Adv. Appl. Microbiol.* **26**:71–87.

Dalton, H., and Higgins, I. J., 1987, Physiology and biochemistry of methylotrophic bacteria, in: *Microbial Growth on C_1 Compounds* (H. W. Van Verseveld and J. A. Duine, eds.), Nijhoff, Dordrecht, pp. 89–94.

Dalton, H., Prior, S. D., Leak, D. J., and Stanley, S. H., 1984, Regulation and control of methane monooxygenase, in: *Microbial Growth on C_1 Compounds* (R. L. Crawford and R. S. Hanson, eds.), American Society for Microbiology, Washington, D.C., pp. 75–82.

Dando, P. R., and Southward, A. J., 1986, Chemoautotrophy in bivalve molluscs of the genus *Thyasira*, *J. Mar. Biol. Assoc. U.K.* **66**:915–929.

Dando, P. R., Southward, A. J., Southward, E. C., Terwilliger, N. B., and Terwilliger, R. C., 1985, Sulphur-oxidizing bacteria and haemoglobin in gills of the bivalve mollusc *Myrtea spinifera*, *Mar. Ecol. Prog. Ser.* **23**:85–98.

Dando, P. R., Austen, M. C., Burke, J. R. A., Kendall, M. A., Kennicutt, I. M. C., Judd, A. G., Moore, D. C., O'Hara, S. C. M., Schmaljohann, R., and Southward, A. J., 1991, Ecology of a North Sea pockmark with an active methane seep, *Mar. Ecol. Prog. Ser.* **70**:49–63.

Davidson, J. A., Cantrell, C. A., Tyler, S. C., Shetter, R. E., Cicerone, R. J., and Calvert, J. G., 1987, Carbon kinetic isotope effect in the reaction of CH_4 with HO, *J. Geophys. Res.* **92**:2195–2199.

DeBont, J. A. M., Lee, K. K., and Bouldin, D. F., 1978, Bacterial methane oxidation in a rice paddy, *Ecol. Bull.* **26**:91–96.

Devol, A. H., and Ahmed, S. I., 1981, Are high rates of sulphate reduction associated with anaerobic oxidation of methane? *Nature* **291**:407–408.

Devol, A. H., Anderson, J. J., Kuivila, K., and Murray, J. W., 1984, A model for coupled sulfate reduction and methane oxidation in the sediments of Saanich Inlet, *Geochim. Cosmochim. Acta* **48**:993–1004.

Diels, L., and Mergeay, M., 1990, DNA probe-mediated detection of resistant bacteria from soils highly polluted with metals, *Appl. Environ. Microbiol.* **56**:1485–1491.

Di Toro, D. M., Paquin, P. R., Subburamu, K., and Gruber, D. A., 1990, Sediment oxygen demand model: Methane and ammonia oxidation, *J. Environ. Eng.* **116**:945–986.

Ehhalt, D. H., 1985, Methane in the global atmosphere, *Environment* **27**:6–33.

Fechner, E. J., and Hemond, H. F., 1992, Methane transport and oxidation in the unsaturated zone of a *Sphagnum* peatland, *Global Biogeochem. Cycles* **6**:33–44.

Fisher, C. R., Fisher, J. J., Oremland, R. S., and Bidigare, R. R., 1987, The importance of methane in the metabolism of the bacterial symbionts of two deep-sea mussels, *Mar. Biol.* **96**:59–71.

Fogel, M. M., Taddeo, A. R., and Fogel, S., 1986, Biodegradation of chlorinated ethenes by a methane-utilizing mixed culture, *Appl. Environ. Microbiol.* **54**:720–724.

Fox, B. G., Froland, W. A., Dege, J. E., and Lipscomb, J. D., 1989, Methane monooxygenase from *Methylosinus trichosporium* OB3b, *J. Biol. Chem.* **264**:10023–10033.

Fox, B. G., Froland, W. A., Dege, J. E., and Lipscomb, J. D., 1990, Haloalkene oxidation by the soluble methane monooxygenase from *Methylosinus trichosporium* OB3b: Mechanistic and environmental Applications, *Biochemistry* **29**:6419–6427.

Frenzel, P., Thebrath, B., and Conrad, R., 1990, Oxidation of methane in the oxic surface layer of a deep lake sediment (Lake Constance), *FEMS Microbiol. Ecol.* **73**:149–158.

Gal'chenko, V. F., Lein, A., and Ivanov, M., 1989, Biological sinks of methane, in: *Exchange of Trace Gases between Terrestrial Ecosystems and the Atmosphere* (M. O. Andreae and D. S. Schimel, eds.), Wiley, New York, pp. 59–71.

Green, J., and Dalton, H., 1986, Steady-state kinetic analysis of soluble methane monooxygenase from *Methylococcus capsulatus* (Bath), *Biochem. J.* **236**:155–162.

Griffiths, R. P., Caldwell, B. A., Cline, J. D., Broich, W. A., and Morita, R. Y., 1982, Field observations of methane concentrations and oxidation rates in the southeastern Bering Sea, *Appl. Environ. Microbiol.* **44**:435–446.

Guckert, J. D., Ringelberg, D. B., White, D. C., Bratina, B. J., and Hanson, R. S., 1991, Membrane fatty acids as phenotypic markers for the polyphasic taxonomy of methylotrophs within the proteobacteria, *J. Gen. Microbiol.* **137**:2631–2641.

Haber, C. L.,, Allen, L. N., Zhao, S., and Hanson, R. S., 1983, Methylotrophic bacteria biochemical diversity and genetics, *Science* **221**:1147–1153.

Hahn, D. Starrenburg. M. J. C., and Akkermans, A. D. L., 1990, Oligonucleotide probes that hybridize with rRNA as a tool to study *Frankia* strains in root nodules, *Appl. Environ. Microbiol.* **56**: 1342–1346.

Hanson, R. S., 1980, Ecology and diversity of methylotrophic bacteria, *Adv. Appl. Microbiol.* **26**:3–39.

Hanson, R. S., Tsuji, K., Bastien, C., Tsien, H. C., Bratina, B., Brusseau, G., and Machlin, S., 1990a, Genetic and biochemical studies of methylotrophic bacteria, in: *Coal and Gas Biotechnology* (C. Aiken and J. Smith, eds.), Institute for Gas Technology, Chicago, pp. 215–231.

Hanson, R. S., Tsien, H. C., Tsuji, K., Brusseau, G. A., and Wackett, L. P., 1990b, Biodegradation of low-molecular weight halogenated hydrocarbons by methanotrophic bacteria, *FEMS Microbiol. Rev.* **87**:273–278.

Hanson, R. S., Netrusov, A. I., and Tsuji, K., 1991, The obligate methanotrophic bacteria *Methylococcus, Methylomonas,* and *Methylosinus,* in: *The Prokaryotes* (A. Balows, H. G. Truper, M. Dworkin, and K. Schliefer, eds.), Springer-Verlag, Berlin, pp. 2350–2364.

Hao, W. M., Scharffe, D., Crutzen, P. J., and Sanhueza, E., 1988, Production of N_2O, CH_4, and CO_2 from soils in the tropical savanna during the dry season, *J. Atmos. Chem.* **7**:93–105.

Harms, N., de Vries, G. E., Maurer, K., Hoogendijk, J., and Stouthamer, A. H., 1987, Isolation and nucleotide sequence of the methanol dehydrogenase structural gene from *Paracoccus denitrificans*, *J. Bacteriol.* **169**:3969–3975.

Harriss, R. C., Sebacher, D. I., and Day, F. P., Jr., 1982, Methane flux in the Great Dismal Swamp, *Nature* (Lond.) **297**:673–674.

Harriss, R. C., Gorham, E., Sebacher, D. I., Bartlett, K. B., and Flebbe, P. A., 1985, Methane flux from northern peatlands, *Nature* **315**:652–654.

Harriss, R. C., Sebacher, D. I., Bartlett, K. B., Bartlett, D. S., and Crill, P. M., 1988, Sources of atmospheric methane in the south Florida environment, *Global Biogeochem. Cycles* **2**:231–243.

Harrits, S. M., and Hanson, R. S., 1980, Stratification of aerobic methane-oxidizing organisms in Lake Mendota, Madison, Wisconsin, *Limnol. Oceanogr.* **25**:412–421.

Hemond, H. F., Nuttle, W. K., Burke, R. W., and Stolzenbach, K. D., 1984, Surface infiltration in salt marshes: Theory, measurement, and biogeochemical implications, *Water Resour. Res.* **20**:591–600.

Henry, S. M., and Grbic-Galic, D., 1990, Effect of mineral media on trichloroethylene oxidation by aquifer methanotrophs, *Micob. Ecol.* **20**:151–169.

Henry, S. M., and Grbic-Galic, D., 1991, Influence of endogenous and exogenous electron donors and trichloroethylene oxidation toxicity on trichloroethylene oxidation by methanotrophic cultures from a groundwater aquifer, *Appl. Environ. Microbiol.* **57**:236–244.

Henson, J. M., Yates, M. V., Cochran, J. W., and Shackleford, D. L., 1988, Microbial removal of halogenated methanes, ethanes, and ethylenes in an aerobic soil exposed to methane, *FEMS Microbiol. Ecol.* **53**:193–201.

Heyer, J., and Suckow, R., 1985, Ökologische untersuchungen der methanoxydation in einem sauren Moorsee, *Limnologica* **16**:247–266.

Heyer, J., Malaschenko, Y., Berger, U., and Budkova, E., 1984, Verbreitung methanotropher Bakterien, *Z. Allg. Mikrobiol.* **24**:725–744.

Higgins, I. J., Best, D. J., and Hammond, R. C., 1980, New findings in methane-utilizing bacteria highlight their importance in the biosphere and their commercial potential, *Nature* **286**:561–564.

Higgins, I. J., Best, D. J., Hammond, R. C., and Scott, D., 1981, Methane-oxidizing microorganisms, *Microbial Rev.* **45**:556–590.

Holtzapfel-Pschorn, A., Conrad, R., and Seiler, W., 1985, Production, oxidation and emission of methane in rice paddies, *FEMS Microbiol. Ecol.* **31**:343–351.

Holtzapfel-Pschorn, A., Conrad, R., and Seiler, W., 1986, Effects of vegetation on the emission of methane from submerged paddy soil, *Plant Soil* **92**:223–233.

Hovland, M., and Thomsen, E., 1989, Hydrocarbon-based communities in the North Sea? *Sarsia* **74**:29–42.

Hyman, M. R., and Wood, P. R., 1983, Methane oxidation by *Nitrosomonas europaea*, *Biochem. J.* **212**:31–37.

Iversen, N., and Blackburn, T. H., 1981, Seasonal rates of methane oxidation in anoxic marine sediments, *Appl. Environ. Microbiol.* **41**:1295–1300.

Iversen, N., and Jørgensen, B. B., 1985, Anaerobic methane oxidation rates at the sulfate–methane transition in marine sediments from Kattegat and Skagerrak (Denmark), *Limnol. Oceanogr.* **30**:944–955.

Iversen, N., Oremland, R. S., and Klug, M. J., 1987, Big Soda Lake (Nevada). 3. Pelagic methanogenesis and anaerobic methane oxidation, *Limnol. Oceanogr.* **32**:804–818.

Janssen, D. B., Grobben, G., Hoekstra, R., Oldenhuis, R., and Witholt, B., 1988, Degradation of trans-1,2-dichloroethene by mixed and pure culture of methanotrophic bacteria, *Appl. Microbiol. Biotechnol.* **29**:392–399.

Joergensen, L., 1985, Methane oxidation by *Methylosinus trichosporium* measured by membrane inlet mass spectrometry, in: *Microbial Gas Metabolism* (R. K. Poole and C. S. Dow, eds.), Academic Press, New York, pp. 287–294.

Joergensen, L., and Degn, H., 1983, Mass spectrometric measurements of methane and oxygen utilization by methanotrophic bacteria, *FEMS Microbiol. Lett.* **20**:331–335.

Jones, R. D., and Morita, R. Y., 1983, Methane oxidation by *Nitrosococcus oceanus* and *Nitrosomonas europaea, Appl. Environ. Microbiol.* **45**:401–410.

Jones, H. A., and Nedwell, D. B., 1990, Soil atmosphere concentration profiles and methane emission rates in the restoration covers above landfill sites: Equipment and preliminary results, *Waste Manage. Res.* **8**:21–31.

Keller, M., Goreau, T. J., Wofsy, S. C., Kaplan, W. A., and McElroy, M. B., 1983, Production of nitrous oxide and consumption of methane by forest soil, *Geophys. Res. Lett.* **10**:1156–1159.

Keller, M., Kaplan, W. A., and Wofsy, S. C., 1986, Emissions of N_2O, CH_4 and CO_2 from tropical forest soils, *J. Geophys. Res.* **91**(D):11791–11802.

Keller, M., Mitre, M. E., and Stallard, R. F., 1990, Consumption of atmospheric methane in tropical soils of central Panama: Effects of agricultural development, *Glob. Biogeochem. Cyc.* **4**:21–28.

Kennicutt, M. C., II, Brooks, J. M., Bidigare, R. R., Fay, R. R., Wade, T. L., and McDonald, T. J., 1985, Vent-type taxa in a hydrocarbon seep region on the Louisiana slope, *Nature* **317**:351–353.

Kennicutt, M. C., Brooks, J. M., Bidigare, R. R., McDonald, S. J., Adkison, D. L., and Macko, S. A., 1989, An upper slope "cold" seep community: Northern California, *Limnol. Oceanogr.* **34**: 635–640.

Khalil, M. A. K., and Rasmussen, R. A., 1983, Sources, sinks and seasonal cycles of atmospheric methane, *J. Geophys. Res.* **88**:5131–5144.

King, G. M., 1990a, Regulation by light of methane emission from a Danish wetland, *Nature* **345**: 513–515.

King, G. M., 1990b, Dynamics and controls of methane oxidation in a Danish wetland sediment, *FEMS Microbiol. Ecol.* **74**:309–323.

King, G. M., Skovgaard, H., and Roslev, P., 1990, Methane oxidation in sediments and peats of a subtropical wetland, the Florida Everglades, *Appl. Environ. Microbiol.* **56**:2902–2911.

King, G. M., Roslev, P., and Adamsen, A. P., 1991, Controls of methane oxidation in a Canadian wetland and forest soils, *Trans. Am. Geophys. Union.* **72**:79.

King, S. L., Quay, P. D., and Lansdown, J. M., 1989, The $^{13}C/^{12}C$ kinetic isotope effect for soil oxidation of methane at ambient atmospheric concentrations, *J. Geophys. Res.* **94**(D): 18273–18277.

Knowles, R., and Topp, E., 1988, Some factors affecting nitrification and the production of nitrous oxide by the methanotrophic bacterium *Methylosinus trichosporium* OB3b, in: *Current Perspectives in Environmental Biogeochemistry* (G. Giovannozzi-Sermanni and P. Nannipieri, eds.), Consiglio Nazionale delle Ricerche–I.P.R.A., Rome, pp. 383–393.

Koch, A. L., 1990, Diffusion: The crucial process in many aspects of the biology of bacteria, *Adv. Microb. Ecol.* **11**:37–70.

Komagata, K., 1990, Taxonomy of facultative methylotrophs, in: *Aerobic Photosynthetic Bacteria* (K. Harashima, T. Shiba, and N. Murata, eds.), Springer-Verlag, Berlin, pp. 25–36.

Krämer, M., Baumgärtner, M., Bender, M., and Conrad, R., 1990, Consumption of NO by methanotrophic bacteria in pure culture and in soil, *FEMS Microbiol. Ecol.* **73**:345–350.

Kuivila, K. M., Murray, J. W., Devol, A. H., Lidstrom, M. E., and Reimers, C. E., 1988, Methane cycling in the sediments of Lake Washington, *Limnol. Oceanogr.* **33**:571–581.

Lamb, S. C., and Garver, J. C., 1980, Batch- and continuous culture studies of a methane-utilizing mixed culture, *Biotechnol. Bioeng.* **XXII**:2097–2118.

Lanzarone, N. A., and McCarty, P. L., 1990, Column studies on methanotrophic degradation of trichloroethene and 1,2-dichloroethane, *Ground Water* **28**:910–919.

Leak, D. J., and Dalton, H., 1986, Growth yields of methanotrophs. 2. A theoretical analysis, *Appl. Microbiol. Biotechnol.* **23**:477–481.

Lee, S., and Fuhrman, J. A., 1990, DNA hybridization to compare species compositions of natural bacterioplankton assemblages, *Appl. Environ. Microbiol.* **56**:739–746.

Lees, V., Owens, N. J. P., and Murrell, J. C., 1991, Nitrogen metabolism in marine methanotrophs, *Arch. Microbiol.* **157**:60–65.

Lidstrom, M. E., 1983, Methane consumption in Framvaren, an anoxic marine fjord, *Limnol. Oceanogr.* **28**:1247–1251.

Lidstrom, M. E., 1988, Isolation and characterization of marine methanotrophs, *Antonie van Leeuwenhoek J. Microbiol. Serol.* **54**:189–199.

Lidstrom, M. E., 1990, Genetics of carbon metabolism in methylotrophic bacteria, *FEMS Microbiol. Rev.* **87**:431–436.

Lidstrom, M. E., and Somers, L., 1984, Seasonal study of methane oxidation in Lake Washington, *Appl. Environ. Microbiol.* **47:**1255–1260.

Lidstrom, M. E., Nunn, D. N., Anderson, D. J., Stephens, R. L., and Haygood, M. G., 1987, Molecular biology of methanol oxidation, in: *Microbial Growth on C₁ Compounds* (H. W. Van Verseveld and J. A. Duine, eds.), Nijhoff, Amsterdam, pp. 246–254.

Linton, J. D., and Buckee, J. C., 1977, Interactions in a methane-utilizing mixed bacterial culture in a chemostat, *J. Gen. Microbiol.* **101:**219–225.

Little, C. D., Palumbo, A. V., Herbes, S. E., Lidstrom, M. E., Tyndall, R. L., and Gilmer, P. J., 1988, Trichloroethylene biodegradation by a methane-oxidizing bacterium, *Appl. Environ. Microbiol.* **54:**951–956.

MacDonald, I. R., Calender, W. R., Burke, J. R. A., McDonald, S. J., and Carney, R. S., 1990, Fine-scale distribution of methanotrophic mussels at a Louisiana cold seep, *Prog. Oceanogr.* **24:**15–24.

Machlin, S. M., and Hanson, R. S., 1988, Nucleotide sequence and transcriptional start site of the *Methylobacterium organophilum* XX methanol dehydrogenase structural gene, *J. Bacteriol.* **170:**4739–4747.

Machlin, S. M., Tam, P. E., Bastien, C. A., and Hanson, R. S., 1987, Genetic and physical analysis of *Methylobacterium organophilum* XX genes encoding methanol oxidation, *J. Bacteriol.* **170:** 141–148.

Martens, C. S., and Berner, R. A., 1977, Interstitial water chemistry of Long Island Sound sediments. I. Dissolved gases, *Limnol. Oceanogr.* **22:**10–25.

Matthews, E., and Fung, I. I., 1987, Methane emission from natural wetlands global distribution, area, and environmental characteristics of sources, *Global Biogeochem. Cycles* **1:**61–86.

Mayer, L. M., Liotta, F. P., and Norton, S. A., 1982, Hypolimnetic redox and phosphorus cycling in hypereutrophic Lake Sebasticook, Maine, *Water Res.* **16:**1189–1196.

Megraw, S. R., and Knowles, R., 1987a, Active methanotrophs suppress nitrification in a humisol, *Biol. Fertil. Soils* **4:**205–212.

Megraw, S. R., and Knowles, R., 1987b, Methane production and consumption in a cultivated humisol, *Biol. Fertil. Soils* **5:**56–60.

Megraw, S. R., and Knowles, R., 1989a, Isolation, characterization, and nitrification potential of a methylotroph and two heterotrophic bacteria from a consortium showing methane-dependent nitrification, *FEMS Microbiol. Ecol.* **62:**367–374.

Megraw, S. R., and Knowles, R., 1989b, Methane-dependent nitrate production by a microbial consortium enriched from a cultivated humisol, *FEMS Microbiol. Ecol.* **62:**359–366.

Megraw, S. R., and Knowles, R., 1990, Effect of picolinic acid (2-pyridine carboxylic acid) on the oxidation of methane and ammonia in soil and in liquid culture, *Soil Biol. Biochem.* **22:**635–641.

Moore, T. R., and Knowles, R., 1989, The influence of water table levels on methane and carbon dioxide emissions from peatland soils, *Can. J. Soil Sci.* **69:**33–38.

Mosier, A., Schimel, D., Valentine, D., Bronson, K., and Parton, W., 1991, Methane and nitrous oxide fluxes in native, fertilized and cultivated grasslands, *Nature* **350:**330–332.

Mountfort, D. O., White, D., and Asher, R. A., 1990, Oxidation of lignin-related aromatic alcohols by cell suspensions of *Methylosinus trichosporium*, *Appl. Environ. Microbiol.* **56:**245–249.

Nagai, S., Mori, T., and Aiba, S., 1973, Investigation and energetics of methane-utilizing bacteria in methane- and oxygen-limited chemostat cultures, *J. Appl. Chem. Biotechnol.* **23:**549–562.

Nichols, P. D., Smith, G. A., Antworth, C. P., Hanson, R. S., and White, D. C., 1985, Phospholipid and lipopolysaccharide normal and hydroxy fatty acids as potential signatures for methane-oxidizing bacteria, *FEMS Microbiol. Ecol.* **31:**327–335.

Nichols, P. D., Henson, J. M., Antworth, C. P., Parsons, J., Wilson, J. T., and White, D. C., 1987, Detection of a microbial consortium including type II methanotrophs by use of phospholipid fatty acids in aerobic halogenated hydrocarbon-degrading soil column enriched with natural gas, *Environ. Toxicol. Chem.* **6:**89–97.

Oldenhuis, R., Vink, R. L. J. M., Janssen, D. B., and Witholt, B., 1989, Degradation of chlorinated aliphatic hydrocarbons by *Methylosinus trichosporium* OB3b expressing soluble methane monooxygenase, *Appl. Environ. Microbiol.* **55**:2819–2826.

Oldenhuis, R., Oedzes, J. Y., Waarde, J. J. v. d., and Janssen, D. B., 1991, Kinetics of chlorinated hydrocarbon degradation by *Methylosinus trichosporium* OB3b and toxicity of trichloroethylene, *Appl. Environ. Microbiol.* **57**:7–14.

O'Neill, J. D., and Wilkinson, J. F., 1977, Oxidation of ammonia by methane-oxidizing bacteria and the effects of ammonia on methane oxidation, *J. Gen. Microbiol.* **100**:407–412.

Oremland, R. S., 1988, The biogeochemistry of methanogenic bacteria, in: *Biology of Anaerobic Microorganisms* (A. J. B. Zehnder, ed.), Wiley–Interscience, New York, pp. 707–770.

Oremland, R. S., and Marais, D. D., 1983, Distribution, abundance, and carbon isotope consumption of gaseous hydrocarbons at Big Soda Lake, Nevada: An alkaline, meromictic lake, *Geochim. Cosmochim. Acta* **47**:2107–2114.

Ott, J., Rieger, G., Rieger, R., and Enderes, F., 1982, New mouthless interstitial worms from the sulfide system: Symbiosis with prokaryotes. P.S.Z.N. I: *Mar. Ecol.* **3**:313–333.

Page, H. M., Fisher, C. R., and Childress, J. J., 1990, Role of filter-feeding in the nutritional biology of a deep-sea mussel with methanotrophic symbionts, *Mar. Biol.* **104**:251–257.

Paull, C. K., Hecker, B., Commeau, R., Freeman-Lynde, R. P., Neumann, C., Corso, W. P., Colubic, S., Sook, J. E., Sikes, E., and Curray, J., 1984, Biological communities at the Florida Escarpment resemble hydrothermal vent taxa, *Science* **226**:965–967.

Paull, C. K., Jull, A. J. T., Toolin, L. J., and Linick, T., 1985, Stable isotope evidence for chemosynthesis in an abyssal seep community, *Nature* **317**:709–711.

Pilkington, S. J., and Dalton, H. J., 1991, Purification and characterization of the soluble methane monooxygenase from *Methylosinus sporium* 5 demonstrates the highly conserved nature of this enzyme in methanotrophs, *FEMS Microbiol. Lett.* **78**:103–108.

Pütz, J., Meinert, F., Wyss, U., Ehlers, R.-U., and Stackebrandt, E., 1990, Development and application of oligonucleotide probes for molecular identification of *Xenorhabdus* species, *Appl. Environ. Microbiol.* **56**:181–186.

Putzer, K. P., Buchholz, L. A., Lidstrom, M. E., and Remsen, C. C., 1991, Separation of methanotrophic bacteria by using percoll and its application to isolation of mixed and pure cultures, *Appl. Environ. Microbiol.* **57**:3656–3659.

Quay, P. D., King, S. L., Lansdown, J. M., and Wilbur, D. O., 1988, Isotopoic composition of methane released from wetlands: Implications for the increase in atmospheric methane, *Global Biogeochem. Cycles* **2**:385–397.

Quayle, J. R., 1987, An eightieth anniversary of the study of microbial C_1 metabolism, in: *Microbial Growth on C_1 Compounds* (H. W. Van Verseveld and J. A. Duine, eds.), Nijhoff, Dordrecht, pp. 1–5.

Reeburgh, W. S., 1980, Anaerobic methane oxidation rate depth distribution in Skan Bay sediments, *Earth Planet. Sci. Lett.* **47**:345–352.

Reeburgh, W. S., 1989, Interaction of sulphur and carbon cycles in marine sediments, in: *Evolution of the Global Biogeochemical Sulphur Cycle* (P. Brimblecombe and A. Y. Lein, eds.), Wiley, New York, pp. 125–159.

Reeburgh, W. S., Ward, B. B., Whalen, S. C., Sandbeck, K. A., Kilpatrick, K. A., and Kerkhof, L. J., 1992, Black Sea methane geochemistry, *Deep-Sea Res.* (Black Sea Issue) **38**:1189–1210.

Remsen, C. C., Minnich, E. C., Stephens, R. S., Buchholz, L., and Lidstrom, M. E., 19889, Methane oxidation in Lake Superior sediments, *J. Great Lakes Res.* **5**:141–146.

Ringelberg, D. B., Davis, J. D., Smith, G. A., Pfiffner, S. M., Nichols, P. D., Nickels, J. S., Henson, J. M., Wilson, J. T., Yates, M., Kampbell, D. H., Read, H. W., Stocksdale, T. T., and White, D. C., 1989, Validation of signature polarlipid fatty acid biomarkers for alkane-utilizing bacteria in soils and subsurface aquifer materials, *FEMS Microbiol. Ecol.* **62**:39–50.

Roulet, N. T., Ash, R., and Moore, T. R., 1992, Low boreal wetlands as a source of atmospheric methane, *J. Geophys. Res.* **97**(D):3739–3749.

Rudd, J. W. M., and Taylor, C. D., 1980, Methane cycling in aquatic environments, *Adv. Aquat. Microbiol.* **1**:77–150.

Rudd, J. W. M., Hamilton, R. D., and Campbell, N. E. R., 1974, Measurement of microbial oxidation of methane in lake water, *Limnol. Oceanogr.* **19**:519–524.

Rudd, J. W., Furutani, A., Flett, R. J., and Hamilton, R. D., 1976, Factors controlling methane oxidation in shield lakes: The role of nitrogen fixation and oxygen concentration, *Limnol. Oceanogr.* **21**:357–364.

Salvas, P. L., and Taylor, B. F., 1984, Effect of pyridine compounds on ammonia oxidation by autotrophic nitrifying bacteria and *Methylosinus trichosporium* OB3b, *Curr. Microbiol.* **10**:53–56.

Sass, R. L., Fisher, F. M., and Harcombe, P. A., 1990, Methane production and emission in a Texas rice field, *Global Biogeochem. Cycles* **4**:47–68.

Schmaljohann, R., and Flügel, H. J., 1987, Methane-oxidizing bacteria in Pogonophora, *Sarsia* **72**:91–98.

Schmaljohann, R., Faber, E., Whiticar, M. J., and Dando, P. R., 1990, Co-existence of methane- and sulphur-based endosymbioses between bacteria and invertebrates at a site in the Skagerrak, *Mar. Ecol. Prog. Ser.* **61**:119–124.

Schütz, H., Seiler, W., and Conrad, R., 1989a, Processes involved in formation and emission of methane in rice paddies, *Biogeochemistry* **7**:33–53.

Schütz, H., Holtzapfel-Pschorn, A., Conrad, R., Rennenberg, H., and Seiler, W., 1989b, A 3-year continuous record on the influence of daytime, season and fertilizer treatment on methane emission rates from an Italian rice paddy, *J. Geophys. Res.* **94**(D)3:16405–16416.

Scott, D., Brannan, J., and Higgins, I. J., 1981, The effect of growth conditions on intracytoplasmic membranes and methane monooxygenase activities in *Methylosinus trichosporium* OB3b, *J. Gen. Microbiol.* **125**:63–72.

Sebacher, D. I., Harriss, R. C., and Bartlett, K. B., 1985. Methane emissions to the atmosphere through aquatic plants, *J. Environ. Qual.* **14**:40–46.

Seiler, W., Conrad, R., and Scharffe, D., 1984, Field studies of methane emission from termite nests into the atmosphere and measurements of methane uptake by tropical soils, *J. Atmos. Chem.* **1**:171–186.

Sexstone, A. J., and Mains, C. N., 1990, Production of methane and ethylene in organic horizons of spruce forest soils, *Soil Biol. Biochem.* **22**:135–139.

Sheppard, J. C., Westberg, H., Hopper, J. F., and Ganesan, K., 1982, Inventory of global methane sources and their production rates, *J. Geophys. Res.* **87**(C):1305–1312.

Sieburth, J. M., Johnson, P. W., Eberhardt, M. A., Sieracki, M. E., Lidstrom, M., and Laux, D., 1987, The first methane-oxidizing bacterium from the upper mixing layer of the deep ocean *Methylomonas pelagica* sp. nov., *Curr. Microbiol.* **14**:285–293.

Simonet, P., Normand, P., Moiroud, A., and Bardin, R., 1990, Identification of *Frankia* strains in nodules by hybridization of polymerase chain reaction products with strain-specific oligonucleotide probes, *Arch. Microbiol.* **153**:235–240.

Smith, R. L., Howes, B. L., and Garabedian, S. P., 1991, *In situ* measurement of methane oxidation in groundwater by using natural-gradient tracer tests, *Appl. Environ. Microbiol.* **57**:1997–2004.

Söhngen, N. L., 1906, Über bakterien, welche methan als kohlenstoffnahrung und energiequelle gebrauchen, *Zentralbl. Bakteriol. Z. Abt. Bd.* **15**:513–517.

Southward, A. J., Southward, E. C., Dando, P. R., Rau, G., Felbeck, H., and Flügel, H., 1981, Bacterial symbionts and low $^{13}C/^{12}C$ ratios in tissues of Pogonophora indicate unusual nutrition and metabolism, *Nature* **293**:616–620.

Southward, A. J., Southward, E. C., Dando, P. R., Barret, R. L., and Ling, R. L., 1986, Chemoautotrophic function of bacterial symbionts in small pogonophora, *J. Mar. Biol. Assoc. U.K.* **66**:415–437.

Stainthorpe, A. C., Salmond, G. P. C., and Dalton, H., 1990, Screening of obligate methanotrophs for soluble methane monooxygenase genes, *FEMS Microbiol. Lett.* **70**:211–218.

Stanley, S. H., Prior, S. D., Leak, D. J., and Dalton, H., 1983, Copper stress underlies the fundamental change in intracellular location of methane monooxygenase in methane-oxidizing organisms: Studies in batch and continuous cultures, *Biotechnol. Lett.* **5**:487–492.

Steudler, P. A., Bowden, R. D., Mellilo, J. M., and Aber, J. D., 1989, Influence of nitrogen fertilization on methane uptake in temperate forest soils, *Nature* **341**:314–316.

Stevens, C. M., and Engelkemeir, A., 1988, Stable carbon isotopic composition of methane from some natural and anthropogenic sources, *J. Geophys. Res.* **93**:725–733.

Stevens, C. M., and Rust, F., 1982, The carbon isotopic composition of atmospheric methane, *J. Geophys. Res.* **87**:4879–4882.

Strand, S. E., and Shippert, L., 1986, Oxidation of chloroform in an aerobic soil exposed to natural gas, *Appl. Environ. Microbiol.* **52**:203–205.

Sweerts, J.-P. R. A., 1990, Oxygen consumption processes, mineralization and nitrogen cycling at the sediment–water interface of north temperate lakes, Ph.D. dissertation, University of Groningen.

Sweerts, J.-P. R. A., Bär-Gilissen, M.-J., Cornelase, A. A., and Cappenberg, T. E., 1991, Oxygen-consuming processes at the profundal and littoral sediment-water interface of a small meso-eutrophic lake (Lake Vechten, The Netherlands), *Limnol. Oceanogr.* **36**:1124–1133.

Topp, E., and Knowles, R., 1982, Nitrapyrin inhibits the obligate methylotophs *Methylosinus trichosporium* and *Methylococcus capsulatus*, *FEMS Microbiol. Lett.* **14**:47–49.

Topp, E., and Knowles, R., 1984, Effects of nitrapyrin [2-chloro-6-(trichloromethyl)pyridine] on the obligate methanotroph *Methylosinus trichosporium* OB3b, *Appl. Environ. Microbiol.* **47**:258–262.

Torsvik, V., Salte, K., Sørheim, R., and Goksøyr, J., 1990a, Comparison of phenotypic diversity and DNA heterogeneity in a population of soil bacteria, *Appl. Environ. Microbiol.* **56**:776–781.

Torsvik, V., Goksøyr, J., and Daae, F. L., 1990b, High diversity in DNA of soil bacteria, *Appl. Environ. Microbiol.* **56**:782–787.

Tsien, H.-C., Brusseau, G. A., Hanson, R. S., and Wackett, L. P., 1989, Biodegradation of trichloroethylene by *Methylosinus trichosporium* OB3b, *Appl. Environ. Microbiol.* **55**:3155–3161.

Tsuji, K., Tsien, H.-C., Hanson, R. S., De Palma, S. R., Scholtz, R., and LaRoche, S., 1990, 16S ribosomal RNA sequence analysis for determination of phylogenetic relationship among methylotrophs, *J. Gen. Microbiol.* **136**:1–10.

Tyler, S. C., Zimmerman, P. R., Cumberbatch, C., Greenberg, J. P., Westberg, C., and Darlington, J. P. E. C., 1988, Measurements and interpretation of $\partial^{13}C$ of methane from termites, rice paddies and wetlands in Kenya, *Global Biogeochem. Cycles* **2**:341–355.

Vogel, T. M., and McCarty, P., 1985, Biotransformation of tetrachloroethylene to trichloroethylene, dichloroethylene, vinyl chloride, and carbon dioxide under methanogenic conditions, *Appl. Environ. Microbiol.* **49**:1080–1083.

Vogel, T. M., Criddle, C. S., and McCarty, P. L., 1987, Transformations of halogenated aliphatic compounds, *Environ. Sci. Technol.* **21**:722–736.

Wackett, L. P., Brusseau, G. A., Householder, S. R., and Hanson, R. S., 1989, Survey of microbial oxygenases: Trichloroethylene degradation by propane-oxidizing bacteria, *Appl. Environ. Microbiol.* **55**:2960–2964.

Wahlen, M., Tanaka, N., Henry, R., Deck, B., Zeglen, J., Vogel, J. S., Southon, J., Shemesh, A., Fairbanks, R., and Broeker, W., 1989, Carbon-14 in methane sources and in atmospheric methane: The contribution from fossil carbon, *Science* **245**:286–290.

Ward, B. B., 1987, Kinetic studies on ammonia and methane oxidation by *Nitrosococcus oceanus*, *Arch. Microbiol.* **147**:126–133.

Ward, B. B., 1990, Kinetics of ammonia oxidation by a marine nitrifying bacterium: Methane as a substrate analogue, *Microb. Ecol.* **19**:211–225.

Ward, B. B., and Kilpatrick, K. A., 1990, Relationship between substrate concentration and oxidation of ammonium and methane in a stratified water column, *Cont. Shelf Res.* **10**:1193–1208.

Ward, B. B., Kilpatrick, K. A., Novelli, P. C., and Scranton, M. I., 1987, Methane oxidation and methane fluxes in the ocean surface layer and deep anoxic waters, *Nature* **327**:226–229.

Ward, B. B., Kilpatrick, K. A., Wopat, A. E., Minnich, E. C., and Lidstrom, M. E., 1989, Methane oxidation in Saanich Inlet during summer stratification, *Cont. Shelf Res.* **9**:65–75.

Whalen, S. C., and Reeburgh, W. S., 1990, Consumption of atmospheric methane by tundra soils, *Nature* **346**:160–162.

Whalen, S. C., Reeburgh, W. S., and Sandbeck, K. A., 1990, Rapid methane oxidation in a landfill cover soil, *Appl. Environ. Microbiol.* **56**:3405–3411.

Whiticar, M. J., in press, Isotope tracking of microbial methane formation and oxidation, in: *Cycling of Reduced Gases in the Hydrosphere* (D. Adams, S. Seitzinger, and P. Crill, eds.).

Whiticar, M. J., and Faber, E., 1986, Methane oxidation in sediment and water column environments–isotopic evidence, *Adv. Org. Geochem.* **10**:759–768.

Whittenbury, R., Phillips, K. C., and Wilkinson, J. F., 1970a, Enrichment, isolation and some properties of methane-utilizing bacteria, *J. Gen. Microbiol.* **61**:205–218.

Whittenbury, R., Davies, S. L., and Davey, J. F., 1970b, Exospores and cysts formed by methane-utilizing bacteria, *J. Gen. Microbiol.* **61**:219–226.

Widdel, F., 1988, Microbiology and ecology of sulfate and sulfur-reducing bacteria, in: *The Biology of Anaerobic Microorganisms* (A. J. B. Zehnder, ed.), Wiley–Interscience, New York, pp. 469–585.

Wilson, J. T., and Wilson, B. H., 1985, Biotransformation of trichlorethylene in soil, *Appl. Environ. Microbiol.* **49**:242–243.

Wolfe, H. J., and Hanson, R. S., 1980, Identification of methane-utilizing yeasts, *FEMS Microbiol. Lett.* **7**:177–179.

Wood, A. P., and Kelly, D. P., 1989, Methylotrophic and autotrophic bacteria isolated from lucinid and thyasirid bivalves containing symbiotic bacteria in the gills, *J. Mar. Biol. Assoc. U.K.* **69**:165–179.

Yavitt, J. B., Lang, G. E., and Downey, D. M., 1988, Potential methane production and methane oxidation in peatland ecosystems of the Appalachian Mountains, United States, *Global Biogeochem. Cycles* **2**:253–268.

Yavitt, J. B., Downey, D. M., Lancaster, E., and Lang, G. E., 1990a, Methane consumption in decomposing sphagnum-derived peat, *Soil Biol. Biochem.* **22**:441–447.

Yavitt, J. B., Downey, D. M., Lang, G. E., and Sextone, A. J., 1990b, Methane consumption in two temperate forest soils, *Biogeochemistry* **9**:39–52.

Yoshinari, T., 1985, Nitrite and nitrous oxide production by *Methylosinus trichosporium, Can. J. Microbiol.* **31**:139–144.

Zajic, J. E., Volesky, B., and Wellman, A., 1969, Growth of *Graphium* sp. on natural gas, *Can. J. Microbiol.* **15**:1231–1236.

Zehnder, A. J. B., and Brock, T. D., 1980, Anaerobic methane oxidation: Occurrence and ecology, *Appl. Environ. Microbiol.* **39**:194–204.

10

Microbial Systems
Patterns in Time and Space

JULIAN W. T. WIMPENNY

1. Introduction

In contrast to the rather uniform and sometimes boring manner in which microorganisms present themselves in the laboratory, systems of microbes in nature form complex populations which often show some type of order in environments which are temporally and spatially heterogeneous in physicochemical composition. Examples of such ecosystems are too numerous to review in detail, however; they include a wide range of systems on a huge spatial scale ranging from nanometers to hundreds of meters.

Pattern formation in bacterial systems implies the idea of organization in space and in time. Heterogeneity as opposed to the more familiar homogeneity opens up a range of possibilities. At its simplest, heterogeneity can simply be chaotic with no obvious order to it. At another level, spatial heterogeneity can give rise to a differentiated ecosystem. This would be true for an algal mat (for a discussion of the spatial organization of algal mats, see articles in the volume edited by Cohen and Rosenberg, 1989, and the contribution by Skyring and Bauld, 1990) as it would be beautifully illustrated in a stratified water column, for example in the Black Sea. At perhaps the most sophisticated level we see the organization of space into pattern. This can be of two types: regular repeating structures like Liesegang rings in certain chemical diffusion systems and the swarming concentric ring pattern produced by certain species of *Proteus*. Or it can imply morphogenetic pattern which at its simplest might be the microbial colony or more complex as with differentiation in the slime mold *Dictyostelium*.

As the systems become more structured, growth takes place in more and more complex yet organized diffusion gradients of various solutes (substrates, products, effector molecules of all sorts, etc.). Where molecular diffusion is the most important solute transport process, solute fluxes are vectorial, having direction as well as magnitude (for a review of the importance of molecular diffusion in microbiology, see Koch,

JULIAN W. T. WIMPENNY • School of Pure and Applied Biology, University of Wales, College of Cardiff, Cardiff CF1 3TL, United Kingdom.
Advances in Microbial Ecology, Vol. 12, edited by K.C. Marshall. Plenum Press, New York, 1992.

1990). Again this is in contrast to the situation in a well-mixed microbial fermentation system. As far as the cell itself is concerned, we note the importance of its response to a very narrow zone immediately surrounding it on whose physicochemical composition it is totally dependent. Before discussing this region in more detail, it is necessary to define some terms which are not commonly defined in microbial ecology yet have been the subject of intense debate in "macro" ecological circles. They are *habitat* and *niche*.

Habitat and Niche

A habitat is a particular set of physicochemical conditions within the space-time continuum which allows expression of the physiological activities, growth, and proliferation of a species or group of species.

Niche, on the other hand, has been traditionally more difficult to define. Hutchinson's (1965) definition emphasizes the multifactorial nature of niche by defining it as an n-dimensional hyperspace, where n is the number of environmental factors affecting survival and reproduction. This *fundamental niche* is determined by the intrinsic genetic properties of an organism. At any particular point in space and in the presence of competitors, these properties may not be completely expressed and this gives rise to *actual* or *realized* niche. That is, when the fundamental niches of two organisms overlap, the realized niche of the poorer competitor will be only part of its fundamental niche.

Whittaker *et al.* (1973) developed the definition further to remove some of the confusion between the ideas of habitat and niche implicit in Hutchinson's definition. They expressed habitat in terms of a hyperspace of physicochemical factors as defined above but distinguished the n-dimensional habitat system from the m-dimensional hyperspace of niche factors representing the activity of the organism. Whittaker combined the two sets of definitions to produce the term *ecotope:*

$$\text{Habitat} + \text{niche} = \text{ecotope}$$

Wimpenny (1981) introduced the term *domain* where the notion of the spatial organization of microbial ecosystems was an essential factor. Domains could be passive reflecting the physicochemical conditions in the environment. These were *habitat domains* (HDs). Or they could reflect the chemical activities of the organism when they were described as *activity domains* (ADs).

Habitat Domains

A particular strain or species of microorganism responds to a wide range of physicochemical factors. For example, it may be able to grow over a broad or narrow range of pH values or temperatures. It responds to pressure, water potential, ionic strength, redox potential, oxygen tension, as well as to a whole range of specific chemical compounds some of which might be substrates while others are inhibitors. It is possible to map the response of an organism to a single environmental factor as a one-dimensional line, to two as a two-dimensional shape, and to three as a solid three-dimensional object (Fig. 1). If further variables are added, a graphical presentation of the response is no longer possible. The response surface then becomes an *n*-dimensional hyperspace where *n* is the number of factors investigated. Each species of organism almost certainly has a unique hyperspace cloud (HSC). Attempts have been made to investigate the effects of a multiplicity of environmental factors on specific organisms. This is an important activity in food microbiology where the aim is to inhibit microbial growth using combinations of agents which if used on their own would be unacceptable to the consumer but acting in concert have little or no detrimental effects on the product (see, e.g., references in Buchanan and Phillips, 1990, Roberts and Ingram, 1973, and McClure *et al.*, 1989).

Wimpenny and Waters (1984) applied the gradient plate technique described by Szybalski and Bryson (1953) in two dimensions at the same time. If arrays of plates were used, more dimensions could be added. A common configuration was pH and NaCl gradients on the gradient plate with a 6 × 6 array of plates covering temperature and a preservative concentration (Wimpenny and Waters, 1987; Peters *et al.*, 1991).

Such plates offer other possibilities, for example in defining the realized habitat domains for competing microbial species. Here, two or more species are inoculated together on the gradient plate. If their growth morphology is sufficiently different, zones of growth can be detected visually. Otherwise, it is possible to replicate the gradient plates onto media selective for each of the competitors.

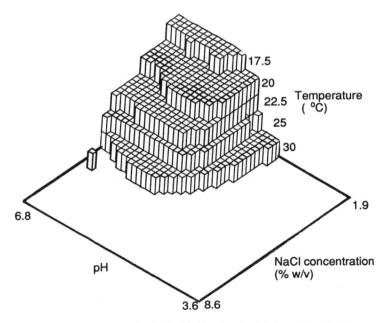

Figure 1. Temperature, pH, and NaCl habitat domain of *Salmonella typhimuium*.

Clearly the hyperspace cloud that characterizes the *potential* habitat domain of an organism will not apply to any single habitat which will be a subset of this, its *realized* habitat domain.

It should be apparent that knowing the habitat domain for a specific organism, it should be possible to determine where in a structured ecosystem it could be found so long as the composition of the habitat is defined—a big caveat of course!

Activity Domains

If the habitat domain reflects the relationship between a species and its environment, the activity domain represents the effect of the cell on the environment. Activity domains are physical spaces around the cell whose physicochemical composition is affected by the biochemical effects of the cell (Fig. 2). Activity domains may be source or sink domains depending on whether they reflect the liberation of a product or the uptake of a substrate. The boundary of an activity domain is that point at which the composition of the habitat ceases to be affected by the cell. In practice, the dimensions of activity domains are quite variable. For example, a collection of cells (a colony or perhaps a layer in a vertically stratified system) will exert a larger influence on the physicochemical environment than will a single cell. What is more, the shape of the activity domain will be influenced by the presence of sources or sinks in the neighborhood of the cell but also by the prevailing pattern of liquid flow.

Interactions between Organisms

Where relevant source and sink domains overlap between species, possibilities for interactions occur. Thus, the product manufactured by one organism constitutes a source domain while the ability to use that product as a substrate indicates a sink domain for the second species. The actual profile of the solute concentration gradient depends on the geometry of the system. In one-dimensional systems under steady-state conditions the gradient is linear. For two- and three-dimensional systems the line will be curved, in the case of a sphere this curve is a hyperbola. In each case we assume that the sink/source is located symmetrically around the relevant source/sink (Koch, 1990). Transfer of material between the two species will distort the domain geometry. Given just two spherical organisms interacting, solute will be transferred between the species, however, in directions away from the receiving cell some product will be dissipated into the environmental sink. Transfer will be optimized if the species form layers close to one another, as might be found in stratified communities.

Interactions will be dominated by the effects of habitat domains. If these overlap for the two species they may be located physically close together. This process becomes most efficient in syntrophic associations. Syntrophic systems couple biochemical reactions together to the benefit of each partner. For example, *"Methanobacillus omelianskii"* originally considered to be a single organism was later shown to be a close association of two species. These were called the "H" and the "S" organisms, respectively (Bryant *et al.*, 1967). The S organism generated hydrogen while oxidizing eth-

Overlapping Habitat domains

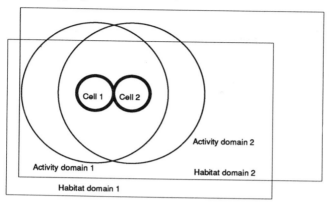

Exclusive Habitat domains

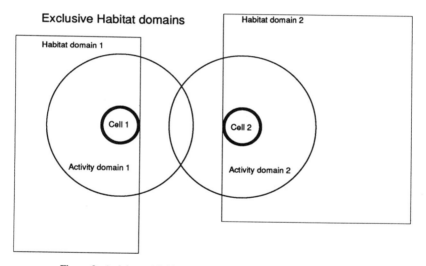

Figure 2. Activity and habitat domain for two species. For details see text.

anol. This was energetically unfavorable unless the hydrogen was removed: this was achieved by the activity of the H organism, a methanogen which required the hydrogen to reduce CO_2. There are numerous other examples of interspecific hydrogen transfer, often not as tightly coupled as this.

A different situation applies to interactions between organisms with incompatible habitat domains. These will interact so long as their activity domains overlap. Here, diffusive transfer of materials can "bridge the gap" between organisms that are unable to coexist in the same physicochemical space. This might be the case for organisms of the sulfur cycle. Here, sulfide-oxidizing bacteria such as *Thiobacillus* spp. which are obligate aerobes oxidize sulfide to sulfate at the expense of oxygen. These are located in the surface layers of sediments or algal mats. Just beneath these in the anaerobic region are sulfate-reducing bacteria, e.g. *Desulfovibrio* spp. which reduce sulfate to sulfide at the expense of an organic reductant. The two reactions, sulfide oxidation and sulfate reduction, form a cycle whose components are distributed by molecular diffusion across the aerobic/anaerobic boundary layer (Fig. 3).

It will be obvious that activity and habitat domains are closely related to the definition of ecotope by Whittaker *et al.* (1973). I prefer to reinterpret Whittaker since the term *niche* seems itself to be the resultant of two factors habitat and activity. The definition of niche now becomes:

The potential *n*-dimensional habitat domain + the potential *m*-dimensional activity domain of an organism = the *potential* niche of an organism

In any one habitat in the presence of other competing organisms, this potential niche is not fully expressed so that:

The actual *n*-dimensional HD + the actual *m*-dimensional AD = the *realized* niche

Transfer and Reaction Zones

The existence of a structured system with physicochemical gradients across it implies stringency on the part of the organisms' ability to grow within it. The vec-

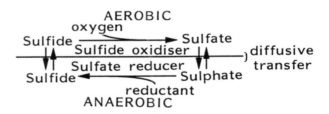

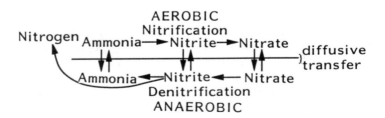

Figure 3. Simple sulfur and nitrogen cycles arrayed across an interface between an aerobic and an anaerobic habitat domain. Molecular diffusion links the two halves of the cycle.

toriality that characterizes such systems will define where exactly in a given space substrates and inhibitors are at appropriate concentrations to allow growth to take place. Imagine a system with opposing gradients of two essential nutrients where transport is by molecular diffusion alone. Only at the point where these nutrients meet will growth occur. Such a domain may be very narrow indeed since the cell is itself a sink for both solutes, and molecular diffusion, at least on a macroscopic scale, is slow enough to be growth rate limiting. Given such a system, it is sensible to define *transfer zones* across which solutes can diffuse and *reaction zones* where substrate utilization, and, generally, therefore growth, takes place. Good natural examples which illustrate such narrow zones are clearly seen in stratified lake communities, where for example a layer of photosynthetic bacteria may be only centimeters thick. Here, position is determined by three factors: the presence of oxygen (an inhibitor), the presence of sulfide (a substrate), and the availability of light as an energy source. The organisms must be in the sulfide-rich–oxygen-poor region but as high as possible to take advantage of sunlight. Practically, they are at the intersection of gradients of light plus oxygen and sulfide.

2. Modeling Structured Ecosystems

It is relevant to consider the way in which spatially heterogeneous microbial systems are investigated in the laboratory. I have discussed the need for such model systems many times before (e.g., Wimpenny, 1981, 1988; Wimpenny *et al.*, 1983) so that only the briefest mention is needed here. We recognize three separate entities: (1) the natural *in situ* system. (2) Part of (1) transferred to a more or less controlled laboratory environment. This is generally described as a *microcosm*. It retains all of the complexity of the *in situ* system. (3) A subset of the natural system where conditions are simplified and tightly controlled and variables altered in an unequivocal fashion. We call this a *model*.

Models can be thermodynamically open systems capable of operating under steady-state conditions or they can be closed where microbial growth is akin to a batch culture. Some, like biofilm models, can be either depending on design.

2.1. Open Model Systems

At least three types of open system exist. These include unidirectionally linked multistage chemostats, bidirectionally linked multistage chemostats (gradostats), and bidirectionally linked systems with cell separation. By and large open models which are spatially heterogeneous, hence incorporating solute diffusion gradients, have rather low spatial resolution. They are therefore not useful from the point of view of pattern formation and recognition.

2.1.1. Multistage Chemostats

Multistage chemostats are fed from a reservoir, at one end only, of what is a cascade system. All nutrients needed for growth enter the system from the one end and there is no reverse transport. As models they can apply to any system where solute transfer is unidirectional. The most obvious of these is soil and related types like landfill operations. They have been applied to sediment systems. In none of these is the model really accurate. This is because in all of these *in situ* systems there is some reverse transfer. The latter is essential for cyclic reactions, e.g., the sulfur or nitrogen cycles in a marine sediment, to take place.

2.1.2. Gradostats

Gradostats solve the problem by adding a second reservoir and weir at the opposite end of the cascade. This introduces bidirectionality allowing the coupling of cyclic reactions. Bidirectionality also means that linked aerobic/anaerobic systems can develop; indeed, almost any system where mutually exclusive habitat domains need to be linked together can be operated in a gradostat, e.g., organisms of a sulfur cycle (Lovitt and Wimpenny, 1981) and *Paracoccus denitrificans* and *Desulfovibrio desulfuricans* grown together (Wimpenny and Abdollahi, 1991).

In order to discern pattern, much greater spatial resolution is needed. Margalef (1967) suggested an ambitious version of gradostat consisting of a three-dimensional array $10 \times 10 \times 10$ of fermenter vessels linked together with programmable pumps! Needless to say, such a system was never built. We have constructed simple 12-vessel gradostat systems though these have so far not proved conspicuously successful. There is the potential for a high-resolution open system based on gradostat principles. The problems are merely technical ones!

2.1.3. Gradostats with Cell Separation

Cell separation, achieved by interposing a permeable membrane between neighboring fermenter vessels, provides bidirectionally linked gradostats where only solutes are transferred between vessels. Such a system was built by R. A. Herbert and his colleagues (Herbert, 1988), and consisted of three vessels each operating as a chemostat, but linked together via membranes permeable to low-molecular-weight solutes but not to cells. In one series of experiments, the three interacting species were in vessel 1, a *Clostridium butylicum* fermenting glucose to ethanol, butyrate, and acetate; in vessel 2, *Desulfovibrio desulfuricans* which reduces sulfate to sulfide at the expense of the fermentation products from vessel 1. Vessel 3 contained *Chromatium vinosum* which was illuminated and photooxidized sulfide from vessel 2 back to sulfate which then diffused back into vessel 3.

2.2. Closed Model Systems

Any system which operates as a batch culture with no inputs or outputs is thermodynamically closed. Many batch systems are partially open. For example, an aerobic microbial colony is open to the atmosphere and gas exchange is possible. Apart from colonies, the only spatially heterogeneous model of value is the gel-stabilized system (Wimpenny *et al.*, 1981). It is discussed in more detail later.

2.3. Biofilm Fermenters

Biofilm is ubiquitous and has been the focus of sustained research in recent years. So far there are few signs of pattern formation in biofilm. The elegant co-aggregation studies of Kolenbrander (1989, this volume) have demonstrated a pattern of binding affinities which reveal a complex organization in populations of oral bacteria. This exciting observation has not so far been detected in other biofilm communities.

The family of model systems used to investigate biofilm is hard to classify properly. Most are closed systems in which biofilm goes through a life cycle: attachment–proliferation–maturation–detachment. These can be regarded as batch systems, though they are often open to solute exchange with the environment due to atmospheric exposure and to imposed flow regimes. It is possible to generate near-steady-state biofilms using flow rates which remove part of the growth so that mature biofilm is at an approximately constant depth. This might be possible in the Rototorque (devised by Characklis, 1990) or in the Robbins device (McCoy et al., 1981). It also takes place in fluidized bed models where biofilm forms by growth and is removed by erosion due to the motion of particles in a turbulent flow regime. Steady- or quasi-steady-state operation was the goal of Coombe et al. (1981) and Peters and Wimpenny (1988) who developed a constant-depth film fermenter where the film surface was constantly being scraped to remove excess growth and to maintain a constant depth.

3. Pattern in Gel-Stabilized Systems

3.1. Description of Gel Systems

If the normal rather chaotic exchange of solutes in a natural environment is replaced by a system which restricts solute transfer to molecular diffusion only, microbial growth can be expressed in sometimes beautiful patterns.

The simplest way to achieve such stability is to add a gelling agent to a microbial growth medium. A simple gel-established model system can be constructed using a 250-ml beaker. At the base of the beaker is a layer of medium containing basal nutrients, a diffusible source (this can be any essential nutrient: a carbon source such as glucose or succinate has been used but also for example H_2S), and finally full-strength agar. After the lower layer has set, an upper layer is poured. This contains the basal nutrients plus a cell inoculum plus a lower concentration of agar to provide a semisolid layer in which cells may grow.

3.2. Simple Moving Boundary Systems

3.2.1. Space Determinants in Gel Systems

Using such a system it is possible to grow an organism at the interface between two essential nutrients. The simplest experiment is to select a nonfermentable carbon source from the source layer and oxygen from the surface. Under these conditions, growth appears at the interface between the two opposing gradients. We have used *Pseudomonas aeruginosa* in countergradients of succinate and oxygen for these experiments. This type of experiment was also simulated using a simple model. The simulation program GELSIM was written for us in FORTRAN by Steve Jaffe. The program could simulate changes in the distribution of up to ten organisms and/or solutes. A range of different growth dynamic equations were supplied as was the ability to write completely new equations to choice. A number of factors were varied in the model to determine their importance as position determinants in a spatially ordered gradient system. The major determinants of position were concentration and diffusion coefficient of the essential nutrients; also, yield coefficient since this is another way of expressing solute concentration (the larger the yield coefficient the smaller the amount of nutrient needed to synthesize a unit weight of cells). Factors that affected the *shape* of the cell distribution curve but not its position were substrate affinity and growth rate. As far as affinity is concerned, the simulations confirm that growth in such a system is dominated by diffusion limitations rather than cell growth dynamic constants. Growth rate *per se* would not anyway be expected to affect position in a diffusion field: it does, however, affect the distribution of cells. Slow growth rates and low affinities broaden the pattern while quick growth and high affinities sharpen it.

Growth of Beggiatoa. An excellent example of simple growth in a gradient system is the growth of *Beggiatoa* in countergradients of oxygen and H_2S (Nelson *et al.*, 1986). Growth position was about 3 mm below the surface of the gel where the sulfide and the oxygen gradients intersected. Control gels were also established without cells. Once more, opposing gradients were established as the sulfide was slowly oxidized chemically by the oxygen. The point of intersection was similar but slightly lower than that seen in the growth system. Simulations (Wimpenny and Jones, 1988) using the same basic data described by Nelson and his colleagues confirmed the position of the growth plate. The simulation made no allowance for motility and chemotaxis; however, it is clear that the organism is motile and did appear to move to the optimum position for growth. One may conclude that organisms can grow to form cell zones at optimum positions in diffusion fields: they may do so more efficiently if they can also move there.

3.2.2. Aerobic and Anaerobic Mixed Communities

3.2.2a. Paracoccus and Desulfovibrio. Abdollahi (1983) used a gel-stabilized model system to investigate the growth of an aerobe (*Paracoccus denitrificans*) and an anaerobe (*Desulfovibrio desulfuricans*) in a lactate gradient with either air or nitrogen as gas phase. Experiments were set up with neither, either, or both organisms incubated aerobically or anaerobically. The two species grew well alone under their appropriate gas phase. While slight growth was detected when the aerobe grew in the absence of oxygen, the sulfate reducer showed no growth at all in the aerobic gel. If the two were grown together under aerobic conditions, both did well. The paracoccus grew best near the surface where the oxygen–lactate gradients met. While the sulfate reducer grew throughout the gel, it appeared to do best close to the surface, possibly benefiting from the lower sulfide concentration in an anaerobic zone just below the air–gel interface.

Clearly, growth of the aerobe reduced the oxygen tension to levels that permit growth of the anaerobe. These experiments suggest that gel-stabilized models are appropriate tools for investigating interactions between selected species.

   3.2.2b. The Oil Storage Tank Water Base Community.   A gel-stabilized model was used by Lovitt to investigate the microbial ecosystem associated with the aqueous phase lying below oil in an oil storage tank (Wimpenny *et al.,* 1981; Wimpenny and Jones, 1988). Water is hard to remove completely from these structures and conditions often favor the prolific growth of bacteria in such a system. They often contain mixtures of aerobic hydrocarbon oxidizers and anaerobic-sulfate reducing species which cause corrosion of the tank itself. The gel-stabilized model consisted of a beaker containing a steel billet, a semisolid layer above this containing an inoculum, and a chemical composition close to that found in natural oil storage tank water bases. Once this layer had set, an oil overlay was put in place and the gel system incubated. Control gels lacking cells showed substantially flat redox potential profiles though there was an oxygen gradient reaching the surface of the steel plate whose corrosion presumably acted as a sink for the oxidant. Where cells were present, an intense reddish banded zone of oxidized iron was detected near the center of the gel. This represented an interface between the aerobic zone (high Eh, O_2 present) and the anaerobic region (black, low Eh, no O_2). Sulfate reducers were detected in this region while hexadecane oxidizers were present in the upper aerobic zone. A peak in aerobic and facultatively anaerobic species was noted toward the center of the gel.

   These experiments demonstrate how a community can become spatially ordered over time if solute transfer is restricted to molecular diffusion. How typical this is of natural ecosystems is less clear. Most samples of material removed from infected storage tank water bases are chaotic, often blackish masses of growth. This may not be really representative of the community because of sampling problems; however, it is unlikely that the system is as organized as well in space as is the gel-model.

3.3. Periodic Phenomena in Gel-Stabilized Systems

   The descriptions above refer to growth that generally follows a simple moving boundary as one or other nutrient becomes depleted. However, in older cultures even in these simple experiments periodic growth bands were seen. This was clearly true in the case of the aerobic/anaerobic mixed culture and was noted after a period of days in cultures of the pseudomonad growing in succinate–oxygen countergradients. It could be said that formation of periodic patterns was, given time, more the rule than the exception. Little is known about "old" periodic structures.

3.3.1. Examples of Periodic Structures

   Repeating growth patterns have been seen in gel-stabilized cultures at least since 1938 when they were described by Williams (1938). Williams regarded them rather as bacterial growth spectra, probably by analogy to cytochrome spectra seen in bacteria using hand spectroscopes by Keilin and others, much in vogue at that time. Band formation took place in tube cultures containing nutrient broth stabilized with 0.75% agar. Bands were generated at elevated oxygen partial pressures (up to 4 atm). The higher the gas pressure or the lower the nutrient concentration, the deeper were the bands in the system. No explanation for band formation was forthcoming; however, elevated oxygen partial pressures are often toxic to bacteria and a toxicity mechanism cannot be ruled out. Bands were noted by Tschapek and Giambiagi (1954) in shake cultures of azotobacter but only when they were fixing nitrogen. It was suggested that band formation was caused by oxygen toxicity. Nitsch and Kutzner (1966) demonstrated banded growth when a streptomycete was grown in a shake culture at very low concentrations of nutrient.

3.3.2. The Bacillus cereus System

The most detailed investigation into banded growth in gel-stabilized systems was carried out on cultures of *Bacillus cereus* (Wimpenny *et al.*, 1981; Coombs and Wimpenny, 1982; Wimpenny *et al.*, 1984).

Periodic growth bands were seen when the organism was grown on an amino acid-based medium in countergradients of glucose and oxygen (Fig. 4). Motility was not involved since bands still appeared in full-strength agar. Increasing glucose and decreasing amino acid concentration caused band formation to move upwards in the gel. Oxygen was necessary as was a glucose gradient. Bands formed sequentially from about the middle of the gel upwards. Various physicochemical gradients were determined down the gel profile. It became clear that large pH changes developed in the gel. An oxygen-dependent oxidative deamination of amino acids led to alkalinization near the surface while anaerobic fermentation of glucose generated organic acids that caused the pH in the gel to fall to around 5.0. It appeared that band formation took place near the junction between an alkaline wave diffusing downwards and an acid wave diffusing upwards through the gel. Simplistically, it seemed that the alkaline products were titrating away the acid allowing the cells to continue to grow. On its own, this proved an inadequate explanation since computer simulations conducted by S. Jaffe (Wimpenny *et al.*, 1984) indicated that this was not capable of "chopping" growth into discrete bands: a simple moving growth boundary should have been all that was seen.

The extra component needed was some sort of asymmetric activation threshold. This could have been hysteresis. Thus, growth led to acid production causing a fall in pH with growth inhibition taking place at a certain pH value. The conversion of inactive to active cells, it was suggested, would then take place at a more alkaline pH value than this. There was no experimental evidence that such hysteresis took place from experiments carried out by W. Jäger and the author. The alternative was based on lag periods. The asymmetry is that growth ceases but that there is a significant lag before it can start again.

To summarize, the following mechanism seems to occur. On incubating the gel, cells at the surface start to grow forming a surface layer. Cells in the body of the gel soon become anoxic and starved so they are in a stationary phase. Cells at the lower interface have excess glucose which they ferment causing the pH to fall, in turn inhibiting further

Figure 4. Growth of *Bacillus cereus* C11 at 30°C in a gel-stabilized model ecosystem. The cells are inoculated uniformly throughout the upper semisolid layer. The basal medium used throughout the system contains salts and casamino acids. Glucose diffuses from the bottom layer and oxygen enters from the surface of the upper layer. Gels shown here were incubated for 0, 2, 4, and 6 days. (Reproduced with permission.)

growth. Now growth can only occur where starved cells in the predominantly acidic gel meet alkaline products diffusing downwards and an energy source (glucose) diffusing upwards. After an appropriate lag period, growth starts at this position forming the first band. Growth here is exponential and since it is anaerobic leads to a large pulse of acidity which spreads away from the first band. Glucose continues to diffuse upwards; where it meets alkali diffusing downwards and at a position which gives *sufficient time* at an appropriate pH value for growth to start, the next band forms. The process then repeats.

3.3.3. Other Examples of Periodic Growth

Many other examples of band formation have been noted: these were reviewed by Wimpenny and Jones (1988). Periodic growth bands have been seen in facultatively anaerobic bacteria, some strict aerobes such as azotobacter and streptomycetes, photosynthetic bacteria including *Ectothiorhodospira* and what was presumed to be a *Rhodopseudomonas*, *Gallionella* in an estuarine sediment and in a benzoate-degrading consortium.

Hans Veldkamp (personal communication) reported an interesting example of periodic growth this time involving two organisms. A lactate-containing medium was seeded with a sample of a surface-illuminated sediment and immobilized with semisolid agar in a measuring cylinder. The measuring cylinder was left on a window ledge illuminated by natural light. The system developed a series of alternating bands of black and purple. It was suggested that the purple bands were due to *Rhodopseudomonas palustris* while the black bands were a sulfate-reducing organism and that by day the photosynthetic bacterium photooxidized sulfide to sulfate and by night the sulfate reducer reversed this process. The system has never been explored further.

The Hoppensteadt and Jäger Salmonella System.   Another system exhibiting spatial periodicities, though not strictly growth in a gel-stabilized model system, is highly relevant to this discussion. Hoppensteadt and Jäger (1979) reported that a salmonella, auxotrophic for histidine, when spread onto a plate containing a well-buffered medium plus glucose would produce rings of growth around a central point on which a drop of histidine solution was placed. The system was modeled mathematically (Hoppensteadt and Jäger, 1979; Hoppensteadt *et al.*, 1984) with a result that was similar to the model formulated by Jaffe (Wimpenny *et al.*, 1984).

3.3.4. Colonial Growth in Gel-Stabilized Systems

So far we have discussed what is effectively one-dimensional stratified growth in diffusion gradients. If the number of cells added to a semisolid medium is progressively reduced, we reach the situation where cells form individual three-dimensional colonies separated from one another. In the end a gel can contain one or a very few colonies generating their own unique pattern both individually and as a group within the system.

3.3.4a. Shake or Sloppy-Agar Culture Manifestations.   Such colonies are often seen as a by-product of viable count determinations in shake cultures at high dilutions. They have been described by Whittenbury (1963) as part of the response of lactic acid bacteria to oxygen tension. Although these were really not mentioned as colony forms *per se*, each species examined generated a unique pattern within the shake tube. In some cases, individual colonies are clearly displayed. For example, Whittenbury's Fig. 14 shows one colony of a sucrose-utilizing mutant strain of *"Lactobacillus plantarum-casei"* group. The colony shows a long fox-tailed shape within the agar. Other colonies, for example of *Streptococcus faecium,* are spherical with hazy zones around them. This type of work needs much more precision to understand what precisely governs the morphology of these colonies. Studies of this form have some practical applications; for example, it is of utmost concern to the food industry how three-dimensional colony growth occurs within the matrix of a food product.

3.3.4b. Three-Dimensional Colony Growth.   So far, very little work has been done on the dynamics of three-dimensional colony formation. It is possible to hazard a guess at some of the constraints on growth. The "perfect" model would be an infinite (large!) but enclosed volume of agar into which a single bacterial cell was inserted near the center. All nutrients would be provided from the gel matrix. This includes, where needed, oxygen. The aerobe is likely to become oxygen limited very quickly because oxygen solubility is very low. The actual growth rate will be a function of the rate at which oxygen is transported by molecular diffusion from the agar block. Other nutrients are likely to be in excess and if no toxic products are formed the colony will continue to grow outwards. The inside of the colony will soon become both anoxic and possibly nutrient deprived as well. These cell will therefore undergo cycles of lysis and limited regrowth on the lytic products. Anaerobic bacteria will naturally grow better, provided oxygen is absent or quickly removed by protective oxygen reduction. Here, product accumulation will become a problem especially if these are organic acids. Acidophilic species like the lactic acid bacteria will do better under these conditions than "normal" bacteria. Facultative anaerobes will show heterogeneous growth with cells at the perimeter using such oxygen as is available while the remaining population grow fermentatively. Once more, pH changes will dominate as colonies grow larger.

Most gel systems are not "infinite." For a facultative anaerobe the presence of an oxygen gradient from a surface will distort the shape of the colony. Growth will extend in the direction of the oxygen where it will become more extensive due to the higher growth yields on oxygen. Such a colony could become mushroom shaped as the "cap" approaches the surface.

Gravitational effects cannot be discounted. Shake tubes often show that a colony can move downwards through a soft agar leaving a trail of smaller colonies behind it. Ideally this type of experiment needs to be carried out in a zero-gravity environment.

Some bacterial species are motile. Motility can lead to periodic effects. Will a developing 3-D colony show periodic structures? If so, they should appear as successive shells of growth rather like onions or Russian dolls? Will outgrowth remain as a shell or could we imagine this highly nutrient-limited growth to take the form of a snowflake? What, anyway, will be the effects of all of the intrinsic species characteristics on the morphology of 3-D colonies?

Numerous techniques need to be applied to 3-D colony growth. These obviously include optical and electron microscopy, needle and microelectrodes, image analysis, core sampling and analysis, etc. Hopefully, enough information will be gained to allow 3-D colony growth to be modeled and through all these approaches understood better.

4. Motility Patterns

There are a growing family of spatial patterns which are due to the motility of organisms. The most famous of these are the concentric rings that different species of *Proteus* form on the surface of an agar plate. More recently, Adler (1966) reported that motile organisms such as *Escherichia coli* form bands or concentric rings when moving in a nutrient gradient. Budrene and Berg (1991) have described the formation of radially orientated aggregation patterns of strains of *E. coli* as they respond to a signal molecule released from the cells.

4.1. Swarming in *Proteus* Species

Hauser more than a century ago in 1885, first described the formation of stable circular patterns in *Proteus* colonies. Since then, there has been considerable work to elucidate the phenomenon, and a range of associated publications including the monograph by Moltke (1927). Swarming has been reviewed by Smith (1972) and by Williams and Schwarzhoff (1978). It is fair to say that the phenomenon, though widely recognized and worked on by numerous different groups, still lacks a single comprehensive explanation. There are at least two and possibly three manifestations of swarming, though they may have a similar mechanism at their base. The common finding that goes back at least as far as Hughes (1957) and Hoeniger (1965a,b) is that sparsely flagellate short rod-shaped bacteria differentiate into long (60–80 μm) cells with up to 150 flagella per cell. The longer swarmers were clearly shown in electron micrographs by Armitage and Smith (1976).

In the first manifestation of swarming, a colony is inoculated centrally on an agar medium. After about 5 hr, differentiation into swarm cells occurs. These move outwards across the agar but at a critical distance they stop moving and dedifferentiate into short nonmotile rods. These then grow forming the first ring. After a period, swarmers are once more produced. These move away from the first ring and the sequence repeats until the edge of the plate is reached. This type of growth was characterized by Armitage and her colleagues (Armitage and Smith, 1976).

A second manifestation of swarming was reported by Bissett and co-workers (Bissett, 1973; Bissett and Douglas, 1976; Douglas and Bissett, 1976). Here, the primary central colony gives rise to swarmers which move across the entire plate in one unbroken sweep. What appears to happen is that after a critical distance from the swarm front or perhaps from the primary colony, some cells (perhaps the majority) dedifferentiate into nonmotile rods and grow forming a thickened zone which appears as the first band. As the swarm front progresses outwards, second and subsequent "casts" of dedifferentiated cells are formed which establish further growth zones appearing as rings. These observations were confirmed by Budriene et al. (1988). According to Douglas and Bissett (1976), ring appearance even in the same strain is very variable and subject to small changes in prevailing physicochemical conditions.

The two processes may not be so very different since they depend on the *time delay* shown by long swarming cells. If they are held up for a significant period at the first ring, mechanism I will be perceived. If there is only a transient delay, mechanism II will hold. Considerable light has been thrown on swarming in *Proteus mirabilis* using time-lapse photography (Shapiro and Trubatch, 1991) (Fig. 5). The sequence of events according to these workers seems clear. A small colony consisting of about 10^5 cells is placed in a 1 μl volume at the center of a plate. At this stage the cells are short rods possessing a few flagella needed for conventional motility. As growth occurs, a small structured disk-shaped colony is formed in which a few long multiflagellate forms soon appear. These then proceed to the periphery of the disk where they then move tangentially to the structure at first soon forming small rafts of up to 10 cells whose flagellar motion is coordinated. These rafts then begin to move away from the periphery as individually coordinated units encapsulated in polysaccharide-containing polymers. These individual rafts give the edge of the primary colony a ragged appearance. The swarm front extends outwards for a period. At some point where the swarmers complete the first phase of migration, a wave of cell division and growth spreads from the central region outwards. As it reaches the edge of the expanding colony, a second wave of swarming cells is formed and moves outwards once more. Second and subsequent flushes show a much more coordinated motion forming a single unified swarm front.

What else is known about the swarming process? It seems that chemotaxis mechanisms are not involved in swarming. Williams and Schwarzhoff (1976) showed that

Figure 5. Photograph of a swarming *Proteus* colony showing ring pattern formation. (Courtesy of J. A. Shapiro).

mutations to negative chemotaxis still produced swarm patterns, that mutants showing normal chemotaxis could not swarm, and perhaps most intriguing, that differentiation to swarmer still took place in cells grown on a thin agar film dialyzed against fresh medium. A key observation is that swarmer formation is, like flagellum synthesis in many other bacteria, under catabolite repression control. A plausible scenario is therefore that cells in the primary colony exhaust easily fermentable substrates and the process of swarmer formation becomes catabolite derepressed. The swarmers move out and soon reach a zone where nutrients are in excess. Swarmers now lose their flagella, dedifferentiate to nonmotile rods, and these, and the cells deposited behind them, start to grow rapidly. The process repeats as the nutrients are depleted in the growth zone. This explanation can account for the first manifestation of swarming.

One more factor must be mentioned. A mechanism based on negative chemotaxis has been in vogue (see, e.g., Armitage *et al.*, 1976). Here, the theory was that a toxic product formed in the primary colony led to negative chemotaxis away from this region. The finding that chemotaxis-negative mutants could still swarm mitigates against such a mechanism.

Finally, swarming has been modeled mathematically (see, e.g., Budriené *et al.*, 1988, and more recently the general form of a model covering different spatial periodicities in microbial systems by Polezhaev and Ptitsyn, 1990). The model assumes that there exist two states of the cells they refer to as vegetative form (VF) and anabiotic form (AF). The structure depends crucially on transitions between the two forms. Solutes are responsible for the changes in structure. These may be growth substrates or products or possibly both. Some asymmetry is required in the model for periodicities to be generated. This can be due to hysteresis or lags.

4.2. Other Motility Patterns

Adler (1966) was the first to report on motility bands in cultures of *E. coli*. He showed that motile cells in tubes containing galactose formed two bands which moved along the tube. The first of these responded to oxygen, the second to galactose gradients as the two nutrients were depleted from the medium. Similar experiments were carried out in semisolid agar in petri dishes. Using mixtures of glucose and galactose, two concentric rings of motile bacteria appeared while three were observed on tryptone agar. Adler regarded these as chemotactic phenomena with different subpopulations of the original inoculum responding to different solutes in the medium. Similar responses have been reported by Nossal (1972) and by Wolfe and Berg (1989). Recently, Budrene and Berg (1991) presented some fascinating examples of pattern formation with cultures of *E. coli*. The experimental system is extremely simple. Cells were introduced at the center of plates prepared from 0.22% agar plus a medium containing amino acids plus a carbon source and where necessary to enhance visibility, a tetrazolium dye. The patterns formed were quite different from concentric rings discussed so far. Groups of cells aggregated to form regularly spaced zones of densely packed cells. The patterns formed resembled, for example, a sunflower head, radial arrays of spots, radially arranged spots, and striped spots with radial tails (Fig. 6).

The explanation of this phenomenon was that the aspartate receptor was necessary for pattern formation. The substance which acts as a local attractant for cells in a particular position, is taken up via the aspartate receptor. It is produced by cells in response to oxidative stress. It was suggested that aggregation was a defense mechanism against oxygen toxicity, since the assemblage of cells would reduce the pO_2 value in the neighborhood of the "colony."

4.2.1. Colony Pattern

Patterns akin to those seen with *Proteus* species have also been reported in colonies of *E. coli* grown in semisolid media in petri dishes (Budriene *et al.*, 1988; Polezhaev and Ptitsyn, 1990). Here, concentric rings of denser bacterial growth were observed. Three types of bacteria were noted: classic motile rod-shaped organisms (VF cells), nonmotile organisms (AF), and occasional long filamentous forms called RF for "running form" seen at the periphery of the structure. The pattern was associated with the nonmotile AF form. It emerged that in common with *Proteus* species, the formation of concentric rings was associated with motility but independent of chemotaxis. In the presence of chemoattractants in the medium, the edge of the growing colony was characterized by a thick-

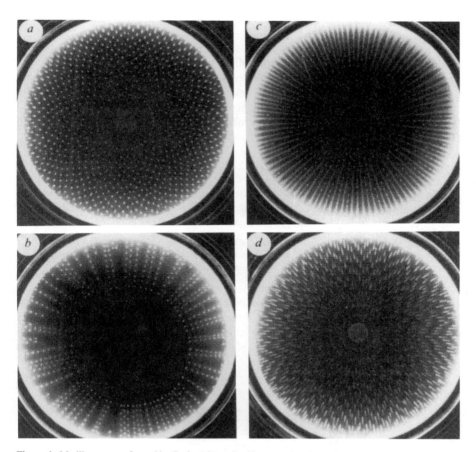

Figure 6. Motility patterns formed by *Escherichia coli* self-aggregating due to the production of a chemoattractant in a semisolid system. (Reproduced with permission.)

ened ring of increased bacterial density. Conversely, in the presence of repellents, there was a diffuse halo rather than a clear ring of migrating cells.

4.2.2. Phage–Bacterial Concentric Rings

There is one interesting observation in the literature that under certain conditions, plaques produced by lytic bacteriophages can show periodic concentric rings, presumed to be of unlysed or possibly regrown bacteria (Ivanitsky *et al.*, 1984). The phage used in this study were T7, T4, and T2 of *E. coli*. Although no explanation was offered for the structures produced, it was clear that increasing the peptone content of the underlying medium made ring production clearer.

5. Fungal Growth Patterns

One of the most intriguing and well-documented periodic phenomena is the appearance of concentric rings in fungal colonies. These are commonly seen by most people; for example, rotting apples infected with *Monilia* species clearly show these rings. They are often seen on agar plates contaminated by fungi, especially species like *Aspergillus niger* (Fig. 7). They reach their zenith from a size point of view in fungal fairy rings which may be many meters across in open field. Indeed, according to Koch (1990), fairy rings up to 4 miles across have been reported.

5.1. Fairy Rings

Fungal fairy rings are indicated by a circle of fungal fruiting bodies. Several species of fungi from the Agaricales, e.g., *Marasmius oreades,* produce these structures which enlarge year by year. As Carlile (1979) noted:

> Perhaps the climax in the development of the fungal colony is seen in the "fairy ring," a colony many meters in diameter, bearing fruiting bodies of a construction sufficiently coordinated and precise as to perhaps qualify them as multicellular individuals.

Fairy rings have been investigated by Boddy and her colleagues (Dowson *et al.,* 1989). A simple experiment solved the problem of the expanding ring, which was whether growth had depleted the inside of the circle of an essential nutrient or whether growth was in some way polarized so that it only took place in one direction—outwards. These workers showed that the second explanation was correct. They simply cut out a

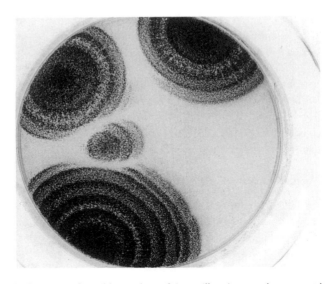

Figure 7. Circular patterns formed by a culture of *Aspergillus niger* growing on a nutrient agar plate.

part of the growing zone and put it back in the soil back to front. Growth then took place toward the center of the ring.

5.2. Rhythmic or Banded Growth

Description of the Phenomenon

Exogenous Rhythms. Among the fungi, rhythmic growth leading to concentric rings of fruiting bodies is generally triggered by an outside stimulus. Such ring structures have been recognized since fungi were first cultured in the laboratory (Werner, 1898). The commonest of these triggers are light, temperature, and humidity; however, there are several chemical triggers which do the same thing. Different fungi show different responses to light. Some are highly sensitive to short light exposures. Thus, exposure to light at 1–3000 lux for a few seconds each day is enough to trigger zonation in *Fusarium discolor sulfureum* (Bisby, 1925, cited by Jerebzoff, 1965). Illumination of a *Penicillium* by only 6 lux in the range of 390–530 nm, after a dark period was sufficient to trigger ring formation. In these experiments a drop in temperature of only 1°C was sufficient to do the same thing (Sagromsky, 1952).

Endogenous Rhythms. Internally directed rhythmic growth with periods of about 1 day (circadian rhythms) is much rarer in fungi than externally triggered changes; however it does occur naturally, more intriguing endogenous mutants are known of organisms which normally need an external trigger. Among naturally rhythmic species is the nematophagous fungus *Arthrobotrys oligospora* whose traps are distributed in bands in the absence of any obvious external trigger (Lysek and Nordbring-Herz, 1981).

"Rhythmic" or "clock" mutants are common among the fungi, e.g., in *Neurospora crassa, Podospora anserina,* and *Penicillium claviforme.*

5.3. Mechanism of Banded Growth

Band formation seems to take place as follows according to Lysek (1984). Primary hyphae starting in the inoculum region on and inside the medium elongate normally. At a point on the periphery the surface hyphae begin to "stale." Their rate of extension slows but they become more highly branched. Meanwhile, subsurface hyphae continue to extend normally and leapfrog the staled hyphae emerging beyond them near the surface. This stops the already retarded hyphae which clearly form the first band. Meanwhile, the subsurface hyphae continue to expand outwards and the process repeats at regular intervals. "Staling" is the trigger for further differentiation leading to the formation of pigments, aerial hyphae, branches, sporangiospores, fruiting bodies, etc.

Lysek discusses what is known about the mechanism of band formation. He points out that a number of chemical agents, many of which interfere with membrane structure and/or permeability to ions, etc., can trigger band formation. Lysek therefore discusses possible mechanisms based on differential ion fluxes at the hyphal tip; however, there seems to be no commonly agreed mechanism that can unequivocally explain the phenomenon.

What seems clear, especially of the rhythmic mutants and strains showing periodic structures in the absence of an external stimulus, is that there must be some internal oscillator which serves the same function.

6. The Bacterial Colony

Microbial colonies appear on the surface of solid substrates in natural habitats (e.g., food products) as well as on the surface of laboratory media. Colonies derived from one or a small group of individual cells form into aggregates which have a characteristic structure which, though strongly dependent on specific environmental factors, often possesses enough morphological characteristics to allow their identification. This aspect of morphogenesis is probably haphazard in the sense that it may not represent a programmed series of instructions as apply in higher organisms. Formation of the detailed structure of a bacterial colony is a combination of two separate factors intrinsic and extrinsic. Intrinsic factors are products of the genetics of the cell itself. They determine the morphology of the individual cell, the mode of cell reproduction, the possession of extracellular appendages (e.g., flagella, fimbriae, pili), production of extracellular products (e.g., exopolysaccharides, proteins), motility, energy metabolism, pigment formation, and so on. Extrinsic factors include the prevailing physicochemical environment which influences the physiology of the cell plus the transport of solutes into and out of the growing colony and the inevitable formation of solute diffusion gradients within the colony and the surrounding medium.

Starting from a single cell, microscopy can reveal the classic dynamics of microbial growth. The cell divides into two, the two form four, the four eight, and so on. This exponential increase generally produces a monolayer on the surface of the plate. The irregularly shaped flattened raft then changes. Cells near the center of the developing colony can no longer push aside their neighbors, and they begin to pile up on top of one another. The process continues and the structure begins to form a clear three-dimensional shape. Now the effect of the environment takes charge and diffusion gradients begin to determine some of the later stages in its development. These gradients have been measured in the case of oxygen tension and pH value (see later); they are presumed also to be present in terms of the nutrients diffusing up into the colony from the agar below. In addition to these gradients, the cells themselves are not inactive. As oxygen becomes limiting and often even when it is not, changes in cell physiology lead to the formation of products many of which are acidic and can lower the pH around the cells producing them. Cellular control mechanisms will naturally respond to changes in local physicochemistry to optimize cell performance. This subtle interplay between gene expression and environment in the end leads to the final colony as perhaps the "best" response of the organism to its environment.

6.1. Microscopy

6.1.1. Light Microscopy

6.1.1a. Surface Illumination. The detailed examination of colony structure even at quite low powers can reveal details of colony structure which are not always obvious to the naked eye. A plate viewing microscope is useful here, especially if it is equipped with both direct incident light as well as transmitted light. Standard geological microscopes are ideal for examining the surface appearance of bacterial colonies. Light micrographs of a range of colonies are shown in Fig. 8. Included here are some of the photographs published by J. Shapiro (Shapiro, 1984, 1985a,b) who has in recent years developed new techniques for studying and recording colonial growth.

     6.1.1b. Transmitted Light.   The very early phases of colonial growth starting from a single cell have been investigated by several groups. Using time-lapse video, Shapiro and Hsu (1989) have carefully monitored these early stages. For growth of colonies of *E. coli* K-12, the first cell division is followed by a relatively sudden movement of the daughter cells toward one another. The cells then reproduce to form what are two pairs of cells located side by side and making a shallow angle to one another. The four cells continue to replicate and at length form an irregular disk and generally follow the pattern outlined at the start of this section.

     Two neighboring microcolonies are generally attracted to one another as is the leading edge of two approaching colonies. Different strains of *E. coli* show subtle

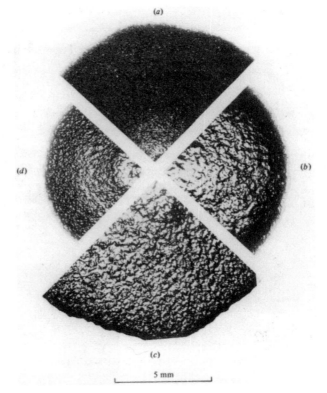

Figure 8. Surface photographs of four different strains of *Bacillus cereus*. Each colony was incubated at 30°C for 48 hr on tryptone soya agar. (a) NCTC 9680; (b) NCTC 9947; (c) C19; (d) D11.

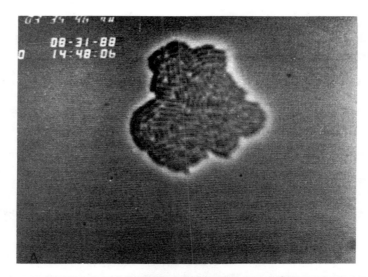

Figure 9. Microcolonies of *Escherichia coli* (a) MS398 and (b) MS2168 seen at an early stage, ca. 3–4 hr and 7.5–11.5 hr, respectively, after inoculation. (Reproduced with permission.)

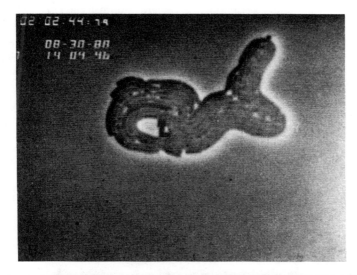

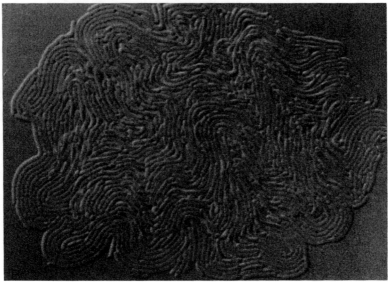

Figure 9. (*Continued*)

differences in cell division and location, so that a specific morphology soon forms in the developing colony (Fig. 9). The early four-cell stage confirms at least four earlier reports produced by Graham-Smith (1910) in *Vibrio cholera,* Hoffman and Franck (1961) using *E. coli* ATCC 8677, Donachie and Begg (1970) using *E. coli,* and Tanaka (1985) with *Agrobacterium tumefaciens.*

While most information is gleaned by direct illumination, a complementary source comes from examining bacterial colonies by transmitted light. Figure 10 shows colonies of *B. subtilis* and *B. cereus* growing on nutrient agar plates. Clear circular patterns are seen in the former but not in the latter organism. These zones may be due to cell lysis; however, this has not been confirmed.

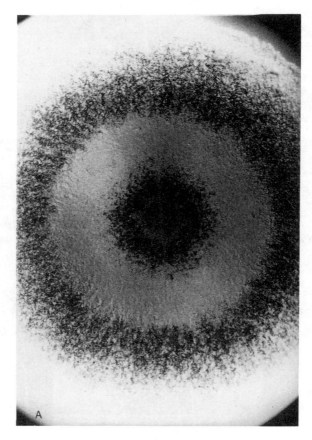

Figure 10. Surface colonies of (a) *Bacillus cereus* and (b) *Bacillus subtilis* viewed by transmitted light. Circular patterns, possibly of cell lysis, appear in the latter but not the former species.

6.1.2. Scanning Electron Microscopy

The scanning electron microscope has been a useful tool for following the development of colonies. The main problem has been the preparation of the colony for microscopy. Drucker and Whittaker (1971a,b) excised agar blocks complete with colonies of organisms including *S. aureus, Candida albicans,* and *Streptococcus* species. These were fixed and examined. Each of these species showed almost spherical cells packed closely together to form simple planoconvex colonies. The appearance of fine strands linking cells together was probably an artifact due to drying of polysaccharides or other extracellular polymers. These authors observed more complex structures with colonies of *Streptococcus mutans;* the latter had colonies differentiated to the extent that there

Figure 10. (*Continued*)

seemed to be a depressed central area where groups of cells formed broad buttresses with space between. On the other hand, cells nearer the periphery were packed more closely together. Springer and Roth (1972) also used the agar block technique to examine two streptococci: *S. pneumoniae* whose colonies were round and entire but had a zone of autolysis near the center, and *S. pyogenes* whose colonies were simple rounded dome-shaped structures with steeply rising edges.

The agar block technique was not always satisfactory and other workers grew colonies on cellulose acetate membranes (Bibel and Lawson, 1972; Todd and Kerr, 1972) or even better, on dialysis membrane strips on top of agar surfaces (Afrikian *et al.*, 1973). The latter photographed cells at the periphery of colonies of *B. cereus* showing the parallel, spaghettilike ranks of long quickly growing cells to be compared with cells nearer the center which were shorter and irregularly located.

Shapiro (1985a, 1987) examined the development of *Pseudomonas putida* and *E. coli* colonies, respectively, Colonies were grown on agar initiated, not as single cells, but as about 10^5 cells in a 1-μl drop. They were fixed *in situ* with osmium tetroxide vapor and then with glutaraldehyde allowed to diffuse to the colonies from wells in the agar. After drying and gold plating, the colonies were examined. The *E. coli* colonies showed a number of concentric rings especially at the periphery of the growing colony. The peripheral region of the colony consists of an extending monolayer with cells showing characteristic whorl-like patterns. The very edge seems to be preceded by a rim of extracellular material. These SEMs clearly reveal the upwardly curved profile described by Wimpenny (1979); however, they reveal further detail which is not so far clearly explicable. It would be interesting to see if the structure revealed by these workers was also present in clones derived from single cell inoculated colonies.

6.2. The Fundamental Structure of a Colony

The morphology of colonies discussed above suggests a significant amount of variability without much common underlying pattern. Can one discern a reasonably consistent pattern to the development of these structures? Assumptions have been made as to structure by some workers. Pirt (1967), in a classic study of colonial growth dynamics, assumed that colonies were substantially flat disks for the purposes of modeling radial growth. Palumbo *et al.* (1971) assumed that colonies of *Pseudomonas fluorescens* were segments of a sphere.

A simple method was developed to determine the physical profile of a range of bacterial colonies (Wimpenny, 1979). After sprinkling with a very fine layer of talcum powder, profiles were measured across colonies by focusing on particles of the powder at regular intervals across the colony meridian. Using this technique, a common architecture (Fig. 11) was revealed for three quite dissimilar bacterial species, *B. cereus, E. coli,* and *Staphylococcus albus*. There is usually a steep and often accelerating rise in height at the edge of the colony to a point where the slope shows a definite change to a flatter profile. In the species tested, the center of the colony is marked by a simple shallow dome; however, there are many examples of colonies which show central concavities, almost certainly due to cell lysis near this central position. The "ledge"

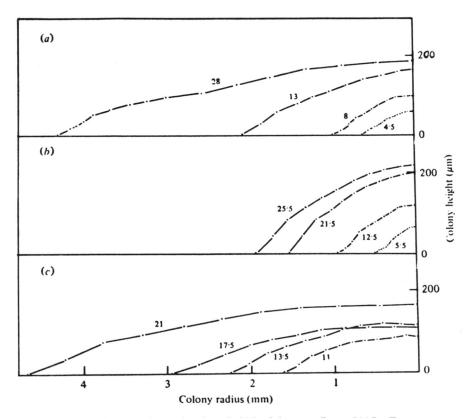

Figure 11. Profiles of colonies of (a) *Escherichia coli*, (b) *Staphylococcus albus*, and (c) *Bacillus cereus* grown for different times on tryptone soya agar plates. Measurements were made by light microscopy. (Reproduced with permission.)

between the steep edge and the flatter central region probably corresponds to the position where unrestricted edge growth becomes diffusion limited or conceivably inhibited by product formation. This will be discussed later.

6.2.1. The Colony Boundary and Radial Growth

It is possible to measure a number of parameters of the growing colony. These include diameter, height, and colony mass. Perhaps the best known of these is diameter from which one deduces the basic measurement of radial growth rate. All workers in the area of colony growth dynamics agree on one thing: radial growth is almost always linear. The earliest reports concerned fungal growth (Fawcett, 1925; Ryan *et al.*, 1943; Brancato and Golding, 1953) and these all obeyed the standard pattern. The fungus *Chaetomium* had linear growth dynamics, but only after a period of exponential increase lasting until the colony reached about 0.2 mm in diameter (Plomley, 1959). After a period of linear radial growth which depends on the organism, on the nutrient concentration, and on the number of colonies competing for nutrients on the plate, growth slows down. On crowded plates, Shrewsbury (1931) showed that there was an abrupt change in diameter increase with colony age in colonies of luminous bacteria. He assumed that nutrients became limited and confirmed this by excising cubes of agar from the immediate vicinity of the colony and replacing these with blocks of fresh nutrient agar. The colonies, whose light emission had ceased, began to glow again.

A general rule seemed to apply in the case of older colonies. That is, linear radial growth gave way, after a certain time, to a linear increase in surface area. Changes in the shape of the colony boundary are an interesting clue as to conditions in the agar. Young colonies are nearly always circular, as often are slow-growing colonies. As the colony ages, the periphery of the structure becomes more irregular. This irregularity becomes

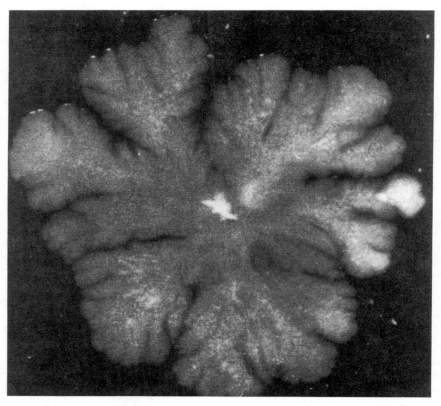

Figure 12. "Snowflake" colony of *Enterobacter aerogenes* grown for 20 days on nutrient agar. (Reproduced with permission.)

extreme in some species after prolonged incubation. For example, Cooper *et al.* (1968) monitored the growth of *"Aerobacter aerogenes"* (now *Enterobacter aerogenes*). After 20 days incubation the colony showed the sort of irregularities characteristic of "snowflakes" (Fig. 12). Colonies showing this intricate pattern seem to be formed by precisely the same mechanism that leads to the appearance of an actual snowflake. That is severe diffusion limitation, in the case of the snowflake it is water vapor in the gaseous phase, while for the colony it is nutrient in the gel phase. It is possible using image analysis to determine the coefficient of circularity of a colony. This was done for *E. coli* (Wilkinson and Wimpenny, unpublished observations) and clearly shows the increase in irregularity as a function of colony age (Fig. 13).

6.2.2. Colony Height

Palumbo *et al.* (1971) examined colonies of *Pseudomonas fluorescens* grown either on glucose salts agar or on a richer medium (tryptone soya agar). Colonies grown on either medium increased in height linearly for at least 50 hr. However, those on the simple glucose salts medium reached only 100 μm in height while the richer medium led to colonies that were about six times as high. Lewis and Wimpenny (1981) investigated the growth of *E. coli* on a range of different media aerobically and anaerobically. In the majority of cases, height increases linearly at least at first. The main exception is seen in colonies grown on the richest medium containing trypticase-soya agar. Colonies reached their greatest height when grown aerobically on either the tryptone soya medium or other medium supplemented with casamino acids either with or without glucose.

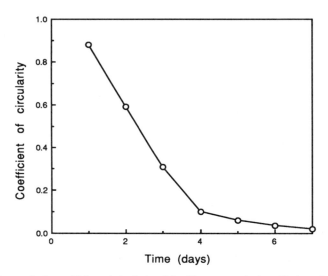

Figure 13. Changes in the coefficient of circularity of *Bacillus cereus* colonies with time. Coefficients were obtained using image analysis software on colony images. (Courtesy of Tim Wilkinson.)

6.2.3. Colony Mass Increase

Palumbo *et al.* (1971) assumed that colonies of a pseudomonad approximated to sections of a sphere and they calculated colony volumes using the appropriate equation after first determining the radius and height of the colony. They indicated that colony volume increased exponentially in young colonies.

Wimpenny and Lewis (1977) measured the absorbance of colonies washed off agar plates, and estimated dry weight from absorbance calibration curves. During the early part of the growth curve, dry weight increased exponentially. Growth data, expressed as doubling times, were calculated and compared with doubling times determined in liquid culture and also with colony respiration doubling time (see later). The data were obtained for five different organisms, two (*Proteus vulgaris* and *Bacillus subtilis*) were active swarmers and covered the agar very quickly. For the latter there was good agreement between respiration and mass doubling times determined for surface growth; moreover, these figures were similar to the doubling times determined in liquid culture. On the other hand, the three nonswarming species grew much faster in liquid than on solid media: however, their respiration and dry weight doubling times as colonies were similar. These data indicate the importance of diffusion limitations in intact colonies.

6.2.4. Effects of Motility

The effects of motility have yet to be systematically evaluated as they help determine both shape and pattern in the bacterial colony. It would be surprising if motility was not extremely important here. At its most extreme, the feathery patterns generated by *Bacillus cereus* var. *mycoides* are due to its motility as are the rings seen in *Proteus* or *E. coli* colonies already discussed (see Section 4).

To summarize, colony growth can be divided into at least three phases: after a lag phase, the young colony develops exponentially. This is sometimes seen as an *exponential* increase in diameter. (2) Quite young colonies soon switch to a linear radial growth rate whose value is dependent on the organism and its physicochemical environment. (3) Older colonies show a linear increase in surface area and under certain circumstances can generate snowflake forms, before they finally stop growing completely.

6.3. Spatial Gradients within Colonies

6.3.1. Oxygen Gradients

The existence of microelectrodes with tip diameters in the 1–5 µm range, provides a useful tool with which to investigate the distribution of oxygen in bacterial colonies. Oxygen measurements have been made in this way by Bungay *et al.* in colonies of *Pseudomonas ovalis* and by Wimpenny and Coombs in *Bacillus cereus* both in 1983. Later, Peters *et al.* (1987) examined the time course of dissolved oxygen changes with age in colonies of *B. cereus, E. coli,* and *Staphylococcus albus.* Young actively growing colonies show very steep oxygen gradients. It is probably true that of all of the solute gradients that apply to structured microbial communities, that for oxygen must be the steepest. Figure 14 shows that this electron acceptor has disappeared after only about 30

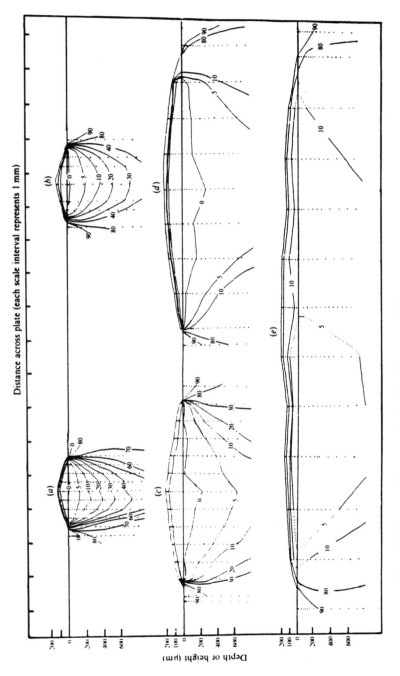

Figure 14. Oxygen profiles across colonies of *Bacillus cereus* and in the underlying agar. (Reproduced with permission.)

μm. As the colony ages, so oxygen penetrates farther. It may seem surprising that very old colonies which might intuitively appear to be anaerobic are generally aerobic throughout. This is because oxidizable substrate has all been depleted.

6.3.2. pH Gradients

Robinson, Wimpenny, and Earnshaw (1991) have, using specific ion microelectrodes, determined pH gradients in and around colonies of *B. cereus* grown on an amino acid medium (casamino acids) in the presence or absence of glucose (Fig. 15). In the absence of glucose, amino acid oxidation leads to alkalinization. Where glucose is present, the growing edge still becomes alkaline while a thickened zone toward the center becomes acidic presumably due to anaerobic glucose fermentation in this zone. These experiments confirm the spatial heterogeneity characteristic of such microbial aggregates. Other electrodes could be used including redox potential, hydrogen sulfide, nitrate and nitrite probes and a number of other ion-exchange electrodes as these become available.

6.4. Differentiation within the Bacterial Colony

The physicochemical changes measured with oxygen and pH microprobes must in turn be reflected in the cell both in terms of the expression of its genetic information and also in terms of its viability.

6.4.1. Distribution of Viability

Very little work has been done on the viability of cells from different regions in the growing colony. In many species there is evidence of cell lysis in the internal regions of the colony; however, there have been no direct measurements of viable counts. Legroux and Magrou (1920) looked at the organization of bacterial colonies microscopically. They stained sectioned old colonies of *Vibrio cholera* with a vital stain and observed that the latter was only taken up by cells at the surface of the colony or of distinct tubes formed by folding and coalescence of ridges and furrows produced by the growing structure. The work suggested that cells were dying and lysing in the body of the colony itself and possibly that the surface aerobic cells were surviving at the expense of the anaerobic moribund organisms.

Greene (1938) reported that spores only formed in the upper regions of colonies of spore-forming species exposed to the atmosphere.

6.4.2. Distribution of Enzymes

It seems clear that the steep gradients measured or assumed in vigorously growing colonies must be reflected by changes in the regulation of metabolic systems within individual cells. This is an area that has received very little attention. Wimpenny and Parr (1979) grew large colonies of *Enterobacter cloacae* on nutrient agar plates. These were cut out of the plate together with the underlying agar and frozen onto an aluminum stub whose base was immersed in liquid nitrogen. The colonies were then sectioned horizontally in 10-μm slices using a cryostat at a temperature of $-25°C$. Sections from the same depth from different colonies were bulked to provide sufficient material. Cells were disrupted ultrasonically and a number of oxidative enzymes were assayed. NADH oxidase and three TCA cycle enzymes all showed significantly higher activities in the upper 100 μm.

6.4.3. Distribution of Growth

Attempts were made to discern the distribution of growth activity within the colony using radioactive tracers (Reyrolle and Letellier, 1979). These workers grew colonies of five different bacterial species up to a certain stage on fragments of cellulose acetate membrane. The latter were then transferred to a similar medium containing tritiated leucine, a marker of protein synthesis, and incubated for 3 or 6 hr. They were then fixed, embedded, and sectioned vertically. Sections were autoradiographed or in some cases stained with toluidine blue. Sections, either from the edge of the colony or near its center, were then examined. Aerobic species, in particular *Pseudomonas aeruginosa* and *Bacillus thuringiensis,* showed little differentiation with respect to tracer distribution, both in young and in older colonies. The related *P. putida* showed significantly more tracer near the upper surface only, toward the center of older colonies. The distribution in the two facultative anaerobes was more interesting. In young colonies of both species, tracer was found adjacent to the agar medium, indicating that most growth was at the expense of the anaerobic fermentation of sugars derived from the medium. The same also seemed to be true in older *E. coli* colonies. The older *Staphylococcus aureus* colonies showed tracer incorporation in a narrow zone near the upper surface of central regions of the colony, and good incorporation near the growing edge of the structure. Where there is a zone near the surface it seems probable that growth is occurring aerobically at the point where oxygen diffusion downwards meets nutrients diffusing upwards. The nature of these nutrients is not known for certain but must include fermentation products that can only be further metabolized by aerobic pathways.

There are unavoidable problems with these experiments. First, the growing colony is transferred to fresh medium containing the tracer. Under these conditions there is an excess of nutrient beneath the colony where naturally this zone would by this time be depleted. The second problem lies in the interpretation of distribution results. Tracer enters the colony from below. It is progressively removed by growth as it diffuses upwards. This means that less and less tracer is available for further growth the higher one proceeds up the colony profile. For example, in all of the *E. coli* results, considerable amounts of incorporation took place adjacent to the agar surface. The question is, would there have been sufficient tracer left to reveal a second zone of growth near the colony surface? It might have been interesting to repeat these experiments growing the facultative anaerobe on a nonfermentable substrate such as lactate aerobically to see where the tracer was located under these conditions. It *ought* to be at a point near the surface where oxygen and lactate meet. There is another problem that this sort of work raises concerning motility in the colony itself. Nothing is known about the part that

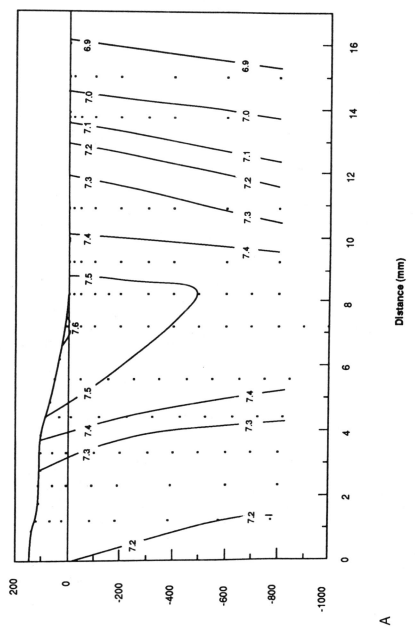

A

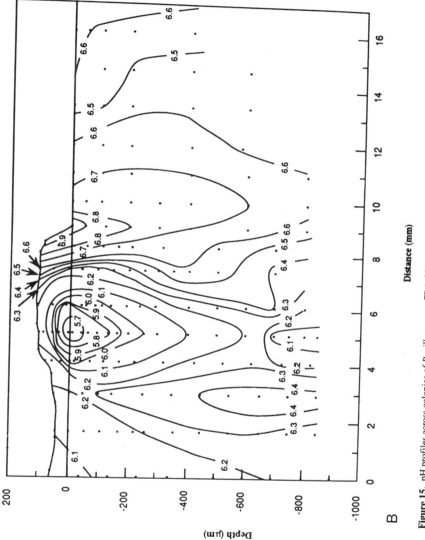

Figure 15. pH profiles across colonies of *Bacillus cereus* CRA 666 and in the underlying agar. The organism was grown on a simple defined medium containing casamino acids without (a) or with (b) added glucose. (Reproduced with permission.)

motility could play in moving bacteria around within the colony, or indeed if this can occur significantly at all.

Net growth can be assessed by determining the light absorption of growing colonies using image analysis. If a time series of growing colonies is recorded, growth over any interval can be obtained by subtraction (Wimpenny and Wilkinson, unpublished). This has been done for *E. coli* colonies and confirms that growth takes place at the edge of the colony.

While this deals with the basic structure of a colony, it says little about the surface detail. Closely related strains of the same species can have quite distinctive differences in pattern. This can be seen in colonies of *B. cereus* grown on the same medium. The reasons for this shift in pattern are quite unclear. They exist and they are reproducible when the strain is grown under the same conditions. It has little to do with the macroscopic shape which are the underlying bones of the colony. They might be regarded as trivial effects of little consequence except that they contribute to a distinct and repeatable morphology. Presumably, such fine grain pattern represents small changes in the *actual* structure of the cell and the *actual* mode of reproduction and the *actual* production of cell appendages and extracellular polymers. This area could be tackled by selecting appropriate mutants.

6.5. Pattern Formation in Bacterial Colonies: Programmed Differentiation?

Two types of differentiation can be seen in growing bacterial colonies. Thus, under appropriate conditions, colonies reveal sectoring and in much older colonies papilla formation. If unstable genetic elements are incorporated into a cell, the frequency of sectoring increases. If these elements are coupled to a color indicator system, the sectoring can be easily visualized. Shapiro used the mu Dlac transposon to fulfill both of these conditions. This transposable genetic element can be expressed at random positions on the genome where it also expresses the β-galactosidase enzyme. Use of a dye like X-gal gives a purple coloration to any regions in the colony where β-galactosidase is induced. Use of this transposon generates sometimes beautiful, flowerlike colonial forms (Fig. 16). These radially organized sectors reflect hereditary changes in the control of growth and gene expression. Each sector derives from a single ancestral cell and is thus a clone.

A second form of colony differentiation has been examined by Shapiro and others. Here there are periodic concentric rings seen in the colony (Fig. 16). Shapiro and Trubatch (1991) regards these rings as a coordinated cellular response to an environmental signal and sees the process as part of an organized morphogenetic phenomenon. If the normal development of the colony is interfered with, for example by putting a glass filament in the path of the growing structure, the colony will grow around the obstacle but its boundary will be altered. However much interference is caused (e.g., by the use of several pieces of filament), the pattern of concentric rings formed remains faithfully coordinated with the pattern forming in the "mother" colony. Shapiro suggests that the fidelity of this response must imply a genetically coordinated morphogenetic action controlled by cell–cell interactions.

What is clear is that the possibility of a programmed morphogenesis must be distinguished from a much more casual response that is the formation of periodic structures due to changes in the physicochemical environment. More research is needed to clarify this important issue.

7. Pattern Formation during Simple Morphogenesis

It is at this point that we change from what are generally accepted to be "accidental" patterns, not programmed into the organism's genome, to patterns that are coordinated goal-oriented activities of the species with putative survival value. I say *generally* because some authors, as has already been discussed, regard pattern formation in bacterial colonies including the swarming colonies of *Proteus* species as genetically programmed with survival value.

7.1. The Myxobacteria

Among prokaryotic organisms the myxobacteria are distinguished by an unusual form of social behavior. That is, they show adventurous and social motility and are capable of differentiating into elaborate fruiting structures. In addition, they show an intriguing periodic behavior called "rippling" which was investigated in detail about 25 years ago by Reichenbach (Reichenbach, 1965, 1966). Over this period Reichenbach produced a series of time-lapse films of myxobacterial colony development and discovered the presence of wavelike structures (Fig. 17). Ripples are a series of evenly spaced ridges, parallel to one another, moving in a pulsating fashion leading to wave propagation from the center to the edge of the colony. These periodicities occur in 5-hr cycles interspersed with a quiescent state. The ripples seem to have a wavelength of 45 to 70 μm and repeat about every 20 min. They travel at 2.2 to 3.7 μm/min (Shimkets and Kaiser, 1982; Shimkets, 1990). The cells are arranged at an angle of 40° to the direction of ripple propagation. Movement of cells in adjacent tracks is in *opposite* direction: every now and then the tracks cross and it is assumed that cells moving from one track to another at crossover points then proceed to alter direction.

The mechanism and control of rippling is not well understood. Motility itself has been well studied in *Myxococcus xanthus*. Two gene clusters have been identified, the A and the S systems. These are both needed for rippling to occur as is the *csgA* gene which codes for an extracellular polypeptide which is a developmental morphogen (Shimkets and Kaiser, 1982).

7.2. *Dictyostelium discoideum*

The classical example of periodic structure formation has been the signaling phenomenon of *Dictyostelium* (Chisholm *et al.*, 1984). *Dictyostelium* is a eukaryotic cellular slime mold. It exists as amoeboid cells which can be raised on bacteria. Starvation triggers a programmed sequence of events leading to the formation of fruiting bodies.

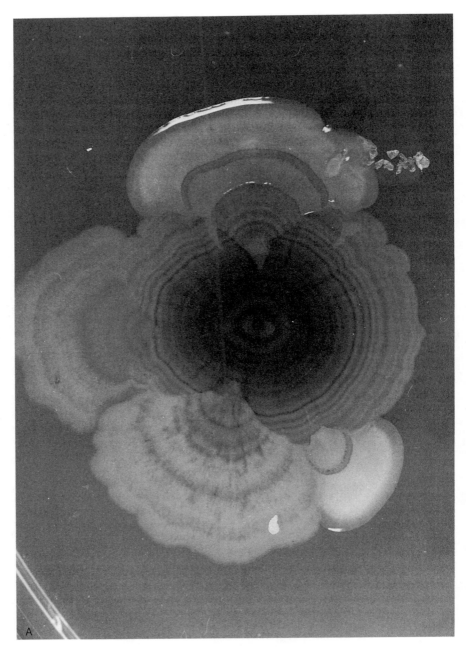

Figure 16. Circular patterns (a) and sectoring (a, b) in colonies of *Escherichia coli* containing the mu dlac transposon. (Courtesy of J. A. Shapiro.)

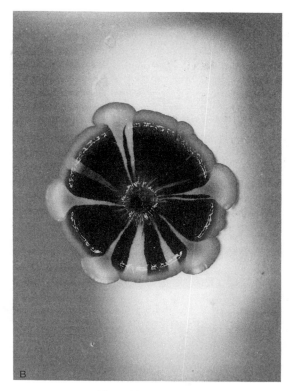

Figure 16. (*Continued*)

Soon after starvation starts, some cells produce pulses of cAMP which acts as a signal leading to chemotactic movement toward the source of the signal (Bonner, 1969). In addition, cells receiving the signal through specific membrane receptor (Newell, 1986) synthesize more cAMP which is transferred outwards acting as signal relay. Prolonged exposure to cAMP desensitizes the receptor and cAMP is degraded by a phosphodiesterase which hydrolyzes cAMP to 5'-AMP. The patterns formed are either concentric rings or spiral shapes (Fig. 18). The waves of cAMP pass regularly over the amoebae and stimulate chemotactic motility. This phase can last for about 2 min followed by a 5-min period of inactivity. The net result of this motion is an accumulation of cells at the center of the concentric rings or the pivot point of the spiral structures.

The chemical pattern revealed by measuring cAMP directly (Tomchik and Devreotes, 1981) led in the end to the cellular differentiation process, as Tyson and Murray (1989) say:

> . . . we see the development of a spatio-temporally periodic chemical prepattern that induces a pattern of morphogenetic movements culminating in the formation of an organized multicellular tissue.

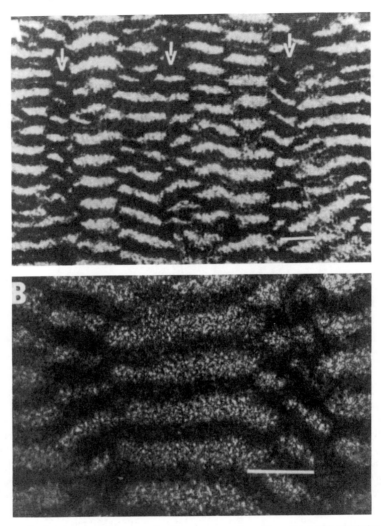

Figure 17. Ripple patterns in aggregating *Myxococcus xanthus*. (Reproduced with permission.)

Tyson and Murray formulate a model which successfully predicts wave formation. This model is based on the extracellular and intracellular cAMP concentrations and the fraction of the cAMP receptor in the active state. This model was given added credence because it was based on reliable biochemical information produced by Van Haastert and DeWit (1984) and Devreotes and Sherring (1985). Spiral wave was predicted by the model. This has a single solution with a rotation period of 14 min and a wave velocity of

Figure 18. Relay signal patterns found when *Dictyostelium* swarm. (Courtesy of Peter Newell.)

0.28 mm/min. This compares well to observed values of 7 min and 0.3 mm/min, respectively (Tomchik and Devreotes, 1981).

Most recently, investigations have concentrated on the motion of individual amoebae using image analysis techniques (Steinbock *et al.*, 1991; Siegert and Weijer, 1991). Such techniques allow the detection of periodic behavior in individual cells even after darkfield optical density changes have dropped to undetectable levels.

7.3. *Polysphondylium pallidum*

Polysphondylium pallidum is another cellular slime mold that has been studied intensively in recent years (Raper, 1984). Swarming cells aggregate and differentiate into a mature fruiting body. The latter produces a series of sorocarps which are whorls of fruiting structures arranged in a regularly spaced series along the length of the stalk. The developing stalk (sorogen) "pinches off" masses of cells at intervals from the bottom upwards. These whorl masses form secondary sorogens which later develop into secondary sorocarps. Cox *et al.* (1988) have investigated the process in some detail. Using specific monoclonal antibodies, they detected a gradient of the pattern-specific antigen Pg101 from tip downwards to the base of the structure. The differentiation process is seen as a balance between two processes: a chemotactic movement toward the stalk apex and a natural tendency for cells to round up and aggregate. A model is proposed based on the processes of short-range activation–long-range inhibition due to Turing (1952) and Gierer and Meinhardt (1972).

8. Principles of Pattern Formation

8.1. Chemical Patterns

8.1.1. Liesegang Rings

Many common objects show evidence of banded structure. These include a number of jewels and semiprecious stones, e.g., agate and malachite. Artificial gel systems containing diffusible reacting molecules form the classic Liesegang rings (Liesegang, 1896). As Hedges (1932) describes the system:

> If a drop of 10 or 20 per cent. silver nitrate is placed on a sheet of gelatin impregnated with 0.4 per cent. of potassium dichromate, silver dichromate is precipitated in the gelatinous medium. Under these conditions however, the precipitate is not continuous, but forms a series of concentric rings, separated by clear spaces in the gel. . . .

A more common model is to incorporate the dilute reactant in a gel in a test tube or measuring cylinder and to add the concentrated reactant to the surface of the gel. Concentric rings and even spiral structures form as a function of time. A good demonstration model system is dilute (say 0.4 M) $MgSO_4$ in 9% gelatin in the lower part of a tube with 11.3 M NH_4OH overlaying this. Rather widely spaced bands of $Mg(OH)_2$ appear in these gels (Muller and Venzl, 1984). Other examples of reacting pairs forming bands under these conditions are described in Hedges (1932): copper phosphate in silica gel, insoluble mercury salts in gelatin, sulfides of manganese, iron, nickel, zinc, and cobalt in gelatin; the diffusion of cadmium or zinc into gelatin or agar gels containing sodium sulfide; insoluble sulfates, ferrocyanides, ferricyanides, cyanides, phosphates, and silicates in silica gel, and many others.

The explanation for Liesegang rings has not been unequivocally determined. Early theories are discussed by Hedges (1932). Most of these are based on work by Ostwald (1925). Here the view is that a supersaturation mechanism is involved. There is seen to be an asymmetry in that as the diffusing solute increases in concentration, precipitation starts after a critical threshold concentration is reached. Precipitation then removes the limiting solute from the neighborhood of the first band. The diffusing solute moves past the first band and no reaction occurs until a point farther along the gel where it reaches the threshold once more. This is a *pre*nucleation mechanism: the threshold and asymmetry involved lead to nucleation and band formation. A more recent explanation (Flicker and Ross, 1974) is quite in contrast to the Ostwald mechanism. The F-R mechanism is based on diffusional instability and while the Ostwald mechanism is local in space and sequential in time the F-R mechanism is global and simultaneous. Müller and Venzl (1984) have systematically investigated Liesegang ring phenomena using the $Mg(OH)_2$ and the PbI_2 systems. They showed, using optical measurements, that a uniform colloid of product is formed early on and that this generates precipitation bands at a later time. Although this seems to be a *post*nucleation mechanism, work subsequently suggests that the largest colloid particles form at the position where the first bands form and that these then enlarge over time. Such an observation remains consistent with the original supersaturation model of Ostwald (1925).

8.1.2. Chemical Oscillators

The Belousov–Zhabotinsky (BZ) reaction has been recognized for more than two decades (Zaikin and Zhabotinsky, 1970). A typical reaction mixture contains cerous nitrate, potassium bromate, sulfuric acid, and malonic acid. If these reagents are mixed together in a flat dish and a redox indicator such as ferroin added, a pattern of concentric rings and spiral structures are formed which oscillate with regular spatial and temporal periodicities. The reaction consists of the oxidation of malonic acid by bromate in acid solution. The main steps in the reaction are as follows: In the presence of Br^- ion, bromate reacts with bromide while the bromous ion falls to a low steady-state concentration (Process I). Now when bromide falls below a critical concentration, bromate oxidizes the reduced form of the catalyst creating a high steady state of bromous acid as this latter reaction is autocatalytic in $HBrO_2$ (Process II). The oxidized form of the catalyst generates more Br^- ions (Process III) which establishes the next loop of the cycle. It is clear that the patterns formed are maintained by energy dissipation in contrast to Liesegang rings which show a "historic" record of a single reaction event occurring as a diffusion front passes through the system.

8.1.3. Turing Structures

Turing patterns are formed by a process of short-range activation–long-range inhibition (Turing, 1952; Gierer and Meinhardt, 1972). If in a diffusion field a reaction (1) stimulates its own rate (positive feedback) but also (2) produces a diffusible inhibitor of the same reaction (negative feedback), the reaction will generate a series of periodic bands of activity. The necessary and sufficient condition for this process to occur is that the pattern generator (morphogen) diffuses more slowly than the inhibitor.

There have been recent reports of purely chemical Turing structures produced in an isothermal single-phase reaction system (Castets *et al.*, 1990; DeKepper *et al.*, 1991). These authors used the chlorite–iodide–malonic acid oscillatory reaction.

8.1.4. Diffusion Limitation and Pattern Formation

Nature generates some of its most beautiful patterns due to changes in phase from gaseous or liquid to a solid phase. This process, especially where it is limited by molecular diffusion, generates whole families of different patterns. One has only to recollect "chemical gardens" where crystals of different inorganic chemicals are dropped into silica gel. One of the most interesting of these diffusion-limited processes is snowflake formation.

8.1.5. Fractal Patterns

Fractal pattern formation should perhaps be given a section of its own. Fractals and chaos theory go hand in hand with fractals perhaps the beautiful very edge of chaos. Fractal patterns are self-similar structures. Examine a fractal pattern. Now take a magnifying glass and look at it ten times enlarged. The smaller patterns which make up the larger appear identical themselves to the larger pattern. Now magnify a small portion of the pattern again. Once more the smaller units are identical to the larger. Pure fractal patterns continue the self-similarity downwards to infinitely small. Pure fractals are a mathematician's delight and are not really relevant to patterns in the real world. For instance, the geographical structure of the British Isles *resembles* a fractal structure. Examine the coast of Scotland on successively larger scales and the bays and inlets and coves and the rocks and stones and streams and maybe the grains of sand all show a similar relationship at each of the different scales. However, these are not true fractals. The self-similarity is not exact and the process cannot be repeated down *ad infinitum*. There is a well-known fractal shape resembling a fern. Once more the resemblance is only superficial! The fractal fern is self-similar, the actual fern is not. In other words, fractal geometry gives no idea of the *mechanism* of pattern formation.

Having said this, it is possible to use the language of fractals and apply it to microbial systems. Thus, an index of irregularity can be determined for bacterial colonies. This was done for a colony of *Clostridium acetobutylicum* by Markx and Davey (1990) in a useful discussion of the applications of fractal geometry and chaos theory in microbial systems. Similarly, fractal indexes have been employed in the analysis of resource capture by cord-forming fungi.

8.2. Pattern-Forming Processes in Biological Systems

An attempt has been made in Fig. 19 to classify pattern-forming phenomena including some common in the chemical world but concentrating on pattern formation in microbial systems. Two main classes of pattern emerge: those that require a constant input of energy for both the formation of the pattern and its maintenance and those that need energy only for the generation of the structure.

In the first group are the signaling events that take place in swarming *Dictyostelium* generating a family of patterns which are almost indistinguishable from BZ reaction patterns. We must also include under this heading traveling bands of microbes moving in chemoattractant gradients first reported by Adler (1966).

The chemical Turing reaction, extremely unusual in purely chemical systems, is the very stuff of differentiation among living organisms and a pattern-forming process that starts to become evident at the more sophisticated end of the microbial world. Chemotactic aggregation can be described as the development of a Turing structure.

In the second class, energy is used in the creation of the pattern in the first case. Pattern formation occurs like a wave traveling through the system. At the active point where reactants are all available under the required conditions, a reaction takes place. The resultant pattern is "historic" in the sense that no energy is needed to maintain it. In

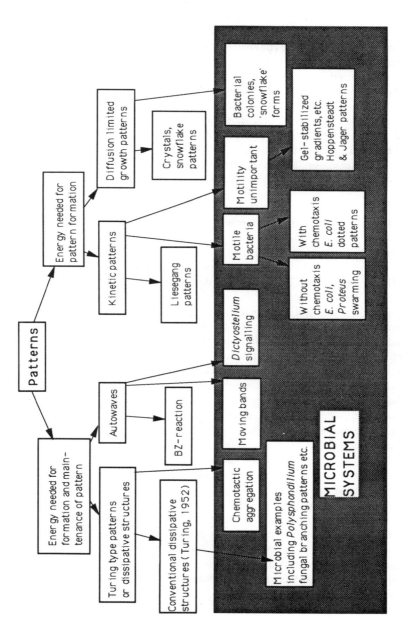

Figure 19. Classification of pattern formation in microbiological systems.

the case of Liesegang ring formation, a stable precipitate forms which remains indefinitely. In banded growth in gel-stabilized gradient systems, energy is dissipated only as the current band is forming. Though viability is retained for some time after band formation, this is irrelevant to the maintenance of the pattern.

These have been called "kinetic" patterns since their formation is dependent on the kinetics of the reactions involved. All require some sort of asymmetric response. This can be by hysteresis or by the introduction of lags before the pattern is formed. In this group, motility is unimportant. A second subgroup where motility is essential to pattern formation includes some of the best known and some of the most beautiful examples of periodic behavior, including swarming in *Proteus* species and the "dotted" patterns recently reported by Budrene and Berg (1991).

Finally, diffusion-limited crystal growth probably relies on the same mechanism that leads to "snowflake" colony growth described most clearly by Cooper *et al.* (1968).

9. The Relevance of Pattern-Forming Processes to Microbial Ecosystems

So now we must return to microbial ecosystems. How does all that we have said regarding "pattern" apply to the way in which microbial communities develop in nature? Having reached this point in the chapter, one is forced to admit a certain sense of failure. Thus, there are very few examples of pattern formation as described here, forming part of a classical microbial ecosystem. There are a few exceptions to this statement. The observations on the growth of *Gallionella* in sediment systems by Perfil'ev and Gabe (1969) beautifully illustrate banded growth patterns with the caveat that the mechanism for their formation has never been investigated. Fungal growth patterns seen on agar plates in the laboratory are commonly observed in wood-decomposing fungi and in species like *Monilia* colonizing fruit.

What *is* clear that the organization of space in physicochemical terms determines both growth and, where it is seen, pattern.

Perhaps we can compare patterns of growth in pure culture systems with patterns of growth in mixed populations? In the latter case the chemical environment differentiates passing through a series of various habitat domains for each different species. The overall structure bears some comparison with a differentiated tissue, with each group of cells carrying out a distinct series of functions. In a sediment system, organisms are arrayed along a redox potential gradient where species are organized according to the presence of a range of electron acceptors, of which oxygen, nitrate, sulfate, and carbon dioxide are the most important. That the community is aligned in order of electronegativity of electron acceptor provides a logical scenario for optimum colonization of the habitat. Stratified water bodies and sediment systems show this type of differentiation clearly. They are substantially one-dimensional systems with reductant ascending and oxidant descending into the system.

In terms of our classification of pattern, such a structured ecosystem is a dissipative structure where energy is spent not only in pattern formation but in its maintenance.

References

Abdollahi, H., 1983, *The effect of oxygen on the growth and behavior of mixed bacterial communities*, Ph.D. thesis, University College Cardiff, Wales.

Adler, J., 1966, Chemotaxis in bacteria, *Science* **153**:708–716.

Afrikian, E. G., St. Julian, G., and Bulla, L. A., 1973, Scanning electron microscopy of bacterial colonies, *Appl. Microbiol.* **26**:934–937.

Armitage, J. P., and Smith, D. G., 1976, The ultra structure of *Proteus mirabilis* swarmers, in: *Society for Applied Bacteriology Technical Series* (R. Fuller and D. W. Lovelock, eds.), Academic Press, New York, pp. 175–185.

Armitage, J. P., Rowbury, R. J., and Smith, D. G., 1976, The role of cyclic adenosine monophosphate in the swarming phenomenon of Proteus mirabilis, *Experientia* **32**:1266–1267.

Bibel, D. J., and Lawson, J. W., 1972, Scanning electron microscopy of L-phase streptococci: Development of techniques, *J. Microsc.* (Oxford) **95**:435.

Bissett, K. A., 1973a, The motion of the swarm in *Proteus mirabilis*, *J. Med. Microbiol.* **6**:33–35.

Bissett, K. A., 1973b, A continuous study of the morphological phase in the swarm of *Proteus*, *J. Med. Microbiol.* **9**:229–231.

Bonner, J. T., 1969, Hormones in social amoebae and mammals, *Sci. Am.* **220**:78–91.

Brancato, F. P., and Golding, N. S., 1953, The diameter of mold colony as a reliable measure of growth, *Mycologia* **45**:848.

Bryant, M. P., Wolin, E. A., Wolin, M. J., and Wolfe, R. S., 1967, *Methanobacillus omelianskii*, a symbiotic association of two species of bacteria, *Arch. Microbiol.* **59**:20–31.

Buchanan, R. L., and Phillips, J. G., 1990, Response surface model for predicting the effects of temperature, pH, sodium chloride content, sodium nitrite concentration and atmosphere on the growth of *Listeria monocytogenes*, *J. Food Prot.* **53**:370–376.

Budrene, E. O., and Berg, H. C., 1991, Complex patterns formed by motile cells of *Escherichia coli*, *Nature* **349**:630–633.

Budrene, E. O., Polezhaev, A. A., and Ptitsyn, M. O., 1988, Mathematical modelling of intercellular regulation causing the formation of spatial structures in bacterial colonies, *J. Theor. Biol.*, **135**:323–341.

Bungay, H. R., Petit, P. M., and Drislane, A. M., 1983, Dissolved oxygen contours in *Pseudomonas ovalis* colonies, in: *Foundations of Biochemical Engineering: Kinetics and Thermodynamics in Biological Systems* (H. W. Blanch, E. T. Papoutsakis, and G. Stephanopoulos, eds.), American Chemical Society, Washington, D.C., pp. 395–401.

Carlile, M. J., 1979, Bacterial, fungal, and slime mold colonies, in: *The Biology and Systematics of Colonial Organisms*, (G. Larwood and B. R. Rosen, eds.), Academic Press, London, pp. 3–27.

Castets, V., Dulos, J., Boissonade, J., and De Kepper, P., 1990, Experimental evidence of a sustained standing Turing-type nonequilibrium chemical pattern, *Phys. Rev. Lett.* **64**:2953.

Characklis, W. G., 1990, Laboratory biofilm reactors, in: *Biofilms* (W. G. Characklis and K. C. Marshall, eds.) Wiley–Interscience, New York, pp. 55–89.

Chisholm, R. L., Fontana,, D., Thelbert, A., Lodish, H. F., and Devreotes, P., 1984, Development of *Dictyostelium discoideum*: Chemotaxis, cell–cell adhesion, and gene expression, in: *Microbial Development* (R. Losick and L. Shapiro, eds.), Cold Spring Harbor Laboratory, Cold Spring Harbor, N.Y., pp. 215–254.

Cohen, Y., and Rosenberg, E. (eds.), 1989, *Microbial Mats: Physiological Ecology of Benthic Microbial Communities*, American Society for Microbiology, Washington, D.C.

Coombe, R. A., Tatevossian, A., and Wimpenny, J. W. T., 1981, Bacterial thin films as *in vitro* models for dental plaque, in: *Surface and Colloid Phenomena in the Oral Cavity: Methodological Aspects* (R. M. Frank and S. A. Leach, eds.), Information Retrieval, London, pp. 239–249.

Coombs, J. P., and Wimpenny, J. W. T., 1982, Growth of *Bacillus cereus* in a gel-stabilized nutrient gradient system, *J. Gen. Microbiol.* **128**:3093–3101.

Cooper, A. L., Dean, A. C. R., and Hinshelwood, C., 1968, Factors affecting the growth of bacterial colonies on agar plates, *Proc. R. Soc. London Ser. B* **171**:175.

Cox, E. C., Spiegel, F. W., Byrne, G., McNally, J. W., and Eisenbud, L., 1988, Spatial patterns in fruiting bodies of the cellular slime mold *Polysphondilium pallidum, Differentiation* **38**:73–81.

De Kepper, P., Castets, V., Dulos, E., and Boissonade, J., 1991, Turing-type chemical patterns in the chlorite–iodide–malonic acid reaction, *Physica D* **49**:161–169.

Devreotes, P. N., and Sherring, J. A., 1985, Kinetics and concentration dependence of reversible cAMP-induced modification of the surface cAMP receptor in *Dictyostelium, J. Biol. Chem.* **260**: 6378–6384.

Donachie, W. D., and Begg, K. J., 1970, Growth of the bacterial cell, *Nature* **227**:1220–1224.

Douglas, C. W. I., and Bissett, K. A., 1976, Development of concentric zones in the *Proteus* swarm colony, *J. Med. Microbiol.* **9**:497–500.

Dowson, C. G., Rayner, A. D. M., and Boddy, L., 1989, Spatial dynamics and interactions of the woodland fairy ring fungus, *Clitocybe nebularis, New Phytol.* **111**:699–705.

Drucker, D. B., and Whittaker, D. K., 1971a, Examination of certain bacterial colonies by scanning electron microscope, *Microbios* **4**:109–113.

Drucker, D. B., and Whittaker, D. K., 1971b, Microstructure of colonies of rod-shaped bacteria, *J. Bacteriol.* **108**:515–525.

Fawcett, H. S., 1925, Maintained growth rates in fungal culture of long duration, *Ann. Appl. Biol.* **12**:191.

Flicker, M., and Ross, J., 1974, Mechanism of chemical instability for periodic precipitation phenomena, *J. Chem. Phys.* **60**:3458–3465.

Gierer, A., and Meinhardt, H., 1972, A theory of biological pattern formation, *Kybernetik* **12**:30–39.

Graham-Smith, G. S., 1910, The division and post fission movement of bacilli when grown on solid media, *Parasitology* **3**:17–53.

Hedges, E. S., 1932, *Liesegang Rings and Other Periodic Structures,* Chapman & Hall, London.

Herbert, R. A., 1988, Bidirectional compound chemostats: Applications of compound diffusion linked chemostats in microbial ecology, in: *Handbook of Laboratory Models Systems for Microbial Ecosystem Research, Vol. 1* (J. W. T. Wimpenny, ed.), CRC Press, Boca Raton, Florida, pp. 99–115.

Hoeniger, J. F. M., 1965a, Development of flagella by *Proteus mirabilis, J. Gen. Microbiol.* **40**:29.

Hoeniger, J. F. M., 1965b, Influence of pH on *Proteus* flagella, *J. Bacteriol.* **90**:275.

Hoffman, H., and Franck, M. E., 1961, Form and internal structure of cellular aggregates in early *Escherichia coli* microcultures, *J. Gen. Microbiol.* **25**:352–364.

Hoppensteadt, F. C., and Jäger, W., 1979, Pattern formation by bacteria, in: *Biological Growth and Spread, Lecture Notes in Biomathematics* ((W. Jäger and J. D. Murray, eds.), Springer-Verlag, Berlin, pp. 68–81.

Hoppensteadt, F. C., Jäger, W., and Poppe, C., 1984, A hysteresis model for bacterial growth patterns, in: *Modelling of Patterns in Time and Space, Lecture Notes in Biomathematics* (W. Jäger and J. D. Murray, eds.), Springer-Verlag, Berlin, pp. 123–134.

Hughes, W. H., 1957, A reconsideration of the swarming of *Proteus vulgaris, J. Gen. Microbiol.* **17**:49–58.

Hutchinson, G. E., 1965, The niche: An abstractly inhabited hypervolume, in: *The Ecological Theatre and the Evolutionary Play,* Yale University Press, New Haven, Conn., pp. 26–78.

Ivanitsky, G. R., Kunisky, A. S., and Tsyganov, M. A., 1984, Study of "target patterns" in a phage–bacterium system, *Springer Series on Synergetics* **28**:214–216.

Jerebzoff, S., 1965, Manipulation of some oscillating systems in fungi by chemicals, in *Circadian Rhythms* (J. Aschoff, eds.), North-Holland, Amsterdam, pp. 183–189.

Kolenbrander, P. E., 1989, Surface recognition among oral bacteria: Multigeneric coaggregations and their mediators, *CRC Crit. Rev. Microbiol.* **17**:137–159.

Legroux, R., and Magrou, J., 1920, Etat organise des colonnies bacteriennes, *Ann. Inst. Pasteur* **34**:417–433.

Lewis, M. W. A., and Wimpenny, J. W. T., 1981, The influence of nutrition and temperature on the growth of colonies of *Escherichia coli* K12, *Can. J. Microbiol.* **27**:679–684.

Liesegang, R. E., 1896, Ueber einige Eigenschaften von Gellerton, *Naturwiss, Wochenschr.* **11**:353–362.

Lovitt, R. W., and Wimpenny, J. W.T., 1981, The gradostat, a bidirectional compound chemostat, and its applications in microbiological research, *J. Gen. Microbiol.* **127**:261–268.

Lysek, G., 1984, Physiology and ecology of rhythmic growth and sporulation in fungi, in: *The Ecology and Physiology of the Fungus Mycelium* (D. H. Jennings and A. D. M. Rayner, eds.), Cambridge University Press, Cambridge, United Kingdom, pp. 323–342.

Lysek, G., and Nordbring-Herz, B., 1981, An endogenous rhythm of trap formation in nematophagous fungus *Arthrobotrys oligospora*, *Planta* **152**:50–53.

McClure, P. J., Roberts, T. A., and Oguru, P. O., 1989, Comparison of the effects of sodium chloride, pH and temperature on the growth of *Listeria monocytogenes* on gradient plates and in liquid medium, *Lett. Appl. Microbiol.* **9**:95–99.

McCoy, W. F., Bryers, J. D., Robbins, J., and Costerton, J. W., 1981, Observations of fouling biofilm formation, *Can. J. Microbiol.* **27**:910–917.

Margalef, R., 1967, Laboratory analogues of estuarine plankton systems, in: *Estuaries: Ecology and Populations* (G. M. Lauff, ed.), Hornshafer, Baltimore, pp. 515–524.

Moltke, O., 1927, Contributions to the characterisation and systematic classification of *Bact. proteus vulgaris (Hauser),* Levin & Munksgaard, Copenhagen.

Müller, S. C., and Venzl, G., 1984, Pattern formation in precipitation processes, in: *Modelling of Patterns in Space and Time, Lecture Notes in Biomathematics* (W. Jäger and J. D. Murray, eds.), Springer-Verlag, Berlin (pp. 254–278).

Nelson, D. C., Jorgensen, B. B., and Revsbech, N. P., 1986, Growth pattern and yield of a chemoautotrophic *Beggiatoa* sp. in oxygen–sulphide microgradients, *Appl. Environ. Microbiol.* **52**:225–233.

Newell, P. C., 1986, Receptors for cell communication in Dictyostelium, in: *Hormones, Receptors and Cellular Interactions in Plants* (C. M. Chadwick, ed.), Cambridge University Press, London, pp. 154–216.

Nitsch, B., and Kutzner, H. J., 1966, Wachstum von Streptomyceten in Schuttelagarkultur: eine neue Methode zur Festellung des C-quellen-spektrums, in: *Symposium on Technische Mikrobiologie,* Berlin, pp. 481–486.

Nossal, R., 1972, Growth and movement of rings of chemotactic bacteria, *Exp. Cell Res.* **75**:138–142.

Ostwald, W., 1925, The theory of Liesegang rings, *Kolloid Z.* **36**:380.

Palumbo, S. A., Johnson, M. G., Rieck, V. T., and Witter, L. D., 1971, Growth measurements on surface colonies of bacteria, *J. Gen. Microbiol.* **66**:137–143.

Perfil'ev, B. V., and Gabe, D. R., 1969, *Capillary Methods for Investigating Microorganisms,* Oliver & Boyd, Edinburgh.

Peters, A. C., and Wimpenny, J. W. T., 1988, A constant depth laboratory film fermenter, in: *Handbook of Laboratory Model Systems for Microbial Ecosystems,* Vol. 1 (J. W. T. Wimpenny, ed.), CRC Press, Boca Raton, pp. 175–195.

Peters, A. C., Wimpenny, J. W. T., and Coombs, J. P., 1987, Oxygen profiles in, and in the agar beneath, colonies of *Bacillus cereus, Staphylococcus albus* and *Escherichia coli, J. Gen. Microbiol.* **133**:1257–1263.

Peters, A. C., Thomas, L. V., and Wimpenny, J. W. T., 1991, Effects of salt concentration on bacterial growth on plates with gradients of pH and temperature, *FEMS Microbiol. Lett.* **77**:309–314.

Pirt, S. J., 1967, A kinetic study of the mode of growth of surface colonies of bacteria and fungi, *J. Gen. Microbiol.* **47**:181-197.

Plomley, N. J. B., 1959, Formation of the colony in the fungus *Chaetomium, Aust. J. Biol. Sci.* **12**:53.

Polezhaev, A. A., and Ptitsyn, M. O., 1990, Phenomenological mechanism of the formation of spatial structures in colonies of bacteria, *J. Nonlinear Biol.* **1**:63–76.

Raper, K. B., 1984, *The Dictyostelids,* Princeton University Press, Princeton, N.J.

Reichenbach, H., 1965, Rhythmische Vorange bei der Schwarmentfaltung von Myxobacterien, *Ber. Dtsch. Bot. Ges.* **78**:102–105.

Reichenbach, H., 1966, Myxococcus spp. (Myxobacteriales) Schwarmentwicklung un Bildung von Protocycten, in: *Encyclopedia Cinematographica film E778/1965* (G. Wolf, ed.), Institut fur den Wissenschaftlichen Film, Gottingen.

Reyrolle, J., and Letellier, F., 1979, Autoradiographic study of the location and evolution of growth zones in bacterial colonies, *J. Gen. Microbiol.* **111**:399–406.

Roberts, T. A., and Ingram, M., 1973, Inhibition of growth of *Cl. botulinum* at different pH values by sodium chloride and sodium nitrite, *J. Food Technol.* **8**:467–475.

Ryan, F. J., Beadle, G. W., and Tatum, E. L., 1943, The tube method of measuring the growth rate of *Neurospora, Am. J. Bot.* **30**:784.

Sagromsky, H., 1952, Der Einfluß des Lichtes auf die rhythmische Konidienbildung von *Penicillium, Flora (Jena)* **139**:300–313.

Shapiro, J. A., 1984, The use of Mu d*lac* transposons as tools for vital staining to visualise clonal and non-clonal patterns of organization in bacterial growth on agar surfaces, *J. Gen. Microbiol.* **130**:1169–1181.

Shapiro, J. A., 1985a, Scanning electron microscope study of *Pseudomonas putida* colonies, *J. Bacteriol.* **164**:1171–1181.

Shapiro, J. A., 1985b, Photographing bacterial colonies, *Am. Soc. Microbiol. News* **51**:62.

Shapiro, J. A., 1987, Organization of developing *Escherichia coli* colonies viewed by scanning electron microscopy, *J. Bacteriol.* **169**:142–156.

Shapiro, J. A., and Hsu, C., 1989, *Escherichia coli* K-12 cell–cell interactions seen by time lapse video, *J. Bacteriol.* **171**:5963–5974.

Shapiro, J. A., and Trubatch, D., 1991, Sequential events in bacterial colony morphogenesis, *Physica D* **49**:214–223.

Shimkets, L. J., 1990, Social and developmental biology of the myxobacteria, *Microbiol. Rev.* **54**:473–501.

Shimkets, L. J., and Kaiser, D., 1982, Induction of coordinated cell movement in *Myxococcus xanthus, J. Bacteriol.* **152**:451–461.

Shrewsbury, J. F. D., 1931, Giant colony culture, *J. Pathol. Bacteriol.* **34**:283–285.

Siegert, F., and Weijer, C. J., 1991, Analysis of optical density wave propagation and cell movement in the cellular slime mould *Dictyostelium discoideum*, in: *Physica D* (H. L. Swinney and V. I. Krinsky, eds.), North-Holland, Amsterdam, pp. 224–232.

Skyring, G. W., and Bauld, J., 1990, Microbial mats in Australian coastal environments, in: *Advances in Microbial Ecology* (K. C. Marshall, ed.), Plenum Press, New York, pp. 461–498.

Smith, D. G., 1972, The *Proteus* swarming phenomenon, *Sci. Prog.* **60**:487.

Springer, E. L., and Roth, I. L., 1972, Scanning electron microscopy of bacterial colonies. I. *Diplococcus pneumoniae* and *Streptococcus pneumoniae, Can. J. Microbiol.* **18**:219–223.

Steinbock, O., Hashomoto, H., and Muller, S. C., 1991, Quantitative analysis of periodic chemotaxis in aggregation patterns of *Dictyostelium discoideum*, in: *Physica D* (H. L. Swinney and V. I. Krinsky, eds.), North-Holland, Amsterdam, pp. 233–239.

Szybalski, W., and Bryson, V., 1953, Genetic studies on microbial cross-resistance to toxic agents. I. Cross resistance of *Escherichia coli* to fifteen antibiotics, *J. Bacteriol.* **64**:489–499.

Tanaka, S., 1985, Cytological studies on *Agrobacterium tumefaciens*. 1. Growth and ultrastructures of the cell, *Yamaguchi Med. Bull.* **34**:25–35.

Todd, R. L., and Kerr, T. J., 1972, Scanning electron microscopy of microbial cells on membrane filters, *Appl. Microbiol.* **23**:1160–1162.

Tomchik, K. J., and Devreotes, P. N., 1981, Adenosine 3', 5' monophosphate waves in *Dictyostelium discoideum*: A demonstration by isotope dilution-fluorography, *Science.* **212**:443–446.

Tschapek, M., and Giambiagi, N., 1954, Die bildung von Liesegang'schen ringen durch Azotobakter bei O_2-hemmung, *Kolloid Z.* **135**:47–48.

Turing, A. M., 1952, The chemical basis of morphogenesis, *Philos. Trans. R. Soc. London Ser. B* **237**:37–72.

Tyson, J. J., and Murray, J. D., 1989, Cyclic AMP waves during aggregation of *Dictyostelium* amoebae, *Development* **106**:421–426.

Van Haastert, P. J. M., and DeWit, R. J. W., 1984, The cell surface cAMP receptor of *Dictyostelium discoideum*: Demonstration of receptor heterogeneity and affinity modulation by nonequilibrium experiments, *J. Biol. Chem.* **259**:13321–13328.

Werner, C., 1898, *Die Bedingungen der Conidienbildung bei einigen Pilzen*, Ph.D. thesis, Basel and Frankfurt.

Whittaker, R. H., Levin, S. A., and Root, R. B., 1973, Niche, habitat and ecotope, *Am. Nat.* **107**:321–338.

Whittenbury, R., 1963, The use of soft agar in the study of conditions affecting the utilization of fermentable substrates by lactic acid bacteria, *J. Gen. Microbiol.* **32**:375–384.

Williams, F. D., and Schwarzhoff, R. H., 1978, Nature of the swarming phenomenon in *Proteus Annu. Rev. Microbiol.* **32**:102–122.

Williams, J. W., 1938, Bacterial growth 'spectrum' analysis. Methods and applications, *Am. J. Med. Technol.* **4**:58–61.

Williams, J. W., 1939, Growth of microorganisms in shake cultures under increased oxygen and carbon dioxide tensions, *Growth* **3**:21–33.

Wimpenny, J. W. T., 1979, The growth and form of bacterial colonies, *J. Gen. Microbiol.* **114**:483–486.

Wimpenny, J. W. T., 1981, Spatial order in microbial ecosystems, *Biol. Rev.* **56**:295–342.

Wimpenny, J. W. T., 1988, The bacterial colony, in: *Handbook of Laboratory Model Systems for Microbial Ecosystems* (J. W. T. Wimpenny, ed.), CRC Press, Boca Raton, pp. 109–139.

Wimpenny, J. W. T., and Abdollahi, H., 1991, Growth of a mixed culture of an obligate aerobe *(Paracoccus denitrificans)* and an obligate anaerobe *(Desulfovibrio desulfuricans)* in homogeneous and heterogeneous culture systems, *Microb. Ecol.* **22**:1–13.

Wimpenny, J. W. T., and Coombs, J. P., 1983, The penetration of oxygen into bacterial colonies, *J. Gen. Microbiol.* **129**:1239–1242.

Wimpenny, J. W. T., and Jones, D. E., 1988, One-dimensional gel-stabilized model systems, in: *Handbook of Laboratory Model Systems for Microbial Ecosystems,* Vol. 2 (J. W. T. Wimpenny, ed.), CRC Press, Boca Raton, pp. 1–30.

Wimpenny, J. W. T., and Lewis, M. W. A., 1977, The growth and respiration of bacterial colonies, *J. Gen. Microbiol.* **103**:9–18.

Wimpenny, J. W. T., and Parr, J. A., 1979, Biochemical differentiation in large colonies of *Enterobacter cloacae, J. Gen. Microbiol.* **114**:487–489.

Wimpenny, J. W. T., and Waters, P., 1984, Growth of microorganisms in gel-stabilised two-dimensional gradient systems, *J. Gen. Microbiol.* **130**:2921–2926.

Wimpenny, J. W. T., and Waters, P., 1987, The use of gel-stabilized gradient plates to map the responses of microorganisms to three or four environmental factors varied simultaneously, *FEMS Microbiol. Lett.* **40:**263–267.

Wimpenny, J. W. T., Coombs, J. P., Lovitt, R. W., and Whittaker, S. G., 1981, A gel-stabilized model ecosystem for investigating microbial growth in spatially ordered solute gradients, *J. Gen. Microbiol.* **127:**277–287.

Wimpenny, J. W. T., Lovitt, R. W., and Coombs, J. P., 1983, Laboratory model systems for the investigation of spatially and temporally organised microbial ecosystems, *Symp. Soc. Gen. Microbiol.* **34:**67–116.

Wimpenny, J. W. T., Jaffe, S., and Coombs, J. P., 1984, Periodic growth phenomena in spatially organised microbial systems, in: *Modelling of Patterns in Time and Space, Lecture Notes in Biomathematics,* Vol. 55 (W. Jäger and J. D. Murray, eds.), Berlin: Springer-Verlag, Berlin, pp. 388–405.

Wolfe, A. J., and Berg, H. C., 1989, Migration of bacteria in semisolid agar, *Proc. Natl. Acad. Sci. USA* **86:**6973–6977.

Zaikin, A. N., and Zhabotinsky, A. M., 1970, Concentration wave propagation in two-dimensional liquid-phase self oscillating systems, *Nature* **225:**535.

Index